East Sussex Church Monuments
1530 - 1830

East Sussex Church Monuments
1530 - 1830

by
Nigel Llewellyn

with additional genealogical research
by John Hawkins
and editorial assistance by
Peter Macleod and Peter Wilkinson

SUSSEX RECORD SOCIETY
VOLUME 93
Issued to members of the Society for the years 2009 and 2010

Published 2011 by
Sussex Record Society
Barbican House,
High Street,
Lewes,
East Sussex, BN7 1YE
© Sussex Record Society and Nigel Llewellyn 2011
ISBN 978 0 85445 075 6

Printed by Hobbs the Printers Ltd., Totton, Hampshire

SUSSEX RECORD SOCIETY

Volumes issued by the Society

Vol. 1 *Marriage Licences at Lewes, 1586-1642*
Vol. 2 *Sussex Fines, 1190-1248*
Vol. 3 *Post Mortem Inquisitions, 1558-1583*
Vol. 4 *Ecclesiastical Returns for East Sussex, 1603; Sussex Poll Book, 1705;
    Sussex MSS in the Harleian MSS; Bishop Praty's Register, 1438-1445.*
Vol. 5 *West Sussex Protestation Returns, 1641-1642*
Vol. 6 *Marriage Licences at Lewes, 1670-1732*
Vol. 7 *Sussex Fines, 1249-1307*
Vol. 8 *Bishop Rede's Register, 1397-1415 (Pt.1)*
Vol. 9 *Marriage Licences at Chichester 1575-1730*
Vol. 10 *Subsidy Rolls, 1296, 1327 and 1332*
Vol. 11 *Bishop Rede's Register, 1397-1415 (Pt. I)*
Vol. 12 *Marriage Licences at Chichester (peculiars), 1579-1730*
Vol. 13 *Cuckfield Parish Register, 1598-1699*
Vol. 14 *Post Mortem Inquisitions, 1485-1649*
Vol. 15 *Bolney Parish Register, 1541-1812*
Vol. 16 *Star Chamber Proceedings, 1500-1558*
Vol. 17 *Ardingly Parish Register, 1558-1812*
* Vol. 18 *Angmering Parish Register, 1562-1687*
Vol. 19 *Sussex Manors and Advowsons, etc., 1509-1833, A-L*
Vol. 20 *Sussex Manors and Advowsons, etc., 1509-1833, M-Z*
Vol. 21 *Horsham Parish Register, 1541-1635*
Vol. 22 *Cowfold Parish Register, 1558-1812*
Vol. 23 *Sussex Fines, 1308-1509*
Vol. 24 *East Grinstead Parish Register, 1558-1661*
Vol. 25 *Marriage Licences at Lewes, 1771-1837, A-L*
Vol. 26 *Marriage Licences at Lewes, 1772-1837, M-Z*
Vol. 27 *Preston Manor Court Rolls, 1562-1702*
Vol. 28 *Sussex Apprentices and Masters, 1710-1752*
Vol. 29 *Abstracts of Documents relating to the Dobell family, 16th-18th cents.*
Vol. 30 *Glynde Parish Register, 1558-1812*
Vol. 31 *Thirteen Custumals of the Sussex Manors of the Bishop of Chichester, c.1256-1374*
Vol. 32 *Sussex Marriage Licences at Chichester, 1731-1774*
Vol. 33 *Sussex Inquisitions (from Bodleian Library), 1541-1616*
Vol. 34 *The Book of John Rowe, Steward to Lord Bergavenny, 1622*
Vol. 35 *Marriage Licences at Chichester, 1775-1800, with Index covering Licences, 1731-1800*
Vol. 36 *Sussex Chantry Records, 1535-1652*
Vol. 37 *Hastings Rape Records, 1387-1474*
Vol. 38 *Chartulary of Lewes Priory (Pt. I), 11th-l4th cents.*
* Vol. 39 *The Buckhurst Terrier, 1597-1598*
Vol. 40 *Chartulary of Lewes Priory (Pt. II), l2th-l4th cents.*
Vol. 41 *Transcripts of Sussex Wills up to 1560, Vol.1 Albourne -Chichester*
Vol. 42 *Transcripts of Sussex Wills up to 1560, Vol.2 Chiddingly -Horsham*
Vol. 43 *Transcripts of Sussex Wills up to 1560, Vol.3 Horsted Keynes –Pyecombe*
Vol. 44 *Records of the Barony and Honour of the Rape of Lewes, 1265-1466*
Vol. 45 *Transcripts of Sussex Wills up to 1560, Vol.4 Racton -Yapton*
Vol. 46 *Chichester Cathedral Chartulary, l3th-l6th cents.*
Vol. 47 *Survey of Robertsbridge Manor, 1567-1570*
* Vol. 48 *The Town Book of Lewes, 1542-1701*
Vol. 49 *Churchwardens' Presentments, (Pt. I), Archdeaconry of Chichester, 1621-1628, 1664-1670*

Volumes marked with an asterisk can be obtained from the Hon. Secretary, Sussex Record Society, Barbican House, Lewes, East Sussex, BN7 IYE. Prices can be found on the Society's website (www.sussexrecordsociety.org)

CONTENTS

ACKNOWLEDGEMENTS

A major Research Grant from the Arts & Humanities Research Council (AHRC) supported the initial project in 2000-2002 to develop a digital database relating to funeral monuments, from which some of the material published here has been taken. Additional AHRC grants supported the research in 2003-05 and through a term of study leave in 2006.

I also acknowledge the support of the University of Sussex in the form of the then Dean, Stephen Burman, and the then Head of Department, Liz James, during the later stages of the work. My immediate colleagues at Sussex tolerated my curiosity about funeral monuments for more than 25 years and I am deeply grateful to them. Dr David Hickman was a leading figure in the original research team that included Dr Tara Hamling, Dr Steffi Knoell, Dr Michelle O'Malley, Dr David Robinson, Dr Hilary Tunley, Dr David Young, staff from the University Photographic Department and the distinguished members of the project Steering Committee. At one stage that project was most valuably supported by a group of local volunteers and I thank everyone involved in the initial stage of the research project.

Since the decision to publish with Sussex Record Society, key members and officers of the society have offered invaluable advice: Professor Brian Short, Roy Hunnisett and, in editorial capacities, Peter Wilkinson and Andrew Foster. Without the expert support and advice and warm encouragement offered by Peter Macleod the contents of this book would still be lying in pieces on my study floor. Valuable, additional expertise and corrective advice on Sussex family history was offered by John Hawkins, whose essential contribution is acknowledged throughout the catalogue and on the title-page. John was ably supported by Steven Blowers in this research. Peter Wilkinson has provided valuable assistance, especially in the checking and copy-editing, throughout the project. Sarah Readman undertook the formidable task of creating the index with unfailing perseverance and accuracy. Roger Davey, Stephen Freeth, Timothy McCann, Ian Nelson, Valerie Mellor, Malcolm Pratt and Christopher Whittick have all provided valuable assistance in elucidating inscriptions.

A number of other individuals helped in different ways: the late Dr Ron Firmin offered lithologic advice, the late Sir Nicholas Pumfrey QC clarified a tricky point of legal history for me and I learned a good deal from Wendy Watson's enthusiasm for "Horsham" stone. IT and library staff in a number of institutions offered much-valued help.

The fieldwork program, which took me to every promising Anglican site in East Sussex during 2005-6 would have failed without the kindness and cooperation of the many members of the diocese of Chichester whose churches I needed to access. From senior church officers, through incumbents (with one unaccountably grumpy exception!) to churchwardens and other lay parishioners, the church community of the county has been enormously supportive and I am grateful to them all. These congregations are working under difficult circumstances to maintain their church as functional buildings and historical sites and everyone interested in local history, from whatever perspective, owes them a great debt. For two years, the fieldwork project was coordinated by Vanessa Sammut whose skills, stamina, good sense and unfailing sense of humour helped see the campaign through to its conclusion. She became the team's leading expert in dealing with the East Sussex clergy and I am very grateful to her.

My immediate family - Clare and Jasper – have proved remarkably tolerant of this long project and will be relieved to hear that I will not be embarking immediately on the survey of West Sussex.

Nigel Llewellyn

INTRODUCTION

This catalogue describes 1409 monuments dating from the period 1530-1830 and identified in 144 East Sussex parish churches. In an accompanying website researchers can find high-resolution images of almost all the objects and, in addition, 200 of these monuments are illustrated in the book itself.[1] Given their history and age, church monuments from this period invariably look very different from the state they were in when first erected, especially in respect of the wording of monumental inscriptions (hereafter M.I.s), which get worn, lost and replaced, often inaccurately, and, in relation to surface colouring and details of decoration and heraldry, all of which are vulnerable to time, malicious treatment, accident and neglect. The entries that follow describe the objects actually found during the course of the church surveys. Those findings have not been edited to conform to other historic records or interpretations, however authoritative they may be. If a ledger stone is engraved with the name 'Smythe', then that is the spelling set out in the catalogue, even if the person commemorated is usually known as 'Smith' from other sources. In the same way, a date will be recorded in the catalogue as it is appears, for example '1691', even when we can be sure that the inscription has been wrongly repainted and the correct date should read '1697'. However, wherever additional or corrective information is available, it has been included in the form of accompanying notes and references. Another point to be stressed is that although we have aimed for complete coverage, there are certainly omissions. Because so many monuments from our period have been lost, for about half the churches surveyed, a final section is included headed 'Additions', in which are listed items not identified during the survey but known about from secondary literature. Future surveys of antiquarian and other manuscript sources relating to East Sussex will, inevitably, increase the numbers of these 'Additions'.

The field-work followed a standard procedure. Each church was given a unique number, e.g. Albourne, St. Bartholomew - 1, Alciston Parish Church - 2, ... Worth, St. Nicholas - 306. Each church entered was surveyed in a clock-wise direction and the objects included were those found within the building that commemorated someone who died between 1530 and 1830. Each of these was then allocated a letter commencing at A so that every monument in East Sussex has a unique identifier, e.g. 1A is the floor mounted brass for Edward Fenner, died 1603 at Albourne, St Bartholomew. Most of the catalogued objects are of stone, for example, engraved floor slabs, framed mural tablets of various sizes and types and, occasionally, more ambitious sculpted monuments. In addition, we include commemorative works in cast iron, engraved brass and on painted panels. The material included ranges in size from enormous architectural tombs, large enough to fill family chapels, to the partial and broken remains of small iron grave markers. Nearly everything was actually made within our period, either around the date of death of the person commemorated, or soon after.

Although there are a few mediaeval monuments in East Sussex churches, significant numbers survive only from the post-Reformation period, hence our starting date of 1530. Since the intention was to collect material evidence for patterns of continuity and change over a long duration, we chose the end point of 1830 to give the survey a full three-hundred year sweep. 1830 also marks a moment of profound historical change, in Sussex as elsewhere in the country, for example, the effects of increasing industrialisation and population growth, of the coming of the railways to the coast and of moves towards Catholic emancipation.

There are many reasons why a survey and published catalogue of East Sussex church monuments will be a valuable addition to the Society's record series. Church monuments are a neglected category; they fall between several fields of scholarly interest. Their inscriptions and heraldry are important to genealogists and family historians. Some carved monuments are sufficiently architectural or sculptural to earn the attention of historians of art and design. Often disrupted but rarely moved to new sites – a rare case is the Pelham monument at Stanmer (244A), originally set up in the City of London – church monuments are rich sources for local historians. In their combination of architectural framing, heraldic display, inscribed text and sculpted forms, monuments create lasting images about individuals and about their families and progeny. They tend to commemorate the higher social orders, nevertheless, in many cases, apart from occasional textual records, church monuments are the only 'portrayals' left of their subjects. In addition to these individual memorial functions, church monuments throw fascinating light on a great number of important historical contexts and issues. The language of their inscriptions tells us about an heir's obligation to his or her benefactor or a widow's or widower's sense of abandonment; they recount the fallen heroes of Britain's early colonial ventures and they evidence the increasing size and fashionability of Sussex's coastal resorts; they proudly proclaim family links to court and state and subtly refer to the manifold, complex and passionate religious differences that marked this period of English history.

The lack of a published record and classification of Sussex monuments was noted as long ago as 1928.[2] It is hoped that the present volume will make a contribution towards meeting that need and it is intended to complete the project by undertaking a parallel survey of West Sussex, with its more than one hundred and fifty churches and several thousand additional monuments. Despite the hard work involved, antiquaries have long recognised the value of county and diocesan surveys of monuments of this kind, although such projects have only rarely been completed. Printed publications like this began with John Weever's *Ancient Funerall Monuments* (1631), which concentrated on compiling monumental inscriptions in the dioceses of London and Norwich. For his own antiquarian reasons, Weever showed very little interest in the material remains of the monuments he catalogued or in monuments built in his own day. Until recently, scholars of monuments have rarely looked across their sets of material to seek answers to questions about patterns of commemoration across space and time, about the local markets and systems of patronage and religious and social histories of all kinds.

This survey had to accommodate the bureaucratic demands that confront researchers in our own day; we obtained permission before visiting churches and since they were invariably locked, we usually had to make appointments. Our photographs were taken with a Leica Digilux 2 camera. The project originated when the Arts and Humanities Research Board (now Arts and Humanities Research Council) launched a competitive grants scheme, which for the first time made available the necessary funding to undertake a county survey of this kind. These resources allowed a research team at the University of Sussex to undertake the field-work and project development needed to work '*Towards a national census of funeral monuments*', as the project was titled. The longer-term ambition, which is to facilitate the creation of a national database of post-Reformation monuments, has yet to be realised but I hope that the publication of the present volume will offer some pointers as to how it might be done.

Although there have been earlier and valuable antiquarian campaigns touching on Sussex tombs, for example, those described by John Farrant in *Sussex Depicted*, most of the material made available in this volume has never been published before. And, the time spent thus far on this project is as nothing compared to the dedication and stamina showed by many previous Sussex historians. Sir Stephen Glynne took almost fifty years to compile his church notes (1825-74) but his interest lay predominantly with mediaeval architecture.[3] In fact, much of the monumental art recorded in this catalogue has long been regarded as deeply unfashionable from the standpoints of period, style and purpose, which are issues that we hope the catalogue will throw light on.

Contexts - Geographical, Demographic, Social and Economic

Our survey uses as an organising principle, the boundaries to the six ancient administrative divisions of Sussex, known by a word with an obscure origin as 'Rapes'. This catalogue records the commemorative art found in the 144 parish churches of the three East Sussex Rapes: Hastings, Pevensey and Lewes. I am unaware of any additional monuments from our period extant in any country house chapels in the county but it would be possible to make an interesting parallel study of commemorative objects in the non-conformist chapels, of which there are many. East Sussex is a strip of country along the south coast with a mixed geographical character and it can be broken down into patches which represent different contexts for the monuments. To the west, the county is dense in small Downland villages. Here too are the county town of Lewes - rare in having several historical parish churches – and the only city, Brighton (or 'Brighthelmstone'), which was steadily expanding in size and importance at the end of our period. To the east of the South Downs, beyond Eastbourne, is a region of low-lying country with boggy ground – often tidal – stretching from beyond Pevensey to East Guldforde on the edge of Romney Marsh and abutting the Kent border. The parish churches are less densely packed in this eastern coastal area which to the north is terminated by the river Rother and had the ancient monastic town of Battle at its centre. Further north, running in parallel with the coast, is a broad strip of higher ground – though lower than the Downs themselves – of Forest and Weald with East Grinstead and Wadhurst as its local centres, both substantial monumental sites. Sandwiched between the Weald and the Downland and running on a west/east axis across the centre of the county, is a broad agricultural area, which in places stretches up to the north as far as the county boundaries with Surrey and Kent. Here the market towns were Hailsham and Ditchling. This was the area crossed by the turnpike road running north and south between London and the coast, which in due course was the route followed by the railway. These developments in transportation slowly encouraged the growth of places such as Cuckfield, where stage-coaches stopped, and Hurstpierpoint, a village transformed by the coming of trains. These geographical characteristics are useful contexts when we consider the kinds of communities that witnessed the setting-up of the monuments in the first instance and the question of transportation across the East Sussex landscape, of which more later.

The East Sussex parish churches in the survey are treated as commemorative sites and from this standpoint they can usefully be sorted into groups on grounds of geography, history and function. Nearly every church we include is medieval either in its actual fabric or in its foundations, although much of the fabric has been entirely replaced or rebuilt. The age of these sites is worth stressing: even in the period covered by the catalogue their antiquity was valued since ancient commemorative sites suggested continuity of dynasty or family and increased the prestige of any new manorial families that managed to associate with them. Since our survey ends c.1830 we include hardly any post-medieval foundations, an exception being the overspill church of St George, Hurstpierpoint, although there are some significant newly-constructed buildings on medieval foundations, for example, St Michael, Lewes, South Malling and Glynde.

Since the ecclesiastical jurisdiction of post-Reformation East Sussex almost all lay in the diocese of Chichester and since the county lacked a cathedral city of its own, the churches in the larger towns were especially important as commemorative sites. These towns were places of formal administrative, legal and commercial functions and they attracted members of the professions and established trades people. Key places in this category were the coastal ports of Rye, Winchelsea, Hastings, Pevensey & Brighthelmstone and inland, Battle, Hailsham, Lewes, Ditchling and East Grinstead. Some of these centres saw major growths of population in the nineteenth century and significant social and economic transformations that were reflected in the appearance of the churches and in their sets of monuments. Especially instructive from this standpoint are the resorts of Brighton and Hastings, which became increasingly fashionable in the early nineteenth century, a social picture clearly painted by the towns' monuments. Lewes, the county town, has four town parish churches in the survey - All Saints, St Anne, St John-sub-Castro and St Michael - a higher total than anywhere else in East Sussex but still a marked decline from the medieval peak of twelve. All Saints lay to the south of the town centre and the parish occupied the west bank of the river Ouse to the top of the hill and beyond northwards as far as Little East Street. By contrast, St Anne's was a small, square parish to the west of the town centre, between the Paddock to the north and the ancient southern town boundary with Southover. St John-sub-Castro occupied the north of the town with the river Ouse on its north-east side and the Paddock to the north-west. Finally, St Michael's was a small central parish, located to the south of the Castle and the High Street and, as with St Anne's, running down to the Southover boundary. From the standpoint of an analysis of the monuments, we can add the churches in Lewes' suburban circle - St John the Baptist, Southover, St Michael, South Malling and St Thomas, Cliffe. Town churches like this retain some of their early-modern character as commemorative sites, despite nineteenth-century enlargements and restorations. To the above list we should add Battle, Cuckfield, Hailsham, Lindfield, Rye and Wadhurst. Their sets of monuments typically include groups to prominent families and the individual citizens who acted as constables, lawyers and mayors. By contrast, members of manorial families tended to be buried out-of-town, near to their ancestral seats. Another category is represented by the monuments in coastal-town churches which often commemorate customs officers or those associated with military and naval service. Several monuments at Seaford and at Newhaven are from the Napoleonic period, although a famous, earlier defensive action is also vividly commemorated at St Michael's, Lewes. Hastings was the only Sussex town in the original set of five Cinque Ports, although Winchelsea and Rye were soon admitted as members, as were in due course Pevensey and Seaford (although on a non-corporate basis).[4]

Early maps of Sussex, such as the 95 printed examples from the period 1575-1830 identified by Kingsley, reveal additional regional identities in relation to the catalogue of monuments.[5] In many of these maps, for example, that drawn in 1723 by Richard Budgen (1695-1731), parts of the territory of Sussex are signalled as possessed by the families whose coats-of-arms are prominently displayed.[6] In the same way, groups of monuments set up in parish churches were designed to confirm the authority of the manorial families of East Sussex on the face of the county. Budgen's was the first large-scale map of Sussex and his practice was carried on at Frant by his son, also named Richard (1730-89). John Cary's map of 1792 displays the turnpike and coaching roads indicative of the social and economic significance of the key towns, many with important sets of family monuments, for example, Cuckfield and Lindfield.[7] There were also more direct points of contact between Sussex map-making and the county's church monuments. Editions of Richard Blore's map of 1693 were dedicated to William Benge, for whose wife see 153A, and cartography was one of the many interests of the famous polymathic natural philosopher Gideon Algernon Mantell (1790-1852), for whom see monument 160A.[8]

Outside the towns, certain sets of monuments reflect the close proximity of some parish churches to great houses. Some of these churches have become increasingly isolated in the countryside as landed estates have expanded around them, pushing residential settlements away from the former village centre. We can see this pattern at Ashburnham, Buxted, Isfield, Stanmer and Withyham. Churchyards in places like these can act as points of connection or relays between the great house and the village, with gates and entrances facing both ways as, for example, at Fletching, Glynde, Northiam and West Firle. In other villages, the parish churches are less strongly associated with the sites of great houses than they were, despite retaining their ancient manorial burial functions. The family tombs included in this group include the Culpepers of Wakehurst Place at Ardingly, the lords of Herstmonceux, the Jeffereys of Chiddingly, the Parkers of Ratton at Willingdon, and the Collins of Socknersh at Brightling. In the seventeenth century, the Pelhams of Halland were buried at Laughton (153D-F), the family having previously used other sites (160D) although subsequently, they shifted to their new estate church at Stanmer (244A).

The forty or so churches of the narrow downland strip are invariably small flint buildings in small parishes, the interiors ill-suited to house anything except small monuments. Some of the churches in this group display monuments that register the local interests of manorial families - the Thomases at Folkington, the Selwyns at Friston and the Dobells at Streat. Others, such as Alfriston, seem quite independent of such manorial pressures. A considerable leap of the imagination is required to reconstruct the original characters of the churches in the coastal districts, now surrounded by dense housing and overtaken by huge increases in population: Bexhill, East Blatchington, Portslade, Seaford and to a lesser extent Winchelsea.

Other distinctive groups of commemorative sites in the county include the twenty or so agricultural villages in western East Sussex, north of the Downs, and the large group of agricultural villages in the south-east of the county: the monuments in many of these areas reflect how isolated these places were, addressing local concerns and often employing different materials and tomb-makers in comparison with the Downland, coastal or Wealden groups. Finally, there are the twenty churches in the forest and Wealden villages to the north and east of the county, some of which are quite large, matching the mediaeval prosperity of villages such as Wadhurst and East Grinstead.

Alongside this slowly evolving pattern of geographical distribution, we should note the parallel social pattern relating to the monuments since through their inscriptions and in other ways they can make direct topical references to historical events, religious, legal and social controversy and even to affairs of state. Broadly speaking, church monuments commemorate the well-to-do and the East Sussex monuments are no exceptions to this rule; they were expensive to set up and they occupy privileged spaces in churches that, after the Reformation, were controlled by local patrons. The lower social orders were rarely the subject of church monuments, a rule proven by exceptions such as the family servant Margaret Becket (131A) or Fanny Cowley (40O) the 'poor but exemplary parishioner' commemorated by the vicar of Brighton. A majority of the total of 1409 monuments included in the catalogue relate to the nobility, the clergy, the gentry, magistrates and other lawyers, established townspeople, officers, gentlemen and their ladies and children. Over time, the social types commemorated by these monuments do slowly broaden, a pattern of change that can be seen c.1600, early in our period overall. Various references in the inscriptions on the monuments, remind us that the later Stuart period was marked by violently contested political change and religious controversy. The very fact that funeral monuments were set up in parish churches meant that any ideological statements they made had to be set within the relatively narrow frame of discursive reference that was appropriate to an established Anglican church space. The mural monument Sir George Courthope (258E) erected in his own memory, perhaps in the midst of the Exclusion crisis but prior to his death in 1685 records his court service and makes pointed reference to his loyalty to the Stuart dynasty.[9] The similarity between the final lines of his memoir, written in 1679, and the text of the M.I. suggests that the latter was written by Sir George himself. At Ringmer, opposing positions in the civil wars of the mid seventeenth century are alluded to in a number of monuments set up in the chancel and in the south aisle (212V, which should be compared with 212 W, X, A, DD and FF).

Navigating their way through the troubled waters of post-Reformation ecclesiastical politics were the parish clergy, men commemorated by many of the monuments recorded in this catalogue. The parish clergy were tomb-subjects whose close attention to rank was often reflected in the wording of M.I.s and requires some introduction. Most of those described as 'curate' were parish priests employed to assist or deputise for a parson. Of parsons themselves there were three kinds, depending on the rules that applied parish-by-parish. The particular 'livings' of parsons who were 'rectors' were drawn both from the greater tithes (covering corn, hay and wood) and the lesser tithes (everything else). Parsons, who were 'vicars', were incumbents of parishes held by monasteries before the Reformation and they received only the lesser tithes. In such parishes, the great tithes, as well as the right to appoint the incumbent had passed after the Reformation to laymen called 'impropriators', who, in turn, sometimes used 'sequestrators' (see 159K). A sub-category, of 'perpetual' vicars, could not be removed from the living at the pleasure of the impropriator, as could other vicars. Curates were entitled to neither greater nor lesser tithes, only to whatever charge the impropriator was required to pay; however, some curates were also perpetual.

These distinctions relating to tithe income, title and rank applied, of course, only to clerics who were ordained priests of the established church and our catalogue lists only monuments in church buildings within the Anglican framework. Nevertheless, during the period covered there were important challenges to the Church of England from several quarters. In East Sussex, a register of recusants was maintained and in the eighteenth century it listed individual Catholics in many villages: in 1717, at Buxted, Framfield and Beckley and in 1724 at East Guldeforde, Eastbourne, Guestling, Little Horsted, Sedlescombe, Westham and West Firle.[10] It was perhaps the case that few of these individuals were of a socio-economic rank that would justify any elaborate commemoration even had their devotional position permitted it. Amongst the higher social orders, significant recusants were the Gages, who were Catholic but loyal and retained the lordship of West Firle. The Porter family at Westham were Catholic as were others at Worth and East Grinstead.[11] Given the protection of the Gages, it is not surprising that at West Firle in 1676, the parish census recorded that there were 43 'papists' registered, as against 107 members of the Church of England, these two factions vastly outnumbering the two recorded Firle non-conformists.[12] In the face of the religious tensions that developed between these families and groupings, some monuments, as we have seen, stressed their subject's loyalty to the established church (212V, 258E).

The kind of data that monuments supply on issues like this is sometimes hard to interpret: the Threele monument at Rye (221A) displays a chronogrammatic inscription about a member of a prominent recusant family, nevertheless commemorated in an Anglican church. The inherent mystification in a chronogram, in which certain letters were picked out by means of differences of size or colour, to signify a Roman date or number alluding to the subject, for example, dates of a life-span or the subject's age, has perhaps contributed to the local notoriety of the Threeles. It is worth noting that there is no evidence to link the use of chronograms with recusancy in other parts of the country.

From the opposing wing of Christian doctrine in England, are the Beard family of Rottingdean, many of whom seem to have been prominent Quakers although some members of the family were buried and commemorated in the parish church (217A-C). The capacity of the established church to accommodate doctrinal breadth is also suggested by the monument (160A) to the radical Whig and Methodist Thomas Mantell, father of the famous surgeon and geologist. In 1676, some years before Mantell's death, the census for his parish at St Michael's, Lewes had recorded that Anglicans outnumbered non-conformists by 251 to 67 with no papists listed.[13] We hope that the material gathered in the catalogue will enable scholars to undertake more thorough studies of how M.I.s and monumental imagery might signal public statements about shades of religious difference in post-Reformation Sussex.

It is important to see the monuments as one element of visual culture within the context of the death ritual overall, which was a long, drawn-out process for our early-modern ancestors, rather than the moment or event that death represents in contemporary culture.[14] However, the monuments themselves rarely refer directly to the practice of the death ritual. The surviving memoirs of Burgess, who was a professional grave-digger at Ditchling in the 1780s, seem not to refer directly to any monuments in the catalogue, which perhaps suggests that grave-diggers had little to do with setting up ledger-stones on church floors. A century earlier, in 1678, Stephen Hatton, the Cuckfield schoolmaster, collected some topical London publications on behalf of Giles Moore, which included at a cost of six pence a printed sheet setting out the words of the recently-passed 'Act for Burying in Woollen'.[15] On quite another social scale, there were hugely costly state and noble funerals, which are much better documented, though rare in relation to Sussex subjects. An exception is the funeral of the Duke of Richmond in 1723, but this took place at Westminster, not at the manorial seat at Goodwood, West Sussex.[16] Heraldry played a crucial role both in grand funerals and in the design of monuments, although the loss of heraldic colour and inaccurate repainting on monumental shields-of-arms makes it well nigh impossible to include accurate verbal descriptions of heraldry in the catalogue.[17] At the funerals of armigerous individuals, those who had been granted, or who had acquired a coat-of-arms, the heraldic hatchment that had already been displayed at the bereaved household during the preceding period of mourning was carried in procession. The hatchments for the late husband of Margareta Randoll (73J) are visibly displayed in a view dated 1784 of their home at Herrings Place.[18] Several East Sussex churches, for example, the atmospheric, isolated church at Hamsey or the busy town-centre church at Lindfield, still display hatchments amongst the monuments and often relating to the same families and individuals. Some of the earlier monuments in the survey, especially those in the chivalric tradition which prevailed into the seventeenth century, had helmets and other knightly paraphernalia hanging above them, e.g. at Battle (20I).

The distribution of monuments by number and date

The catalogue includes details on 1409 monuments in 144 locations, an average of nearly ten monuments per church. If we distribute these data across time, roughly on the basis of the lead subject's date of death, we find that the pattern shows a steady increase in the number of surviving monuments. This trend is not unexpected since it partly results from steady improvements in the survival rate for more recent monuments. However, the numbers may also reflect the death-rate and, furthermore, fluctuations in the numbers of surviving monuments certainly follow fluctuations in the numbers originally, a pattern reflecting changes in fashion, in habit, in the economy, or levels of increasing or decreasing enthusiasm for commemorative art on the part of tomb-subjects, executors or other patrons. Although the source-material specifically relating to Sussex is rare, we have no reason to believe that the patronage pattern for the county differed from other areas of England. A large percentage of monuments were erected by their subjects within their own life-times, though this becomes less common during the eighteenth century and afterwards. More complex and costly monumental projects were the subject of preliminary discussion and the production of estimates and legal contracts (West Firle 281D). As we shall see, as far as the choice of tomb-maker was concerned, more modest patrons looked to locally-based makers although their grander neighbours had to cast their net more widely, to London or even abroad. According to the letter of the ecclesiastical law, monuments represented structural changes to church fabric and so required a 'faculty' but few examples of formal documents, such as this, relating to monuments, have survived.[19]

After the reformation, there was a steady growth in the number of monuments erected in Sussex and within this overall trend, there are significant periodic peaks in the 1620s, the 1630s, 1670s, the 1680s, the 1720s and steadily through the 1820s.

Decade	Count	%	Decade	Count	%
1530s	5	0.4	1690s	41	3.3
1540s	1	0.1	1700s	54	4.3
1550s	5	0.4	1710s	58	4.6
1560s	1	0.1	1720s	62	4.9
1570s	3	0.2	1730s	60	4.8
1580s	7	0.6	1740s	42	3.3
1590s	13	1.0	1750s	54	4.3
1600s	9	0.7	1760s	49	3.9
1610s	21	1.7	1770s	61	4.8
1620s	29	2.3	1780s	56	4.4
1630s	32	2.5	1790s	71	5.6
1640s	21	1.7	1800s	86	6.8
1650s	29	2.3	1810s	112	8.9
1660s	37	2.9	1820s	131	10.4
1670s	46	3.6	1830 itself	18	1.4
1680s	47	3.7			
			Total	1261	100.0
			Undated	148	
			All Monuments	1409	

By contrast, there are periods of decline in the 1640s, the 1690s, the 1740s and the 1780s. It seems likely that the survival rate of monuments, as recorded in the catalogue, is indicative of the original numbers of monuments set up overall, although it would also be reasonable to argue that the social, economic and religious controversies of the seventeenth-century Civil War explain the very low numbers of monuments relating to the period 1644 – 52, as might later political uncertainties after 1688 and around 1745. By contrast, the steep rise in numbers c.1600 matches national trends as the ranks of the tomb-subjects broadened socially, swelled for the first time by the professional classes - divines, lawyers and teachers.[20]

Any analysis of the geographical distribution of monuments is markedly vulnerable to the distorting impact of chance and local circumstances. The extraordinary survival of eighty ledger stones on the floor at Rye represents about 6% of the total survey of East Sussex monuments in what is merely 0.6% of the county land area. The floors at Ticehurst, Wadhurst and Waldron are also exceptional sites, filled with surviving ledger stones. The really impressive sets of wall monuments are found in the larger, market towns, especially those which have long-established families in their vicinities, for example, Brighton, Cuckfield, Eastbourne, East Grinstead, Hastings, Hurstpierpoint, Lewes and Ringmer. The numbers of monuments in these churches represent a major percentage of the total in East Sussex overall and are important survivals on grounds of their carving styles and artistic quality and the financial investment they represent. If we consider the total numbers of monuments over the whole 300-year period, we find that the densest distributions lie in the coastal strip, areas which were sparsely populated until the later eighteenth century but which then experienced very rapid growth to reach high levels of population and economic activity, levels matched by correspondingly high numbers of monuments. By contrast, in the south-eastern quarter of the county, which never became fashionable and with the notable exception of Rye, there are, generally, fewer monuments.

The monuments as material survivals

Any attempt to understand how monuments functioned needs a mental reconstruction of the circumstances that determined their original viewing. Leaving aside how they have ended up and how we found them during the survey, how were monuments initially located within the churches? There was no standard practice but there were common patterns in relation to the distribution of monuments in side chapels, in chancels and choirs and in the nave and side aisles. During the years covered by the catalogue, these spatial contexts were affected by a number of important liturgical and other changes that had an impact on the way in which the monuments were seen. During the Georgian period, congregations were increasingly seated in relative comfort and given sight of the key points within the church space, allowing them to witness the devotional rituals at the east end, to hear sermons and bible-readings by means of direct visual and audial contact with pulpit and lectern.[21] Spatial trends such as these encouraged the use of floor and wall for monuments and discouraged free-standing tombs in aisles and occupying valuable liturgical space in the chancel. Sometimes, tensions developed between the demands of liturgical practice and the personal, familial and hereditary interest of patrons, who valued commemorative spaces that gave them the opportunity for social display. The very presence of a monument might be important in establishing manorial rights, for example, the mural monument for the insolvent politician, businessman and financier Arnold Nesbitt proudly proclaims him as 'Lord of Icklesham' (140F); it was erected by his heir after his death in 1779 in order to help secure the succession thrown into jeopardy by Nesbitt's failed enterprises. The grander families owned their own private burial spaces in chapels and used them as commemorative sites generation after generation. The importance of continuity was such that traditional burial places were maintained even when the family were no longer living locally or had purchased manors elsewhere. The Frewens continued to be buried and commemorated at Northiam although they had become lords of other estates. The existence of the mural monument for Jeremiah and Jane Curteis of c.1800 (276B) at Wartling is explained in the inscription. Jeremiah was of Rye and both he and his wife are buried at Tenterden in Kent. The seat of their only son, Edward-Jeremiah, was at Windmill Hill, near Wartling, where he succeeded the Luxfords (see 276A) and established a burial place for his family and, as the M.I. puts it, for 'its Descent & Alliance', in succession to Tenterden. Until well into the nineteenth century, East Sussex monuments continued to stress the importance of manorial possession and family succession as an established right. At key moments in the lengthy histories of some families, great commemorative campaigns were sometimes launched in response to changing fortune and political necessity. The Shurleys of Isfield - newly wealthy under the early Tudors - made a chapel for themselves, erected elegant and fashionably decorated seating and built a squinch through the wall into the chancel to allow the family to sit separately from other parishioners without losing direct visual contact with the host elevated at the mass. Succeeding generations of the family then erected grand wall tombs in this space; first, John Shurley, the dynastic founder who had first bought the estate and whose will of 1527 includes a request for a tomb, then his third son and heir Edward (died 1558), whose tomb had built into its very foundations the grave marker of Gundreda, a totemic element from the remains of the Priory of St Pancras at Lewes; then Thomas, the eldest son of Edward (died 1571); finally, his descendent Sir John Shurley (died 1631).

At the other end of the monumental range are ledger stones, in effect, part of the church flooring and, in consequence, extremely vulnerable to disruption. Although much work remains to be done, it is clear that some ledgers remain in situ, or nearly in situ, while others have been removed to quite new locations within the church. It is probably safe to assume that few small monuments have escaped some disruption and that few of them remain in their exact original locations. The question of causes for damage to church monuments is hotly debated amongst scholars. Sometimes, the excuses for change were practical, for example, the installation of a new organ or heating system. In two nearly adjacent churches north of the Downs, the original ledgers appear to have been dispensed with entirely and replaced during nineteenth-century restorations by other markers. At Selmeston new brasses were made and at Berwick (25B-E), the ledgers were replaced by a uniform set of grave markers, simply engraved with name and date.

In this same church, a fine organ has quite recently been installed, which totally obscures an important seventeenth-century mural monument.

Cast-iron railings were commonly used to protect post-Reformation monuments, especially those set up against walls or freestanding in aisles and although few survive, the strength of the Sussex iron industry suggests that it is likely that they were made locally. In a letter dated 24th June 1749, John Fuller, the son of John Fuller of Brightling, wrote to Samuel Remnant, his agent, about some iron-founding business: '*I desire you will ask Mr Bowen, about my cast barrs for my Fathers Monument ...*' and in a later letter (17th August 1752), also to Bowen, Fuller asks for the rest of the iron rails to be cast, since the stones [for the monument] were ready cut and awaiting collection at Lewes.[22]

Style and Type

The existence of a local iron industry explains one of East Sussex's, near-unique contributions to the history of English monumental art, the extraordinary sets of cast ledgers that are encountered in several of the county's churches, most famously, at Wadhurst. These iron ledgers have been studied but rarely in the broader context of other parallel genres of commemorative art.[23] To summarise Willatt's authoritative account, these iron floor slabs are found in (but not far beyond) the iron-working area of the Weald, in about twenty churches. In fact, they are found hardly anywhere else in England. A total of about one hundred examples have been identified and they are mainly dedicated to the commemoration of iron-masters and their families; these iron ledgers do not commemorate the gentry. In terms of their production, the evidence suggests that they were made as a side-line, or alongside other cast iron goods, not by specialists. In particular, there is a significant interchange of function and manufacture between these commemorative ledgers and firebacks.[24] Production started in the sixteenth century and peaked in the seventeenth, going into sharp decline after c.1710.[25] Later examples complement cast inscriptions comprising letters and digits with ornamental and heraldic devices. In general, these iron ledgers employ a habitual element of repetition, as might be expected with a casting technique. Willatt has identified a group of seven slabs (the so-called 'AETATIS SUIE' series), with death dates between 1653 and 1667, probably all made in the same foundry at Wadhurst and employing re-used pattern blocks.[26] The chiselled incision of M.I.s into pre-cast slabs – rather than casting lettering and numbers into them – is a rarer development and one that took place after 1700.

In parallel with the local Sussex tradition of iron ledgers runs the production of incised lettering in stone slabs, a class of commemorative art found across England and of great historical importance but because of the inaccessibility of the material and a lack of a comprehensive corpus of photographs, little studied, at least in the post-Reformation period. In his will of 1546, Richard Stapleigh sought burial at Twineham, under a 'greater' stone for himself and a 'lesser' for his wife.[27] Writing her will (1554), Barbara Cumber of Pevensey noted that after her burial at Westham, William Fermer should provide two '*grete stones graven and thone [*one of them*] to be laid upon my late Husbande John Cumber and thother upon my selfe*'.[28] Directions concerning ledgers were often highly specific; for example, at

Winchelsea, where the will of George Lewis, 1553, directed that he be buried in St Nicholas' Chapel, *'under the whytt marble stone ... And the sayd stone to be layd upon one agayne Immedyately which stone ys myn own ...'.*[29] Robert Middleton, the vicar of Cuckfield, required that a stone be engraved to cover his late wife, that it be plain, not costly, and have *'both our epitaphs not too nigh lest the rail of the Communion Table cover it. I would have the reader told that I lie on her right hand'*, sure enough the engraved text read: *'On his left hand lieth the body of Mary ....'.*[30]

Many of these ledgers are now so worn that they represent a major challenge to cataloguers, although the present collection suggests that a good deal is possible with care, effort and a digital photography. Depending on material used, location and traffic across the church floor, some ledger inscriptions probably became worn quite quickly. G.S. Butler found the engraved lines on a ledger as hard (or as easy) to read in the 1860s as they are today and Horsfield noted that lines engraved c.1665 were virtually obliterated by the 1820s.[31]

Occasionally, it is possible to identify characteristics on lettering or decoration of ledgers which indicate the involvement of a particular workshop or the hand of a particular engraver and it is to be hoped that future close study of the photographs illustrating this catalogue will enable scholars to identify patterns of production and patronage. One group of engraved ledgers can be identified, deploying a characteristic fleur-de-lys motif crossing a decorative border in the four corners of the slab. This motif is carved on both black stone and other coloured freestone slabs, all dating from the last quarter of the eighteenth century, possibly as early as the mid 1760s.[32] The occurrence of the motif on slabs at Alfriston (4G) and at Lindfield (164U) - commemorating respectively William Batchelor and his wife and daughter - suggest that the family returned to a single maker as the need arose. Most of the ledgers in this group are found in churches in an area centred on Lewes, which was perhaps where they were made.[33]

Most of the East Sussex mural monuments are made of carved stone and the county survey shows every stage in the style history of monumental design in the county. The earliest stage covered by this catalogue is illustrated by a group of wall monuments, in a late Perpendicular style, erected to commemorate members of the social elite. Monuments like this date from both the pre- and post-Reformation periods and cross the present-day county boundary between East and West Sussex. The devotional changes marked by the Reformation determine the symbolic content of these tombs but not their overall architectural plan and their designs were affected by the turbulent histories of the religious institutions. The enormous arched monument to the Lords Dacre at Herstmonceux (131D) was first erected c.1500 and then revised in its form after 1539 when additional family effigies were moved to Herstmonceux from nearby Battle Abbey. We find a similar pattern at Slaugham (234D) where the Coverts set monuments up in the late 1520s and revised them in the late 1540s. The Oxenbridge monument at Brede (38C, dated 1537) is a similar object but in a plainer style with a projecting tomb-chest. It is carved from Caen stone, much sought after on the Sussex coast as a building material and enthusiastically salvaged from the ruins of Lewes Priory.[34] Two monuments at Isfield (145A-B), the former using some Purbeck 'marble', probably both date from after 1558 and are part of a campaign by the Shurleys to register their presence as lords of that manor. Finally, two other monuments in this stylistic group – very similar to each other - probably result from patron-families copying one another: they are at Selmeston (227C, dated 1532) and at Hamsey (120G, ordered after 1538) and are both built into niches in sanctuary north walls and display quatrefoil decorations and ornamental cresting.

Late Elizabethan and Jacobean monuments were often erected to commemorate the socially ambitious but they tend to use and reuse a relatively narrow range of motifs and components. East Sussex has a small set of monuments from this period, the low number illustrating the lack of major political players on the national stage amongst the county families at this time. They conform to the standard types, employing combinations of native and imported materials - primarily alabaster - and were London-made. Given the notorious state of the Sussex roads, transporting brittle, heavy loads such as ambitious carved stone monuments must have been a considerable challenge and we have to assume that coastal and navigable river waterways were used as much as was possible.

In the Elizabethan and Jacobean period, there are two significant trends in the forms that monuments took, the first associated with a short period c.1580 when a rather austere classicizing style was fashionable (145C, 234F) and when the supplementary effigial portraiture was as often carried out in brass as it was in stone (145C, 281B-E). In the second period, the Jacobean monuments use a greater variety of materials and they deploy more complex combinations of colour and decorative pattern. Their monumental effigies take the form of armoured knights carved in stone, either recumbent or kneeling against prayer-desks set in niches (56M, 72M, 112B, 201A) and flanked by standing angel-like figures, a device that remained current in the reign of Charles I (56D, 72P, 280C-D). In general, East Sussex is very short of important works by the great names of this important period of tomb-making; nothing in the county can be convincingly attributed to Nicholas Stone, Epiphanius Evesham, or William Wright.[35]

During the seventeenth century, monuments increasingly start to exploit allegorical combinations of verbal and visual conceits to communicate complex devotional and metaphysical ideas, for example, the engraved Carleton monument at Cuckfield (72G). Most dramatic of all in this period are East Sussex's unique contributions to England's small but select collection of funeral monuments that display the emotional devices of the full-blown theatrical Baroque. For this reason, the extraordinary works of the mid-1670s by Bushnell and Cibber at Ashburnham (11D) and Withyham (302J) are probably the most important works of English sculpture included in this catalogue.

The years around 1700 saw the introduction of a number of standard forms and themes, many imported as monumental ideas from continental sources, for example, Baroque Rome, via well-traveled sculptors originating from the Netherlands and elsewhere in north-west Europe. 39S and 71D are small wall monuments using a simulated textile effect to display a M.I., a Roman Baroque device initially developed by Gian Lorenzo Bernini (1598-1680) and perhaps first brought into England by Francis Bird.[36] James Gibbs's engraved *Book of Architecture* (1728) seems to have been an important source of some of these ideas, such as the ubiquitous pyramidal backdrop to the monumental composition (72H) and the naked boys, often in pairs or trios, playing within and around drapery and garlands of vegetation, which it seems were invented by the Flemish sculptor Duquesnoy (1597-1643) and which spread across Europe, from the mid-1680s, in cartouche form, in a type popularised initially by Arnold Quellin (1653-86). The quality of many of the small Baroque tablets that appear in the catalogue is often spectacular, although many are located high in side aisles and hard to see (72N-O). The frames of heraldic cartouches on eighteenth-century mural monuments of this kind are frequently the most Baroque element in the whole composition and in their playful ornament seemingly inconsistent with other sculptural elements (119A, 147D or 216A). Quite why heraldic devices could be playfully framed without a loss of dignity when inscribed texts demanded more austere presentation has yet to be explained.

A broader range of classical eighteenth- and nineteenth-century style-variants are represented by the signed and often documented work of sculptors who had a national reputation, many of whom are represented in the county: Flaxman,[37] Westmacott, Chantrey, Nollekens at Withyham (1802) and less known figures such as Rouw at Brightling c.1830. This shift towards a national market for monument-production paralleled the early nineteenth-century increase in numbers of costly public monuments being set up which was coupled with an attendant decline in the numbers of large monuments erected for private families and individuals in village churches. Explanations lie not only in the economic turn-down during Britain's long Revolutionary and Napoleonic wars against the French and pressing, alternative priorities for spending amongst private patrons but the inescapable fact that chapels and church walls were increasingly filling up with monuments. Under these circumstances, smaller mural monuments became an attractive option and were produced increasingly in regional workshops that gradually became firms, turning out well-designed small monuments, for example, that of Thomas King of Bath and the Fishers of York.[38] As we shall see, the monumental production of Parsons of Lewes needs to be seen within this tradition. The evidence of the monuments catalogued suggests that the markets operated on two major axes: on one hand the patrons' use of local suppliers and on the other a fashionable focus on London and beyond. Lewes was clearly a manufacturing centre for monuments of different kinds throughout the period covered by this survey. There were also other centres of manufacture in the east of the county, for example, at Rye, but these workshops seemed unable effectively to penetrate the markets to the north of the county. It is significant that 186A, at Northiam, is signed by a Canterbury maker, and was not supplied by an East Sussex tomb-maker.

The best example of mass production of monuments in the early nineteenth century is perhaps the firm established by John Bacon the Elder (1740-99), whose unpretentious smaller monuments are found in innumerable village churches. These were usually designed using standard themes and formal types, with the actual cutting left in the hands of assistants, an arrangement that was encouraged by Bacon's invention of a new kind of easily-handled pointing machine, designed to replicate carved stone forms.[39] His second son, John II (1777-1859) carried the firm on from 1799 to c.1808, working in partnership with Charles Manning who died 1812, (see 221WW and 221XX) and there were later successors too (see 234I, 276F and 299R).

Exactly how the national markets for monuments operated is not yet fully understood.[40] For East Sussex, we have rare documented references to tomb-making but these are not always easy to link to extant monuments. For example, on 9th November 1787, at Ditchling, a '*Mr. Rowland made an end of setting up of Toombes – He and 2 of his men came last Thursday. Set up one for Looker Chatfield 1 for Mr Beadle 1 for Mr Joseph Chatfield and Mrs His Wife, etc'.*[41] These were almost certainly churchyard monuments. By far the best documented manufacturer of East Sussex monuments was the Lewes firm of Parsons. Latter Parsons was town Headborough in 1815, a constable in 1827 and a juryman as late as 1832.[42] As Rupert Gunnis long ago pointed out, the firm flourished from the late 1780s to about 1860 and at his yard at Eastgate, Latter Parsons was joined by his son.[43] Church monuments must have been a staple of the Parson yard's output but he also worked on the ashlar masonry of the Lewes County Hall (1808) and his subscription to Horsfield's antiquarian account of Lewes published in 1824 suggests that he saw himself as more than merely an artisan mason.[44] As might be expected, the Parsons shop developed commercial relationships with their colleagues in allied trades. As John Farrant has shown, in c.1800, May and Parsons were selling a typical churchyard head-and-foot tomb stone of Porland stone, with linking iron rails, for £4-5, plus the cost of transport.[45] Church monuments from the Parsons yard – often but not always signed – can be found across the county. At Seaford, there is a large concentration, many signed: to Nathaniel Harrison, died 1855, and to Ann Soper, died 1845, on the west wall of the nave, and to James Walker, died 1831, and to Sarah Jane Michell, died 1836, on the south wall of the tower. At South Malling, the mural monument to Charles Harrison, died 1832, on the south wall of the nave is probably by Parsons although only the Avalanche Disaster memorial on 1836 on the north wall is signed. At Uckfield, there is a monument by Parsons in the south aisle.

The output of the Parsons yard at Lewes was relatively pedestrian in its use of materials, combinations of colour and choice of forms, but some other East Sussex monuments from this period are exotic imports, the most striking being the mural monument for Georgina Naylor, died 1806, at Herstmonceux (131E). This ambitious work includes a death-bed scene in bas relief with an angel and distraught relatives around the deceased and records Naylor's death at Lausanne in Switzerland on Easter Sunday 1804. It was carved many years later by a Danish sculptor called Kesels (1784-1836) employed by her children.

The contrast between the local and the foreign is a powerful theme running through the catalogue of monuments and is an issue that throws valuable light on the choices made by patrons and tomb-makers about sculptural materials. In the heyday of the Parsons workshop, all the East Sussex makers were using imported black and white marbles, for example, John and Major Vidler of Hastings (the latter working in the 1820s and '30s), John Smith of Rye (flourished from the mid 1810s to c.1850), Williams of Brighton whose practice was perhaps taken over in 1829 by Bennett.[46] But none of these early makers is well documented and the four monuments signed by Williams (1C, 49C, 75A and 195D) show a wide variety of styles, which makes attribution of these kinds of non-figural works extremely challenging, though deserving additional research. John Marten of Tenterden is an intriguing figure who seems to have operated both as a mason and as a painter of church panels. At Ticehurst, the Lord's Prayer is painted on a wooden panel, signed and dated by Marten in 1764. Another figure of considerable interest is the multi-talented Walter Gale, schoolmaster and practitioner of several trades including the engraving of tombstones (and ledgers?) and the painting of church boards (commemorative and heraldic?). Gale also had literary interests and wrote an ambitious response to the important set of monuments at Withyham in his diary.[47] A Parsons contemporary was Isaac Hargraves, also of Lewes, who surfaces briefly in the mid 1790s and signs a rather delicate and inventive mural tablet at Horsted Keynes (137C). By contrast, for an earlier Lewes maker, John Morris, the record is fuller: he worked from the 1750s through to 1775, was an expert in freestone and a member of a dynasty stretching back to the early years of the century when his grandfather, Arthur, worked under Dubois at Stanmer House.[48] In the later 1750s, John Morris worked at Glynde Place and was still active as late as 1775 when he signed the Lushington monument (93K) at Eastbourne, pendant to a Willard monument (93H), which must be another of his works, as is perhaps an earlier Lushington monument (93A). It is also known that Morris owned fragmentary panels from the late Elizabethan Goring monument in St Michael's, Lewes (160H), which came into his possession in partial settlement of a debt and which later reappeared in the collection of C.F. Bridgeman, his business successor.

Most local East Sussex stone was hardly suitable for carved monuments. At Heathfield, this fact was confronted head on by the Harmer family, who used local clays to develop a style of cast terracotta decorative panel, which were used on monuments and for similar purposes. There are examples in the churches at Hailsham, Heathfield, Mayfield, Wadhurst and Warbleton and in several East Sussex churchyards (for example, Glynde). The key figure in this practice was Jonathan Harmer, briefly in the United States in the late 1790s, whose cast clay motifs also appear in cast iron form (at Wartling churchyard) suggesting a willingness to transfer between techniques in the search for business.[49] This pattern is confirmed by the discovery that the Lewes clockmaker John Holman engraved at least one monumental brass (see 157P).

As the name suggests, the so-called Sussex Marble is a local version of Wealden marble of the 'large Paludina' type. The stone is also known as Bethersden, Kentish, Petworth (the Kirdford quarry here is a main source), Laughton and Winklestone (from the fresh-water univalves fossilized in it). It is a blue-grey limestone, mottled with green and yellow ochre and in nature it is tight-grained and it takes a high polish. By the nineteenth century, the small pits in which it is found had been worked out and although it was in use from the Norman period, very few monuments in this survey feature the material. In fact, Sussex Marble is more commonly used in West Sussex, Kent and Surrey than in East Sussex.[50]

These observations on availability, carving potential and cost bring us finally to the key question of what motivated the East Sussex patrons to pay for monuments to be erected in their parish churches, not always with the full backing of their fellow parishioners. In 1734, Mr Stapley of Hickstead - for the family see Twineham - attended a vestry meeting at Cuckfield called by '*Mr Sergison, concerning the setting up of a Monument in the Chancel on the North Wall. The Vicar opposed him. But the Vestry decided it should be erected*' and 72H remains there to this day: it still has supporters and detractors![51] Sometimes the local incumbents must have been victors in such disputes, whether or not they were the patrons of particular chapels or chancels and on occasions they managed their church spaces to the direct advantage of their own families. 93A is a remarkable monument erected to the memory of Henry Lushington, son of the vicar of Eastbourne (of the same name), killed in India in 1763 after a harrowing incarceration in the infamous 'Black Hole' of Calcutta. His father had an elegant monument erected in the niche formerly occupied by the Easter sepulchre on the north sanctuary wall, perhaps the most prestigious commemorative site in the church. 93A was moved to the west end of the church in 1851, after the Rev Henry Lushington's influence had waned. At Rye, a remarkable M.I. alludes to what must have been a heated dispute about burial rights, so heated in fact that perpetual reference to it was made in the engraved text. The ledger installed in the south transept floor (now in the north transept) in memory of Ralph and Anne Norton, some time after 1750, by their daughters Catherine and Elizabeth, notes that the request of the elderly couple '*to be laid near each other*' had been denied '*by the wanton Exercise of Power*'. At Salehurst, another ledger records the deaths of Robert Fowle and his son in the 1680s in simple terms although in the 1650s the Fowle family's rights on burial in the chancel there had been disputed by the vicar.[52]

Throughout the period covered by the catalogue, the commitment of families to their pedigrees and marriage connections remains undiminished and is one of the key messages communicated by the monuments. The Willards were buried at Hailsham and at Eastbourne and at the latter church Thomas Willard (died 1794) is commemorated together with his widow and their children by means of a monument of c.1810 (93G), which also names family members as far back into history as 1559. At Hailsham, in 1839, the family supplemented the Eastbourne monuments by erecting another tablet setting out their pedigree.

Other M.I.s were concerned more with personal devotion, spirituality and bereavement, for example, the extraordinary self-deprecating, moralizing wording on 258H, a ledger that notes that Samuel Newington's widow Anne (died 1757) both remarried and died on a Saturday. By contrast with the intimate quirkiness of this observation, the M.I.s on the more public-facing Hooper cenotaphs at Beckley and Hailsham stress the family's charitable donations, increasingly an important theme for monuments through the eighteenth century. Some M.I.s are narrowly, even eccentrically, topical in their wording, for example, the reference on 20D at Battle to the 'United Ionian Islands', a nomenclature that applied to Cephalonia for a short period only, or on nearby 20B, the wording of which demonstrates that the text must have been agreed during the brief period between the Battle of Salamanca and Wellington's elevation to his dukedom.

The corpus of M.I.s made available by the catalogue and the accompanying illustrations will take a great deal of further analysis but some preliminary findings can be signaled here. These inscriptions are intended to be permanent statements, to establish and maintain positions by means of symbolism, fact (sometimes chosen selectively) and narrative. Historical research will help deal with the silences and omissions that can be identified in these commemorative texts, as well as supplementing the commentary they represent. Allen Grebell, of a long-established Rye family, having reached the age of 50 and having been elected mayor of the town was murdered in 1742 'by the cruel stab of a sanguinary butcher' called Breads, whose intended victim had apparently been the previous mayor, James Lamb.[53] The M.I. on Grebell's ledger (221T) is silent on what his contemporaries would have regarded as a 'Bad Death', the shameful details of which were thought inappropriate to be perpetuated by a memorial.

The social and historical value of the texts collected in these M.I.s is immense: we learn that unmarried women of a certain age could be recorded as 'Mrs'[54] and that gender difference can be indicated by language, for example, on 306M where the biography of a cleric is set out in Latin while that of his wife is in English. Many of these commemorative texts are concerned with didactic messages, in the tradition of the *memento mori*, an aspect of spirituality that survived the Reformation. In fact, some M.I.s suggest that the pattern of religious change could be slow. A ledger at Worth (306I) commemorating a lady who died in 1679 still uses the orthodox Roman wording '*On whose soule Jesus have mercy*' and there are earlier examples engraved when Reformation statutes expressly forbade such sentiments.[55]

Once the field-work on West Sussex has been undertaken and the results published, a complete catalogue of Sussex church monuments, 1530-1830, will allow historians to tackle these and many other complex research questions. Meanwhile, it is hoped that the publication of this set of Sussex records will play some role in furthering scholarly and public understanding of church monuments, a fascinating aspect of historical material and visual culture and a valuable part of the county's heritage.[56]

Nigel Llewellyn

Lewes

16 September 2010

Notes

1   Website address is www.sussexrecordsociety.org. For more material and commentary on many of the general issues touched on in this introduction see *Funeral Monuments in post-Reformation England* (2000) by Nigel Llewellyn.

2   In a warm review of Katherine Arundel Esdaile's *English Monumental Sculpture since the Renaissance* appeared in *Sussex Notes and Queries*, 2 1928 32

3   Glynne worked too late for consideration by Farrant. See the list of locations covered by Glynne in *SNQ* VIII 1940-41 158ff and a longer account in *SNQ* XVI (2) 1963-7 53-62.

4   Nairn & Pevsner (42).

5   Kingsley (91-6)

6   Kingsley (57 and 63)

7   Kingsley (101)

8   Kingsley (166-8)

9   Courthope (*SAC* 51 65-98) and an edition by SC Lomas was published by the Royal Historical Society with a transcript at p.95

10 Ford (*passim*)

11 Manning (*SAC* 106 103-112) superseded by Caplan (*SAC* 116 19-29)

12 Cooper (*SAC* 45 142ff.)

13 ibid

14 For an introduction to the visual culture of the English death ritual *The Art of Death*, (1990), by Nigel Llewellyn

15 For Burgess see Sawyer (*SAC* 40 144ff); for the woollen burial act see Bird (118) and for records reflecting this burial custom see Putron (*SAC* 18 190-3), submitted by the then vicar of Rodmell.

16 Steer (*SAC* 98 156ff)

17 The photographs of the monuments do, however, allow us to include these records, visually rather than verbally.

18 Farrant (201)

19 Renshaw (*SAC* 49 47-65)

20 For the general increase in monuments c.1600, see Llewellyn *(Monuments)*

21 S Berry (*SAC* 142 107ff)

22 Crossley & Saville (252 & 272)

23 Willatts (*SAC* 125 99-103) with a microfiche illustrating additional examples. See now Hodgkinson..

24 See Ardingly (8) Addition.

25 Nairn & Pevsner (58)

26 At Maresfield (172G), Salehurst (222BB and CC) and at Wadhurst (270SS, TT, W and YY)

27 Rice & Godfrey (IV 261) and Introduction to Twineham (263) and for later ledgers to this family 263A, C and D.

28 Rice & Godfrey (IV 333)

29 Rice & Godfrey (IV 365)

30 J. Cooper (*SAC* 50 12) and see Cuckfield (72) Addition 4

31 An anonymous ledger at Rye (221O) and a ledger to an anonymous male member of the Wood family, c.1665, at West Hoathly (283G).

32 Monuments 4G, 159L, 164Q, 164U, 292C & 298E

33 The outlier being the later slab at Westham (292C)

34 Maurice Howard, *The Building of Elizabethan and Jacobean England* (2007), pp. 24-28 & footnote and Richard K. Morris, '*Monastic Architecture: Destruction and Reconstruction*' in D. Gaimster and R. Gilchrist, eds, The Archaeology of

Reformation, 1480-1580, Leeds, 2003, pp. 235-51.

35   White (*Biographical Dictionary*)

36   Whinney (96)

37   Flaxman is best studied at Chichester Cathedral especially the important early monument to William Collins, for which see David Bindman (ed) *John Flaxman R.A.*, London, Royal Academy of Arts exhibition catalogue 1979 113-115.

38   Whinney (319, 361)

39   Whinney (308-110). Our knowledge of Bacon's practice will be transformed by the imminent publication of a major study by Dr Sarah Rees Jones of the University of York.

40   The major research project at the University of Glasgow, 'Mapping the Practice and Profession of Sculpture in Britain and Ireland 1851-1951' led by Dr Anne Compton and ending in 2010 will throw considerable light on these questions.

41   Sawyer (*SAC* 40 147)

42   Smith (206, 256, 292)

43   Gunnis (*Dict.* 292)

44   Horsfield (1824 I xiii)

45   Farrant (292)

46   See his tablets from the 1840s at Bolney

47   Blencowe (*SAC* 9 182ff)

48   See *SAC* 70 222

49   On the Harmer terracottas see Perceval Lucas, Heathfield Memorials, 1910; Gunnis (*Dict.*); and R.G.H. d'Elboux in *SNQ* 12 1948-9 54-7

50   See the monuments at Isfield and Slaugham. For Sussex Marble see G.H. Kempson's note in *SNQ* 5 1934-5 26-7 and I learned a good deal on the topic from personal communications from the late Dr Ron Firmin.

51   Turner (*SAC* 23 68-9)

52   See 222X and for the dispute Hussey (*SAC* 25 161). Lucy Fowle was well connected which perhaps enabled her to influence the outcome of the dispute.

53   See Vidler in *SNQ* XI 1946-7 49-51

54   See 222O commemorating Mary Peckham (d.1805)

55   See Hooe (135) Additions 1-2

56   Since this project was started, I have learned of the national photographic survey of monuments, designed for publication on CD-ROM or DVD and now intended to be consulted by means of the internet (See Cameron B Newham 2009)

ABBREVIATIONS

Abbreviation	Description
(H)	Height
(L)	Length
(W)	Width
add. or Add.	additional or Additional
aet	aetatis or at the age of
AM	Artium Magister (or MA)
an. reg.	anno regni or year of the reign
bap.	baptised
Bart.	Baronet
BCL	Bachelor of Canon/Civil Law
BL	British Library
BLG	Burke's Landed Gentry
BM	British Museum
bur.	buried
CCEd	Clergy of the Church of England database
d.	died
DD	Doctor of Divinity
DMS or D.M.S.	Dis Manibus Sacrum, or sacred to the spirits of the dead
Esq.	Esquire
ESRO	East Sussex Record Office
f.	folio
fl.	floruit or flourished
Gent.	Gentleman
IGI	International Genealogical Index
IPM	Inquisition Post Mortem
JH	John Hawkins
Knt.	Knight
Lieut.	Lieutenant
Lieut-Col. and Lt. Col.	Lieutenant Colonel
LLD	Doctor of Laws
M.I.	Monument Inscription
MP	Member of Parliament
MS(S)	manuscript(s)
NADFAS	National Association of Decorative & Fine Arts Societies
NBI	National Burial Index
NL	Nigel Llewellyn
ODNB	Oxford Dictionary of National Biography
PRO	Public Record Office
Regt.	Regiment
SAC	Sussex Archaeological Collections
SCM	Sussex County Magazine
SFHG	Sussex Family History Group
SNQ	Sussex Notes & Queries
SRS	Sussex Record Society
STD	Doctor of Sacred Theology
TAQ	terminus ante quem or the latest date for an event
TNA	The National Archives
TPQ	terminus post quem or the earliest date for an event
V&A	Victoria & Albert Museum
VCH	Victoria County History

BIBLIOGRAPHY

Introductory note

Most titles and articles cited in the text have been included in the following bibliography. References to items cited only once in the text have been given their full title there but have not been listed here - nor have references to short notes in journals.

Titles of separate books (as opposed to articles) have normally been cited in the text with a short title, e.g. Comber, J. *Sussex Genealogies – Ardingly Centre* is listed as Comber (*Ardingly* pp) where pp identifies the page number(s). Where the book has multiple volumes the referenced volume is shown as vv. For clarity, the entry for authors of separate books also includes the short title citation.

Articles are identified with the author's name, book, volume (vv) and page (pp).

André, J.L., 'Female Head-Dresses, Exemplified by Sussex Brasses', *SAC* vol. 42 (1899) pp 1-18

André, J.L., 'Battle Church', *SAC* vol. 42 (1899) pp 214-236

Armytage, G.J., *Musgrave's Obituary prior to 1800*, Harleian Society (1899-1901) 6 vols.; cited as Armytage (*Musgrave* vv pp)

Armytage, G.J., *A Visitation of the County of Kent 1663-1668.*, Harleian Society (1906); cited as Armytage (*Kent* pp)

Arnold, F.H., 'Memoir of the Rev. E. Turner, M.A., V.P.', *SAC* vol. 25 (1873) pp 213-219

Attree, F.W.T., 'Monumental Inscriptions in Ditchling, Church and Churchyard', *SAC* vol. 28 (1878) pp 132-147

Attree, F.W.T., 'Wivelsfield, History of the Parish', Pt. I *SAC* vol. 35 (1888) pp 1-60 and Pt. II *SAC* vol. 36 (1889) pp 19-74

Attree, F.W.T., *Post Mortem Inquisitions in Sussex 1485-1649*, SRS vol. 14 (1912); cited as Attree (*SRS* 14 pp)

Attree, F.W.T. & Booker J.H.L., 'The Sussex Colepeppers', Pt. I *SAC* vol. 47 (1904) pp 47-81; Pt. II *SAC* vol. 48 (1905) pp 65-98

Awty, B. & Whittick, C., 'The Lordship of Canterbury, iron founding at Buxted', *SAC* vol. 120 (2002) pp 71-81

Bacon, J., *Liber Regis vel Thesaurus Rerum Ecclesiasticarum* (1786); cited as Bacon (pp)

Bannerman, W.B., *The Visitations of Sussex 1530, 1633-4.*, Harleian Society (1905); cited as Bannerman (*Sussex* pp)

Bax, A.R., 'Inscriptions in the church and churchyard of Lindfield, co. Sussex', *SAC* vol. 37 (1890) pp 151-172

Bax, A.R., 'Inscriptions in the churchyard and crypt of St. Clements Hastings', *SAC* vol. 49 (1906) pp 105-119

Bell-Irving, E.M., *Mayfield - The Story of an Old Wealden Village* (1903); cited as Bell-Irving (pp)

Berry, S., 'Laughton Church chancel and other major church alterations in and around Lewes, East Sussex, c. 1740 – 1810', *SAC* vol. 142 (2004) pp 107ff

Berry, W., *Pedigrees of the Families in the County of Sussex* (1830); cited as W. Berry (*Sussex* pp)

Berry, W., *Pedigrees of the Families in the County of Hampshire* (1833); cited as W. Berry (Hampshire pp)

Betham, W., *Baronetage* (1801-5) 5 vols.; cited as Betham (vv pp)

Bindoff, S.T., *The House of Commons 1509-1558*, The History of Parliament Trust (1982) 4 vols.; cited as Bindoff (vv pp)

Birch, R., *Sussex Stones* (2006); cited as Birch (pp)

Bird, Ruth (ed.), *The Journal of Giles Moore of Horsted Keynes, 1655–1679*, SRS vol. 68 (1971); cited as Bird (pp)

Blaauw, W.H., 'Wakehurst, Slaugham and Gravetye', *SAC* vol. 10 (1858) pp 151-167

Blencowe, R.W., 'Extracts from the Journal and Account Book of Timothy Burrell ...', *SAC* vol. 3 (1850) pp 117-172

Blencowe, R.W. , 'Extracts from the Journal of Walter Gale, Schoolmaster at Mayfield', *SAC* vol. 9 (1857) pp 182-207

Blencowe, R.W. , 'Extracts from the MSS ... of William John Campion ... and of Sir Thomas Maryon Wilson', *SAC* vol. 10 (1858) pp 1-35

Blencowe, R.W., 'Extracts from the memoirs of the Gale Family', *SAC* vol. 12 (1860) pp 45-60

Brent, C.E., *Georgian Lewes 1714-1830: the Heyday of a County Town* (1993); cited as C. Brent (pp)

Brent, J., 'The Pooles of Chailey and Lewes', *SAC* vol. 114 (1976) pp 69-80

Budgen, W. (ed.), *Abstracts of Documents relating to the Dobell Family*, SRS vol. 29 (1924); cited as Budgen (*Dobell* pp)

Budgen, W., *Old Eastbourne, its Church, its Clergy, its People* (c. 1912); cited as Budgen (*Eastbourne* pp)

Burke, B., *General Armory* (1884); cited as R. Burke (*Armory* pp)

Burke, J., *Extinct and Dormant Baronetcies* (1841) 2nd edition; cited as J. Burke (*Baronetcies* pp)

Burke's Landed Gentry various editions, from 1834; cited as BLG (edn. [i.e. year] pp)

Burtchaell G. & Sadleir T., *Alumni Dublinenses 1593-1860* (1935) 3 vols.; cited as Burtchaell & Sadleir (vv pp)

Butler, G.S., 'The Vicars of Rye and their Patrons, with the mural, slab and headstone inscriptions in the Parish Church ...', *SAC* vol. 13 (1861) pp 270-301

Butler, G.S., 'Inscriptions in Icklesham Church', *SAC* vol. 14 (1862) pp 258-62

Butler, G.S., 'Topographia Sussexiana, an attempt towards forming a list of the various publications relating to the county of Sussex', *SAC* vol. 15 (1863) pp 214-30; vol. 16 (1864) pp 273-290; vol. 17 (1865) pp 169-184; vol. 18 (1866) pp 87-110

Butler, G.S., 'The Church of St Mary, Rye', *SAC* vol. 22 (1870) pp 124-133

Caffyn, J., *Sussex Schools in the 18th Century*, SRS vol. 81 (1998); cited as Caffyn (pp)

Caplan, N., 'The Sussex Catholics, c. 1660-1800', *SAC* vol. 116 (1978) pp 19-29

Chapman, R., 'The Parochial History of Hamsey', *SAC* vol.17 (1865) pp 70-103

Clarke, A.W.H., *The Visitation of Sussex 1662*, Harleian Society (1937) vol. 89; cited as A. Clarke (*Sussex* pp)

Clarke, S., 'S. Nicholas Church, Brighton', *SAC* vol. 32 (1882) pp 33-74

Clayton, C.E., 'Hangleton and its History', *SAC* vol. 34 (1886) pp 167-184

Cleere, H. & Crossley, D., *The Iron Industry of the Weald* (1995); cited as Cleere & Crossley (pp)

Clergy of the Church of England database (ongoing project); www.theclergydatabase.org. uk ongoing project

Cockayne, G.E., *Complete Baronetage* (1983 reprint) 6 vols in 1; cited as Cockayne (*Baronetage* vv pp)

Cockayne, G.E., *The Complete Peerage* (1987 reprint) 14 vols. in 6; cited as Cockayne (*Peerage* vv pp)

Comber, J., *Sussex Genealogies – Horsham Centre* (1931); cited as Comber (*Horsham* pp)

Comber, J., *Sussex Genealogies – Ardingly Centre* (1932); cited as Comber (*Ardingly* pp)

Comber, J., *Sussex Genealogies – Lewes Centre* (1933); cited as Comber (*Lewes* pp)

Cooper, G.M., 'Berwick Parochial Records', *SAC* vol. 6 (1853) pp 223-243

Cooper, J.H., 'Old Cuckfield Families', *SAC* vol. 41 (1898) pp 203-215; vol. 42 (1899) pp 19-53; vol. 43 (1900) pp 1-44 & pp 279-280

Cooper, J.H., 'The Vicars and Parish of Cuckfield', *SAC* vol. 45 (1902) pp 1-33; vol. 46 (1903) pp 94-113; vol. 50 (1907) pp 1-19

Cooper, J.H., 'The Coverts - Part II', *SAC* vol. 47 (1904) pp 116-147

Cooper, J.H., 'Cuckfield Families: The Wardens', *SAC* vol. 49 (1906) pp 89-104

Cooper, W.D., *The History of Winchelsea* (1851); cited as W. Cooper (pp)

Cooper, W.D., 'Royalist Compositions in Sussex during the Commonwealth', *SAC* vol. 19 (1867) pp 91-120

Couchman, J.E., 'Sussex Church Plate', *SAC* vol. 53 (1910) pp 198-266; vol. 54 (1911) pp 123-258; vol. 55 (1912) pp 126-219

Courthope, F.G., 'Extracts from the Memoirs of Sir George Courthope, 1616-1685', *SAC* vol. 51 (1908) pp 65-98

Crawfurd, R.P. (ed.), *East Grinstead Parish Register, 1558-1661, SRS* vol. 24 (1917); cited as Crawfurd (pp)

Crossley, D. & Saville, R., *The Fuller Letters, 1728-1755, SRS* vol. 76 (1991); cited as Crossley & Saville (pp)

Cruikshanks, etc., *The House of Commons 1690-1715*, The History of Parliament Trust (2002) 5 vols.; cited as Cruikshanks (vv pp)

Dallaway, J. & Cartwright, E., *Parochial Topography Bramber Rape 1830* ; cited as Dallaway (*Bramber* pp)

Davey, L.S., *The Street Names of Lewes* (1981) revised edition; cited as L. Davey (pp)

Davey, R.(ed.), *East Sussex Land Tax, 1785, SRS* vol. 77 (1991); cited as R. Davey (pp)

Davidson-Houston, Mrs C.E.D., 'Sussex Monumental Brasses', *SAC* vol. 76 (1935) pp 46-114; vol. 77 (1936) pp 130-194; vol. 78 (1937) pp 63-125; vol. 79 (1938) pp 74-130; vol. 80 (1939) pp 93-147

D'Elboux, R.H., 'Sussex Monumental Brasses Addenda', *SAC* vol. 86 (1947) pp 118-125

D'Elboux, R.H., 'Jonathan Harmer's Terracottas', *SNQ* vol. XII (1948-9) pp 54-57

De St. Croix, W., 'Parochial History of Glynde', *SAC* vol. 19 (1867) pp 47-90

Dennis, R.N., 'Monumental Inscriptions, East Blatchington', *SAC* vol. 13 (1861) p 302

Dunkin, E.H.W., 'History of the Deanery of South Malling', *SAC* vol. 26 (1875) pp 9-96

Dunkin, E.H.W., *Calendar of Sussex Marriage Licences – Archdeaconry of Lewes, August 1586 to March 1642-3, SRS* vol. 1 (1901); cited as Dunkin (*Licences 1586-1643* pp)

Dunkin, E.H.W., *Calendar of Sussex Marriage Licences – Archdeaconry of Lewes 1670 to 1728-9, and Deanery of South Malling 1620 to 1732, SRS* vol. 6 (1907); cited as Dunkin (*Licences 1670-1729* pp)

Dunkin, E.H.W., & Penfold, E.W.D., *Calendar of Sussex Marriage Licences – Archdeaconry of Lewes and Deanery of South Malling, 1772-1837, SRS* vol. 25 & 26 (1917 & 1919); cited as Dunkin & Penfold (*Licences* pp)

Eardley, F.S., *Horsted Keynes, Sussex - The Church and Parish of St. Giles* (1939); cited as Eardley (pp)

Eeles, H.S., *Frant - A Parish History* (1947); cited as Eeles (pp)

Ellman, E., 'Crawley Monumental Inscriptions', *SAC* vol. 24 (1872) pp 301-3.

Elvin, C.N., *Handbook of Mottoes* (1860) revised 1971; cited as Elvin (pp)

Emden, A.B., *Biographical Register of Cambridge to 1500* (1963); cited as Emden (pp)

Esdaile, K.A., *English Monumental Sculpture since the Renaissance* (1927); cited as Esdaile (*EMS* pp)

Esdaile, K.A., 'Notes on the Sackville monuments at Withyham Church', *SNQ* vol. IV (1932-33) pp 120-1.

Esdaile, K.A., 'Some Sussex Monuments 3: Cibber's Sackville Monument at Withyham', *SNQ* VIII (1940-41) pp 185-7

Esdaile, K.A., 'An incised slab at Cuckfield', *SAC* vol. 82 (1942) pp 96-103

Esdaile, K.A., *English Church Monuments, 1510-1840* (1946); cited as Esdaile (*ECM* pp)

Fairbairn, J., *Fairbairn's Crests* (1986); cited as Fairbairn (pp)

Farrant, J.H., 'The Making of Francis Grose's Antiquities', *SAC* vol. 131 (1993) pp 152-158

Farrant, J.H., *Sussex Depicted: Views and Descriptions 1600 – 1800, SRS* vol. 85 (2001); cited as Farrant (pp)

Figg, W., 'On Bishopstone Church', *SAC* vol. 2 (1849) pp 272-284

Fitzgerald-Uniacke, R.G., 'The Barhams of Shoesmiths in Wadhurst', *SAC* vol. 56 (1914) pp 110-160

Ford, W.K., *Chichester Diocesan Surveys, 1686 and 1724, SRS* vol. 78 (1994); cited as Ford (pp)

Foster, J., *Alumni Oxonienses* (From 1891) Pt. I 1500–1714, 4 vols; Pt. 2 1715-1886, 4 vols.; cited as Foster (*Al Ox* Pt. vv pp)

Foster, J., *Peerage, Baronetage and Knightage of the British Empire for 1880*; cited as Foster (*Peerage* pp)

Godfrey, W.H. (ed.), *The Book of John Rowe, Steward of the Manor of Lord Bervavenny, 1597-1622, SRS* vol. 34 (1928); cited as Godfrey (pp)

Godfrey, W.H., 'Church of St. Anne, Lewes', *SAC* vol. 69 (1928) pp 159-69

Godfrey, W.H., 'The Parish Church of St. Andrew, Bishopstone', *SAC* vol. 87 (1848) pp 164-83

Godfrey, W.H. & Salzman, L.F. (eds.), *Sussex Views from the Burrell Collection, SRS* Jubilee volume (1951, reissued 2001); cited as Godfrey & Salzman (pp)

Godman, P.S., 'Allotment of Sittings in Sedlescombe Church', *SAC* vol. 52 (1909) pp 96-9

Gomme, G.L, *Topographical History of... Sussex... [from] The Gentleman's Magazine from 1731-1868* (1900); cited as Gomme (pp)

Gower, G.L., 'Monumental Inscriptions from the Church at Horsted Keynes, Sussex', *SAC* vol. 34 (1886) pp 107-120

Grayling, J.F., 'Notes on St. Peter's Church, Twineham', *SAC* vol. 59 (1918) pp 113-5

Grose, F., *Antiquities of England & Wales* (ca. 1770/80s) Date and no. of volumes depend on edition.; cited as Grose (Edn. vv pp)

Gunnis, R., *Dictionary of British Sculptors 1660 – 1851* (1968 edn.); cited as Gunnis (*Dict.* pp)

Gunnis, R., 'Monuments by John Flaxman in Sussex', *SAC* vol. 97 (1959) pp 82-88

Hannah, I.C., 'Crawley', *SAC* vol. 55 (1912) pp 1-18

Harper, R.W.E., *Heraldry in Wadhurst Church*, (c. 1980); cited as Harper (*Heraldry* pp)

Harrison, L., *Inspiring Sussex Gardeners*, (2008); cited as Harrison (pp)

Hasler, P.W., *The House of Commons 1558-1603*, The History of Parliament Trust (1981) 3 vols.; cited as Hasler (vv pp)

Hennessy, G., *Chichester Diocese Clergy Lists* (1900); cited as Hennessy (pp)

Henning, B.D., *The House of Commons 1660 – 1690*, The History of Parliament Trust (1983) 3 vols.; cited as Henning (vv pp)

Hoare, H.R., 'Notes on... St Thomas à Becket, Framfield', *SAC* vol. 4 (1851) pp 291-304

Hodgkinson, J., *The Wealden Iron Industry*, The History Press (2008); cited as Hodgkinson (pp)

Hodson, L.J. and Odell J.A., *Ticehurst: The Story of a Sussex Parish* (1925); cited as Hodson & Odell (pp)

Holgate, M.S. (ed.), *Sussex Inquisitions (from Bodleian Library), 1541-1616, SRS* vol. 33 (1927); cited as Holgate (pp)

Holland, S., 'Monumental Inscriptions, Poynings', *SAC* vol. 15 (1863) pp 231-3

Horn, J.M., *Fasti Ecclesiæ Anglicanæ 1300-1541, vol. VII, Chichester Diocese* (1964); cited as Horn (*Fasti 1300-1541* pp)

Horn, J.M., *Fasti Ecclesiæ Anglicanæ 1541-1857, vol. II, Chichester Diocese* (1971); cited as Horn (*Fasti 1541-1857* II pp)

Horn, J.M., *Fasti Ecclesiæ Anglicanæ 1541-1857, vol. VII, Ely, Norwich, Westminster and Worcester Diocese* (1992); cited as Horn (*Fasti 1541-1857* VII pp)

Horsfield, T.W., *The History and Antiquities of Lewes and its Vicinity* (1824) 2 vols.; cited as Horsfield (*Lewes* vv pp)

Horsfield, T.W., *The History, Antiquities and Topography of the County of Sussex* (1835) 2 vols.; cited as Horsfield (*Sussex* vv pp)

Humphery-Smith, C.R., *Armigerous Ancestors* (1997); cited as Humphery-Smith (pp)

Hussey, R.C., 'Some entries in Salehurst Parish Books', *SAC* vol. 25 (1873) pp 152-162

Huth, E. (ed.), *The Parish Registers of Bolney, Sussex 1541-1812, SRS* vol. 15 (1912); cited as Huth (pp)

Huxford, J.F., *Arms of Sussex Families,* (1982); cited as Huxford (pp)

International Genealogical Index; www.familysearch.org; cited as IGI

Irwin, D., *John Flaxman, 1755 – 1826; Sculptor, Illustrator, Designer* (1929); cited as Irwin (pp)

Johnstone, H., *Churchwardens Presentments (17th century) Part II: Archdeaconry of Lewes*, SRS vol. 50 (1950); cited as Johnstone (pp)

Kent, T., *Sussex Silver and its Makers* (2002); cited as Kent (pp)

Kingsley, D., *Printed Maps of Sussex 1575-1900*, SRS vol. 72 (1982); cited as Kingsley (pp)

Lambarde, F., 'Coats of Arms in Sussex Churches', SAC vols. 67-75 (1926-35)

Leeney, O.H., 'Ancient Sussex Churches in the Ecclesiologist', SAC vol. 83 (1942/3) pp 137-50; vol. 84 (1944-5) pp 114-52; vol. 86 (1947) pp 155-186; vol. 87 (1948) pp 184-207; vol. 88 (1949) pp 157-178.

Leslie, K.C. and Short, B., *An Historical Atlas of Sussex*, (1999); cited as Leslie (pp)

Lewis, J.M., *Welsh Monumental Brasses. A Guide*, National Museum of Wales (1974); cited as J. Lewis (pp)

Lewis, S., *A Topographical Dictionary of England* (1844) 5th edition, 4 vols.; cited as S. Lewis (vv pp)

Ley, J., 'Waldron, its Church…', SAC vol. 13 (1861) pp 80-103

Livett, G.M., 'Three East Sussex Churches: Battle, Peasmarsh, Icklesham', Pt. II SAC vol. 47 (1904) pp 35-46 and Pt III SAC vol. 48 (1905) pp 38-64

Llewellyn, N, *Funeral Monuments in post-Reformation England*, (2000); cited as Llewellyn (*Monuments* pp)

Llewellyn, N, *The Art of Death*, (1990); cited as Llewellyn (*Art of Death* pp)

Loder, G.W.E. (ed.), *The Parish Registers of Ardingly, 1558-1812*, SRS vol. 17 (1913) Loder, G.W.E. (ed.) The Parish Registers of Ardingly, 1558-1812, (SRS vol. 17, 1913); cited as Loder (pp)

Lower, M.A., 'Historical and Archaeological notices of Iron Works …', SAC vol. 2 (1849) pp 169-220.

Lower, M.A., 'Memorials of the Town, Parish & Cinque Port of Seaford', SAC vol. 7 (1854) pp 73-150.

Lower, M.A., 'Parochial History of Chiddingly', SAC vol. 14 (1862) pp 207-258

Lower, M.A., 'Sussex Iron Works and Iron Masters', SAC vol. 18 (1866) pp 11-16

Lower, M.A., 'Notes on the Family of Whitfeld or Whitfield …', SAC vol. 19 (1867) pp 83-90

Lower, M.A., 'Sir William Springett & the Springett Family', SAC vol. 20 (1868) pp 34-46

Lower, M.A., 'Some Notices of Charles Sergison, Esq.', SAC vol. 25 (1873) pp 62-84

Manning, R.B., 'Anthony Browne, 1st Viscount Montague; the influence in county politics of an Elizabethan Catholic nobleman', SAC vol. 106 (1968) pp 103-112

Matthews, A.G., *Calamy Revised* (1934); cited as Matthews (pp)

Mercer, E., *Oxford History of English Art, 1553-1625*, (1962) vol. VII; cited as Mercer (pp)

Metcalfe, W.C., *Visitation of Hertfordshire 1634*, Harleian Society (1886); cited as Metcalfe (pp)

Mosse, H.R., *The Monumental Effigies of Sussex 1250-1650* (1933) 2nd edition; cited as Mosse (pp)

Musgrave, C., *Life in Brighton* (1981) revised edition; cited as Musgrave (pp)

Nairn, I. & Pevsner, N., *The Buildings of England – Sussex* (1965); cited as Nairn & Pevsner (pp)

Namier, L. & Brooke, J., *The House of Commons 1754 – 1790*, The History of Parliament Trust (1985) 3 vols.; cited as Namier & Brooke (vv pp)

National Burial Index for England and Wales, Third Edition (CDROM), Federation of Family History Societies CD ROM

Newham, C.B., *Towards an Inventory of Church Monuments in England*, Church Monuments XXIV (2009) pp 118-126; cited as Newham (pp)

Nichols, J.G., *The Topographer and Genealogist* (1848-1858) Multiple vols.; cited as Topographer (vv pp)

Oswald, A., 'Firle Place, Sussex', Country Life, for Viscount Gage (1972)

Oxford Dictionary of National Biography

Phillips, M., 'Pedigree & Genealogical Memoranda relating to the Family of Pellatt', SAC vol. 38 (1892) pp 99-128; vol. 39 (1894) 55-93

Physick, J., *Designs for English Sculpture 1680-1860* (1969); cited as Physick (pp)

Povey, K., 'John Flaxman's Monuments in Sussex Churches', Sussex County Magazine vol. II (1928)

Pullein, C., *Rotherfield: The Story of Some Wealden Manors* (1928); cited as Pullein (pp)

Putron, P. de, 'Burial in Woolen', SAC vol. 18 (1866) pp 190-193

Radcliffe, A.F., 'Dobell of Streat', SAC vol. 66 (1925) pp 123-135

Ray, J.E., 'The Church of SS Peter and Paul, Bexhill', SAC vol. 53 (1910) pp 61-108

Ray, J.E., 'The Parish Church of Herstmonceux, and the Dacre Tomb', SAC vol. 58 (1916) pp 21-64

Remnant, G.L., 'Jonathan Harmer's Terracottas', SAC vol. 100 (1962) pp 142f-148; vol. 102 (1964) pp 52-54

Renshaw, W.C. (ed.), *Ecclesiastical Returns for 81 parishes in East Sussex made in 1603*, SRS vol. 4 (1905); cited as Renshaw (pp)

Renshaw, W.C., 'Notes from the Act Books of the Archdeaconry Court of Lewes', SAC vol. 49 (1906) pp 47-65

Renshaw, W.C. (ed.), *The Parish Registers of Cuckfield, Sussex, 1598-1699*, SRS vol. 13 (1911); cited as Renshaw (*Cuckfield Registers* pp)

Renshaw, W.C., 'Some clergy of the Archdeaconry of Lewes & South Malling Deanery', SAC vol. 55 (1912) pp 220-277

Rice, R. Garraway (ed.), *Sussex Apprentices and Masters 1710 to 1752*, SRS vol. 28 (1922); cited as Rice (pp)

Rice, R. Garraway & Godfrey, W.H. (eds.), *Transcripts of Sussex Wills...to 1560...vols.1-3; 4.*, SRS vols. 41-43 (1935-38); vol. 45 (1941); cited as Rice & Godfrey (vv pp)

Richardson, J., 'Inscriptions in Alfriston Churchyard', SAC vol. 17 (1865) pp 240-44

Rush, H.J., 'Wivelsfield Church', SAC vol. 22 (1870) pp 50-56

Rylands, W.H., *Visitations of Hampshire 1530, 1575, 1622, 1634*, Harleian Society (1913); cited as Rylands (pp)

St. Mary's Church, Eastbourne, Monumental Inscriptions, BPN Publications; cited as St. Mary's (*Inscriptions* pp)

Salt, M.C.L., 'The Fullers of Brightling Park', SAC vol. 104 (1966) pp 63-87; vol. 106 (1968) pp 73-88; vol. 107 (1969) pp 14-24

Salzman, L.F., *The History of the Parish of Hailsham* (1901); cited as Salzman (*Hailsham* pp)

Salzman, L.F., *A Calendar of Post Mortem Inquisitions... Sussex... 1 to 25 Elizabeth*, SRS vol. 33 (1903); cited as Salzman (*Inquisitions* pp)

Salzman, L.F., *The Parish Registers of Glynde, Sussex 1558-1812*, SRS vol. 30 (1924); cited as Salzman (*Glynde Registers* pp)

Salzman, L.F. (ed.), *The Town Book of Lewes 1542-1701*, SRS vol. 48 (1945-6); cited as Salzman (*Lewes Town Book* pp)

Sautter, M., 'Exhibition ... of Lewes Clocks', Sale Catalogue, WF Bruce Ltd (2003)

Sawyer, F.E., 'The Ecclesiastical History of Brighton', SAC vol. 29 (1879) pp 181-210

Sawyer, F.E., 'Recent Sussex Bibliography (1864-1881)', SAC vol. 32 (1882) pp 201-212

Sawyer, J, 'Some extracts from the Journal and Correspondence of Mr John Burgess, of Ditchling, Sussex 1785-1815', SAC vol. 40 (1896) pp 131-161

Sedgwick, R., *The House of Commons 1715-1754*, The History of Parliament Trust (1970) 2 vols.; cited as Sedgwick (vv pp)

Shaw, W.A., *The Knights of England* (1906) 2 vols.; cited as Shaw (vv pp)

Sherlock, P., *Monuments and Memory in Early Modern England*, Ashgate Aldershot (2008); cited as Sherlock (pp)

Simmons, H., 'Monumental Inscriptions, Seaford', SAC vol. 12 (1860) pp 242-253

Simmons, H., 'Monumental Inscriptions, Bishopstone', SAC vol. 19 (1867) pp 185-8

Smith, V. (ed.), *The Town Book of Lewes 1702-1837*, SRS vol. 69; cited as Smith (pp)

Steer, F.W., 'The Funeral Account of the First Duke of Richmond & Lennox', SAC vol. 98 (1960) pp 156ff

Steer, F.W. (ed.), *A Catalogue of Sussex Maps*, SRS vol. 66 (1968); cited as Steer (pp)

Stephenson, M., *A List of Monumental Brasses in the British Isles* (1926) 1964 edition; cited as Stephenson (pp)

Summers, P., *Hatchments in Britain, vol. 5 – Kent, Surrey & Sussex* (1985); cited as Summers (pp)

Sussex Archæological Collections, ongoing series from Vol. 1, 1848

Sussex Churches, Guides, Sussex Historic Churches Trust; cited as Sussex Churches (Parish pp)

Sussex County Magazine, vols. 1-30 (1927-55); cited as *SCM* (vv pp)

Sussex Marriage Index up to 1837, Sussex Family History Group (CD ROM)

Sussex Notes & Queries (1926-1971) 17 vols.

Sussex Record Society, ongoing series from Vol. 1, 1901

Thomas-Stanford, T., *An Abstract of the Court Rolls of the Manor of Preston...*, *SRS* vol. 27 (1921); cited as Thomas-Stanford (pp)

Thorne, R.G., *The House of Commons 1790-1820*, The History of Parliament Trust (1986); cited as Thorne (vv pp)

Tittler, R., *Accounts of the Roberts Family of Boarzell, Sussex c. 1568-1582*, *SRS* vol. 71 (1977-9); cited as Tittler (pp)

Turner, E., 'Uckfield Past and Present', *SAC* vol. 12 (1860) pp 1-22

Turner, E., 'Isfield Place with notes respecting the family of Shurley', *SAC* vol. 18 (1866) pp 124-136

Turner, E., 'The Stapley Diary', *SAC* vol. 18 (1866) pp 151-162

Turner, E., 'Otehall', *SAC* vol. 19 (1867) pp 61-70

Turner, E., 'The Mode of Life of a Sussex Gent', *SAC* vol. 23 (1871) pp 36-72

Turner, E., 'Brasses in Sussex Churches', *SAC* vol. 23 (1871) pp 129-191

Turner, E., 'A Brief Sketch of the History of John Rowe, Esq.', *SAC* vol. 24 (1872) pp 85-98

Tyler, E.J., *The Clockmakers of Sussex*, The Watch and Clock Book Society Ltd; cited as Tyler (pp)

Venn, J. & J.A., *Alumni Cantabrigienses* (1752-1900) Pt. 1 to 1751; Pt. 2 1752-1900 10 vols.; cited as Venn (Pt. vv pp)

Victoria County History, (ongoing series) founded in 1899; cited as *VCH* (vv pp)

Vivian, S.P., *The Manor of Etchingham cum Salehurst*, *SRS* vol. 53 (1953); cited as Vivian (pp)

Wace, A., *The Story of Wadhurst* (1923); cited as Wace (pp)

Wagner, A.R., 'The Wagners of Brighton and their Connections', *SAC* vol. 107 (1959) pp 35-57

Whinney, M., *Sculpture in Britain 1530-1830* (1988) revised by J. Physick; cited as Whinney (pp)

Whistler, R.F., 'The Relics of King Charles I at Ashburnham Place', *SAC* vol. 36 (1888) pp 160-171

White, A., *A Biographical Dictionary of London Tomb Sculptors c.1560-c.1660*, Walpole Society vol. 61 (1999); cited as White (pp)

Wilde, S.D., 'Fletching, Parish and Church', *SAC* vol. 4 (1851) pp 231-242

Willatts, R., 'Iron graveslabs: a sideline of the early iron industry', *SAC* vol. 125 (1987) pp 99-113

Wood, A.à, *Fasti Oxonienses* (1813-1820) 4 vols.; cited as Wood (vv pp)

Wright, P., *Frant - The Story of a Wealden Parish* (1982); cited as Wright (pp)

GLOSSARY

Item	Description
acanthus	a representation of the ornamental foliage of this common Mediterranean plant; a decorative motif in classical architecture
achievement	an escutcheon with adjuncts, or bearing, often showing a full coat of arms (including crest, motto, etc.)
architrave	in classical architecture, the horizontal element supported by capitals or pilasters
armiger	a person entitled to heraldic arms
baldachin (or Italian baldacchino)	a ceremonial canopy over an altar, throne, tomb, etc.
baluster	a series of ornamental short posts, often supporting a rail or flanking a niche
balustrade	a railing supported by balusters, especially forming an ornamental parapet
Baroque [style]	highly ornate style of the 17th and 18th c.
bas-relief	sculpture or carving in which the figures project slightly from the background
cartouche	a scroll-like ornamental, framed space
caryatid	a pillar in the form of a draped female figure supporting an entablature
chancel	part of the church near the altar reserved for the clergy, the choir, etc.
cherub (or plural cherubim)	a representation of a winged child or the head of a winged child
chrisom	a white robe put on a child at baptism, and used as its shroud if it died within the month
clerestory	an upper row of windows in a large church above the level of the aisle roofs
column	a free-standing, supporting element in classical architecture, with circular shaft, usually with capital and base mouldings, sometimes 'attached' and if in miniature a colonette
corbel	a projection of stone, timber, etc., jutting out from a wall to support a weight
composite	a late (Roman) order of classical architecture, combining elements of the Corinthian and Ionic orders
Corinthian	an order of classical architecture, exploiting acanthus decoration in its capital; the third of the original Greek orders following Doric and Ionic
cornice	a horizontal moulded projection crowning a structure
Decorated	the second stage (14th c.) of English Gothic with increasing use of decoration and tracery; the style that follows Early English

dentil	each of a series of small rectangular blocks as a decoration under the moulding of a cornice
Doric	of the oldest, sturdiest and simplest of the orders of classical architecture
Early English	the first stage (12th-13th c.) of English Gothic with pointed arches
egg-and-dart	an ornamental device often carved in wood, stone, or plaster, consisting of an egg-shaped object alternating with an element shaped like an arrow, anchor or dart
entablature	in classical architecture, the upper or horizontal element, the section supported by columns or pilasters comprising architrave, frieze and cornice
escutcheon	a shield or emblem bearing a coat of arms
finial	an ornament finishing off the apex of a roof, pediment, canopy, etc.
freestone	any fine-grained stone which can be cut easily, especially sandstone or limestone
gadroon	an ornamental moulding consisting of convex curves in a series forming an ornamental edge like inverted fluting
guttae	small cone-shaped projections decorating the architrave in classical architecture, properly in Doric but in other orders too
hatchment	a large panel, invariably of wood and usually diamond-shaped, displaying a deceased person's armorial bearings, carried in the funeral then affixed to that person's tomb, etc.
herm	(lit. the god Hermes): male head or bust on a pedestal.
mantling	ornamental drapery behind and around a shield
memento mori	Latin; translates as 'remember you must die'; also used generically to refer to symbolic and verbal exhortations to 'remember your own mortality'
metope	a square space between triglyphs in a Doric frieze, sometimes blank, sometimes decorated, for example, with paterae
Norman	the first stage (11th and 12th centuries) in English mediaeval architecture and prevalent style in that period, with rounded arches, windows and doorways
ogive (adjective ogival)	a pointed arch with a flattened double or 'S' curve
oolite (adjective oolitic)	a sedimentary rock, usually limestone, with visible, sometimes prominent, fossilised forms, often layered and of rounded form
palimpsest brass	used of an inscribed monumental brass, which has been turned and engraved with new inscriptions and devices on the reverse side
palmette	an ornament of radiating petals like a palm leaf
patera (plural paterae)	a circular ornament, resembling a dish, often worked in relief on friezes and set in metopes

pediment	the front surmounting a portico, façade or niche, in elevation, segmental or triangular
Perpendicular	the third stage (14th-16th c.) or style of English Gothic with vertical tracery in large windows; following Decorated
pietra dura (Italian: ' hard stone')	a method of inlaying coloured marbles or semi-precious stones into a stone base, often in geometric or flower patterns
pilaster	a rectangular column, especially one projecting from a wall
predella (Italian: 'altar-step')	used for a frieze of painted or carved panels set below the main panel or panels of a composite altar-piece or other composition
putto (plural putti)	a representation of a naked child, cherub or (sometimes) Cupid in (especially post-Renaissance) art
quatrefoil	a four-pointed or four-leafed figure, especially as an ornament resembling a flower or clover leaf
rance or raunce	a type of red marble, often with white or blue graining, that comes from Belgium
Renaissance	the culture and style of classical revival, in England developed in the 16th c.
revetment	a retaining wall
ribbon-work	decoration applied by manipulating ribbons into patterns; see too strap-work
rocaille (French: rock), rococo	a light, decorative 18th style often based on asymmetrical rock and shell motifs
sanctuary	the part of the chancel containing the altar
sarcophagus	a stone coffin, especially one adorned with a sculpture or inscription
serliana	after the Renaissance architectural theorist, Sebastiano Serlio, a tripartite window, door, or blind architectural feature consisting of a central opening with a semicircular arch over it springing from two entablatures each supported by two columns or pilasters flanking narrower flat-topped openings on either side.
spandrel	the almost triangular space between one side of the outer curve of an arch, a wall, and the ceiling or framework
strap-work	ornamentation imitating plaited straps; close to ribbon-work (q.v.)
tomb-chest	a coffin-like element in monumental design, usually carved in stone, sometimes supporting effigies, inscriptions and ornament
tonsure	the shaving of the crown of the head
touch	soft black marble mined near Tournai
transept	of a church with a crossed-shaped plan, the whole arm, or the north or south part at right angles to the nave
triglyph	an ornamental tablet with three vertical grooves, alternating with metopes in a Doric frieze
volute	a spiral scroll characteristic of Ionic capitals and also used in Corinthian and composite capitals

INTRODUCTION TO THE CATALOGUE

The Catalogue is arranged alphabetically by name of parish. All the parishes of East and West Sussex were listed alphabetically and each was numbered: Albourne = 1, Alciston = 2, Aldingbourne = 3, etc. This volume only includes material in the three East Sussex Rapes.

Each parish entry starts with the place name and church dedication and is followed by a short introductory passage about the place and the church, covering the building history of the church - especially as it relates to the creation of commemorative spaces – aspects of local history, important antiquarian treatments of the monuments, any distinctive or significant trends in the monuments.

The works commemorated in each parish entry reflect the field-work procedure, which was to enter the building by the main door and, as far as was practicable, turn left and take a clock-wise, often spiralling, route round the building cataloguing every item encountered whether on floor or wall. Works found in porches and vestries were included.

Every monument is uniquely distinguished: its church number is followed by a letter, e.g. 1A, 1B, etc. The sequence of elements in each catalogue entry is as follows:

> Catalogue Number
> Title (including monument type, main subject and date)
> Location
> Dimensions (in centimetres, width before height)
> Condition and state
> Description (design, materials, authorship)
> Monumental Inscription (or M.I., transcription or précis)
> Cataloguers' Observations

Where research identifies that there are monuments that are missing or lost then a list of these additional monuments is appended to each parish.

Dates are shown as day month year corresponding to the entry on the memorial. For clarity, dates from 1st Jan to 25th March prior to the date change in 1752 are shown as, for e.g., 3 Feb 1749/50. Where the catalogue has a complete transcription of the M.I., then that transcription retains the date in its original form.

Additional information supplied by John Hawkins for the Cataloguers' Observations is prefixed by the initials "JH". References to books and articles are normally given in shortened form; the full details are given in the Bibliography. The Glossary defines many of the architectural terms used to describe the monuments.

Unless the monument was inaccessible or obscured then it has been photographed and, where appropriate, a close-up has been taken of individual components or parts. These 3,400 photographs have been added to a web site that mirrors the catalogue for use by researchers and family historians. The web site at www.sussexrecordsociety.org contains the catalogue and all of these photographs. 200 photographs have been included as high quality plates in this volume. They represent the wide variety of monuments in East Sussex and each plate has notes appended to highlight the artist or other salient features.

LIST OF PLATES

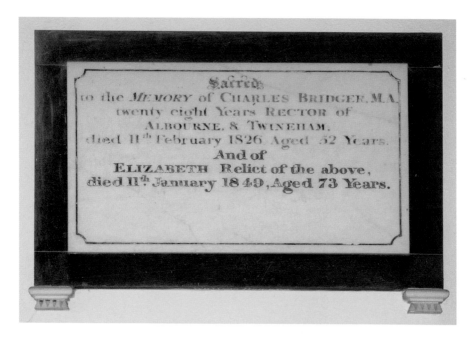

Plate 1 - Williams of Brighton signed a small number of simple black and white tablets; he was one of several makers meeting increased market demand for monuments in the 1820s.
Mural monument for Rev. Charles BRIDGER, d. 1826
Albourne, St. Bartholomew 1C

Plate 2 - The decorative *fleur-de-lys* motif engraved in the corners of this ledger stone is found in a group of similar stones carved in the 1780s, probably from a workshop at Lewes.
Ledger for William BATCHELOR, d. 1783
Alfriston, St. Andrew 4G

Plate 3 - A set of conventional post-Reformation brasses commemorating one of the Culpeper
daughters of Wakehurst Place, comprising her figure at prayer, her family arms and an inscription.
Floor mounted brasses for Elizabeth CULPEPER, d. 1634
Ardingly, St Peter 8C

Plate 4 - Notable features of this tablet from c.1740 are the high, curved pediment, the death's head
decoration on the apron and the carved floral panels flanking the inscription.
Mural for John READ, d. 1738
Arlington, St. Pancras 9E

Plate 5 - In dramatic contrast with the restrained orthodoxy of 11E (see Plate 8), this vast *tableau* uses
Baroque devices and poses to express the grief of the bereaved husband.
Wall monument for Jane, Countess of MARLBOROUGH, d. 1672
and her husband William ASHBURNHAM, d. 1679
Ashburnham, St. Peter 11D

Plate 6 - Alongside her distraught husband and also in antique dress, the Countess is shown not dead but propped up on one elbow, receiving her coronet from a flying *putto*.
Wall monument for Jane, Countess of MARLBOROUGH, d. 1672 and her husband
Ashburnham, St. Peter 11D

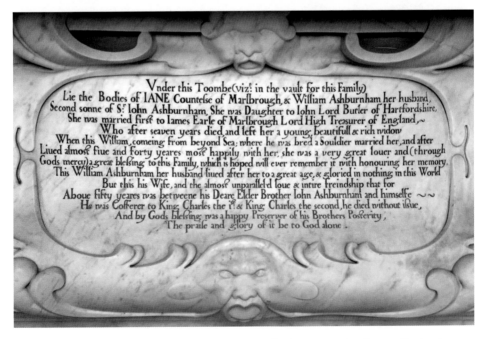

Plate 7 - The inscription is mounted in a highly inventive Baroque cartouche; the wording touches on questions of social rank and emphasises affection and personal loss.
Wall monument for Jane, Countess of MARLBOROUGH, d. 1672 and her husband
Ashburnham, St. Peter 11D

Plate 8 - This type of composition was established in the 1610s and its *retardataire* features are in
keeping with the lengthy inscription's emphasis on genealogy and land ownership.
Wall monument for John ASHBURNHAM, d. 1671
Ashburnham, St. Peter 11E

Plate 9 - A caryatid is a rare classicising feature on an English monument of c.1730;
it exemplifies the ambitious monumental patronage of the Medley family.
Mural monument for Susanna MEDLEY, d. 1704
Barcombe, St. Mary 16F

Plate 10 - At John Raynes' death, Conniborrow Park passed to the Medley family, who perhaps paid
for this highly inventive anthropomorphic cartouche framing his coat-of-arms.
Mural monument for John RAYNES, d. 1687
Barcombe, St. Mary 16C

Plate 11 - A simple white-on-black tablet records the loss of Major Swain's wife and daughter while he
was helping liberate part of what is now Greece from Ottoman control.
Mural monument for Harriett SWAIN and her daughter Mary-Ann, both d. 1821
Battle, St. Mary the Virgin 20D

Plate 12 - A Midlands alabaster tomb for one of Henry VIII's courtiers, its *all'antica* Roman lettering
and decorated balusters are fashionable Renaissance features rare in Sussex.
Free-standing tomb-chest for Sir Anthony BROWNE, d. 1548 and his first wife Alice, d. 1540
Battle, St. Mary the Virgin 20I

Plate 13 - The set of brasses includes heraldry and a captioned figure, the Latin inscriptions describe
Wythins' academic career and touch on the theme of the *memento mori*.
Floor-mounted brasses for John WYTHINS, d. 1615
Battle, St. Mary the Virgin 20J

Plate 14 - Commemorative accounts of the subject's charitable acts became increasingly popular in the eighteenth century, as in the Hooper monuments both here and at Hailsham (119F). Mural monument for Odiarne HOOPER, d. 1769 and many descendants
Beckley, All Saints 21E

Plate 15 - A mural design but resting on the church floor, the only substantial monument at Beddingham is a remarkably late (1790s) example of a Baroque broken pediment. Wall Monument for Alexander CARR, d. 1790 and members of his family
Beddingham, St. Andrews 22A

Plate 16 - The church was restored in the 1850s; there are numerous repositioned grave-markers in the floor; this one is carefully cut and perhaps a replacement for the original.
Grave marker for Augustin METCALFE, d. 1672
Berwick, St Michael and All Angels 25B

Plate 17 - A highly inventive design with a number of unusual combinations such as the playful adaptation of the acanthus leaf motif in the apron framed by drape-like scrolls.
Mural monument for Thomas MILNER, d. 1722
Bexhill, St. Peter 26B

Plate 18 - Commissioned in London by the subject's uncle, it includes a slate-like inscription panel and, below in the apron, the marble version that would become increasingly fashionable.
Mural monument for Rev. Thomas DELVES, d. 1677/8
Bexhill, St. Peter 26C

Plate 19 - The Hurdis tablets link rural Sussex clerical life with the national literary scene; below the commemorative tablet, the poet William Hayley contributes an elegy to his late colleague.
Mural monument for Rev. James HURDIS, d. 1801
Bishopstone, St. Andrew 31B

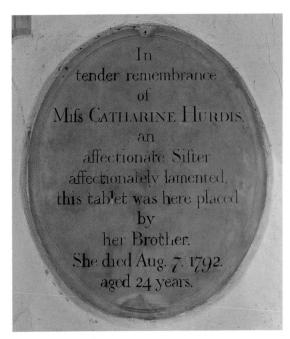

Plate 20 - Hurdis was deeply affected by the death of his sister Catherine but, although being
Professor of Poetry at Oxford, restricts himself to a modest, anonymised inscription.
Mural monument for Catharine HURDIS, d. 1792
Bishopstone, St. Andrew 31D

Plate 21 - Typical of the mid eighteenth-century are the florid lettering and the cavalier treatment of
the pediment - entablature omitted and transformed into an angled frame.
Mural monument for Mary BURGESS, d. 1755
Bishopstone, St. Andrew 31E

Plate 22 - This ledger, with its prominent achievement-of-arms in mid-relief and lengthy inscription, has been trimmed at the edges and reset amongst Victorian floor tiles.
Ledger for Rev. Vere MUNN, d. 1736 and Elizabeth MUNN, d. 1758
Bodiam, St Giles 32A

Plate 23 - As has frequently occurred elsewhere, many monuments here were relocated to the tower wall after the restoration of the church; note the elegant Latin interpolation in the MI.
Mural monument for Elizabeth BALCHEN, d. 1778 and John BALCHEN, d. 1785
Bodiam, St Giles 32D

Plate 24 - The Tempest family were lords of the manor at Bodiam; the decoration mixes a neo-classical Greek-key moulding below with Baroque-style acanthus above.
Wall monument for John TEMPEST, d. 1820 and Sarah TEMPEST, d. 1810
Bodiam, St Giles 32E

Plate 25 The early nineteenth-century monuments at Brede are installed in a group on the north chancel wall; the ledgers are earlier in date and grouped in the south-east chapel.
Brede, St. George 38

Plate 26 - In its original location, in the pre-Reformation Oxenbridge Chantry chapel, the composition of this Caen-stone knight's tomb is dominated by armour and heraldry.
Wall monument for Sir Goddard OXENBRIDGE, d. 1531, erected 1537
Brede, St . George 38C

Plate 27 - The serpents entwining a vase, signal a memorial for a physician; erected by his grateful patron, this is, in fact, a cenotaph since Dr Blair was buried in London.
Mural monument for Dr. Primrose BLAIR, d. 1819
Brightling, St. Thomas à Becket 39F

Plate 28 - This weeping *putto* from the 1680s is evidence that several of the many mural monuments erected for the Collins family at Brightling are of the highest quality.
Mural monument for Thomas COLLINS, d. 1671, Margaret Collins, d. 1681 & William Collins, d. 1690
Brightling, St. Thomas à Becket 39J

Plate 29 - The brasses commemorating the infant son of the Rector, Thomas Pye, typify late Elizabethan emblematics as they play off his pious character against the family name.
Brasses for Thomas PYE, d. 1592
Brightling, St. Thomas à Becket 39U

Plate 30 - Three of these cast lead slabs survive at Brighton (see too 40GG-HH), dating from
around 1700; they appear to commemorate those involved in re-roofing the church.
Wall-mounted lead slab commemorating Edward LOWE and others, dated 1677
Brighton, St Nicholas of Myra 40BB

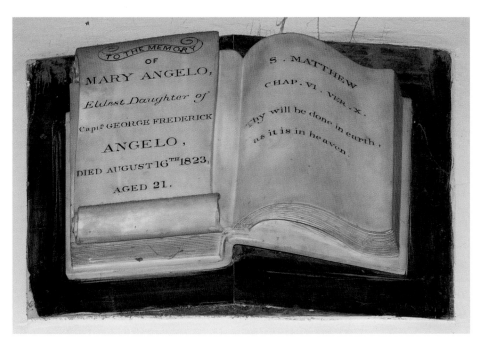

Plate 31 - An ingenious early nineteenth-century variant on the standard white-on-black type; an open
book with biography inscribed on the left and Biblical quotations on the right.
Mural monument for Mary ANGELO, d. 1823
Brighton, St Nicholas of Myra 40OO

Plate 32 - The idealised female subject borne aloft in the arms of an angel, carved here by the younger Westmacott, who had largely took over his father's practice by this date.
Mural monument for Frances Crosbie FAIRFIELD, d. 1830
Brighton, St Nicholas of Myra 40SS

Plate 33 - Flaxman had an extensive and successful monumental practice, his works combining allegory (Faith and Hope), symbolism and orthodox neo-classical design principles.
Mural for Rev. John COURTAIL, d. 1806
Burwash, St. Bartholomew 45L

Plate 34 - The damaged inscription panel of this mural monument suggests that it has been moved
from a location that would have better suited its attenuated proportions.
Mural monument for Nathaniel CRUTTENDEN, d. 1770
Burwash, St. Bartholomew 45O

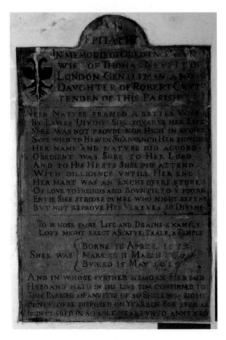

Plate 35 - Unusually formed of three abutting sections, this tablet for a Burwash woman was set up by
her husband, a Londoner; it describes her piety and his charitable bequests.
Mural monument for Obedience NEVITT, d. 1619
Burwash, St. Bartholomew 45Q

Plate 36 - An outstanding example of the large-scale Baroque cartouche, with heraldic devices above
the ornamental surround combining curtains, cherubim and trumpets denoting fame.
Mural cartouche for Anthony SAUNDERS, d. 1719
Buxted, St. Margaret The Queen 47E

Plate 37 - This is Regnart's version of an important early nineteenth-century motif, taken both
from Goethe and antiquity - the draped widow mourns at the funerary urn.
Mural monument for George MEDLEY, d. 1796, and his widow's parents
Buxted, St. Margaret The Queen 47G

Plate 38 - The patron of 48A, Fuller of Rosehill, also erected monuments at Brightling (39);
here, Nollekens gives unusual emphasis to the complex carved panel of trophies.
Mural monument for John FULLER, d. 1810
Catsfield, St Laurence 48A

Plate 39 - Designed and carved in c.1760, many years after the subject's death, this elegant mural monument is carefully shaped to fit the space available in the chancel.
Mural monument for George GORING, d. 1728, his wife and children
Chailey, St. Peter 49I

Plate 40 - The faded inscription includes a digit, which has clearly been corrected to read '1' not '2'.
Mural monument for John Trayton FULLER, d. 1811
Chalvington, St Bartholomew 50A

Plate 41 - One of number of remarkable seventeenth-century tombs at Chiddingly, unique in the county for its coloured inlays and for the urn as its centrepiece, rather than an effigy.
Mural monument for Margaret JEFFERAY, dated 1620
Chiddingly, Parish Church 56D

Plate 42 - The large proportions of the achievement-of-arms and the decorative scrolls, the wreathed border to the tablet and the sobering skulls are all typical of the 1660s.
Mural monument for Stephen FRENCH, d. 1666
Chiddingly, Parish Church 56E

Plate 43 - This vast wall monument was erected some thirty years after the death of
Sir John Jefferay and fills the south transept, which had to be rebuilt to accommodate it.
Wall monument for Sir John JEFFERAY, d. 1578, and descendants, dated 1612
Chiddingly, Parish Church 56L

Plate 44 - Sir Edward Montagu had the Jefferay monument built - at the request of his late wife,
Jefferay's daughter – and included a standing statue of himself in the composition
Wall monument for Sir John JEFFERAY, d. 1578, and descendants, dated 1612
Chiddingly, Parish Church 56L

Plate 45 - The use of plaster rather than carved stone is rare in East Sussex; here the material is moulded to form a decorative surround to this modest cartouche.
Mural monument for Ann LUXFORD, d. 1729
Clayton, St John The Baptist 61C

Plate 46 - An interesting tablet by Westmacott that in its virtuoso rendering of fabrics and use of an exotic marble for the baseplate suggests both Dyson's and Hastings' fashionability.
Mural monument for Jeremiah DYSON, d. 1813
Crowhurst, St. George 71D

Plate 47 - Reversing the standard convention, Thomas Adey has carved a life-sized figure of Truth
holding a representation of the subject in the form of a portrait medallion.
Standing wall monument for Charles SERGISON, d. 1732
Cuckfield, Holy Trinity 72H

Plate 48 - The Flaming Heart and the Clasped Scripture engraved onto the Carleton monument
reflect the intense early seventeenth-century interest in religious symbolism.
Mural monument for Guy CARLETON, d. 1628 and his nephew and niece
Cuckfield, Holy Trinity 72G

Plate 49 - The formal language of obelisks, scaled friezes and kneeling figures derives from the
many much larger monuments set up at about this date at Westminster Abbey.
Mural monument for Ninian BURRELL, d. 1614
Cuckfield, Holy Trinity 72M

Plate 50 - One of many Burrell monuments at Cuckfield, this small but exquisite marble cartouche, with its foliate and scrolled surround, is set too high easily to be seen.
Mural monument for Timothy BURRELL, d. 1717
Cuckfield, Holy Trinity 72O

Plate 51 - Young Ninian Burrell prays towards the high altar as the niche curtains are parted by two attendant angels: an interesting mixture of piety, fashionability and theatricality.
Mural monument for Ninian BURRELL, d. 1628
Cuckfield, Holy Trinity 72P

...ounted at Dallington, takes the form of an engraved lozenge, ...t it appears never to have been nailed through.
... brass for Ann CRAUFURD, d. 1771
... St. Giles (also St. Margaret) 73A

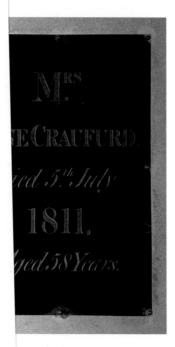

Plate 33 - Taking the simplest possible form, this engraved brass plate was perhaps originally designed to mark the burial place in the floor but is not very worn.
Wall-mounted brass for Jane CRAUFURD, d. 1811
Dallington, St. Giles (also St. Margaret) 73G

Plate 54 - A version of the scroll conceit, first invented by Nicholas Stone for the Caesar monument at Great St Helens in the City of London in the early seventeenth century. Mural monument for Robert RANDOLL, d. 1783, and his daughter, d. 1759 Dallington, St. Giles (also St. Margaret) 73l

Plate 55 - Parsons' workshop in Lewes turned out church monuments – mostly small-scale wall tablets – over many years: this is probably their most ambitious signed work known. Mural monument for William CHAMBERS, d. 1808 East Blatchington, St Peter 82B

Plate 56 - A cast iron slab of an especially rustic kind from the heart of the Wealden industrial belt:
note the letters reversed in error and the relative scale of text to ornament.
Wall-mounted iron slab for Anne FORSTER, d. 1591
East Grinstead, St Swithun 86H

Plate 57 - The brothers Payne died within a few months of one another, having been domestic
partners for forty years and doughty supporters of monarchy, episcopacy and piety.
Mural monument for Robert and Henry PAYNE, both d. 1708
East Grinstead, St Swithun 86S

Plate 58 - A rough, local cast-iron slab, that appears to have been salvaged after the church fire of 1684 and put to work as a hearth-plate, to fit which its corners were trimmed.
Iron floor slab for Francis HASELDEN, d. 1616
East Grinstead, St Swithun 86BB

Plate 59 - An accomplished portrait bust to commemorate the adolescent son of the vicar of Eastbourne, who died at Calcutta, established by the East India Company in 1690.
Wall monument for Henry LUSHINGTON, d. 1763
Eastbourne, St Mary 93A

Plate 60 - A rare case of a monument signed (by John Morris, mason-sculptor based in Lewes)
in the full academic manner, "invenit et sculpsit", that is, both designer and carver.
Mural monument for Mary LUSHINGTON I, d. 1775, and Mary Lushington II, d. 1811
Eastbourne, St Mary 93K

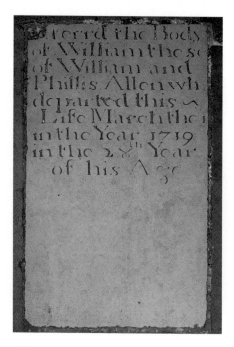

Plate 61 - A good number of these creamy-yellow freestone ledgers survive at Eastbourne, in this
case, the lettering which fills only half of the space available, was never added to.
Ledger for William ALLEN, d. 1719
Eastbourne, St Mary 93T

Plate 62 - Highly decorated and with some rare combinations of colour and pattern, parts of the inscription suggest that the engraver was not fully briefed on the wording to be used.
Mural monument for Thomas ALCHORNE and others, dated 1735
Eastbourne, St Mary 93MM

Plate 63 - The low-relief sailing vessel signals Britain's expanding foreign and colonial interests in the early nineteenth century; both subjects died suddenly and in distant parts.
Mural monument for James RANKING, d. 1827, and John RANKING, date of death unknown
Eastbourne, St Mary 93TT

Plate 64 - The so-called Sheffield mausoleum is a commemorative environment unique in
East Sussex; the open door reveals the lower parts of a vast wall of inscriptions.
The SHEFFIELD Mausoleum, late 18th century
Fletching, St. Andrew & St. Mary 107C

Plate 65 - Built in a neo-Gothic style, near to the site of the Sheffield Park family pew, the wall
commemorates generations of the Holroyd family and their friend Edward Gibbon.
The SHEFFIELD Mausoleum, late 18th century
Fletching, St. Andrew & St. Mary 107C

Plate 66 - The initiative for this much restored late Elizabethan canopy tomb was taken by the
subject's widow, 'herself livinge' when it was erected but pictured as if also dead.
Standing wall monument for Richard LECHE, d. 1596, and his wife Charity
Fletching, St. Andrew & St. Mary 107D

Plate 67 - A marble cartouche that is typical of the very high quality of the mural monuments of
c.1700 at Folkington, which have been recently restored to the highest standard.
Mural monument for Lady Barbara THOMAS, d. 1697
Folkington, St Peter 108C

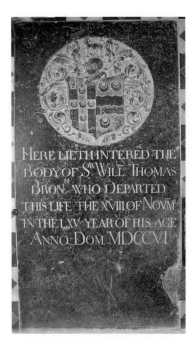

Plate 68 - This ledger stone is directly linked with its matching monument - erected for a Baronet -
and its bold lettering makes a confident declaration of his local authority.
Ledger for Sir William THOMAS, d. 1706
Folkington, St Peter 108E

Plate 69 - An elegant standing monument of various subtly coloured marbles with standing *putti*
supporting the heraldry; its patron was the heir, William Dobell of Streat (250B).
Wall monument for Sir William THOMAS, d. 1706
Folkington, St Peter 108H

Plate 70 - Several Elizabethan Gages are commemorated at Firle but others are commemorated here by a small monument probably by the same London maker, Garret Johnson.
Mural monument for the GAGE family, dated 1595
Framfield, St Thomas à Becket 110I

Plate 71 - The richly decorated pediment, over the simple tablet, is in a studied but showy Grecian form of the neo-classical style associated with Sir Richard Westmacott.
Mural monument for Sarah WOODWARD, d. 1823, and others
Framfield, St Thomas à Becket 110Q

Plate 72 - Around 1830, tomb designers started to employ various kinds of mediaeval design – in this case the flat 'Tudor' arch – in contrast with the prevalent classical forms.
Mural monument for Catherine Erskine ROWLAND, d. 1829
Frant, St Alban 111C

Plate 73 - The prominent signature on the base of the urn in the centre of Peirce's non-figurative composition indicates the increasing confidence and social prestige of tomb-makers.
Mural monument for Charles BROWN, d. 1754
Frant, St Alban 111D

Plate 74 - A grand but entirely orthodox Jacobean wall-monument of a type that occurs across
England; the ancient Selwyn line is stressed despite the evident lack of male progeny.
Mural monument for Thomas SELWYN, d. 1613/4, and Elizabeth his wife
Friston, St Mary the Virgin 112B

Plate 75 - A curiosity: the flattened ogival arch and handling of detail suggests that this was made -
by the otherwise unknown HW Dodd - many years after the subject's death.
Mural monument for Philip VAN CORTLANDT, d. 1814
Hailsham, St. Mary the Virgin 119B

Plate 76 - With its colour combinations of pink and other marbles, elegant lettering and delicate swags 119D is reminiscent of Adam's interior decorations, in the Roman manner.
Mural monument for Rev. Thomas HUBERSTY, d. 1793
Hailsham, St. Mary the Virgin 119D

Plate 77 - A simple composition allowing concentration to rest on the family coat-of-arms and the virtues of the deceased, described as '*a faithful and truly pastoral vicar*'.
Mural monument for Odiarne HOOPER, d. 1769
Hailsham, St. Mary the Virgin 119F

Plate 78 - A highly inventive and unusual design: note the flaming lamps, the decorative fluted
pilasters and the playful combination of winged heads - Death's and a cherub's.
Mural monument for Anthony TRUMBLE, d. 1733
Hailsham, St. Mary the Virgin 119G

Plate 79 - A transitional design, positioned in the north chancel where an Easter Sepulchre would
have stood, with a flattened, early Tudor arch and Perpendicular cresting.
Wall monument for Edward MARWICK, d. 1538
Hamsey, St. Peter 120G

Plate 80 - Unusual for the early date of its broken pediment and the obelisk which backs the lost arms on the central pedestal; the M.I. has a powerful moralising and didactic message.
Mural monument for Richard RANDES, d. 1640
Hartfield, St Mary 123I

Plate 81 - An unusual composition: the aim to give centre stage to the inscription tablet is somewhat offset by the insertion of a second M.I. between the huge scrolled corbels.
Mural monument for Horatio MARTELLI, d. 1817
Hastings, St. Clements 125B

Plate 82 - A magnificent example of urban confidence; lavish patronage has exploited the expensive materials to the full; the cluster of three cherubs are of very high quality.
Mural Monument for John COLLIER, d. 1760
Hastings, St. Clements 125N

Plate 83 - The simplest possible rendering of an urn – the dominant monumental motif of its day – displaying a M.I. registering Hastings' attraction to fashionable visitors in the 1820s.
Mural monument for Magnus JACKSON, d. 1830
Hastings, All Saints 126A

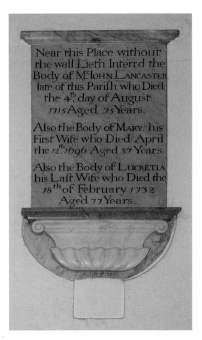

Plate 84 - An eccentric combination of a single pedestal displaying the M.I.,
set on an corbel in the form of an Ionic capital.
Mural monument for John LANCASTER, d. 1715, his wives Mary, d. 1696, and Lucretia, d. 1732/3
Herstmonceux, All Saints 131B

Plate 85 - A highly accomplished relief carving; a death-bed scene in a neo-classical setting; seen
from below, an angel waits to transport the soul of the deceased.
Mural monument for Georgiana NAYLOR, d. 1806
Herstmonceux, All Saints 131E

Plate 86 - The largest Gothic wall tomb in the county, formed from an arch punched through the
chancel wall, bringing the effigies into direct devotional engagement with the altar.
Wall tomb for the Lords DACRE, dated late 15th century and early 16th century
Herstmonceux, All Saints 131D

Plate 87 - The little-known Lewes-based tomb-maker Hargraves adopts the neo-classical decorative
vocabulary and a near-exclusive contrast of black and white.
Mural monument for Richard WYATT, d. 1816
Horsted Keynes, St Giles 137C

Plate 88 - The simplest possible form of grave-marker; a square slate block with engraved initials
and no date, marking the burial place of Richard Wyatt (see Plate 87)
Grave marker for 'RW', no date
Horsted Keynes, St Giles 137N

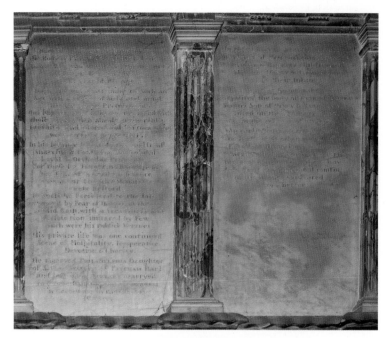

Plate 89 - The long M.I. alludes to Courthope's child-hood experience of the anarchy of the Civil War of the 1640s; its dense lines fill the space between simple fluted Doric pilasters.
Mural monument for Peter COURTHOPE, d. 1724/5
Hurstpierpoint, Holy Trinity 139/1L

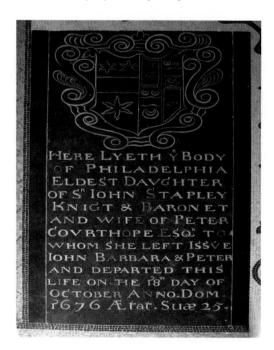

Plate 90 - A beautifully preserved example of late seventeenth-century ledger engraving; the handling of the figure '1' is characteristic; probably set up by the subject of Plate 89
Ledger for Philadelphia COURTHOPE, d. 1676
Hurstpierpoint, Holy Trinity 139/1U

Plate 91 - The contrasting ages and life-spans of the subjects are reflected in the two scripts
used on the M.I., the top 7 lines are some 50 years older than the lower 7 lines.
Mural monument for John BORRER, d. 1793
Hurstpierpoint, Holy Trinity 139/1X

Plate 92 - The workshop of John Marten at Tenterden, Kent also supplied eastern Sussex;
the M.I. remains silent on the dramatic scandals of Nesbitt's political and commercial careers.
Mural monument for Arnold NESBITT, d. 1779
Icklesham, All Saints 140F

Plate 93 - Elizabethan classical architecture such as this relied heavily on the use of pattern books, the probable source for the characteristic squat Doric order, rare at this date.
Wall monument for Thomas SHURLEY, d. 1579, and his wife, d. 1571
Isfield, St. Margaret 145C

Plate 94 - In its high quality materials and its stress on lineage, 145D demonstrates how quickly the Shurleys were transformed from court servants to established local magnates.
Wall monument for Sir John SHURLEY, d. 1631, and his two wives
Isfield, St. Margaret 145D

Plate 95 - Unusual for its overlapping low-relief portrait heads in a simple roundel, a device
combined here with familiar motifs such as the sarcophagus and large torches.
Mural monument for Charles ROCHESTER, d. 1758
Jevington, St. Andrew 147D

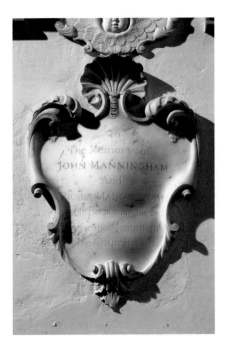

Plate 96 - A small, late but quite memorable cartouche of unexpected beauty; its shell-forms and
undulating tablet are the creation of an unknown but expert practitioner.
A cartouche for John MANNINGHAM, d. 1751, and Thomas
Jevington, St. Andrew 147F

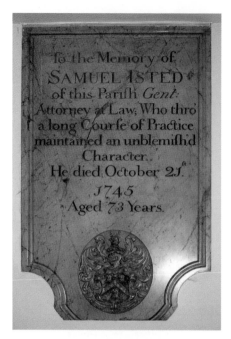

Plate 97 - Taking the form of a floor slab but not apparently worn by footprints, the large lettering
stresses Isted's honesty; Lewes was a major centre for the legal professions.
Mural monument for Samuel ISTED, d. 1745
Lewes, All Saints 156H

Plate 98 - A standard neo-classical formula – unframed, monochrome, using simple 'Greek' shapes;
the subjects (not apparently of Lewes) were fashionable and cosmopolitan.
Mural monument for the LEWIS family, erected after 1825
Lewes, St Anne 157A

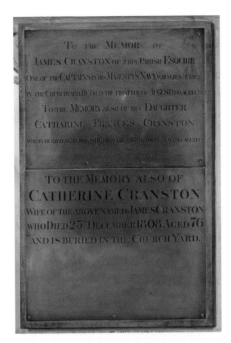

Plate 99 - The lower of this pair of engraved brass plates is signed by the clock-maker Holman;
it suggests that skilled metal-workers could work across a range of products.
Wall-mounted brass for James CRANSTON, d. 1790, and his family
Lewes, St Anne 157P

Plate 100 - One of many tablets of this type in Lewes; thirty-five years elapsed between the deaths of
Elizabeth's two husbands, the latter a man some twenty years her junior.
Monument for Elizabeth RIDEOUT, d. 1774, Richard PAYNE, d. 1732/3, & Richard RIDEOUT, d. 1767
Lewes, St Anne 157Q

Plate 101 - In the nineteenth century, St John-sub-Castro's monuments were removed from the
demolished mediaeval church and grouped in the chancel of the new church.
Mural monument for Ann and Daniel LA PLA, d. 1771 and 1774
Lewes, St. John-Sub-Castro 158D

Plate 102 - An exercise in a simple, standard formula, one of several used by the Westmacotts,
combining Greek elements with a Mannerist inversion of the pointed pediment.
Mural monument for Louisa Maria BALDOCK, d. 1819
Lewes, St John The Baptist (Southover) 159I

Plate 103 - In a 'predella' below the main effigies, Pelham's children kneel in gendered groupings,
flanking an hour-glass, a popular Elizabethan *memento mori* symbol.
Mural monument for Sir Nicholas PELHAM, d. 1559, and his wife Anne (SACKVILLE)
Lewes, St. Michael 160D

Plate 104 - Susanna's body was returned for burial to the Lewes parish church of her maternal
grandfather and her parents commissioned a monument from Rogerson of London.
Mural monument for Susannah BULL, d. 1794
Lewes, St Thomas a Becket, Cliffe 161B

Plate 105 - Draped urns were highly fashionable in the late 1700s; Lindfield was a large parish covering over much of Haywards Heath and has an important set of monuments.
Mural monument for Sarah and Richard BOARD, d. 1765 and d. 1782
Lindfield, All Saints 164D

Plate 106 - The well-to-do Board family looked not southwards to Lewes for this monument but northwards, to the highly accomplished Thames-side workshop of T and G Marshall.
Mural monument for William and Harriot BOARD, d. 1790 and d. 1809, and their children
Lindfield, All Saints 164G

Plates 107 & 108 - Lindfield has a unique set of hatchment-like commemorative boards, typically with octagonal or diamond-shaped painted fields edged with Latin inscriptions.
Painted Arms of William and Harriot BOARD, d. 1790 and d. 1809, and Dorothy Newton, d. 1730
Lindfield, All Saints 164N

Plate 109 - The Kidders were an ancient Maresfield family and the main purpose of 172C is to record
the subject's lineage; the heraldic supporter is turned here into a pictorial motif.
Mural monument for Edward KIDDER, d. 1817
Maresfield, St. Bartholomew 172C

Plate 110 - The death of a young mother was frequently the occasion for the erection of monuments,
in this case, in the church of her husband, the parish rector.
Mural monument for Louisa RIVETT, d. 1798
Maresfield, St. Bartholomew 172E

Plate 111 - The M.I.s on most iron slabs are cast into the metal but they could also be engraved;
note the delicacy of the entwined foliage and play on 'AGE' and the figure '8'.
Iron Slab for Thomas SANDS, d. 1708
Mayfield, St Dunstan 173H

Plate 112 - A high quality version of the Goetheian motif of the widow weeping over the urn here with
unusual yellow half-columns; the Bakers were very prominent at Mayfield.
Mural monument for Thomas BAKER, d. 1782, and his wives, Marthanna, d. 1780 and Ann, d. 1804
Mayfield, St Dunstan 173I

Plate 113 - Oliver's design is unusually inventive with playful curves on the inscription tablet and the entablature and a reversal of the usual pattern of arms above and cherub below.
Mural monument for George and Philadelphia BAKER, dated 1765
Mayfield, St Dunstan 173R

Plate 114 - For a lawyer; a variation on the standard Jacobean self-facing kneeler type with unidentified mourners, possibly angels, reclining on the broken scrolled pediment.
Mural monument for Thomas AYNSCOMBE, d. 1620, and Katherine his wife, d. 1633
Mayfield, St Dunstan 173T

Plate 115 - Dating probably from the early 1740s, the panels of coloured marbles in the place of
fluted pilasters are unusual; the M.I. ends with a reference to death as the great leveller.
Mural monument for Thomas HICKES, d. 1736
Mountfield, All Saints 177A

Plate 116 - Emphasising a densely scripted M.I. and without figuration, a design that could have been
floor-mounted but is now on a wall in the Frewen chapel, added in the 1840s.
Mural monument for Sir Edward FREWEN, d. 1723, and his wife Selina, d. 1714
Northiam, St Mary 186D

Plate 117 - Erected in memory of the absentee lord of the manor by his executrix, in fulfilment of her
duty; the dramatic dark grey death's head is the only concession to figuration.
Mural monument for Thomas Holles PAYNE, d. 1800
Ovingdean, St Wulfran 192F

Plate 118 - Perhaps the earliest monument in the county to a Shelley, one of Sussex's most prominent
and commemorated families; 'Labour' and 'Rest' flank the coat-of-arms.
Mural monument for Richard SHELLEY, d. 1594
Patcham, All Saints 195C

Plate 119 - The workshop of John Bacon was one of England's most productive although by this date he was not personally directly involved in carving every commission.
Mural monument for Elizabeth DELVES, d. 1819
Peasmarsh, St Peter and St Paul 197F

Plate 120 - A spacious and ancient church but short of monuments; only this outline remains of what must have been a substantial wall-tomb, perhaps originally similar to Plate 94.
Wall monument for John WHEATELY, d. 1616
Pevensey, St. Nicholas 201A

Plate 121 - A unique survival; an engraved floor slab commemorating a brewer, his name originally
inlaid in brass; both stone and deceased come from the Low Countries.
Floor slab for Cornelis ZOETMANS, dated c.1530
Playden, St. Michael 203C

Plate 122 - The north sanctuary wall is a prestigious position for a monument and an appropriate
choice for a man who was not only the rector but also had the living in his gift.
Mural monument for Rev. William HAMPTON, d. 1770, and his wife Mary, d. 1793
Plumpton, St. Michael 204F

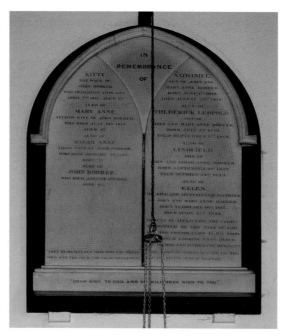

Plate 123 - The monument reduced to a framed, inscribed panel; Brine – a London maker – signed
two other monuments at Portslade immediately alongside this one.
Mural monument for the BORRER family, from 1811
Portslade, St Nicholas 206J

Plate 124 - One of three matching mural tablets chronicling the lives and ministries of the Cluttons,
rectors of Portslade, from the time of Ralph (d.1761) to John (d.1815).
Mural monument for Ralph CLUTTON, d. 1761
Portslade, St Nicholas 206O

Plate 125 - An interesting monument in a transitional style; the draped urn was a somewhat passé motif by the early 1830s, while the faceted column shafts signal the Gothic revival.
Mural monument for Dame Mary BALL, d. 1832, and Sir Alexander John BALL, d. 1809
Poynings, Holy Trinity 207A

Plate 126 - The antique motif of trophies-of-arms - the draped canon and captured standards - is adapted for a senior officer in the Royal Artillery during the Napoleonic period.
Mural monument for Lt-Col. Abraham DU VERNET, d. 1806
Ringmer, St. Mary the Virgin 212D

Plate 127 - The carved cherubs on this important mural reveal how tasks could be allocated within the high quality of these two contrasts with those below.
Mural for Sir Herbert WHALLEY, d. 1689
Ringmer, St. Mary the Virgin 212Z

Plate 128 - The subject, who died in the Civil War siege of Arundel, is presented as an ancient hero with his own curled tresses but also, remarkably for this date, dressed in a toga.
Mural for Sir William SPRINGETT, d. 1643
Ringmer, St. Mary the Virgin 212GG

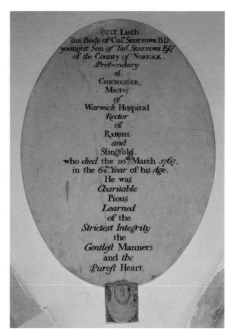

Plate 129 - The only mural monument at Rodmell; for a distinguished cleric; an elegant inscription on an unframed tablet, its oval shape increasingly popular towards 1800.
Mural monument for Rev. Charles SKOTTOWE, d. 1767
Rodmell, St. Peter 214I

Plate 130 - A very competent early eighteenth-century engraved ledger for a member of a prominent clerical family, the lettering sizes carefully adjusted at the end of line two.
Ledger for Rev. Thomas PELLING, d. 1732
Rottingdean, St Margaret 217D

Plate 131 - Brasses from the early 1800s are rare, this one possibly commemorates a young visitor to Brighton and can be compared with the Cranston brass at Lewes (Plate 99).
Wall-mounted brass for Fanny HUNTER, d. 1807
Rottingdean, St Margaret 217I

Plate 132 - At Rye, both mural monuments and engraved ledger stones set into the church floor commemorate generations of the Proctor family and their kin, many of them sailors.
Mural monument for members of the PROCTER family, including James, d. 1809
Rye, St. Mary 221B

Plate 133 - Dozens of ledger stones remain on the floor at Rye; detail shows a display of
memento mori imagery – crossed bones and a prematurely lost rose bud.
Ledger for Ann LONG, d. 1725, and descendants
Rye, St. Mary 221X

Plate 134 - The Bacon workshop maintained its commercial success as it passed through various
hands and directors using a standard formal vocabulary of draped urns and wreaths.
Wall monument for Elizabeth WOOLLETT, d. 1810
Rye, St. Mary 221XX

Plate 135 - The back-plate refers distantly in its shape to the form of the classical obelisk, it supplies
a ground for a simply juxtaposed oval M.I. and proud achievement-of-arms.
Mural monument for Chiswell SLADE, d. 1787
Rye, St. Mary 221NNN

Plate 136 - This set of motifs is repeated in many monuments in the north aisle at Rye, dating from
c.1820-30; the Haddocks were prominent in the town's shipping community.
Mural monument for Mary HADDOCK, d. 1823
Rye, St. Mary 221OOO

Plate 137 - Flaxman has signed this fluted urn on a plinth adorned with acanthus; it probably dates
from the very late 1790s and alludes, metaphorically, to a wreath in decay.
Monument for Thomas OWENS, d. 1769, Elizabeth WELLER, d. 1781, Catharine OWENS, d. 1797
Rye, St. Mary 221QQQ

Plate 138 - It is very unusual for the tablet to be formed on the pattern of an heraldic escutcheon;
the M.I. – Malabar (SW India) – refers to the expansion of British colonial interests.
Mural monument for William PROSSER, d. 1795, and his family
Rye, St. Mary 221VVV

Plate 139 - Probably not in its original location and unsigned but showing the standard Bacon
workshop elements of a ledged sarcophagus with ball-and-claw feet (as in Plate 136).
Mural monument for Daniel SLADE, d. 1826
Rye, St. Mary 221WWW

Plate 140 - With Wadhurst, Salehurst has a remarkable collection of cast-iron slabs, showing all the
basic features of the type, including occasional erroneous reversals of the cast letters.
Cast iron slabs for Silvester PECKHAM, d. 1712/3 and others
Salehurst, St Mary the Virgin 222L

Plate 141 - Some Salehurst families commissioned engraved stone ledgers rather than locally
produced memorials in cast iron, perhaps to register their upward social mobility.
Ledgers for William PECKHAM, d. 1737, and others
Salehurst, St Mary the Virgin 222R

Plate 142 - Black and white dominate most early nineteenth-century monuments; delicate inlaid trim in
rance stone and a curvaceous apron like this would soon become outmoded.
Mural monument for Esther ATKINS, d. 1807
Seaford, St Leonard 224B

Plate 143 - There is a small number of early Tudor wall-tombs in Sussex (see too Hamsey); this one
displays late Gothic features such as the chest quatrefoils and the cresting above.
Wall monument for Dame Beatris BRAY, dated 1532
Selmeston, St Mary 227C

Plate 144 - The floor monuments have been repositioned or replaced with black and red
mid-nineteenth-century brasses, here combined with the original eighteenth-century arms.
Floor-mounted brass for Ann COX, d. 1741
Selmeston, St Mary 227F

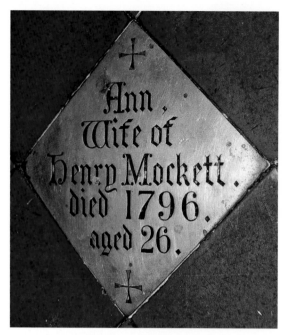

Plate 145 - One of a set of four, the diamond or lozenge shape of this mid-Victorian replacement for a
lost eighteenth-century grave marker is perhaps an echo of the original form.
Brass grave marker for Ann MOCKETT, d. 1796
Selmeston, St Mary 227G

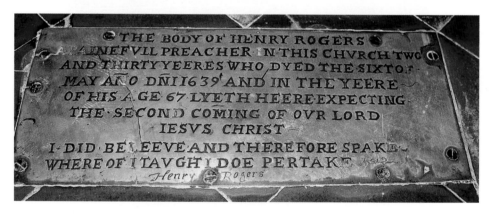

Plate 146 - A rare survival amongst the monuments at Selmeston, an original brass plate from the
mediaeval church; rare too is the implied signature of the final two lines in the M.I.
Floor-mounted brass for Henry ROGERS, d. 1639
Selmeston, St Mary 227H

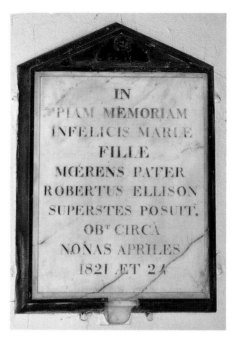

Plate 147 - It is highly unusual for a simple early nineteenth-century inscription tablet such as this to be set in a moulded metal frame, all cased in a cast or stamped tin border.
Mural monument for Mary ELLISON, d. 1821
Slaugham, St Mary 234B

Plate 148 - Elaborately flourished ornamental scripts proliferated before the style was thrown out in a wave of neo-classical reaction; the opening 'Near' is a remarkable invention.
Mural monument for Dionysius BARTLEE, d. 1773
Slaugham, St Mary 234C

Plate 149 - At the cusp of Reformation, a wall-tomb displaying brass figures on the back wall representing the subject and his many wives, escutcheons and a 'Resurrection'.
Wall monument for Richard COVERT, d. 1547
Slaugham, St Mary 234D

Plate 150 - The Elizabethan or Anglican version of the wall-tomb type in Plate 149; the shift to the Reformed theology is suggested by the kneeling figure using a prayer-book.
Wall monument for Jane FETYPLACE (COVERT), d. 1586/7
Slaugham, St Mary 234E

Plate 151 - Rather than grouped below the effigies of the father and mother, the whole clan of children are shown kneeling to the east, named by the initial letters over their heads.
Wall monument for Richard COVERT, dated 1579
Slaugham, St Mary 234F

Plate 152 - Commemorating the founder of Brighthelmstone as a fashionable spa and in its notably non-Christian M.I. (in Latin and, more rarely, Greek) citing Russell's medical skills.
Mural monument for Richard RUSSELL, d. 1759
South Malling, St. Michael 239B

Plate 153 - Having built a great house at Stanmer as a sign of their political power, the Pelhams moved this ancestral tomb from its previous City of London site into the estate church.
Mural monument for Sir John PELHAM, d. 1580, his wife and his son Oliver, d. 1584/5
Stanmer Parish Church 244A

Plate 154 - A memorial for the patron's mother, carved many years after her death by Isaac Hargraves of Lewes, whose career is largely undocumented and unresearched.
Mural Monument for Elizabeth SCRASE, d. 1732
Stanmer Parish Church 244D

Plate 155 - An enormous and important mural monument of exceptional quality; it combines elegant
carving, decorative combinations of coloured stones and a moralising M.I.
Mural monument for Mary DOBELL, d. 1764
Street Parish Church 250A

Plate 156 - A family group comprising a delicate matching pair of oval tablets with decorated frames of
about 1799, complemented by a plain rectangular tablet slightly later in date.
MARCHANT family monuments
Street Parish Church 250F,G & H

Plate 157 - An immense cast-iron ledger probably commissioned by the subject's daughter, heir to the
Gott furnace at Lamberhurst; given the huge scale, this is a technical triumph.
Iron ledger for Martha GOTT, d. 1732/3, and descendants
Streat Parish Church 250L

Plate 158 - This magnificently 'struck' lettering was commissioned by the vicar to honour his parents: the engraved hand points to the place of burial, now surrounded by later tiles.
Ledger for Diones GEERE and his wife Dina, both d. 1743
Tarring Neville, St. Mary 254A

Plate 159 - Sir George Courthope (d.1685) was a dedicated patron of monuments; he wrote the inscription on his own (258E) and erected this eccentric combination for his parents.
Mural monument for Sir George, d. 1642, and Lady Alice COURTHOPE
Ticehurst, St Mary 258F

Plate 160 - Confidently restored heraldry on an elegant cartouche to commemorate yet another George Courthope; c.f. Plate 159, note the style change over the intervening sixty-year period.
Mural monument for George and Albinia COURTHOPE, d. 1714 and 1717
Ticehurst, St Mary 258G

Plate 161 - White or grey marble ledgers on this scale are rare; this magnificent example uses the standard composition of centred lines of engraved text under a coat-of-arms.
Ledger for John ROBERTS, d. 1741
Ticehurst, St Mary 258M

Plate 162 - The architecture of this monument is a simple composition with carefully sawn and
assembled panels framing the M.I. tablet; only the apron and brackets are curved.
Mural monument for Elizabeth JACKSON, d. 1756
Uckfield, Holy Cross 264D

Plate 163 - A set of brasses once on the sanctuary floor; Fuller was the founder of an important
county family and had many charitable interests; he is shown as a devout layman.
Wall-mounted brasses for John FULLER, d. 1610
Uckfield, Holy Cross 264F

Plate 164 - An extremely confident exercise in late Baroque design; note the scrolled borders to the cartouche and the cherubs' heads set into the mantling round the achievement.
Mural cartouche for John EGLES, d. 1750
Uckfield, Holy Cross 264M

Plate 165 - Smith set up a business at Rye exploiting and developing the designs of John Bacon; this is a variant of a standard type, the sarcophagus on a base, seen from the side.
Mural monument for William Cooper WOODHAMS, d. 1826, and his wife Catherine, d. 1870
Udimore, St. Mary 265A

Plate 166 - A simple memorial erected by a leader of local society in memory of the life and extreme old age of a fellow-parishioner known simply by her social rank as 'Widow'.
Mural monument for [Mary] MARSHALL, d. 1798
Udimore, St. Mary 265G

Plate 167 - In the porch and illustrating the local terracotta work of Harmer; his are the decorative inserts such as the winged cherubim and flanking vases set above the entablature.
Mural monument for Mary Georgiana LUCK, d. 1817
Wadhurst, St. Peter & St. Paul 270C

Plate 168 - Illustrating the simplest possible form of cast-iron memorial making; the subject's initials pressed into the casting sand to create a repeated motif across the ledger.
Floor slabs: Edward CHANDLER, d.1673; John SAUNDERS, d.1675; Dorothy ALCHERNE, d.1688
Wadhurst, St. Peter & St. Paul 270K,L & M

Plate 169 - The pose of the figure, turning outwards from her prayer-desk to engage with the onlooker, was adopted by tomb-makers in the mid 1600s, across England.
Mural monument for Mary DAVISON, d. 1651
Wadhurst, St. Peter & St. Paul 270X

Plate 170 - Palmer's London-made monument is the most ambitious work at Wadhurst, with
elaborately carved cartouche, mourning *putti* and free-standing fluted columns.
Mural monument for John BARHAM, d. 1723/4
Wadhurst, St. Peter & St. Paul 270EE

Plate 171 - A rare example of special metal-working skills from what was the heart of the Wealden
iron industry; brass figures and letters are set into an iron slab.
Floor slab for Judith LEGAS, dated 1747
Wadhurst, St. Peter & St. Paul 270ZZ

Plate 172 - The female mourner at her husband's tomb was a standard device by 1800; but this monument was perhaps erected at the Harcourt's wife's death making it a curious choice of motif.
Mural for Martha HARCOURT, d. 1796, and her husband Henry, d. 1800
Warbleton, St. Mary 273B

Plate 173 - Probably the most accomplished portrait on any East Sussex monument, the robed bust on a pedestal by Michael Rysbrack relates to a preliminary drawing in the V&A.
Mural for Sir John LADE, d. 1740
Warbleton, St. Mary 273C

Plate 174 - This shows a rare economy of form with its inscription complemented only by the symbolic dropped rose bud on the pediment alluding to the fourteen year-old subject.
Mural monument for Mary Barrett Curteis INGLIS d. 1827
Wartling, St Mary Magdalene 276E

Plate 175 - A mural monument of high quality on a modest scale; a mourning child attends an urn draped and representing the deceased in the form of a neo-classical portrait medallion.
Mural monument for Caroline Sarah CURTEIS d. 1825
Wartling, St Mary Magdalene 276F

Plate 176 - 'Labour' and 'Rest' were popular personifications on monuments c.1600, alluding both to an active and useful life and in death, the expectation of the resurrection.
Mural monument for Susan TIRREY, d. 1637
West Dean (near Eastbourne), All Saints 280C

Plate 177 - An important London-made monument, perhaps intended to mark Thomas' rise in social status from a member of Lewes' legal circle to the owner of a country estate.
Mural Monument for William THOMAS, d. 1639/40 and his wife Anne, d. 1625
West Dean (near Eastbourne), All Saints 280D

Plate 178 - The angel makes a gesture of honour towards Thomas and his wife, who are shown
kneeling to our right, which in heraldic terms is the lesser or 'sinister' side.
Mural Monument for William THOMAS, d. 1639/40 and his wife Anne, d. 1625
West Dean (near Eastbourne), All Saints 280D

Plate 179 - As Roman Catholic recusants, the Gages came under political suspicion; John Gage's
ambitious family monuments were partly designed to signal their loyal, public service.
Brasses for Thomas and Elizabeth GAGE, both d. 1590
West Firle, St. Peter 281C

Plate 180 - The set of tombs at Firle is the work of the immigrant Netherlands carver, Garret Johnson; this is the largest monument, erected to commemorate Gage's parents. Tomb-chest for Sir John GAGE, d. 1556, and his wife Philippa made in the late 1590s
West Firle, St. Peter 281F

Plate 181 - The figure of the deceased is shown as a shrouded corpse, a motif in the *memento mori* tradition; the MI refers to the Duke of Norfolk, the subject's blood relative.
Brass for Mary HOWARD, d. 1638
West Firle, St. Peter 281G

Plate 182 - In late mediaeval tomb-chests, M.I.s were carved into the chamfered edges
(see Plate 12 at Battle); here the M.I. is cast into the iron slab's edge, leaving the centre vacant.
Wall-mounted iron slab for Richard INFIELD, d. 1619
West Hoathly, St Margaret 283M

Plate 183 - Another variant on the basic cast-iron slab, this time with the MI not set round the edge but
in bands across the centre, a pattern that recurs at East Grinstead (86BB).
Wall-mounted slab for Richard INFIELD, d. 1624/5
West Hoathly, St Margaret 283N

Plate 184 - A view that reveals both the thickness and the untreated faces of a finished ledger stone, engraved, painted black, lifted from the floor and set up against the wall.
Wall-mounted ledger for Katherine INFIELD, d. 1623
West Hoathly, St Margaret 2830

Plate 185 - The obelisk, a symbol of eternity since the Elizabethan period through its association with the ancient pyramid, is adapted to form the back plate supporting an oval tablet.
Mural monument for John Meres FAGGE, d. 1769
Westham, St Mary 292V

Plate 186 - The bringing together of elements that appear not to belong (the vast urn, the heraldry) perhaps reflects restorations undertaken after bomb damage in World War II.
Standing monument for Sir Thomas PARKER, [d. 1663], grandson Sir Robert Parker, d. 1691, others
Willingdon, St. Mary the Virgin 297A

Plate 187 - A monument dominated by a mid-relief image of a kneeling figure with a prominent widow's hood; she is surrounded by decorative symbols; below is a crudely shaped apron.
Mural monument for Elinor PARKER, d. 1598/9
Willingdon, St. Mary the Virgin 297F

Plate 188 - A very neat version of the standard Jacobean niched epitaph; the armoured figure, small
M.I. and modest coat-of-arms are flanked by elegant strapwork panels.
Mural monument for Sir John PARKER, d. 1617
Willingdon, St. Mary the Virgin 297P

Plate 189 - Perhaps the highest in quality of the many monuments to the Parkers at Willingdon; the
carved cherubs' wings, their heads, mantling and foliate decoration are all exquisite.
Cartouche monument for William PARKER, d. 1727
Willingdon, St. Mary the Virgin 297S

Plate 190 - Ledger stone carving of a very high quality to commemorate the parish priest; this detail
shows the escutcheon of arms, raised in mid-relief, in cretaceous limestone.
Ledger stone for Rev. William EDWARDS, d. 1731, and his wife Frances
Wilmington, St. Mary & St. Peter 298C

Plate 191 - The west wall of the south aisle at Winchelsea is packed with monuments
(some duplicates) erected after the church restorations of the Peninsula War period.
Winchelsea, St. Thomas 299O,P,Q,R,S,T,U & V

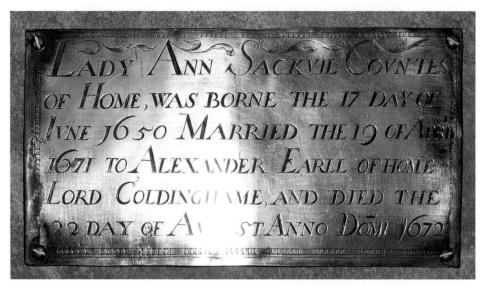

Plate 192 - The elaborate flourishes of the opening words of this engraved inscription contrast with
the sad account of the short life of Ann Sackville, Countess of Home
Wall-mounted brass for Lady Ann SACKVIL, Countess of Home, d. 1672
Withyham, St Michael and All Angels 302C

Plate 193 - Nollekens employs the sentimental device of a group of mourning *putti*, assembled round
the urn, in contemplation of the portrait bust of the third Duke of Dorset.
Mural monument for John Frederick SACKVILLE, 3rd Duke and Earl of DORSET, d. 1799
Withyham, St Michael and All Angels 302E

Plate 194 - In sharp contrast with Nollekens' (Plate 193), Flaxman's version gives greater prominence
to the portrait medallion and includes one single widow-like figure.
Mural monument for George John Frederick SACKVILLE, 4th Duke of DORSET, d. 1815
Withyham, St Michael and All Angels 302G

Plate 195 - Dominating the centre of the chapel, the free-standing *tableau* for the Earl of Dorset's son shows the dramatic intensity of bereavement on a level unmatched in Sussex.
Freestanding monument for Thomas SACKVILLE, d. 1675, his father Richard, d. 1677, erected 1678
Withyham, St Michael and All Angels 302J

Plate 196 - Cibber poses the parents meditating on the figure of their dead son shown not defunct but reclining, his death symbolised by the skull he clutches in his left hand.
Freestanding monument for Thomas SACKVILLE, d. 1675, his father Richard, d. 1677, erected 1678
Withyham, St Michael and All Angels 302J

Plate 197 The SACKVILLE chapel contains the most important set of monuments in East Sussex
with signed and documented works by Cibber, Nollekens, Chantrey and Flaxman.
Withyham, St Michael and All Angels 302

Plate 198 - An unusual composition with a spiral-fluted urn carrying the inscribed tablet as the
centre-piece; in the pediment above, the self-devouring snake symbolises eternity.
Mural monument for William LAMBE, d. 1823
Worth, St Nicholas 306A

Plate 199 - The gadroon ornament is prominent in a frieze between the inscription tablet and the scrolled apron; this is a late occurrence of a decoration more usually employed c.1600.
Mural monument for John SHELLEY, d. 1713
Worth, St Nicholas 306E

Plate 200 - The figure of the mourning widow at the urn, in diaphanous drapes, is here presented in a distorted pose, perhaps aimed at raising the emotional intensity of the monument.
Mural monument for Catharine BETHUNE, d. 1808
Worth, St Nicholas 306R

LIST OF CHURCHES

(1) ALBOURNE, St. Bartholomew

Mainly by Scott 1859, except the chancel - Nairn & Pevsner (395), and see plan in *SNQ* (5 183); for the earlier church, which was reported in 1724 to be fine, see Gomme (180); there was a dispute over a gallery (Ford 120); no monuments cited in Horsfield (*Sussex* II 253-5).

Albourne, 1A Floor-mounted brass for Edward FENNER, d. 1603
- Centre of nave floor, West of chancel arch.
- 35(W) x 12.5(H) — Good; polished.
- A rectangular brass plaque, screwed to floor; M.I. (5 lines, engraved); head to the West.
- Edward Fenner, Gent., d. 21 Jul 1603.

1. Are there recusant sentiments in this inscription: 'deceased in the true faith of Christ'?
2. JH notes that Davidson-Houston (*SAC* 80 147) quotes Dallaway (2 2 291) referring to this as 'a brass now removed from the church'.

Albourne, 1B Ledger for Rev. Benjamin HOFFMAN, d. 1711
- Centre of chancel floor, West of sanctuary rail.
- 98(W) x 198(L) — Sound: crack across centre.
- Escutcheon, then M.I. (engraved) fill black slab; head to West.
- Rev. Benjamin Hoffman, rector of Albourne and Woodmancote, d. 17 Apr 1711, aet 59; his wife, Anne, daughter of Rev. Robert Blithman, M.A., rector of Eversleigh, Hampshire; their issue - Brandon (already dead), Benjamin, Robert, Anne.

1. The words 'Faithful Minister' suggest that the patron was not Benjamin Hoffman himself.
2. Transcribed by Gomme (180).
3. For heraldry see Lambarde (*SAC* 72 2-18).
4. JH notes that Rev. Benjamin Hoffman, MA, was rector of both Albourne and Woodmancote 1682-1711, see Hennessy (20, 166).

Albourne, 1C Mural monument for Rev. Charles BRIDGER, d. 1826 [Plate 1]
- Chancel, North wall, above head height.
- 86(W) x 66(H) — Very good.
- White on black baseplate; M.I. tablet (5 lines + 3 lines, engraved) in upper 75%; engraved and black border; 2 white corbels with dentils; signed (beneath) 'WILLIAMS. BRIGHTON'.
- Rev. Charles Bridger, M.A., rector of Albourne and Twineham for 28 years, d. 11 Feb 1826, aet 52; his widow, Elizabeth, d. 11 Jan 1849, aet 73.

1. 1C is the least imposing of the four tablets signed by Williams in East Sussex (see 49C, 75A and 195A).
2. JH notes that Rev. Charles Bridger, MA, was rector of both Albourne and Twineham 1798-1826, see Hennessy (20, 152).

(2) ALCISTON Parish Church

Architectural history uncertain; chancel originally longer - Nairn & Pevsner (394-5); for a view by Lambert see BL Add. MS 5676 f.73; chancel pavement reported missing in 1686 and in 1724 it was generally in a poor state, especially the South side (Ford 53, 162).

Alciston, 2A Ledger for W[illiam] MERES, d. 1623
- Chancel floor, near North wall.
- 57(W) x 95(L) — Worn.
- M.I. in Roman capitals (engraved) in East end of a freestone slab; head to East.

W MERES G

1623

1. In situ - Horsfield (*Sussex* I 333).
2. Note that the 'S' is reversed on the slab.
3. NBI records the burial of William Meres on 16 Oct 1623 at Alciston.

Alciston, 2B Ledger for John MERES, d. 1641
- Chancel floor, near South wall.
- 57(W) x 95(L) — Fine.
- M.I. in Roman capitals (engraved) in upper 30% of freestone slab; head to East.
- John Meres, d. 12 Jul 1641; his father, Thomas Meres.

1. Horsfield (*Sussex* I 333).
2. For licence to marry for John Meres of Alciston, Gent., with Joan Acheson of Pevensey 27 Jan 1638, see Dunkin (*Licences 1586-1643* 245).
3. One Thomas Meres of Alciston, Gent., was licensed to marry Mary Heath of Piddinghoe, 25 Sep 1637, see Dunkin (*Licences 1586-1643* 242).

(4) ALFRISTON, St. Andrew
A large 14th-century church, Decorated into Perpendicular - Nairn & Pevsner (396); for a plan, see *SNQ* (III 12); for views see BL Add. MS 5678 f.233; 5676 f.72; 5671 f.62; in 1686 some of the paving was missing (Ford 53). No mural monuments were erected on the church walls, perhaps avoiding the mediaeval wall paintings; the walls were bare by 1825 (see Ade's drawing ESRO ACC 340). The early 18th century Vincent hatchment was not matched by monuments - a lack noted in *Gent's Mag* 1767, see Gomme (181), perhaps due to the absence in Alfriston of a dominant family (sensible suggestion in the Church Guide). However, there is an important set of ledgers, some now hard to access, and 4B offers a rare chance to gauge a ledger's thickness. The parish clerk, James Richardson, recorded the inscriptions in 1865, see Richardson (*SAC* 17 240-4). Horsfield (*Sussex* I 330-2) cites no M.I.s here.

Alfriston, 4A Ledger for John BROOKE, d. 1680
- North transept floor, West end, against North wall, partly obscured by furnishings.
- 63(W) x 120(L) — Very worn.
- M.I. (4 lines) in upper 30% of freestone slab; head to East.

> [HERE] LYETH BVRIED THE
> [BODY O]F IOHN BROOKE OF
> [THIS P]ARISH WHO DIED IVNE
> [THE 10ᵀᴴ] 1680 AGED 46 YEARES

1. Not noted by Richardson (*SAC* 17 243-4).
2. Perhaps related to the licence to marry, dated 24 Jun 1676, for one John Brooke of Berwick to Elizabeth Howell of Alfriston, see Dunkin (*Licences 1670-1729* 34).

Alfriston, 4B Ledger for Thomas CHOWNE, d. 1724
- North transept floor, centre, South of 4C-D.
- 86(W) x 167(L) — Fine; damaged North edge.
- M.I. (5 lines, engraved) in upper 40% of polished black slab; head to West.

> HERE LIETH INTER'D THE
> BODY OF THOMAS CHOWNE
> ESQ^r WHO DEPARTED THIS
> LIFE THE 16th DAY OF SEPTEM^{br}
> 1724 AGED 45 YEARS

1. 4B was transcribed by Richardson (*SAC* 17 243) and is in situ.
2. Thomas Chowne and his father (see 4D) were descendants of the first Thomas Chowne (d.1639) a lay theologian of Place House, Frog Firle (author of *Collectiones Theologicarum quarundam Conclusionum ex diversis Auctorum sententiis excerptae*, 1635). A later Thomas (d.1788), whose collections were destroyed by fire in 1765, was an historian of Sussex.

Alfriston, 4C Ledger for Phebe CHOWNE, d. 1713
- North transept floor, centre, North of 4B.
- 86(W) x 169(L) — Good.
- M.I. (11 lines, engraved) in upper 60% of polished black slab; head to West.
- Phebe Chowne d. 17 Dec 1713, aet 31; youngest daughter and co-heir of William Westbrook, Esq., Ferring; and wife of Thomas Chowne, Esq.,

1. For Phebe Chowne's husband see 4B.
2. Transcribed in Richardson (*SAC* 17 243) and in situ.

Alfriston, 4D Ledger for Thomas CHOWNE, d. 1688
- North transept floor, centre, North of 4B-C.
- 93(W) x 182(L) — Very worn; pitted; corners damaged; restored (cement).
- M.I. (13 lines, Latin, engraved) in upper 60% of black slab; head to West.
- Thomas Chowne, armiger, d. 19 Jul 1688, aet 46; his wife Elizabeth d. Oct 1688, aet 38; their son, also Thomas Chowne.

1. In a different stone to 4B-C.
2. Dated [?] 1707.
3. Patron appears to be their son, also Thomas Chowne, as cited in 4B.
4. Transcribed in Richardson (*SAC* 17 243).

Alfriston, 4E Ledger for William GYLES, d. 1719
- South transept floor, South-East corner, partly obscured by furnishings.
- 82(W) x 148(L) — Worn; damaged (East side).
- M.I. (5 lines, engraved) in upper 50% of polished black slab; head to South.
- William Gyles, Gent., d. 4 Jan 1719, aet 76.

1. Transcribed Richardson (*SAC* 17 243) and in situ.
2. Perhaps related to licence to marry dated 2 Oct 1697 for William Gyles of Alfriston and Anne Atwood of Waldron, see Dunkin (*Licences 1670-1729* 167).

Alfriston, 4F Ledger for [J]ohn BROOKE, d. 1680 [?]
- South transept floor, South side, to left of 4G, partly obscured by furnishings.
- 90(W) x 190(L) — Very worn.
- M.I. (engraved) in upper 50% of polished, pink, freestone slab; head to West.

... BURIED THE
....JOHN BROOKE OF
.... WHO DIED IVNE ...

... AGED 59 YEARES

1. Not noted by Richardson (*SAC* 17 243-4).
2. NBI records the burial of John Brooke on 14 Jun 1680 at Alfriston.

Alfriston, 4G Ledger for William BATCHELOR, d. 1783 [Plate 2]
- South transept floor, South side, left of 4F, East end obscured by furnishings.
- 90(W) x 190(L) — Very worn.
- M.I. (7 lines, engraved) in polished, pink, freestone slab; head to West; fleurs-de-lys in corners.

To the Memory of
WILLIAM BATCHELOR
LATE OF THIS *PARISH* GENT
WHO DEPARTED THIS LIFE
APRIL THE 16TH 1783

AGED 30 YEARS

1. The fleur-de-lys motif recurs on the ledger for William Batchelor's wife and child at Lindfield (164U) and elsewhere in the county in the 1770-80s (159L, 164Q, 164U).
2. Transcribed Richardson (*SAC* 17 244) and in situ.
3. For other Batchelors see Alfriston Additions 5-6.

Alfriston, 4H Ledger for William GYLES, Jnr., d. 1724
- South transept floor, South wall, towards South-West corner.
- 112(W) x 194(L) — Worn.
- M.I. (6 lines, engraved) in upper 50% of large, polished, black slab; head to West.
- William Gyles, d. 3 Sep 1724, aet 39; eldest son of William Gyles, Senior.

1. Transcribed Richardson (*SAC* 17 244) and in situ.
2. Note the decorative spacing amongst the letters.
3. Perhaps related to a licence to marry of 2 Oct 1697 for William Giles of Alfriston and Anne Atwood of Waldron, see Dunkin (*Licences 1670-1729* 167).

Alfriston, 4I Ledger for Ann BROOKE, d. 1673
- South transept floor, against South wall, South-West corner.
- 63(W) x 147(L) — Worn; edges fine.
- M.I. (8 lines, engraved) in upper 50% of pink, shelly, freestone slab; head to North.
- Ann Brooke, d. 1 Apr 1673, aet 47; her husband, John Brooke.

1. Not noted by Richardson (*SAC* 17 243-4).
2. For Ann Brooke's husband see 4A.

Alfriston, 4J Ledger for [Ja]mes BROOKE, d. 1667
- South transept floor, against South wall, in far South-East corner, partly obscured by furnishings and plumbing.
- 52(W) x 147(L) — Worn; cracked.
- M.I. (engraved) in upper 30% of polished, pinkish, shelly, freestone slab; head to North.

...LYETH THE BODY
...MES BROOKE OF
...PARISH WHO
...THE 30 OF OCTOBER
...DOM 1667
...D 82 YEARS

1. Not noted by Richardson (*SAC* 17 243-4).
2. From a material rare in East Sussex but used for 4G-I. .
3. NBI records the burial of James Brooke on 2 Nov 1667 at Alfriston.

Alfriston Additions
Noted and transcribed by Richardson (*SAC* 17 243-244):
(1) Robert North, minister of Alfriston 45 years, d. 1709, age unknown (slab in chancel).
(2) Joan North, widow, buried 20 Jul 1671 (slab in chancel).
(3) Susan Crosby, d. 20 Jul 1800, aet 8 (slab in chancel).
(4) William Henry Chown, d. 25 Mar 1747, an infant (slab in North transept).
(5) William Batchelor Jnr., d. 3 May 1754, aet 26; his wife Ann; their son Thomas, d. 13 May 1753, aet 1.
(6) Martha Batchelor, d. 5 Nov 1752, aet 51; wife of William Batchelor, Snr., d. 21 Dec 1752, aet 52.

(8) ARDINGLY, St. Peter

Decorated South aisle and chancel; North aisle and vestry 1887 - Nairn & Pevsner (397); church plan in *SNQ* (X 102); Grimm's 1782 view from North-East, see Godfrey & Salzman (Pl. 4); necessary repairs were reportedly underway in 1724 (Ford 121); Ardingly is, in effect, the Wakehurst Place estate church; the Culpepers held the estate between 1468 and 1694 and the chancel was established as their burial place early in the 16th century, see Attree & Booker (*SAC* 47 65) & BL Add. MS 5672 f.38 (Burrell); however, the request by Thomas Culpeper in 1571 for tombs at Ardingly for himself, his father and grandfather, with 'escriptions ...graven in brasse...fayer & comlie', seems to have been ignored.

Ardingly, 8A Mural monument for Timothy BROWNE, d. 1804

- Chancel North wall, above head height.
- 80(W) x 170(H) — Good.
- M.I. (14 lines, final 5 lines added after 1824; engraved, black) in upper 60% of a very flat freestone [?] panel, set portrait-wise; resting on a moulded shelf over a curved and decorative apron; at top, shoulders and scrolls rising to a decorative shell motif; around the M.I., an inset, scrolled black border.

> Near this Place are
> Deposited the remains
> of TIMOTHY BROWNE A.M.
> Rector of this Parish and Vicar of
> West Hoathly in this County. In
> the Discharge of the sacred Dut
> ies of his Office he was indefa
> tigable. He was the tender and affe
> tionate Husband and a kind indulgent
> Parent, to his Friends open and sin
> cere, to his Neighbour obliging and
> affable, to the Poor charitable and
> humane. He died the 28th of Oct
> 1804 in the 83rd Year of his Age
> Sincerely lamented by all who knew
> him. Go Reader and imitate his
> Virtues.
> Also ELIZABETH relict of the
> said TIMOTHY BROWNE who died
> April 1 1824 at Bromley College
> KENT
>
> Aged 77 years

1. Noted by Horsfield (*Sussex* I 260).
2. Pendant with 8E, perhaps both post-date 1804.
3. Timothy Browne was inducted at Ardingly in 1757, vicar of West Hoathly from 1771, buried in the chancel at Ardingly, aet 82, on 3 Nov 1804 (Loder 191).

Ardingly, 8B Mural monument for Purnell Thomas HICKS, d. 1824

- Sanctuary North wall, above head height.
- 82(W) x 84(H) — Fine; faded.
- M.I. (11 lines, engraved, faded) in upper 50% of a simple unframed white marble tablet against a black baseplate; 2 block corbels.
- Rev. Purnell Thomas Hicks, rector of Ardingly for 5 years, d. 23 Dec 1824, aet 28.

1. Horsfield (*Sussex* I 260).
2. JH notes that Rev. Purnell Thomas Baptist Hicks, MA, was rector at Ardingly from 1820 until his death.

Ardingly, 8C Floor mounted brasses for Elizabeth CULPEPER, d. 1634 [Plate 3]

- Sanctuary floor, South of centre.
- Brass 1: 19(W) x 21(H) — Fine. Brass 2: 43(L) — Fine. Brass 3: 46(W) x 19(H) — Fine.
- 3 brasses on a modern slab; (1) an escutcheon; (2) female figure standing with hands clasped in prayer; (3) M.I. (6 lines, engraved); head to West.
- Elizabeth Culpeper, d. 6 Dec 1634, aet 7; eldest daughter of Sir William Culpeper, Bart., of Wakehurst Palce, and his wife, Jane.

1. In situ - Horsfield (*Sussex* I 259); Stephenson (502); Turner (*SAC* 23 134); Phillips (*SAC* 38 120) - with illustration; Lambarde (*SAC* 69 199) and Davidson-Houston (*SAC* 76 61) - illustrated.
2. Elizabeth Culpeper buried on 8 Dec 1634, see Loder (151) from Parish register; for Culpeper genealogy see Blaauw (*SAC* 10 154); She is granddaughter of Sir Edward Culpeper and the Elizabeth Culpeper commemorated by 8D; the wife of Sir William Culpeper (1602-78) was Jane Pellatt of Bolney, see Attree & Booker (*SAC* 48 98).
3. Willatts (*SAC* 125 106) suggests that this and 8D are London-made brasses.

Ardingly, 8D Floor mounted brass for Elizabeth CULPEPER, d. 1633

- Sanctuary floor, against South wall.
- Slab: 76(W) x 170(L) — Worn. Brass 1: 22(W) x 24(L) — Fine. Brass 2: 69(L) — Fine. Brass 3: 52(W) x 26(L) — Fine.
- 3 brasses mounted on an ancient slab; (1) escutcheon; (2) female figure standing with hands clasped in prayer; (3) M.I. (8 lines engraved) within a decorative border; head to West.
- Elizabeth Culpeper, d. 10 Sep 1633; daughter of William Farnefold, Esq., of Steyning; and wife of Sir Edward Culpeper, Knt., of Wakehurst Place.

1. In situ - Horsfield (*Sussex* I 259); Stephenson (502); Turner (*SAC* 23 134); Lambarde (*SAC* 69 198) and Davidson-Houston (*SAC* 76 59-61) - with illustration, transcribed and translated.
2. Parish register for 23 Aug 1633; 'The La: Eliz. Culpeper, an old woman, was buried in the Chancell 4 foote from the south-window' (Loder 151); 8D is wrongly dated 1632 in some sources (Church Guide) and the M.I. is at variance with the register entry.
3. Elizabeth and Edward were married 1584; Sir Edward was buried 9 Apr 1630, after which Dame Elizabeth moved to Bolney to live with her son Sir William Culpeper, Bart. and his wife Jane Pellatt; Their daughter Katherine (1597-1623) married Richard Infield, of Gravetye (1599-1624), see an iron slab at West Hoathly 283M, see Willatts (*SAC* 125 106); Edward Culpeper was still living in 1628, see Blaauw (*SAC* 10 154); Elizabeth was grandmother of another Elizabeth commemorated by 8C.
4. Both 8C and 8D were probably London-made.

Ardingly, 8E Mural monument for Timothy BROWNE, d. 1763

- Chancel South wall, above head height.
- 80(W) x 170(H) — Good.
- Description - see 8A.

Near this Place
is Interred the Body of
TIMOTHY BROWNE, Gent.
Who died November 24th 1763
Aged 80 Years
Also ELIZABETH daughter of
the said TIMOTHY BROWNE
and MARY his Wife
who died October 6th 1776
in her 55th year
[Likewise?] MARY Relict of
the said TIMOTHY BROWNE
who died October 9th 1778

in her 82nd year

1. See Horsfield (*Sussex* I 259-60) – date given as 1768.
2. Pendant with 8A; perhaps both post-date 1804.
3. Another cleric named Timothy Browne [son?] was in receipt of glebe and tithe rentals in 1785 (R. Davey 4).
4. Parish register notes burial of Mary Browne on 15 Oct 1778 (Loder 180, 183-4), the burial of Timothy Browne himself on 27 Nov 1763 and the burial of Elizabeth Browne on 10 Oct 1776.

Ardingly, 8F Wall mounted slab for Ann FORSTER, d. 1591
- South aisle, South wall, on back wall of a recess.
- 80(W) x 60(H) — A fragment; fine.
- M.I. (in raised relief) cast within an ornamental border on an iron slab.
- Ann Forster, d. 18 Dec 1591; eldest daughter of Thomas Aynsford, Esq.; husband unknown; issue 2 sons, 5 daughters, none named.

1. JH notes that this is not a genuine memorial, but one of several copies, cast as firebacks, see additions note 1.

Ardingly Additions
(1) A copy of the cast iron fireback and grave marker for Ann Forster, a descendant of Richard Wakehurst, was formerly in the church (Church Guide); Holgate 'The Anne Forster Grave-slab' (*SAC* 59 130-1) reports how the fireback and grave marker came to light at Ardingly; Willatts (*SAC* 125 109-10) notes that the original grave marker at Crowhurst, Surrey was retained for use in making firebacks due to its complex patterns; other versions are at East Grinstead (see 86H) and Anne of Cleves House, Lewes. Lambarde (*SAC* 69 199).
(2) A ledger with arms is reported beneath choir stalls: Elizabeth, infant daughter of Anthony and Margery Bickerstaffe, d. 1628.

(9) ARLINGTON, St. Pancras
A flint church with Anglo-Saxon and later mediaeval phases - Nairn & Pevsner (399-400); for a view by Lambert from South-East see BL Add. MS 5676 f.74; for a plan see *SNQ* (VI 53); interior heavily restored in the late 19th century with pews moved and floors excavated, see Powell 'Notes on Arlington Church' (*SAC* 38 184-188); reports of 1686 and 1724 suggest that condition was poor (Ford); amongst the ledgers, Horsfield (*Sussex* I 321) notes only 9E but the Additions to Arlington were probably lost late in the 19th century when 9A-D were re-positioned.

Arlington, 9A Ledger for William CHILDREN, d. 1692
- North aisle floor, towards West end; North-West of a group of 4.
- 85(W) x 135(L) — Worn; pitted.
- M.I. (4 lines, engraved) in upper 25% of a freestone slab; head to West.
- Hardly legible; William Children, d. 9 Jan 1692, aet 27.

Arlington, 9B Ledger for Richard CHILDREN, d. 1687
- As 9A, North-East of a group of 4.
- 77(W) x 138(L) — Fair; pitted.
- M.I. (7 lines, engraved) in upper parts of a freestone slab; head to West.
- Richard Children, buried 11 Jun 1687, aet 11; son of George Children of Tunbridge.

1. Perhaps related to the Richard Children of Arlington, licensed to marry Mary Cox of Hailsham on 25 Feb 1690, see Dunkin (*Licences 1670-1729* 122).

Arlington, 9C Ledger for Elizabeth CHILDREN, d. 1692/3
- As 9A, South-West of a group of 4.
- 70(W) x 115(L) — Fine.
- M.I. (6 lines, engraved) in upper 30% of a freestone slab; head to West.
- Elizabeth Children, widow, d. 23 Jan 1692/3, aet 54.

1. Perhaps related to the Richard Children of Arlington, licensed to marry Mary Cox of Hailsham on 25 Feb 1690/1, see Dunkin (*Licences 1670-1729* 122).
2. NBI records burial of Unnamed Children 24 Jan 1693 at Arlington.

Arlington, 9D Ledger for Elizabeth CHILDREN, d. 1690
- As 9A, South-East of a group of 4.
- 58(W) x 132(L) — Worn.
- M.I. (10 lines, engraved) in a freestone slab; head to West.
- Elizabeth Children, bur. 20 Dec 1690, aet 27; daughter of Richard Children.

1. Perhaps the daughter of Richard Children, see 9B.

Arlington, 9E Mural for John READ, d. 1738 [Plate 4]
- North aisle wall, East of pier, at head height.
- 76(W) x 130(H) — Very good; repainted.
- M.I. (7 lines, engraved, black) on a panel; all in cream, white and grey marbles; a semi-circular curved pediment and cornice; below, corbels, base mouldings and a skull with scroll.
- John Read, Gent., of Arlington, d. 15 Apr 1738, aet 50.

1. Noted by Horsfield (*Sussex* I 321).
2. John Read of Arlington, Gent., was licensed to marry Elizabeth Milward of Hastings on 20 Sep 1704, see Dunkin (*Licences 1670-1729* 90); for a later member of the Milward family see 125A.
3. 9E is unusually 'composite' and uncertain for so small a piece, with unusual floral decoration in the flanking sections, and in the spaces between the various kinds of marble.
4. For an earlier John Read see Arlington Addition 4.

Arlington, 9F Monument for Henry MASON, d. 1800, and his wife Mary, d. 1840
- Nave, South wall, East of South door, high up.
- 80(W) x 170(H) — Inaccessible.
- M.I. (16 lines, engraved, gilded) on a slate oval tablet; limestone baseplate of rough obelisk form; above, in low relief, swags and urn.
- Henry Mason, Esq., of Winkinghurst, Sussex, died at Hailsham 4 Feb 1800, aet 55; his wife Mary, d. 7 Apr 1840, aet 83.

1. Not noted by Horsfield (*Sussex* I 321) and likely to be after 1840.

Arlington Additions
<u>Horsfield (*Sussex* I 321):</u>
(1) Alice Page, d. 1657, wife of Richard Page, also d. 1657.
(2) William Stapley, son of William, d. 1679.
(3) William Stapley, d. 1694.
(4) John Read, of Wilbies, 1694 (see 9E).

(11) ASHBURNHAM, St. Peter

The excellent pre-classical 17th-century interior is well preserved - painted reredos, pulpit, West gallery, box pews, iron railings, tombs, etc.; the earlier church (dedicated to St. Peter) was made over to the household of the Ashburnham family (the church stands alongside Ashburnham House). The new church of 1665 (dedicated to SS Peter & James) is mock-Perpendicular - Nairn & Pevsner (400-1); plan see *SNQ* (X 132-3); view from North-East, as if isolated from the house, see Godfrey & Salzman (Pl. 13) and was consecrated on 13 Jul 1667. The building, together with the two monuments in the North chapel, see early photograph in Whistler (*SAC* 36 168), rebuilt on an ancient site, evidence an acute sense of style decorum and history on the part of the makers and patrons. John Ashburnham (1603-71) Groom of the Bedchamber to Charles I, rebuilt house and church; he was fined under the Commonwealth; his grandson John was created Baron Ashburnham in 1689 and in 1703 referred to the N. Chapel as 'an ancient chapel belonging to my family' (dedicated to St. James). John Ashburnham constructed a family vault extending beneath chancel and both chapels, reported as containing 40 family coffins, see Whistler (*SAC* 36 168, n.10); a family pew was in South-East chapel but had become a vestry by the early 1960s.

Ashburnham, 11A Ledger for John ASHBURNHAM, d. 1679
- Nave floor, centre, towards the West end.
- 44(W) x 45(L) — Worn; damaged (lower side).
- M.I. (engraved) on a pale yellow freestone slab; head to West.

Iohn ſon of

Mʳ Tho: Aſhburn

ham died.1679

1. Noted in situ in Whistler (*SAC* 36 168, n.10).
2. For John Ashburnham's marriage to Alice Osborne, of Westham, widow on 27 Aug 1629, see Dunkin (*Licences 1586-1643* 177).

Ashburnham, 11B Ledger for Rebecca NETHERCOTT, d. 1682
- Nave floor, centre, East of 11A.
- 55(W) x 84(L) — Very worn.
- M.I. (engraved) on a pale grey freestone slab; head to West.

Rebecca eldeſt da-

ughter of Anthony

Nethercott Clerk

and Elizabeth his

wife

Aged 8 years was

buried ... day of

April 1682

1. The lettering infill is still partly visible.

Ashburnham, 11C Ledger for Frances COSTER, d. 1726
- Nave floor, centre, East of 11B.
- 76(W) x 131(L) — Worn.
- M.I. (engraved) in upper 50% of a pale yellow freestone slab; head to West.

> Here Lyeth Inter'd
> the Body of M^rs
> Frances Cofter Mother
> of the Revd Arthur
> Cofter Vicar of this
> Place who Died at
> Battle July the 17.1726
> *Aged 73 years*

1. NBI records the burial of Francis Coster on 20 Jul 1726 at Ashburnham.

Ashburnham, 11D Wall monument for Jane, Countess of MARLBOROUGH, d. 1672 and her husband William ASHBURNHAM, d. 1679 [Plates 5, 6 & 7]

- North chapel, against West wall.
- 434(W) x 520(H) x 187(D); (tomb chest) 233(L) — Excellent; local damage.
- On a white marble tomb chest topped by a polished black ledger, to our left, lies the semi-recumbent effigy of the Countess; to our right, William, in Roman armour, kneels in supplication; behind and above, a baldacchino, topped by an achievement; more arms on the back wall (all in grey marble), being arranged by cherubim, one of whom crowns the Countess; on the face of the tomb chest, M.I. (engraved, black) on a panel with decorative scrollwork; to the sides, on 4 pedestals, trophies as attributes of nobility.
- Jane, Countess of Marlborough; died before her husband (of 44 years) William Ashburnham, second son of John Ashburnham; no issue; her father, John, Lord Butler of Hertfordshire; her first husband, for 7 years, James, Earl of Marlborough, Lord High Treasurer, etc.

1. In situ - Horsfield (*Sussex* I 558-9).
2. The Baroque approach in this work by John Bushnell d. 1701 (documented: Gunnis *Dict.*) has often been noted but equally often misunderstood (Nairn & Pevsner 401).
3. Its 'great pretension' quoting the local vicar, see Whistler (*SAC* 36 168, note 10).
4. William (see biography by C Brooks in *ODNB*) was second son of Sir John Ashburnham and younger brother of John (see 11E) and honoured here by virtue of his marriage to Jane, the widow of James, Earl of Marlborough.
5. Also noted by *Gent's Mag* 1786 ii 853 reported in Gomme (190) and by Lambarde (*SAC* 68 223) noting arms.
6. A view by Grimm (1788) in BL Add. MS 5670 ff.68-9; first published by Esdaile in Walpole Society XV (then in *SNQ* IX 2-3), noting that the cherub places wreath of immortality on her head.
7. The four flanking pedestals also used by Bushnell at his monument at Fulham to Lord Mordaunt.
8. The influences are typically eclectic - English heraldry (following training with Burman), flying cherubs in the Italian/Dutch tradition, French passioned husband.
9. Noted by Whinney (97-100 & Pl. 61) who notes that Bushnell was not trusted by patrons, who tended to prefer to commission Gibbons or Cibber (ibid 101).
10. For Bushnell, see, Linda Boreau, 'John Bushnell in Venice' (*Church Monuments* XIV 1999 88-103 p.96 and Pl. 9).
11. NBI records the burial of Jane Asburnham on 28 Mar 1672 at Ashburnham.

Ashburnham, 11E Wall monument for John ASHBURNHAM, d. 1671 [Plate 8]

- North chapel, against the North wall.
- 267(W) x 504(H) x 128(D); tomb-chest 252(L) — Excellent; some staining; slate front panel cracked.
- In white and grey marble and black slate; three recumbent effigies in white marble with hands clasped in prayer and with feet to the East on a tomb-chest; John Ashburnham between his two wives, 1 shrouded; on the front of the chest, kneeling children as mourners (4 sons and 4 daughters) centred on a prayer desk; above and behind, and carried on polished black columns, M.I. (engraved) on slate tablet on back wall; over, an arched superstructure with scrolled pediment and achievement.
- John Ashburnham, Esq. of Ashburnham, d. 15 Jun 1671, aet 67; his father, Sir John

Ashburnham who died in Fleet Prison; Sir John's wife was daughter of Sir Thomas Beaumont, of Staughton, Leicestershire; she died aet 74, buried at St. Andrew Holborn; John Ashburnham's first wife was Frances, daughter of William Holland of West Burton; their issue - 8; his second wife was Elizabeth, daughter of Christopher Kenn of Somerset, and widow of Lord Poulett of Hinton St. George, Somerset, she died aet 70.

1. In situ - Horsfield (*Sussex* I 558-9); drawn by Grimm (1788) in BL Add. MS 5670 ff.68-9; noted by Nairn & Pevsner (400-01); *Gent's Mag* 1786 ii 853 quoted by Gomme (190).
2. Attributed by Mr Bloxham to Nicholas Stone, see Whistler (*SAC* 36 168, note 10).
3. Lambarde (*SAC* 68 223) notes the heraldry.
4. Esdaile (*SNQ* IX 2) regards 11E as by Burman though it is not documented; she reflects on Burman's troubled relationship with his former master, Bushnell, maker of 11D; White (13-15) does not comment on Esdaile's attribution to Burman, for whom see A. White's biography in *ODNB*.
5. 11E parodies a monument of some 50-60 years earlier.
6. Very occasionally, the maker's contemporary sensibility is apparent, e.g. in the fabric hanging from the circular scroll-ends in the pediment and the form of the brackets beneath the flanking columns.

(15) BALCOMBE, St. Mary

Recently repaired in 1724 (Ford); major changes were made to the church (except for the tower) in 1847-50 - Nairn & Pevsner (401) and perhaps again in 1873 (*SNQ* V 56); see DJW Piper 'Henry Chatfield' *SNQ* (XVI 16ff) for an account of the dominant local family; Balcombe Addition (1) was perhaps lost during these 19th-century church restorations.

Balcombe, 15A Ledger for the sons of Rev. John CHATFIELD, d. 1779
- South-East chapel floor, East of chancel arch, partly obscured by furnishings.
- 65(W) x 88(L) — Very worn.
- M.I. on freestone slab; head to West.

In Memory of
The Sons of yᵉ Rev
... John Chatfield
... Ann his wife who
dyed infants
... March ...
...37
Janʳʸ 14 ... 74
... ye 2nd 17.9
... 6 ...

1. Chatfield was rector at Balcombe 1740-49; his successors were still being taxed on parish lands in 1785 (R. Davey 8).
2. Licence to marry of John Chatfield of Cuckfield and Anne Moor of Wivelsfield, 13 Apr 1692, see Dunkin (*Licences 1670-1729* 137).
3. For the Moor monuments at Wivelsfield see (303).

Balcombe, 15B Ledger for Robert WYATT, d. 1657
- South-East chapel floor, immediately West of 15A, partly obscured by furnishings.
- 65(W) x 61(L) — Fine; damaged edges; length reduced(?).
- M.I. (5 lines, engraved) in upper 50% of a black slab; head to West; perhaps cut at East end.

HERE LYETH BVRIED THE BODY
OF ROBERT WYATT ELDEST
SONNE OF FRANCIS W[YATT]
WHO DYED ...

... BER IN ...

1. Horsfield (*Sussex* I 260) gives the date 8 Oct 1657.

Balcombe, 15C Ledger for Rev. Thomas CHATFIELD, d. 1730
- South-East chapel floor, immediately West of 15B, partly obscured by furnishings.
- 100(W) x 201(L) — Fine; worn.
- M.I. (engraved) fills surface of a black slab; head to West.

IN MEMORY ..
of yᵉ *Revᵈ* Mᴿ THOMAS ..
Rectʳ of this *Pariſh* who ...
1730 Aged ...

And *alſo* of yᵉ Revᵈ *Mᴿ THO: CHA...*
Rectʳ of this Pariſh who was Son of *a*
foreſaid THOMAS & DIED JUNE Yᴱ 5ᵀᴴ
1740 AGED 46

And Alſo of *SARAH* CHATFIELD *Widow*
of yᵉ aforeſaid THOMAS CHATFIELD SENᴿ
who *died* May yᵉ 13ᵗʰ 1766
Aged 96

And alſo of *Mᴿ JOHN CHATFIELD*
Son of the REVᵒ Mᴿ JOHN CHATFIELD
and ... his Wife who died Jan
1769 Aged ...

Alſo of the Revᵈ Mᴿ JOHN CHATFIELD
Rector of this Pariſh who ...
... THOMAS CHATFIELD S ...
who died October 2...

Aged 71

1. Thomas Chatfield was the first of several Chatfields who were rector at Balcombe: Thomas (1693-1730), another Thomas (1730-40), John (1740-79) and Henry (1779-1819).
2. For licence to marry of Thomas Chatfield, of Balcombe, clerk, and Sarah Bray, of Balcombe, 20 Jun 1693, see Dunkin (*Licences 1670-1729* 147).
3. Horsfield (*Sussex* I 259-60) notes 15C and that Thomas Chatfield [Snr] d. 4 Aug 1730, aet 75. He gives a fuller transcription; John Chatfield, d. 4 Jan 1769, aet 27, son of Rev. John Chatfield and Ann his wife.

Balcombe, 15D Ledger for Robert SPENCE, d. 1656
- South aisle floor, towards East end.
- 85(W) x 169(L) — Sound; worn.
- M.I. (engraved) in Latin and English fills most of the centre of a black slab; head to West.
- Robert Spence, Esq., d. 15 Jan 1656, aet 66[?]; his son, John Spence of Malling; his grandson, also John Spence, d. 20 Sep 1713, aet 49.

1. Noted by Horsfield (*Sussex* I 260) who says Robert Spence died aet 56.
2. The Spences were an ancient Norfolk family, for whom see South Malling (239E, G and H).
3. NBI records that Robert Spence was buried at Balcombe on 17 Jan 1658.

Balcombe Additions
Horsfield (*Sussex* I 260):
(1) A mural monument? – Rev. Henry Chatfield, d. 12 Nov 1819, aet 63, '39 yrs as rector'.
(2) Elizabeth Chatfield, d. 23 mar 1811, aet 28, daughter of (1) above.
(3) Henry Chatfield, 25 Dec 1811, aet 19, son of (1) above.
(4) 2 other sons of (1) above.

(16) BARCOMBE, St. Mary

South aisle & vestry rebuilt 1879-80, chancel added to earlier nave in 13th century (*SNQ* X 149 - with plan) - Nairn & Pevsner (403); for a view by Lambert from North-East see Godfrey & Salzman (Pl. 14) (BL Add. MS 5677 f.24); condition fine in 1724 (Ford); for exterior mural monuments see Lambarde (*SAC* 71 144-5); Barcombe has an important set of monuments dating from c.1700 relating to two local families linked by marriage (16A,C,D,E and F): the Raynes were owners of Conniborrow Park until 1685 when John Raynes left the estate to his sister, Susanna Medley.

Barcombe, 16A Mural monument for Anne RAYNES, d. 1632

- Chancel, North wall, West end, above head height.
- 61(W) x 30(H) — Good.
- M.I. (9 lines, engraved) of Latin fills an unframed slate panel.
- Anne Raynes, d. 9 Jul 1632; daughter of William Stonestreat, of Lewes, Gent.; and wife of Edward Raynes, Gent.; issue - Richard Raynes.

1. Noted by Horsfield (*Sussex* I 222).
2. Erected by Richard Raynes in 1680, following the death of Edward Raynes (see 16E).

Barcombe, 16B Mural monument for Robert CRAYFORD, d. 1683

- Chancel, North wall, East end, above head height.
- 51(W) x 74(H) — Very good.
- A cartouche; drapes falling from a cherub reveal M.I. (10 lines, engraved, black) of Latin on a convex oval panel; below, a death's head.
- Robert Crayford, d. 1683, aet 63, scholar (Gonville & Caius College, Cambridge).

1. Robert Crayford was rector at Barcombe 1671-83; he had also been vicar of East Grinstead 1658-71. He supplied Giles Moore with some books on 23 Sep 1678, via his son Robert Crayford, Jnr., see Bird (118).

Barcombe, 16C Mural monument for John RAYNES, d. 1687 [Plate 10]

- Chancel, South wall, East end, above head height.
- 82(W) x 149(H) — Good; faded; worn.
- A cartouche; two putti hold back drapes to reveal M.I. (9 lines, shallow engraved) on more drapery; below, swags; beneath a cherub and a central fluted corbel; above, scrollwork around an escutcheon.
- John Raynes d. 23 Oct 1687, aet 53[?]; partly illegible.

1. Noted by Horsfield (*Sussex* I 222) and dated 1687; and see Lambarde (*SAC* 71 143) noting arms.
2. For John Raynes' daughter see 16F.
3. NBI records the burial of John Raynes on 15 Nov 1687 at Barcombe.

Barcombe, 16D Ledger for John MEDLEY, d. 1682

- South aisle floor, East end, alongside 16E.
- 55(W) x 143(L) — Good; worn.
- M.I. (9 lines, engraved) in upper parts of a light brown freestone slab; head to West.
- John Medley, d. 10 Oct 1682 aet 8; eldest son of Thomas Medley, Gent., and his wife Susanna.

1. For Susanna Medley, see also 16F.
2. Not mentioned in Horsfield.

Barcombe, 16E Ledger for Edward RAYNES, d. 1677

- South aisle floor, East end, alongside 16D.
- 95(W) x 95(L) — Very worn.
- M.I. (engraved) fills surface of a light brown freestone slab; hardly legible; head to West.

- Edward Raynes, Gent., d. 16 Aug 1677, aged about 80.

1. The estate at Barcombe was bought by Edward Raynes, a Lewes lawyer, for his niece and heir, Susanna, see 16F; she married Thomas Medley (1645-1728) in 1672 (Farrant 154-5).
2. Not mentioned in Horsfield.

Barcombe, 16F Mural monument for Susanna MEDLEY, d. 1704 [Plate 9]

- South aisle, South wall, East end, at head height.
- 180(W) x 365(H) — Excellent.
- Magnificent in white and grey marble; elegant draped caryatids, standing on ornamental bases, flank M.I. (engraved black) in upper 50% of a panel set portrait-wise, with cherub over; caryatids support an entablature and a heavy scrolled and broken pediment; urn in the centre; below, ornamental apron, moulded, with escutcheon in Baroque frame.
- Susanna Medley, died at Coneyborough, Barcombe, 5 Apr 1704, aet 62; wife of Thomas Medley, Esq.; heir to her brother, John Raynes, Gent.; monument erected 1730 by her youngest son Edward Medley.

1. Noted by Horsfield (*Sussex* I 222 - 'handsome', with aet as 63); in situ and arms noted in Lambarde (*SAC* 71 143); 1730 given as date of death in Nairn & Pevsner (403) - also caryatids and individualist qualities of 16F noted; in fact, 1730 is the TPQ.
2. For patron and Susanna Medley's youngest son see 16D; for her father see 16C.
3. Farrant (154-5) notes Edward Medley (1680-1754) was builder of Coneyborough in the 1710-20s.
4. 16F is the work of a high quality tomb-maker.
5. JH notes that Horsfield (*Sussex* I 222) mentions inscription to Edward Medley, Esq., formerly of Coneyburrows, ob. 1730. Not clear if this was a separate item; it could have been part of 16F.

Barcombe, 16G Ledger for Elizabeth LUCAS, d. 1769 and her uncle Edward, d. 1776

- Nave floor, West end, East of tower chapel.
- 110(W) x 198(L) — Fine: worn (arms).
- Escutcheon, then M.I. (engraved) fills surface of a black (slate?) slab; head to West.
- Elizabeth Lucas, d. 29 Aug. 1769 aet 37; daughter of John Lucas, Esq. of Longford, Barcombe; also Edward Lucas, (brother of John), d. 2 Feb 1776, aet 81.

1. Not mentioned in Horsfield. In situ c.1930 – see Lambarde (*SAC* 71 143) noting arms.

(20) BATTLE, St. Mary the Virgin

A Norman church, rebuilt in Perpendicular - Nairn & Pevsner (407-8); for plan see *SNQ* (XI 7); John Smith of Rye and James Whitehead (1817) were working in the town and at the Abbey, Gunnis (*Dict.* 357, 431), although there are no signed monuments by them in the church; 20I is of national significance. Horsfield (*Sussex* I 530) makes the point that there are other monuments that he is unable to mention because of lack of space.

Battle, 20A Mural monument for Edmund CARTWRIGHT, d. 1823

- North aisle, North wall, near East end, at head height and above.
- 187(W) x 167(H) — Very good.
- In off-white marble; tabernacle of three 'pages' on a black base; cornice over; below, basement and a shelf; M.I. (left) - 3 engraved verses; M.I. (centre): beneath a pointed pediment - biography; M.I. (right) - 3 verses; signed (lower left): 'M.VIDLER. SC. HASTINGS'.
- Edmund Cartwright, D.D. F.R.S., poet, formerly fellow of Magdalen College, Oxford, rector of Goadby Marwood, Leicestershire and prebendary of Lincoln, 24 Apr 1743 - 30 Oct 1823; monument erected by his widow, Susanna.

1. In situ - Horsfield (*Sussex* I 529-30).
2. Gunnis (*Dict.* 409) as by Major Vidler, who worked locally and at Battle Abbey (1811-1818).
3. Patron was his widow Susannah.
4. Cartwright was a cleric of poetic inclination.
5. JH notes that Edmund Cartwright died at Hastings on 30 Oct 1723 and NBI records burial on 8 Nov 1823 at Battle.

Battle, 20B Mural monument for Lieutenant-Colonel [John] KINGSBURY, d. 1813

- North aisle, North wall, West of North door, high.
- 70(W) x 93(H) — Very good.
- A flat cornice with hanging garlands; above M.I. (23 lines, engraved, black) on an unframed panel; over a black slate base.
- Lt. Col. Kingsbury, Queens Royal Regiment, d. 14 Aug 1813, aet 46; saw action at Gibraltar, Egypt, Portugal, Spain and with Wellington.

1. 20B was erected by Kingsbury's fellow officers to a hero of the Peninsula War.
2. The M.I. includes no family history.
3. 20B must have been ordered after 3 Oct 1812, when Wellington was elevated to a marquessate (after the Battle of Salamanca on 22 Jul 1812) and before his elevation to a dukedom on 4 May 1814.
4. NBI records burial of John Kingsbury in August 1813 at Battle.

Battle, 20C Mural monument for Edward DONNE, d. 1847

- North aisle, North wall, over North door, high.
- 90(W); (H) inaccessible — Good; faded; dirty.
- In trapezoidal shape; thin black baseplate with a pointed top; grey marble panel of same shape, unframed; 2 corbels; a moulded cornice; wreath in pointed pediment; signed (lower right): 'BEDFORD / 256 OXFORD STREET / LONDON'.
- Edward John Donne, died at Woodlands, Battle 15 Nov 1847, aet 28; his father, also Edward Donne, of Harley St. London; Edward John was survived by his parents.

1. Not listed by Gunnis (*Dict.*).
2. Perhaps after 1847.
3. NBI records burial of Edward Donne on 20 Nov 1847 at Battle.

Battle, 20D Mural monument for Harriett SWAIN and her daughter Mary-Ann, both d. 1821 [Plate 11]

- North aisle, North wall, East of North door, high.
- 63(W) x 77(H) — Very good; faded.
- A thin black baseplate; M.I. (24 lines, engraved, black) on unframed panel, set portrait-wise; flat cornice.
- Harriett Swain, died at Cefalonia, 12 Oct 1821, aet 37; wife of Major Swain, (36th Regiment); their daughter Mary-Anne Swain, d. 25 Jul 1821, aet 6; Harriett and Mary-Ann Swain both buried at St. Spiridion, Argostoli, Cefalonia.

1. Formerly 'opposite the pulpit' - Horsfield (*Sussex* I 529-30).
2. Erected by the husband / father.
3. They died on Cephalonia, the Ionian islands being then under the protection of Britain and referred to as the United States of Ionia after treaty of Paris, 5 Nov 1815 (arrangement ended 1864).

Battle, 20E Mural Monument for Giles WATTS, d. 1792

- North aisle, North wall, East of North door, above head height.
- 69(W) x 63(H) — Very good; faded.
- No baseplate; M.I. (9 lines, engraved, black) on unframed panel set landscape-wise; 2 block corbels; cornice and blank pointed pediment.
- Giles Watts, physician, d. 1 May 1792, aet 67; his widow, Mary Watts d. 24 Dec 1815, aet 92.

1. Although Mary Watts is mentioned before Giles Watts in the M.I., 20E seems to pre-date her death in 1815.
2. Giles Watts, son of John Watts, of Battle, was apprenticed to Robert Young, of Battle, surgeon on 11 Nov 1743, see Rice (201).

Battle, 20F Mural monument for Robert WALLACE, d. 1824
- North Choir aisle, North wall, North-East corner, very high.
- Small (inaccessible) — Very good condition; paint splashes.
- M.I. (6 lines, engraved, black) on unframed panel; above, a blank pointed pediment; thin black baseplate; signed (lower right): 'VIDLER & Co'.
- Robert Alexander Paterson Wallace, Esq., died at Hastings, 29 May 1824 aet 22.

1. Vidler (from Hastings see 126C-D) worked a good deal at Battle, see Gunnis (*Dict.*) and 20A.

Battle, 20G Mural Monument for Mary BIRCH, d. 1807
- North choir aisle, North wall, North-East corner, high, below 20F.
- 95(W) x 120(H) — Very good; faded.
- In white marble on a thin black baseplate; flat cornice; black shelf under pedestal; unsigned.
- Mary Birch, 1748 - Aug 1807; wife (41 years) of the late Rev. Thomas Birch, rector of South Thoresby, Lincolnshire; surviving issue, 9 unnamed.

1. Patrons of 20G were subject's children.
2. Mary Birch was the mother of the Rev. Thomas Birch (d.1840) and the grandmother of his many daughters all of them commemorated nearby.
3. The shelf arrangement on 20G is close to that on 20A (signed by Vidler).

Battle, 20H Mural monument for the daughters of the Rev. Thomas BIRCH, undated
- North Choir aisle, North wall, high, upper left of a group of 4 monuments.
- Inaccessible — Very good.
- Thin black baseplate; M.I. on panel of sarcophagus shape; cornice and pointed top; feet on a base.
- Katharine Anne, d. 1820; Jane Christian, d. 1822; Frances Margaret Eliza, d. 1835; Maria Rosaria, d. 1839 and Salvadora Hannah, d. 1840; all daughters of Thomas and Maria Rosaria Birch.

1. Katharine, Jane, Frances, Maria and Salvadora were granddaughters of Mary Birch (see 20G).
2. JH notes that their father Thomas Birch was vicar of Battle 1801-40; prebendary of Bishopshurst 1823-40 and vicar of Bexhill 1836-40, where he is buried. NBI records burials of the Birch daughters: Katharine Ann on 10 Mar 1820, Jane Christian on 20 Apr 1822, Frances Margaret Eliza on 26 May 1835, Maria Rosaria on 11 Jun 1839 and Salvadora Hannah on 8 Feb 1840, all at Battle.

Battle, 20I Free-standing tomb-chest for Sir Anthony BROWNE, d. 1548 and his first wife Alice, d. 1540 [Plate 12]
- Between Sanctuary and North choir aisle.
- 136(W) x 240(L) x 120(H) — Fine; many repairs; local losses (effigial hands).
- 2 recumbent effigies; heads to West; female to male's left (female to South of male); over her head, a tabernacle; male in armour; tomb-chest with balusters, putti, arms on sides; M.I. in English on chamfered edge.

(1 on the West side):
HERE LIETH THE RIGHT HONORABLE
SIR ANTONIY BROWNE, KNYGHT

(2 on south side)

OF THE GARTERE

MASTER OF THE KYNGS MAIESTES HORCYS

AND ONE OF THE HONORABLE PRIVE COUNCEL

OF OUR MOST DRAD SOVEREYAN LORDE AND

VICTORYOUS PRINCE KYNG

(3 on east side)

HENRY THE EYGHT

AND DAME ALLIS HIS WYFE WHICHE ALIS

DECESID THE 31 DAY

(4 on north side)

OF MARCHE A°. DNI. 1540.

AND THE SAYD SIR ANTHONY DECESID 6 DAY

OF MAY A°. DNI. 1548 ON WHOIS SOWIS

AND ALL CRISTEN IHU. HAVE MARCY

1. Formerly in niche on North side of choir - Horsfield (*Sussex* I 529) and see also Gomme (168) and Lambarde (*SAC* 68 226-7) - noting arms; so embedded in the wall that some of the M.I. could not be read by Andre (*SAC* 42 229-31); Milles in Farrant 93 and Grose 1777 Diary in Farrant 119.
2. Drawn by Grimm (BL Add. MS 5670 f.35).
3. Anthony Browne lived c.1500-1548; for his career at court see WB Robinson in *ODNB* and on his estate acquisitions see M Howard, *The Early Tudor Country House* (1987); for his elaborate funerals see Turner (*SAC* 6 54-6) (Ashmole MS 818/12).
4. 20I was erected after the death of Alice Browne, daughter of Sir John Gage of West Firle (see 281 Intro) on 31 Mar 1540.
5. Browne left up to £20 in his will for its completion (see e.g. North side of M.I.).
6. There have been a number of unpersuasive attempts to link the design of 20I with the Westminster Abbey tombs of the Florentine Torrigiano and unspecified French sources (e.g. David Starkey (ed.), *The English Court 85-6* (1987)).
7. The material used is Midlands alabaster.
8. It is probable that Anthony Browne commissioned 20I together with another monument for his Fitzwilliam sons-in-law at Tickhill, Yorkshire, for whom he acted as executor (see P. Biver, 'The Tickhill and Battle monuments' *Yorkshire Arch. Journal* XX 279-83).
9. 20I shows a progressive Renaissance design, e.g. the Roman lettering, see Nairn & Pevsner (408), for which there are national parallels at Bodmin, Cornwall and Farringdon, Berkshire.
10. Armour from this monument supposedly sold Christies 1887 (*SAC* 36 247).
11. His garter plate is at the BM, see Andre (*SAC* 42 229-31).

Battle, 20J Floor-mounted brasses for John WYTHINS, d. 1615 [Plate 13]
- Sanctuary floor, South of centre.
- Ledger: 82(W) x 178(L) — Fine; dented. Brasses - panel of arms: 25(W) x 30(H); figure/captions: 89(H); large M.I.: 50(W) x 25.5(H); smaller M.I.: 53(W) x 12(H) — Worn but fine;
- Brasses on a black marble ledger; above, rectangular panel of arms; then, male figure, robed with captions rising left and right; below, 2 M.I.s (9 lines and 4 lines, engraved) in Latin.
- John Wythins, from Chester, scholar of Oxford, STD, dean and vicar of Battle for 42 years, d. 18 Mar 1615, aet 84; quotations from Job.x.1 and Philip.i.3.

1. In situ; drawn by Grose 1777 in Farrant (122); Horsfield (*Sussex* I 529); Stephenson (503); Turner (*SAC* 23 136); Andre (*SAC* 42 233); Gomme (191-2); Lambarde (*SAC* 68 228) - noting arms; and Davidson-Houston (*SAC* 76 80-2).
2. John Wythins was Cheshire born, Oxford educated STD [DD], Brasenose, 1570 see Wood (I 1800), and possibly Vice-chancellor but some claim there has been confusion between a Vice-chancellorship of the University and the vice-principalship of his College; he was also dean and vicar of Battle; his descendant, Mrs F Newnham, presented a silver flagon to the church in 1705, see Couchman (*SAC* 55 183).

Battle, 20K Ledger for John HAMMOND, d. 1761, his wife Eleanor, d. 1797 and others

- South-East chapel floor, at entrance, near South wall, with (modern) gates set into it.
- 100(W) x 182(L) — Good.
- M.I. (17 lines [6+3+4+4], engraved) on a black slab; head to West.
- John Hammond, Gent., d. 17 Dec 1761, aet 48; his wife Eleanor, d. 11 Jan 1797, aet 84; their issue - another John Hammond, d. 10 Mar 1760, aet 5; also William Hammond, brother to John Hammond, Snr, d. 20 Apr 1749, aet 34.

1. Perhaps lettered in the late 1790s? John Hammond's widow was taxed on parish lands in 1785 (R. Davey 12).
2. Perhaps John Hammond was a surgeon active in Battle, see Rudkin '18th Century Medical Practice' (*SCM* I 510).

Battle, 20L Ledger for John HAMMOND, d. 1711 and his wife Joan, d. 1700

- South-East chapel floor, at entrance, North of 20K, with (modern) gates set into it; An unusually large ledger.
- 125(W) x 150(L) — Worn.
- M.I. (8 lines, engraved) in upper 50% of a slab; head to the West.
- John Hammond, d. 9 Jan 1711, aet 73[?]; his wife, Joan, d. 24 Jan 1700, aet 69.

Battle, 20M Mural cartouche for William WATSON, d. 1689

- South-East chapel, North wall, North-East corner, high.
- 110(W) x 205(H) — Fine; repaired.
- M.I. (12 lines engraved, black) on a convex cartouche; arms above; cherubim in the folds.
- William Watson, LLD, dean and vicar of Battle for 25 years and canon of Chichester, d. 10 Apr 1689, aet 51.

1. Formerly in chancel Horsfield (*Sussex* I 529-30); Andre (*SAC* 42 233-4); Lambarde (*SAC* 68 228 - noting arms).
2. Not high quality; possibly exposed to water damage at some stage?
3. JH notes that William Watson was LLD of St. John's, Cambridge. He was dean and vicar of Battle 1663/4-89; rector of Old Romney, Kent 1670; prebendary of Wightring in Chichester Cathedral 1673-89. See Venn (1 4 351) and Horn (*Fasti 1541-1857* II 60).

Battle, 20N Ledger for George WORGE, d. 1765

- Beneath safe in South Chapel.
- 110(W) x 215(L) — Fine.
- Black slab; head to West.
- Ledger for George Worge, Esq., d. 1765, aet 60; his wife, Elizabeth, d. 10 Oct 1766, aet 60, a daughter of John Collier, Esq., of Hastings.

1. Noted by Horsfield (*Sussex* I 529-30) and Lambarde (*SAC* 68 228) noting arms.
2. Noted by Andre (*SAC* 42 234).
3. For Worge see 93II.

Battle Additions

Davidson-Houston (*SAC* 76 80), with illustration and transcription.
(1) Inscribed brass for Elizabeth, d. 3 Oct 1597, widow of Thomas Haye, Gent., (on chapel floor), as late as 1784 (citing BL Add. MS 6344 f.790); there was also a M.I. for Haye himself (d. 17 Feb 1591).
Horsfield (*Sussex* I 529-30), Stephenson (503), Gomme (191) from *Gent's Mag* 1825 16, Turner (*SAC* 23 137-8), Davidson-Houston (*SAC* 76 78-80) with illustration and transcription.
(2) A pair of brasses with M.I.s to Elizabeth (1597), widow of Thomas Alfray, Gent., in the nave and Thomas Alfray, 1589, aet c.50; Elizabeth was daughter of Ambrose Comfort; married 31 years, issue son and daughter; M.I. stresses physical strength of Thomas Alfray; Davidson-Houston locates these in North chancel aisle floor; it was complete in Burrell's day (BL Add. MS 5697 f.15); the Alfrays were ironmasters (see 302A and 26A).

(21) BECKLEY, All Saints

13th-century aisle arcades with Victorian dormers - Nairn & Pevsner (412-13) and a modern chapel South of chancel; plan in *SNQ* (XI 33); reportedly fine in 1686 (Ford); by 1724, chancels of both the rector and Sir John Shelley, Bart. in need of repair; external view by Grimm 1784, BL Add. MS 5670 f.13, see Godfrey & Salzman (Pl. 17); in 1777, Grose found nothing worth drawing (Farrant 120); the consistent widths of the ledgers 21F-21I suggest that they have been relocated as a group.

Beckley, 21A Mural monument for Samuel REEVES, d. 1823 and his wife Elizabeth, d. 1836

- South aisle wall, West of the South door; at head height.
- 77(W) x 67(H) — Very good; fading.
- A grey marble panel on rectangular slate backplate; straight cornice; M.I. (6 + 5 lines, engraved); unsigned.
- Samuel Reeves, Gent., d. 8 Apr 1823, aet 67; his wife Elizabeth, d. 12 Aug 1836, aet 90, daughter of Walter and Elizabeth Waters.

1. Probably after 1836.
2. Father-in-law commemorated in 21G.

Beckley, 21B Mural monument for Richard POLLARD, d. 1794

- North-East chapel, West wall; above head height.
- 70(W) x 174(H) — Very good, water staining (edges), faded.
- In marble; above, an urn in half-relief on a block base; a convex oval panel set portrait-wise, bordered with black inset squares; below, a corbel decorative with foliage and hemispheres; M.I. (11 lines, engraved very shallow, black).

HIS

disconsolate WIDOW

and

affectionate DAUGHTER

DEDICATE this TABLET

to the

memory of RICHARD POLLARD

late of RYE

Ob. 17TH JUNE 1794

On Tombs Encomiums are but vainly spent

A virtuous Life is the best MONUMENT

1. Horsfield (*Sussex* I 510) describes this as formerly in nave and dated 1794, aet 58; after 1791.
2. Crudely shaped oval suggests local work.
3. NBI records burial of Richard Pollard 20 Jun 1794 at Beckley.

Beckley, 21C Mural monument for Mildred LEWIS, d. 1826

- South sanctuary, North wall, West end; above head height.
- 71(W) x 45(H) — Very good.
- A white marble panel on a black baseplate; M.I. (10 lines, engraved, black); signed (lower left): 'M.Vidler. SC. Hastings'.
- Mildred Lewis, d. 9 Oct 1826, aet 77; widow of Rev. H. Lewis; and sister of the late Rev. Dr Bethune of Rowfant House, Sussex.

1. Formerly North side of chancel - Horsfield (*Sussex* I 510).
2. For the tomb patronage of the Bethunes, see 306S-T.

Beckley, 21D Mural monument for Elizabeth HOOPER, d. 1819

- Sanctuary North wall, centre, above head height.
- 77(W) x 90(H) — Fine; fading.
- Unframed; white marble on a black baseplate set portrait wise; M.I. (19 lines, engraved, black).
- Mrs Elizabeth Hooper, of Hailsham, d. 8 Oct 1819; financial details of her charitable donation.

1. In situ - Horsfield (*Sussex* I 510).
2. Elizabeth was daughter of Odiarne Hooper (see 21E) both with cenotaphs at Hailsham (119E-F).
3. Gunnis (*Dict.* 292) attributes this 1819 memorial to Parsons, but says it commemorates Odiarne Hooper.

Beckley, 21E Mural monument for Odiarne HOOPER, d. 1769 and many descendants [Plate 14]

- Sanctuary North wall, East end, above head height.
- 151(W) x 210(H) — Good; faded.
- In mixed marbles; below, coloured hard-stone decorative; above the M.I., a fluted frieze; a moulded entablature between the 2 M.I.s; coloured heraldry on apron.
- Odiarne Hooper, clerk, d. 2 Aug 1769, aet 68; Ann, his wife d. 4 Mar 1775, aet 75; their issue - Odiarne, son, d. 19 Dec 1734, aet 12; John, son, died an infant; Mary, daughter, d. 21 Jun 1749, aet 21; Ann, daughter d. 22 Aug 1760, aet 14; John, d. 29 Dec 1766, aet 36; Thomas, d. 2 Nov 1803, aet 78; Elizabeth d. 8 Nov 1819, aet 84.

1. Noted by Horsfield (*Sussex* I 510); in situ Lambarde (*SAC* 68 218).
2. Odiarne Hooper was educated University College, Oxford; instituted vicar at Mayfield 1730, East Guldeford 1736 and Hailsham 1753, see Dunkin (*SAC* 26 70); he supported schooling in Beckley (for his bequest see Caffyn 44); his first son, also Odiarne, was extensively taxed on parish lands in 1785 (R. Davey p.16); he is also commemorated at Hailsham (119F).
3. The design of the two Hooper tombs at Hailsham (119F and 119E) is similar.
4. Gunnis (*Dict.* 361) notes a letter of 1749 associating Richard Spangen of Camberwell with three monuments at Hailsham for Mr Hooper.
5. Do the Beckley and Hailsham tombs form a set?

Beckley, 21F Ledger for Thomas and Mary HOOPER, undated [post 1753]

- Choir floor, East end.
- 114(W) x 198(L) — Sound, worn.
- Escutcheon, then M.I. (Latin, engraved) fills surface of a black slab; head to West.
- Thomas Hooper, A.M., vicar of Beckley (52 years), died aet 79; son of Thomas Hooper of Mayfield; his wife, Mary Lloyd of London; their issue - 7 children, including Odiarne.

1. Thomas Hooper (1673-1753) was presented to the living at Beckley in 1699; later he was vicar of Hailsham and rector of Wimborne St. Giles and Wimborne All Hallows in Dorset; In 1752 he was succeeded at Beckley by a grandson, also Thomas Hooper (d.1804).
2. Patron of 21F is the son, Odiarne, for whom see 21E (see also Farrant 158 re the Hooper family).

Beckley, 21G Ledger for Walter WATERS, d. 1772 and his family

- Choir floor, West end.
- 114(W) x 195(L) — Very good.
- M.I. (engraved) fills surface of a black slab; head to West; final 5 lines added after 1811.
- Walter Waters, Gent., d. 11 Aug 1772, aet 67; his wife, Elizabeth 21 Jan 1785, aet 78; their issue - John, d. 25 Dec 1764, aet 21; Young, d. 16 Sep 1767, aet 29; Walter, d. 8 Mar 1774, aet 32; Mary, d. 13 Aug 1811 aet 76.

1. Probably set up by Mary Waters (sister? of Elizabeth Reeves, see 21A), after 1785.

Beckley, 21H Ledger for Elizabeth LLOYD, d. 1720

- Nave floor, East end.
- 114(W) x 199(L) — Good, some wear.
- Escutcheon, then M.I. (Latin, engraved) fills 90% of a black slab; head to West.
- Elizabeth Lloyd, d. 31 Mar 1720, aet 85; daughter of John Odiarne of Wittersham, Kent, and his wife Thomasina [?], daughter of William Davy of Hobbs, Beckley; and wife of Gerard Lloyd, d. c.1676; their issue - Elizabeth.

1. Moved from chancel entrance - Lambarde (*SAC* 68 218).
2. Plate was given to the church in memory of Elizabeth Lloyd in 1729 - see Couchman (*SAC* 55 200).
3. Patron of 21H is the daughter, Elizabeth.

Beckley, 21I Ledger for Thomas HOOPER, d. 1803 and his sister Elizabeth, d. 1819

- Nave floor, centre.
- 114(W) x 198(L) — Worn but legible, large crack across centre.
- M.I. (7 lines, engraved) in upper 30% of a black slab; head to West.
- Thomas Hooper, clerk, rector of Beckley d. 2 Nov 1803, aet 78; Elizabeth Hooper of Hailsham, d. 8 Nov 1819, aet 84.

1. 21I commemorates 2 children of Odiarne Hooper, see 21D-E.

Beckley, 21J Ledger for John HOLMAN, no date

- Nave floor, West of centre.
- 85(W) x 171(L) — Very worn.
- M.I. (?6 lines, engraved) at West end of a black slab; head to West.

HERE LIETH Yᴱ BODY OF

IOHN HOLMAN[?] PATRON OF

...BECKLEY ...

[remainder illegible].

1. Probably late 17th century [?].
2. The patron of Beckley in 1603 was Sir George Browne, by grant from his mother, see Renshaw (*Ecclesiastical Returns* 6).

Beckley, 21K Anonymous ledger, no date

- Nave floor, opposite South door.
- 66(W) x 174(L) — Very worn; cracked from East to West (South side).
- Cream freestone slab.

1. Probably datable within our period.
2. Possibly commemorating John Fuller?

Beckley Additions

Horsfield (*Sussex* I 510):
(1) Notes M.I. for Jeremiah and Sarah Smith, both d. 1782, aet 66 and 62.
(2) Unspecified black slabs to Fuller and Hobbs. Could these be 21J and 21K?

(22) BEDDINGHAM, St. Andrews

The church arcades are c.1200 - Nairn & Pevsner (413); for plan see *SNQ* (II 141); for external views by Lambert, 1780 from North-East and South-East see BL Add. MS 5676 ff.79-80; reports of 1686 and 1724 suggest that the state of repair was fine (Ford).

Beddingham, 22A Wall Monument for Alexander CARR, d. 1790 and members of his family [Plate 15]

- North aisle, against South wall, at East end.
- c.155(W) x c.213(H) — Good; some repairs; colour.
- M.I. (17 lines [10 + 7], engraved and black) on white marble panel; simple, black marble frame of pilasters with decorative plaster roses as capitals and plinth moulding; above, a broken, pointed pediment in grey-veined marble; in centre, achievement in Baroque frame on a foot.
- Alexander Carr, d. 9 Jun 1790, aet 33; his father, also Alexander Carr, d. 3 Jan 1797, aet 72; his mother, Rebecca Carr, d. 27 Jul 1792, aet 72; his sister, Charlotte, d. 26 Sep 1790, aet 28; his brother and the eldest son, Sir Thomas Carr, Knt., d. 9 Jun 1814, aet 65.

1. In situ - Horsfield (*Sussex* I 340) and Lambarde (*SAC* 70 151) describing arms.
2. Style of letters on M.I. suggests a TPQ for 22A of about 1793.
3. One Thomas Carr was tenant of Alexander Carr's lands by 1785, see R. Davey (19).
4. 22A is perhaps linked to a licence to marry dated 27 Jun 1781 for Alexander Carr, of Rottingdean, Gent. and Elizabeth Beard, of Chailey, aged 22, see Dunkin & Penfold (*Licences* 77), if so, Elizabeth is not commemorated on 22a (or on 139/1CC); she perhaps died many years after the patron of 22A, assumed here to be Sir Thomas Carr (d.1814).

Beddingham, 22B Ledger for Samuel YOUNG, d. 1736.

- Sanctuary floor, before and in part obscured by altar.
- c.80(W) x c.118(L) — Fair; missing letters; edges worn.
- M.I. (12 lines engraved) on freestone slab; head to the East.

SAMVEL YOVNG THE SON
OF CHRISTOPHER
YOVNG WHO DYED
THE 30TH DAY OF
SEPTEMBER 1689
AGED 65 YEARS.

ALSO HERE LIETH THE
BODY OF SAMVEL SO..
OF THE AFORESAID SAM..V...
YOVNG WHO DYED ..HE
3rd OF MAY 1736 A..ED
66 YEARS.

1. Raised chancel step is of a later date and lines 1-2 are missing, so 22B may have been moved. Not in Horsfield.
2. May relate to a licence to marry, dated 12 Feb 1693-4, for Samuel Young and Anne Jenner, both of Beddingham, see Dunkin (*Licences 1670-1729* 151).

(25) BERWICK, St. Michael & All Angels

Nairn & Pevsner (414-15) note the over-restoration of 1856, e.g. North arcade; for an early view see Lambert (BL Add. MS 5676 f.73); in 1724, the church fabric was reported to be fine (Ford). 25B & C probably replace earlier ledger stones.

Berwick, 25A Ledger for George HALL, d. 1668
- Vestry floor, North of chancel.
- Dimensions, condition and description unknown — Obscured and inaccessible.

> GEORGE HAL[L], RECT[ER] OF THIS CHVRCH
> HIS NAME SPEAKS ALL LEARNING HYMANE
> AND DIVINE HIS MEMORY PRECIOVS BOTH TO THE
> MVSE[S] AND THE GRACE[S] HIS EXTRACTION
> FROM TWO ROYAL[L] COLLEGES THE ONE AT
> ETON THE OTHER AT CAMBRIDG. TOGETHER
> WITH HIS SON GEORGE BOTH OR'GEN[AL] AND
> TRANSCRIPT ARE HERE REREPOSED IN HOPE
> OF A JOYFV[L] RESVRRECTION THE FIRST
> VNBORNE IENVA[RY] THE 15 1668

1. See G. Cooper (*SAC* 6 239) for transcription.
2. The M.I. is also reported in the Church Guide.

Berwick, 25B Grave marker for Augustin METCALFE, d. 1672 [Plate 16]
- Chancel floor, near South wall.
- 30.5(W) x 15(L) — Fair.
- M.I. (2 lines engraved) on a slate slab.

> AVGVSTIN METCALFE
> 1672

1. Set in later paving.
2. Probably a later replacement.

Berwick, 25C Grave marker for John HAWES, d. 1743
- Chancel floor, West end, near South wall.
- 30.5(W) x 15(L) — Fine.
- M.I. (2 lines, engraved) on a slate slab.

> IOHN HAWES
> 1743

1. For licence to marry, dated 28 Nov 1695, for John Hawes of Berwick, clerk and Francis Hay, of Westham, see Dunkin (*Licences 1670-1729* 159); he was instituted 19 Feb 1694 (Ford).
2. 25C is set in later paving; probably a later replacement.
3. Lambarde (*SAC* 70 147) describes arms.

Berwick, 25D Grave marker for William HAWES, d. 1784
- Chancel floor, West end, centre.
- 30.5(W) x 15(L) — Fine.
- M.I. (2 lines, engraved) on a slate slab.

> WILLIAM HAWES
> 1784

1. Set in later paving; probably a later replacement.

Berwick, 25E Floor monument for John NUTT, dated 1653
- Chancel floor, West end, near North wall.
- 30.5(W) x 15(L) — Fine.
- M.I. (2 lines, engraved) on a slate slab.

> IOHN NVTT
> 1653

1. For licence to marry for John Nutt, clerk, of Berwick, to Anne Duncke, of Whatlington 4 May 1620, see Dunkin (*Licences 1586-1643* 118). Anne presented plate to the church in 1630, see Couchman (*SAC* 55 158); for her family see 295A.
2. 25E is set in later paving and probably a later replacement. See also 25H.

Berwick, 25F Mural monument for Louisa Elizabeth WEST, d. 1821

- West tower, South wall, now obscured by an organ.
- 104(W) x 76(H) — Very poor; local losses (decorative details).
- M.I. (engraved) on a white marble tablet; on a shallow black baseplate with a pointed top and squared bottom; signed (lower left): 'C Smith ft Norton Street, London'.

In the vault of Kensington Church Middlesex
Are deposited the mortal remains of
Louisa Elizabeth wife of the Revd Harry West AM rector
And fourth daughter of the late Harry Vere 1st Esqr
of Aston Hall in the county of York and formerly Governor of Bengal:
She departed this life on 10 September 1821 aged 40 years
With the nobler virtues that elevate our nature
She possessed the softer talents that adorn it.
Pious humble benevolent candid and sincere
She fulfilled the duties of humanity
And her heart was warm with all its best affections. Calm and resign'd to
The dispensations of heaven leaving
Her disconsolate friends to deplore her
Loss & to cherish the remembrance of
That worth. They honour'd living and
Lament in death. To the memory of the best of wives. The best of
Friends. He for whom she join'd

Those tender names dedicates this marble.

1. Described by Horsfield (*Sussex* I 329) (with unusual enthusiasm) as a beautiful cenotaph in statuary marble, bordered with black.

Berwick, 25G Mural monument for John HAWES, d. 1743

- West tower, South wall, far South-West corner, now obscured by an organ.
- 80(W) x 180(H) — Condition inaccessible.
- M.I. on a tablet, framed by decorative work and Ionic pilasters; topped by a cornice; above, a decorative scrolled pediment; below, an apron with arms & a cherub.

This Chancel contains the Bodies
of *JOHN HAWES* A.M. Rector
of this Chvrch & Vicar of Alcifton
47 years who died Ian 3^d
A.D. 1743 Æt 75,
Of *Frances* his wife (Daughter
of JOHN HAY Esqr & *Elizabeth*
his wife of Little Horfted in
this County) who died Iuly 27
AD 1740 Æt 67
Of Six of Their Children viz
William 1706
Edward 1707
Mary 1711
Ann 1712
An.. 1712
& *Frances* 1742
And of *William Hawes* Gent. their

Unckle who died A.D. 1700 Aet 70

and on the shield of arms:

Hawes

... pritchard

Se nom Hosier

... 1727 A.D. 1730

1. Noted but not located by Horsfield (*Sussex* I 329).
2. M.I. suggests that 25G was formerly at the East end.
3. In situ c.1929 - see Lambarde (*SAC* 70 147) noting arms.
4. The date of death for the child Frances must be an error.
5. For licence to marry dated 28 Nov 1695 for John Hawes of Beddingham, clerk and Francis Hay, of Westham, see Dunkin (*Licences 1670-1729* 159).

Berwick, 25H Mural monument for John NUTT, d. 1653 [sic] and his wife Ann, d. 1661

- West tower, North wall, high, obscured by an organ and inaccessible, since 1987.
- c.120(W) x c.300(H) — Damaged (extent unknown).
- 2 portrait busts (male to left, female to right), in 17th century dress, in oval framed niches, on plinths; above, an achievement, swags and fruit; below, M.I. on rectangular panel (final lines added), a cornice over; base mouldings; flanked by scrolls; below, a cherub on an ornamental scrolled apron.

HERE
LIETH THE BODY OF JOHN NVTT BACHEL[OR]
OF DIVINITIE PREBEND OF
CHICHISTER
RECTOR OF BERWICK & BOXHILL
HE DYED
IN DECEMBER: 1656.
HERE LYE[TH] ANN HIS WIFE

SHE DIED IN MAY THE [2] 1661

1. Horsfield (*Sussex* I 329) saw 25H in the chancel; seen in situ by Lambarde (*SAC* 70 147) noting arms and noted by Nairn & Pevsner (414-15).
2. First seen by this author in September 1979, prior to the installation of the organ, when the high quality of the portrait busts suggested an attribution to Edward Marshall.
3. There are errors in the M.I.: 'Boxhill' for 'Bexhill' (with later correction attempted).
4. Also noted by Ray (*SAC* 53 105) is the faint '3' added near the date 1656, an accurate correction reflecting the date on Nutt's grave marker (25E).
5. For an engraved view of 25H and a biography entry on John Nutt see Cooper 'Berwick Parochial Records' (*SAC* 6 224).
6. His wife (from 1620), Ann Nutt was daughter of John Dunck, Vinehall, Whatlington (for whom see 254A).
7. JH notes that Horsfield, Lambarde and Nairn & Pevsner all quote year of death as 1656, but see note 4 above. NBI also confirms 1653, as does Venn (1 3 272).

(26) BEXHILL, St. Peter

Aisles completed by the Perpendicular period, two bays added in 1878, as was the chancel - Nairn & Pevsner (415-6); condition reportedly fine in 1724 (Ford); extensive alterations, see Ray (*SAC* 53 61-108); view from North-East in Godfrey & Salzman (Pl. 18), with of its present urban setting (BL Add. MS 5676 f.34, by Lambert).

Bexhill, 26A Mural monument for Richard ALFRAY, d. 1698

- South aisle wall, West end, facing East.
- 99(W) x 97(H) — Good; dirty.
- Moulded and patterned marble frame; M.I. (7 lines, engraved, gilded) in upper 50% of slate panel.
- Richard Alfray, of Bexhill, d. Battle 17 Apr 1698, aet 22.

1. Noted by Horsfield (*Sussex* I 429-30) who also notes a floor slab for another Richard Alfray, d. 3 Nov 1684.
2. JH notes that Richard Alfray d. 1684 was the father of Richard d. 1698, see W. Berry (*Sussex* 244-5).

Bexhill, 26B Mural monument for Thomas MILNER, d. 1722 [Plate 17]

- North aisle, West end, on North face of pier, at head height.
- 120(W) x 210(H) — Excellent.
- Scrolled pilasters with black capitals flank a tablet set portrait-wise with M.I. (12 lines, engraved, black) filling upper 75% of tablet; black cornice and eccentric open scrolled pediment round an achievement; below, splendid scrolled apron with 2 cherub's heads as corbels.
- Thomas Milner, vicar of Bexhill for 37 years, buried 3 Dec 1722, aet 70; his wife, Rachel, buried 18 Sep 1712, aet 65.

1. Noted but not located by Horsfield (*Sussex* I 429-30); in situ in Lambarde (*SAC* 68 232) who notes arms.
2. See Ray (*SAC* 53 107) for biography of Thomas Milner (MA of Magdalene College, Cambridge); succeeded at Bexhill in 1685, aged 34.
3. Plate was presented to the church from his estate. See Couchman (*SAC* 55 184).
4. Good quality cherubim.
5. Some unusual combinations in this design.
6. Datable c.1723.

Bexhill, 26C Mural monument for Rev. Thomas DELVES, d. 1677/8 [Plate 18]

- North aisle, West wall, West end, South of West window, high.
- Inaccessible — Very good.
- Black marble tablet, set portrait-wise, with M.I. (15 lines, engraved, gilded); flanking, plain pilasters; above, moulded cornice and moulded open, curved pediment round an achievement; below, black base moulding, then 2 moulded brackets flanking a curved apron with additional M.I. (7 lines, engraved, black).
- Thomas Delves, vicar of Bexhill for twenty plus years, d. 22 Mar 1677/8, aet 46; his many virtues; his uncle, Nicholas Delves, of London, Alderman and Merchant Taylor.

1. In situ - Horsfield (*Sussex* I 430) and Lambarde (*SAC* 68 232) noting arms.
2. Patron of 26C was Thomas Delves' uncle, a City merchant.
3. JH notes that despite the claim on the monument that he was vicar of Bexhill for twenty years and upwards, he was at Bexhill from his presentation on 5 Jul 1661 until his death – less than 17 years. See Ray (*SAC* 53 106) and Hennessy (31).
4. NBI records burial of Thomas Delves on 23 Mar 1677/8 at Bexhill.

Bexhill, 26D Mural monument for Gillery PIGOTT, d. 1814

- North aisle, West wall, North of West window, high up.
- Inaccessible — Very good.
- Neat, fluted pilasters and upper and lower frame round white marble tablet set portrait-wise filled with M.I. (engraved, black); black decorative border to M.I.; above, modest pilasters and moulded cornice; on top, draped urn in low relief.
- Gillery Pigott, Esq., d. Hastings 8 May 1814, aet 53; second son of (another) Gillery Pigott, late of Great James St, Bedford Row, London, merchant; his great-grandmother, Isabella, heiress of Thomas Gillery of Newcastle; his wife, Charlotte, daughter of John and Rt. Hon. Lady Mary Archer, of Welford, Berkshire.

1. Always located near to 26E.
2. Noted by Horsfield (*Sussex* I 430).
3. Patron is widow.
4. Emphasis on the geometric, for example, in the fluted framing.

Bexhill, 26E Mural monument for James CRANSTON, d. 1770

- North aisle, North wall, North-East corner, high.
- c.70(W); (H) unknown — Very good; pigment losses.
- Cartouche; M.I. (12 lines, engraved, black) on convex surface, framed by elegant drapes; arms above; below in centre, fluted, splayed, scrolled bracket.

- James Cranston, rector of Stowting, Kent for 45 years, b. Feb 1692, died Kewhurst, Bexhill, 8 Dec 1770; son of (another) James Cranston, of Hastings, and his wife Cordelia; his grandfather, Thomas Delves.

1. Always located near to 26D - Horsfield (*Sussex* I 430) and Lambarde (*SAC* 68 232) noting arms.
2. Visible in pre-1878 restoration photograph in Ray (*SAC* 53 74).
3. Relocated close to original position in rebuilt North aisle.
4. JH notes that James Cranston had been curate of Bexhill during the period 1723-42, and perhaps for longer (see CCEd). He was BA of Jesus College, Cambridge, and rector of Stowting, Kent, 1725-71, see Venn (1 1 413).

Bexhill, 26F Mural monument for Thomas PYE, d. 1610
- North aisle, North wall, at East end, high.
- 71(W) x 75(H) — Excellent.
- M.I. (10 lines, engraved, black) on a modern panel with a plain block base and decorative top (scrolls, shell).
- Rev. Thomas Pye, rector of Bexhill, rector of Brightling and prebendary of Selsey, d. 1610; family origins in Staffordshire.

1. Horsfield (*Sussex* I 430) gives a biographical account of Thomas Pye, but does not mention 26F or its predecessor.
2. One Elleanor Pye, of Bexhill, widow, was licensed to marry William Pelsant, clerk, also of Bexhill, on 17 Apr 1610, see Dunkin (*Licences 1586-1643* 73).
3. Thomas Pye, d. 31 Jan 1610, held the benefice in 1603, see Renshaw (*Ecclesiastical Returns* 6); he was scholar, linguist and a dedicated guardian of the church fabric, see Ray (*SAC* 53 94 & 104-5).
4. See 39U for a brass commemorating Thomas Pye's infant son.

Bexhill, 26G Floor mounted brass for William and Samuel SATTERLEY, both d. 1809
- South aisle floor.
- 25(W) x 40(H) — Very good.
- M.I. (8 lines, engraved) on unframed brass plate, head to West.
- William Satterley, d. 29 Jan 1809, aet 30; Samuel Satterley, d. 7 May 1809.

Bexhill Addition
Horsfield (*Sussex* I 430).
(1) Describes a flat stone in the nave, for Sir John Evelyn, Bart. of Wotton in Surrey, who died 14 May 1833, aged 75. NBI says he was buried here 18 May 1833.

(31) BISHOPSTONE, St. Andrew
Saxon, extended in the Norman and Early English periods, restored 1849 & 1885 - Nairn & Pevsner (418-9) and Godfrey (*SAC* 87 164-183); fabric reportedly fine in 1724 (Ford) when the living was held by Ezechial Bristed (for whom, see 164Q); for M.I.s see Simmons (*SAC* 19 185-188); for pre-restoration illustration by Sharpe - none showing monuments - see Godfrey (ibid.); monuments apparently reinstated after 19th-century restoration.

Bishopstone, 31A Ledger for [Ann] Wife of Henry DALLINDEAR, d. 1640
- North aisle floor, aligned with North door.
- 98(W) x 150(L) — Pitting; wear; corners lost; legible.
- M.I. (6 lines, engraved) in upper end of freestone slab; decorative motifs in corners; head to West.

> HERE VNDER LYETH THE
> WIFE OF HENRY DALLIN
> DEAR THE DAFTER OF
> ROBART HANSONE WHO
> DIED THE 28 OF
>
> IANVARY ANO 1639

1. In situ - Horsfield (*Sussex* I 272).
2. 19th century pews have been cut into the corners.
3. Perhaps for the daughter of the Robart Hansone who stood surety in 1628-9 for a licence to marry, see Dunkin (*Licences 1586-1643* 172).
4. JH notes that Henry Dallinder married Ann Hanson by licence 23 Apr 1639 at East Hoathly (Sussex Marriage Index).

Bishopstone, 31B Mural monument for Rev. James HURDIS, d. 1801 [Plate 19]

- North-East choir wall, North-East corner, facing West, at head height.
- (1) Lower: 62.5(W) x 38(H); (2) Upper: 67(W) x 79(H) — Good; local damage to (2).
- (1) is a M.I. (8 lines, engraved and black, signed 'W.Hayley Esq[r]') on a rectangular tablet; a thin engraved border.
  (2) is a M.I. (15 lines, centred, engraved and black) on a raised oval tablet of grey marble.
- Rev. James Hurdis, D.D., Professor of Poetry, Oxford and vicar of Bishopstone; d. 23 Dec 1801, aet 38; patron his four unnamed sisters.

1. In situ - Horsfield (*Sussex* I 272); noted by Figg (*SAC* 2 279).
2. M.I. restored in 1926 by Mr Bowden Smith.
3. Transcribed by Simmons (*SAC* 19 18); and see *SNQ* (XI 157); Godfrey (*SAC* 87 180) and Tattersall 'A Literary Discovery - Letters of James Hurdis to William Cowper' (*SCM* 1 26-29).
4. Biography of James Hurdis in *ODNB* by C Whittick with full bibliography stressing his reactionary views and his emotional dependence on his sisters; he had enlarged the family vault at Bishopstone at the death of his favourite sister Catherine some 10 years before his own death; for Hurdis' father see 31C; 31B was erected by James Hurdis' four surviving sisters; for Hurdis pedigree see Lower (*SAC* 7 134-6) and *SNQ* (XV 229); James Hurdis became vicar in 1791 and his family (mother, six sisters) lived at Little Hallands at nearby Norton; his career as a poet determined the second epitaph supplied by his colleague and correspondent William Hayley; the latter, the biographer of Cowper, was an antiquarian associate of Grose and Burrell (Farrant), whose summer residence was at Eartham, West Sussex, see Irwin (9-11).
5. The design of upper part of 31B matches James Hurdis' own monument for his sister (31D).

Bishopstone, 31C Ledger for James HURDIS, d. 1769

- Choir floor.
- 97(W) x 181(L) — Worn; recut.
- M.I. (3 lines, engraved) in upper parts (W) of a sandstone slab; head to the West.

> JAMES HURDIS GENT.
> DIED [20 JUN] ... 1769
> AGED 59 YEARS.

1. Noted by Horsfield (*Sussex* I 272), Simmons (*SAC* 19 186), Godfrey (*SAC* 87 181).
2. M.I. on 31C was recut by Bowden Smith in 1926 (see note on 31B).

Bishopstone, 31D Mural monument for Catharine HURDIS, d. 1792 [Plate 20]

- South-East choir wall, South-East corner, facing West, above head height.
- 67(W) x 79(H) — Fading; local damage (above).
- M.I. (12 lines centred, engraved, black) on grey marble oval tablet, set portrait-wise.
- Catherine Hurdis, d. 7 Aug 1792, aet 24; a brother, unnamed.

1. In situ; transcribed Simmons (*SAC* 19 186), noted by Godfrey (*SAC* 87 181).
2. James Hurdis (see 31B), patron of 31D, wrote to the poet Cowper on 31 Aug 1792 of his sense of

loss at Catherine Hurdis' death and proposing a M.I.; Cowper's revisions are partly reflected in the text, only part of which appears on 31D, see Tattersall (*SCM* 1 223-5).

Bishopstone, 31E Mural monument for Mary BURGESS, d. 1755 [Plate 21]
- South-East choir wall, South-East corner, facing West, at head height, below 31D.
- 77(W) x 72(H) — Worn; repaired.
- M.I. (5 lines, engraved and black) on white marble tablet; pointed gable top; no entablature; base mouldings; simple slate pilasters flanking; below, simple blocked corbels and curved apron, both in grey marble; shabby ball finial.
- Mary Burgess, d. 13 Apr 1755, aet 84.

1. In situ; transcribed Simmons (*SAC* 19 186) and noted by Godfrey (*SAC* 87 181).
2. Note the eccentric composition and ornamental letter 'N'.

(31) Bishopstone Addition
Horsfield (*Sussex* I 272):
(1) Elizabeth Forth, widow, d. 1639, aet 76.

(32) BODIAM, St. Giles
Early English, reported to be in fine condition in 1686 and 1724 (Ford) but subjected to a major restoration of 1845-56 - Nairn & Pevsner (419); Leeney (*SAC* 84 123-6); a new tiled floor in the chancel; plan in *SNQ* (XI 103) and Douglas Simpson 'The Moated Homestead, Church, and Castle of Bodiam' (*SAC* 72 74-83); for a view, see Godfrey & Salzman (Pl. 22), seen from South-East. South wall of chancel now obscured by modern chapel; mediaeval brasses relocated to tower West wall some time after 1847, as was 32C; the many owners of the Castle during our period were not commemorated in Bodiam.

Bodiam, 32A Ledger for Rev. Vere MUNN, d. 1736 and Elizabeth MUNN, d. 1758 [Plate 22]
- Nave floor, North-East side.
- 86(W) x 187(L) — Worn; dirty; sound.
- Escutcheon then M.I. (17 lines, engraved) fills a black slab; head to West.
- Rev. Vere Munn, vicar of Bodiam for 22 years, d. 31 Aug 1736, aet 59; his wife, Elizabeth, d. 27 Sep 1758, aet 78; daughter of Rev. William Wilkin, vicar of Heathfield.

1. Noted by Horsfield (*Sussex* I 524).
2. NBI records burial of Elizabeth Munn on 4 Oct 1758 at Bodiam.

Bodiam, 32B Ledger for [James] CROKER, d. 17[34]
- Nave floor, alongside and South of 32A.
- 93(W) x 155(L) — Very worn; cracked.
- Escutcheon, then M.I. (engraved) fills a cream freestone slab; head to West.

1. Horsfield (*Sussex* I 524) notes James Crocker, alias Croker, 1734 and Elizabeth his wife 1739.

Bodiam, 32C Mural monument for Susanna TEMPEST, d. 1746/7
- Tower, South wall, East end, at head height.
- 41(W) x 55(H) — Battered; cracked; worn.
- M.I. (8 lines, engraved) on upper 60% of a grey slate tablet.
- Susanna Tempest, d. 4 Jan 1746/7, aet 26, second wife of George Tempest, Gent., of Cranbrook.

1. Formerly on the floor, Horsfield (*Sussex* I 524) saw this located alongside other Tempest monuments.
2. For descendants of George Tempest, see 32D-E.

Bodiam, 32D Mural monument for Elizabeth BALCHEN, d. 1778 and John BALCHEN, d. 1785 [Plate 23]

- Tower, South wall, alongside and West of 32C.
- 57(W) x 66.5(H) — Fine; dirty.
- M.I. (12 lines + 2 lines, engraved and black, English and Latin) fills an unframed white marble tablet.
- Elizabeth Balchen, d. 31 Jul 1778, aet 22; daughter of George and Elizabeth Tempest of Cranbrook, Kent; and wife of John Balchen, of London, d. 9 Jan 1785, aet 38.

1. Cited by Horsfield (*Sussex* I 524).
2. The sequence of George Tempest's wives is unclear.

Bodiam, 32E Wall monument for John TEMPEST, d. 1820 and Sarah TEMPEST, d. 1810 [Plate 24]

- Tower, South wall, alongside and West of 32D.
- 89(W) x 66(H) — Fine; faded; local damage (lower edge).
- M.I. (8 lines, engraved and black) fills a white marble trapezoidal tablet; grey baseplate with pointed top; below, Greek key decorative; above, scrolled pediment with acanthus decorative.
- John Tempest, Esq., of Cranbrook, d. 23 Mar 1820, aet 72; his wife, Sarah, d. 24 Jan 1810, aet 60.

1. In 1785, John Tempest was an owner here but not an occupier (R. Davey 23).
2. Unusual mix of Baroque (acanthus) and Neo-classical decorative elements.

Bodiam Additions

Horsfield (*Sussex* I 524) [lost in 1845 restoration?]:
(1) Nathaniel Hiland, 1694.
(2) William Bird, Gent., 1713.
(3) Stephen Sivyer, Gent., 1761 and his wife Mary 1759.

(33) BOLNEY, St. Mary Magdalene

Norman and later and North aisle of 1853, Nairn & Pevsner (421); for plan see *SNQ* (XI 103); for a view from South-West by Grimm, see Godfrey & Salzman (Pl. 24), from BL Add. MS 5672 f.25; in 1714 Anthony Stapley noted that the church had 'just been repaired and beautified', see Turner (*SAC* 18 153); Horsfield (*Sussex* I 251) noted that most of the M.I.s were illegible. The flooring has been extensively renewed leaving little original.

Bolney, 33A Ledger for Thomas DENNETT, d. 1767

- Porch floor.
- 78(W) x 176(L) — Worn.
- M.I. (engraved) in upper 25% of a pale freestone slab; head to North.

In Memory of
Thos DENNETT Efq^r
who departed this life
March ye 2^d 1767 Aged

4[7] Years

1. Horsfield (*Sussex* I 251) noted other Dennett slabs in churchyard but not 33A.
2. The porch was built in 1718.
3. For licence to marry dated 19 Oct 1707 for Thomas Dennett, of Woodmancote, Gent. and Jane Hole, also of Woodmancote, see Dunkin (*Licences 1670-1729* 196); Thomas Dennett, of Cowfold, was buried 6 Mar 1767, baptised 8 Mar 1720, son of John and Susan Dennett, deceased, see Huth (47, 188).

Bolney, 33B Floor-mounted brass for John PELLATT, d. 1625
- Sanctuary, East end, North corner.
- Slab: 90(W) x 155(L) — Worn. Brass: 46(W) x 15(H) — Fine.
- M.I. (5 lines, engraved) on a rectangular brass panel; head to East; mounted on a freestone slab.
- John Pellatt, Esq., d. 22 Oct 1625, aet 41, buried 22 or 24 Oct, son and heir apparent to Sir Benjamin Pellatt Knt.

1. In situ - Horsfield (*Sussex* I 251); see Pellatt pedigree in Phillips (*SAC* 38 112), which also notes burial of Jane, a daughter 29 Aug 1616; noted in Davidson-Houston (*SAC* 76 88-89) - with illustration and transcription.
2. John Pellatt's wife was Ann, daughter of Thomas West, Lord De La Warr; their daughters - Mary (buried 25 Sep 1625), Dorothy (buried 27 Sep 1625), Susan (buried 7 Sep 1624), Anne (buried 29 Aug 1616 or baptised 26 Sep 1616) and son Thomas (buried 11 Jan 1613), also the baptisms of Rose (28 Sep 1623), Susan (11 Jul 1622), Katherin (6 Jan 1620), Dorothy (6 Aug 1618), Ane (26 Sep 1616), Thomas (27 Dec 1612), see Huth (26-29, 30-1, 46-7, 49-50.).

Bolney, 33C Floor-mounted brass for Anne BERKELEY, d. 1601
- Sanctuary, East end, South corner.
- Slab: 77(W) x 150(L) — Worn Brass: 64(W) x 22(H) — Fine.
- M.I. (10 lines, engraved) on a brass cut wider to the East and narrower to the W, head to East; mounted on a freestone slab.
- Anne Berkeley, d. 5 Jan 1601, aet 70; daughter of John Ashburnham, of Ashburnham; her first husband, John Bolney, Esq., of Bolney; her second husband, Thomas Culpeper, Esq., of Wakehurst; her third husband, Henry Berkeley, Esq., lawyer.

1. In situ - Horsfield (*Sussex* I 25); Davidson-Houston (*SAC* 76 88).
2. The pedigree in Blaauw (*SAC* 10 154) and Huth (9, 11, 55, 64, 67) give details of Anne Berkeley's earlier husbands and issue. First husband was John Bolney whom she married on 28 Jul 1556 at Bolney. He died 1557 and was buried on 4 Nov 1557 at Bolney. Second husband was Thomas Culpeper of Ardingly who married Anne on 15 Oct 1565. He died 1571 or 2. Thomas Culpeper was brother of John Culpeper of Wakehurst, d. 1565, his nephew inheriting the nomenclature 'of Wakehurst'. Anne's third husband was Henry Berkeley whom she married on 27 Aug 1572 at Ardingly. He was father of John, baptised 22 Jun 1567 and buried 7 Jan 1572, and Harrie, baptised 17 Oct 1569.

(38) BREDE, St. George
Norman & later, Perpendicular chancel and South chapel (1537) - Nairn & Pevsner (422-3); views by Lambert (BL Add. MS 5670 f.18 & 5676 f.14); plan in *SNQ* (XI 124); in 1686, the rector's chancel had bad pavements, which still needed repair in 1724; Mr Horne's West chancel had by then been repaired (Ford); Brede estate purchased by Sir Edward Frewen, of Brickwall, Northiam in 1708 and remained in that family until 1936 (Farrant); but the Frewens were buried at Northiam (see 186).

Brede, 38A Mural monument for Mary Anne DAVIES, d. 1792
- North nave pillar, near East end, at head height.
- 75(W) x 45(H) — Excellent.
- M.I. (6 lines, gilded, Latin) on a dark grey unframed marble plaque.
- Mary Anne Davies, 18 Aug - 2 Oct 1792.

1. Note the self-conscious neo-classicism of M.I. (text and lettering).

Brede, 38B Mural monument for Felicia Elizabetha Selby HELE, d. 1829
- Chancel, North wall, at head height.
- 97(W) x 185(H) — Excellent; fading; colour.
- Curved backplate; reclining, draped figure mourns over a gilded urn; moulded cornice;

below, a framed M.I. (many lines, engraved and black) in pedestal form against a square base; on apron, extravagantly gilded rosettes on square corbels; between, escutcheon and motto; signed (under lower edge): 'M. W. JOHNSON, NEW RD, LONDON'.

- Felicia Hele, d. 10 Oct 1829, aet 59; one of three daughters of Rt. Rev. George Horne, bishop of Norwich, etc and Felicia Elizabetha, daughter of Philip Burton of Burton Lazars, Leicestershire, Hatton Garden, London and Eltham, Kent; and wife of Robert Selby Hele, rector, etc., nephew of John Hele of St. Pancras and Devon; issue of Robert and Felicia Hele - 15 (8 survive).

1. In situ - Horsfield (*Sussex* I 515) just erected; Lambarde (*SAC* 68 219-220) noting arms; Nairn & Pevsner (423).
2. Near other Hele monuments, another similar to her husband (d. 1839), also by Johnson.
3. Robert Selby Hele was well connected and a chaplain-in-ordinary to George IV.
4. For MW Johnson, of London, fl.1820-60, see Gunnis (*Dict.* 220) who misspells as Hale.

Brede, 38C Wall monument for Sir Goddard OXENBRIDGE, d. 1531, erected 1537 [Plate 26]

- Lady Chapel (Oxenbridge Chantry), against South wall.
- 194(W) x 188(H) — Fine; restoration; discolouration and staining (lower).
- In Caen stone; against wall; a recumbent armoured figure on tomb-chest, faces East, hands clasped in prayer, heraldic supporter at feet, head on helmet on pillow; on tomb-chest, escutcheons and dentil mouldings; behind and above, panels with cornice and frieze with triglyphs; flanking pilasters with grotesques and other decorative; in centre, the date 1537; no other M.I.; below, on floor, base mouldings.

1. In situ – Francis Grose 1777 (Farrant 120); Horsfield (*Sussex* I 515); Lambarde (*SAC* 68 220) noting arms; Mosse (31-2); Nairn & Pevsner (423) - associated with Perpendicular South chapel, with Oxenbridge arms on North-East corner pier dated as late as 1618.
2. Goddard Oxenbridge specified burial here, see will of 17 Jun 1530, proved 27 Oct 1531 in Rice & Godfrey (1 199); his wives were Elizabeth Etchingham and then Anne Fienne; his brother founded the Oxenbridge chantry at St. George Chapel, Windsor.
3. 38C was restored [shortly?] before Jul 1982 (NL visit).
4. Architectural details more crudely cut than effigial details; deep lines of the face suggest use of a death-mask.
5. Note the early Renaissance ornament in late Perpendicular building – Grose thought 38C to be fine but older than its date of 1537 - a reflection of late 18th-century (mis)understandings about 16th-century design.

Brede, 38D Ledger for Thomas ADES, d. 1813

- South-East chapel floor, North side.
- 78(W) x 161(L) — Very worn.
- M.I. (many lines, engraved) in upper 50% of a freestone slab; decorative border; head to West.

In a Vault
beneath this Stone lieth
the remains of

THOMAS ADES
Son of John & Mary Ades
of this Parish
who departed this Life
April 15th. 1813

Aged Six Months

Brede, 38E Ledger for ... ADES, no date

- South-East chapel floor, centre, South of 38D, largely carpeted.
- c.73(W) x c.161(L) — Very worn.
- M.I. (engraved) in upper 50% of a freestone slab; head to West.

...lieth the [body of]
...RANT ADES
... [of] THOMAS & MARY
...this Pariſh:
...victim to the
...death on March 7th
...
... and 6 months.
... Creator in the days
...

1. Perhaps 1660s?
2. JH notes that on 2 Sep 1764, Dorothy Durrant Ades, daughter of Thomas and Mary, was baptised at Brede (see IGI).

Brede, 38F Ledger for Thomas ADES, d. 1811

- South-East chapel floor, South side, entirely carpeted.
- 77(W) x 165(L) — Fine?
- M.I. (engraved) in upper 25% of freestone slab, with a double border.

... beneath this Stone
lieth the remains of
THOMAS ADES
late of this Parish
who Died 7th March 1811.

Aged 78 Years

1. As early as 1785, Thomas Ades was an important tenant of the owner Rev. Thomas Frewen Turner (R. Davey 25).
2. Surveyed in 2000-02, not seen by NL.

Brede, 38G Ledger for [John TILDEN] who d. 1730 and his wife Alice

- South-East chapel floor, South side, West end, entirely carpeted.
- 78(W) x 170(L) — Fine?
- M.I. (engraved) in upper parts of black slab (slate?).

Here lieth interr'd
the Body of ...DEN gent
who died Octo^{br} 30 MDCCXXX
Aged 61 Years
Also

ALICE his Wife who died
July 15 MD ...V
Aged 67 Years
They left life one Son
and one Daughter
GEORGE ...

1. Surveyed in 2000-02, not seen by NL.
2. NBI records burial of John Tilden on 3 Nov 1730 at Brede.

Brede Additions

Horsfield (*Sussex* I 515):
(1) A confused entry describing M.I.s in the chancel to various members of the Horne family: Mrs Elizabeth Horne, wife of Mr Samuel Horne, rector, 1686; another 1663; another 1682; Samuel Horne also 1686.

(39) BRIGHTLING, St. Thomas à Becket

The church is mainly 13th-14th century, with a few puzzling modern additions [18th century?]; the porch is dated 1749; the roughly equal size of chancel and North chapel is hard to explain - Nairn & Pevsner (424-5); for a plan see *SNQ* (XI 147); for view from South-East by Grimm (1784), see BL Add. MS 5670 f.64; in 1724 condition reportedly fine (Ford); monuments originally in the floor were reset as murals during the 1903 restoration; there is a remarkable series of 14 monuments commemorating many generations of the Collins family, Lords of the Manor of Socknersh (10 Collins monuments dated 1667-1717); the Fullers followed the Collins; a house site was acquired by Thomas Fuller in 1698 and from 1703, possessed by John Fuller (1680-1745), ironmaster and honouring his wife, renamed Rose Hill; their son was John II (1706-55); his son, John III (1757-1834) was patron of the young JMW Turner (Farrant); this Fuller (known as 'Mad Jack') won the local parliamentary seat from Col. Sergison at Cuckfield (72), redecorated the interior of the church and erected several monuments, his own (too late for this survey) signed by Henry Rouw of London (for Fuller, 1757-1834, see biography in *ODNB* by JPJ Entract); compared to his architectural patronage (see his ambitious pyramidal mausoleum built 1810 at Brightling and his ownership of Bodiam Castle from 1829), Fuller's monuments are very conventional; Willatts (*SAC* 125 107) lists 6 iron slabs here, all pre-cast and incised, intended for churchyard use.

Brightling, 39A Brasses for Richard GLYD, d. 1618 and Martha his wife, d. 1619

- Nave, West wall, near South-West door, at head height.
- Stone: 65(W) x 164(H); Three brasses: 52(W) x 16.5(H); 49.5(W) x 13.5(H); 54(W) x 18(H) — Good.
- 3 brasses on a freestone slab, mounted on the wall.

(M.I. on top brass)

HERE LYETH BVRIED RICHARD GLYD WHOSE VNPARTIALL
LOVE, WISE COVNCELL, & EQVALL CARE SOE TRAINED VP, AND
PROVIDED FOR HIS SIX SONNES THAT THEY OWE MORE THEN THE
DEAD LETTER OF THIS INSCRIPTION CAN EXPRESSE. HOW MVCH OTHER
ARE INDEPTED VNTO HIM, LET THEM CONFESSE. WHO WHEN HE HAD RVNNE
AN EVEN COVRSE, ALMOST. 70. YEERES AT THAT PLACE WHERE HE WAS
VPON NEW YEERS DAYE BORNE, HE COMFORTABLY DEPARTED THIS
LIFE VPON EASTER DAYE THE 5. OF APRILL 1618

(M.I. on middle brass)

HIS NEIGHBOVRS BREASTS WILL COMMON PLACE BOOKES MAKE
WRITT FVLL OF'S PRAYSE WHO'S NEXT FOR INDEX TAKE
THEIR SVCCESSORS OF TH'VNBORNE AGE WILL CRYE
TAUGHT BY TRADITIONS FAYTH HERE GLYD DOTH LYE
PROVE FREINDS VNKIND. THIS MARBLE STONE SHALL WEEPE.
AND TIME IN SHEDING TEARS WITH APRILL KEEPE

(M.I. on bottom brass)

HERE LYETH MARTHA THE LOVING WIFE TO RICHARD GLYD AND
DEAR CAREFVLL MOTHER OF 6 SONNES VNTO WHOM THEY OWE
A GREATER TRIBVTE OF DVTY THEN THIS STONE CAN CONTAYNE,
OR THE WORLD IMAGINE WHO WHEN SHE HAD LEDD A VERTVOVS
RELIGIOVS, BLAMELES LYFE NEARE 63 YEERES RESIGND HER
HAPPY SOVLE INTO ITS MAKERS HANDS THE 24 APRIL 1619

REST BLAMELESSE SOVLE: FREINDS NEIGHBOVRS ALL BIDD SLEEPE
THOV HAST NOE FOES WAKING THY GHOST TO KEEPE.
SLEEPE NEARE THY MATE APRILL YOV BOTH INTOMBS
WHY SHOVLD ONE FLESHE, ONE HART TAKE VP TWO ROOMES

1. Noted by Horsfield (*Sussex* I 567), Stephenson (504).
2. Formerly on the floor, then on North aisle wall see Davidson-Houston (*SAC* 76 96) with illustration.

Brightling, 39B Wall-mounted ledger for Edward ENGLISH, d. 1661
- On West wall, under the tower, now a vestry.
- 74(W) x 155(L) — Worn, damaged, repaired.
- Arms then M.I. (10 lines, engraved) on a slate slab, now wall-mounted.

A PRISONER OF HOPE
EDWARD ENGLISH ESQ: OBIJT
MAIJ ANNO DOM : 1661
ÆTATIS SVI 33
HE HAD ONE SONNE & 6 DAUGHTERS
BY HIS ONLY WIFE ELIZABETH
[DAUGH]TER OF HENRY WILLIANS
...
...
...[LEFT] WITH 5 DAUGHTERS
[BLES]SED ARE THE DEAD THAT DIE IN THE LORD

1. Noted by Horsfield (*Sussex* I 567).
2. Edward English owned Brightling Park (Church Guide).

Brightling, 39C Wall-mounted ledger for Elizabeth COLLINS, d. 1676
- On North wall, under the tower, now a vestry.
- 88(W) x 195(L) — Good; damaged; faded.
- Arms then M.I. (19 lines, engraved, Latin) on a freestone slab.
- Elizabeth Collins, d. 13 Jun 1676, aet 52 [?]; daughter of Peter Farnden, of Selscomb
  [Sedlescombe?]; and widow of Thomas Collins; also, a nephew, one Peter G...

1. Noted by Horsfield (*Sussex* I 567).
2. Patrons were [?] Elizabeth Collins' surviving children; for her husband see 39D.
3. English word 'Aged' written over the Latin 'Aetatis'.
4. Heraldry on memorial not mentioned by Lambarde (*SAC* 68 221-2).

Brightling, 39D Wall-mounted ledger for Thomas COLLINS, d. 1667
- On North wall, under the tower, now a vestry.
- 88(W) x 197(L) — Good.
- Close to 39C (his wife); M.I. (engraved, centred).
- Thomas Collins, of Socknersh, armiger and magistrate, d. 30 Dec 1667, aet 67; his wife
  Elizabeth, daughter of Peter Farnden, armiger.

1. Patron was Thomas Collins' widow Elizabeth (see 39C); for his wife 1 see 39T.
2. Collins, a Presbyterian, was responsible for the parish register during the Commonwealth period
   (see church guide).
3. 39D was formerly in sanctuary - Davidson-Houston (*SAC* 76 96-7).
4. Heraldry on memorial not mentioned by Lambarde (*SAC* 68 221-2).

Brightling, 39E Mural monument for William SHIELD, 1829
- North nave clerestory, high.
- Inaccessible — Fine.
- An unframed white marble tablet with arched top; above, a portrait roundel in low relief,
  facing East, beneath a draped wreath; lower, M.I. (14 lines, engraved, black); below that, a

blocked base moulding on 2 block corbels with paterae; signed (below): 'PETER ROUW, Sculptor, Portland Road, LONDON'.
- William Shield, Esq., royal musician, d. 25 Jan 1829, aet 80, buried at Westminster Abbey; patron John Fuller, of Rose Hill, Esq.

1. Noted by Gunnis (*Dict.* 332) as by Peter Rouw, for William Shield and dated 1830; followed by Nairn & Pevsner (425).
2. Fuller's first commission as a patron (see 39F).
3. JH notes that Shield's biography by R.H. Legge, revised by B.M. Zon in *ODNB* mentions no connection with Brightling.

Brightling, 39F Mural monument for Dr. Primrose BLAIR, d. 1819 [Plate 27]
- North chancel arch pier, West face, at head height.
- 100(W) x 131(H) — Excellent; faded.
- Mostly white marble; on a pedestal in low relief, an urn; entwined snakes for handles; grey slate baseplate; below M.I. on an unframed rectangular panel; simple block corbels.
- Dr. Primrose Blair, naval Physician, d. 27 Jan 1819, aet 59, buried St. Martins [-in-the-Fields], London; patron, John Fuller, Esq.

1. Attributed to Chantrey by Gunnis (*Dict.* 94); noted by Nairn & Pevsner (425).
2. Primrose Blair was buried in London.
3. The snakes refer to his profession as a doctor.
4. The patron was John Fuller, see Salt (*SAC* 104).

Brightling, 39G Mural monument for Thomas COLLINS, d. 1709 and his wife Margaret, d. 1720
- On North aisle chapel (Lambarde) wall, North-West corner.
- 90(W) x 184(H) — Excellent; faded.
- M.I. (engraved; final 3 lines added) on a white marble cartouche; drapery and cherubim surrounds; above, arms; below, a pedestal with scrolls, foliage and a laurel wreathed death's head.
- Thomas Collins, of Socknersh, d. 13 Dec 1709, aet 80; his wife, Margareta, d. 2 May 1720, aet 85; daughter of Henry Cox, of Swanmore, Southampton.

1. In situ; noted by Horsfield (*Sussex* I 567) and Lambarde (*SAC* 68 220) noting arms.
2. Presumably dating from soon after 1709.
3. The quality of the carving is very high.
4. Very close in authorship to 306B.

Brightling, 39H Anonymous ledger, d. 1802
- On North aisle chapel wall, near West end, below 39G.
- 50(W) x 37(L) — Poor, worn.
- M.I. (7 lines, shallow engraved) on a rough freestone slab.

April 26th 1802:

Aged 11 Years.

When bl ...Youth & Beauty is ...

Death pl... is in ye Grave

Take care Young Folks ye precious Time to

In living mindful of your latter End

1. Relocated here [from the churchyard?].

Brightling, 39I M.I. on brass commemorating John BATYS' bequest, 1635
- North aisle chapel, North wall, at head height, between windows.
- Slab: 61(W) x 147(H); Brass: 50(W) x 47(H) — Fine.
- M.I. (engraved) on a brass plate on a freestone slab; alongside earlier brasses (one now missing).

- Also cited is Sir Thomas Sackvill, Knt.; also Thomas, Lord Coventry, Lord Keeper.

1. Original location unknown; supposedly discovered some 200 years after Batys' death, at the bottom of a deep well on the South Downs (see Burrell in BL Add. MS 5679 f.47).
2. Noted by Horsfield (*Sussex* I 567), Turner (*SAC* 23 140-41) with transcription and Davidson-Houston (*SAC* 76 91-3) with illustration.
3. A 17th-century inscription attached to a 15th-century monument, clarifying and confirming the terms of a legal bequest is highly unusual.
4. Was the Presbyterian registrar Thomas Collins (see 39D) somehow associated with the patronage of 39I?

Brightling, 39J Mural monument for Thomas COLLINS, d. 1671, Margaret Collins, d. 1681 and William Collins, d. 1690 [Plate 28]
- North aisle chapel, North wall, on wall in North-East corner.
- 70(W) x 160(H) — Excellent.
- M.I. (15 lines, engraved) on white marble convex cartouche, scrolled edges; mourning cherubs left and right; below, a crowned death's head as bracket; above, splendid scrolled achievement.
- Thomas Collins, buried 29 Aug 1671; Margaret Collins, buried 26 Jan 1681; William Collins, buried 9 Jun 1690; their parents, also Thomas Collins, Esq., of Socknersh, Brightling and Margaret, daughter of Henry Collins, of Swanmore, Hampshire, heir to William Collins, Esq., her uncle, of Corhampton, Hampshire.

1. In situ; noted by Horsfield (*Sussex* I 567); Also Lambarde (*SAC* 68 221) heraldry described.
2. The carving of 39J is of very high quality, for example the teardrops on the cherub's cheeks.

Brightling, 39K Mural monument for Henry COLLINS, d. 1753
- North aisle chapel, North wall, across North-East corner.
- 75(W) x 163(H) — Excellent; faded.
- M.I. (15 lines, engraved) on white marble convex cartouche; decorated scrolls on edges; below, a cherub as bracket; above, achievement; 2 cherubs flanking.
- Henry Collins, Esq., of Socknersh, d. 20 Mar 1753, aet 41; his father also Henry Collins; his mother, Mary Plumer, of Hollingbourne, Kent; his wife, a daughter of James Venables, Esq., of Woodcotts, Hampshire.

1. In situ; noted by Horsfield (*Sussex* I 567) and Lambarde (*SAC* 68 222) heraldry described.
2. M.I. points out that Henry Collins was last of line.
3. The rare and complex location - across the corner of the church - appears to have been chosen for its display potential, rather than out of necessity.

Brightling, 39L Wall-mounted slab for Marie COLLINS, d. 1618
- North aisle chapel, North wall, North-East corner, at head height.
- 87.5(W) x 54(L) — Fair.
- M.I. (6 lines, engraved) on a pale sandstone slab.

HERE LYETH BVRIED THE
BODYE OF MARIE COLLENES
THE LASTE WIFE OF THOMAS
COLENES LAT ONER OF
SOCKNERSH DIED THE 8 OF IULI
1618

1. Relocated here.
2. 39L appears to be the earliest Collins monument extant at Brightling.
3. Not mentioned by Horsfield.

Brightling, 39M Wall-mounted slab for Henry COLLINS, d. 1705/6
- North aisle chapel, East wall, low.
- 53(W) x 68(H) — Very good; stained, faded.

- M.I. (9 lines, engraved, centred)) on an unframed marble slab.
- Henry Collins, d. 13 Jan 1705/6, an infant; son of another Henry Collins, Gent., of Socknersh, and his wife, Mary.

1. Relocated here.
2. 39M-R commemorate the issue of Henry and Mary Collins (see 39S).

Brightling, 39N Wall-mounted slab for Margaret COLLINS, d. 1697
- North aisle chapel, East wall, low.
- 61(W) x 89(H) — Very good; stained.
- M.I. (10 lines, engraved, centred) on an unframed marble slab.
- Margaret Collins, d. 5 Jun 1697, an infant; daughter of Henry Collins, Gent. of Socknersh, and his wife Mary.

1. Relocated here.
2. Noted by Horsfield (*Sussex* I 567).
3. 39M-R commemorate the issue of Henry and Mary Collins (see 39S).

Brightling, 39O Wall-mounted slab for Thomas COLLINS, d. 1698/9
- North aisle chapel, East wall, low.
- 61(W) x 89(H) — Good; stained, faded.
- M.I. (8 lines, engraved, centred) on an unframed marble slab.
- Thomas Collins, d. 20 Mar 1698/9, an infant; son of Henry Collins, Gent., of Socknersh, and his wife, Mary.

1. Relocated here.
2. Noted by Horsfield (*Sussex* I 567).
3. 39M-R commemorate the issue of Henry and Mary Collins (see 39S).

Brightling, 39P Wall-mounted slab for Mary COLLINS, d. 1703/4
- North aisle chapel, East wall, low.
- 61(W) x 89(H) — Very good, faded.
- M.I. (9 lines, engraved, centred) on an unframed marble slab.
- Mary Collins, d. 10 Feb 1703/4, aet 1; daughter of Henry Collins, Gent., of Socknersh, and his wife, Mary.

1. Relocated here.
2. Noted by Horsfield (*Sussex* I 567).
3. 39M-R commemorate the issue of Henry and Mary Collins (see 39S).

Brightling, 39Q Mural monument for Margaret COLLINS, d. 1719
- North aisle chapel, East wall, low.
- 61(W) x 95(H) — Good, faded.
- M.I. (7 lines, engraved) in upper 60% of a veined marble slab.
- Margaret Collins, d. 20 Dec 1719, an infant; daughter of Henry Collins, Gent., of Sockbersh, and his wife, Mary.

1. Relocated here.
2. Noted by Horsfield (*Sussex* I 567).
3. 39M-R commemorate the issue of Henry and Mary Collins (see 39S).

Brightling, 39R Ledger for William COLLINS, d. 1713
- North aisle chapel, East wall, low.
- 55(W) x 60(H) — Good, faded.
- As 39Q.
- William Collins, d. 3 Sep 1713, an infant; son of Henry Collins, Gent., of Socknersh, and his wife, Mary.

1. Relocated here.
2. Noted by Horsfield (*Sussex* I 567).
3. 39M-R commemorate the issue of Henry and Mary Collins (see 39S).

Brightling, 39S Mural monument for Henry COLLINS, d. 1743 and his wife Mary, d. 1746

- North aisle chapel, East end, South of window, above head height.
- 80(W) x 174(H) — Very good.
- M.I. (12 lines, engraved) in 2 stages, on white marble cartouche; scrolled and draped edges; below, winged death's head bracket; above, achievement.
- Henry Collins, Esq., of Cornhampton, Hampshire, d. 13 Nov 1743, aet 69; his wife, Mary, d. at Cornhampton, 12 Sep 1746, aet 68.

1. In situ; noted by Horsfield (*Sussex* I 567) and Lambarde (*SAC* 68 222) noting arms.
2. The effect of the crumpled material is remarkable.

Brightling, 39T Wall-mounted brass for Mary COLLINS, d. 1648

- North aisle chapel, East wall, at head height, below 39S.
- Stone slab: 41(W) x 74(H); Brass: 53(W) x 21(H) — Fine.
- M.I. (engraved) on brass plate mounted in centre of freestone slab.
- Mary Collins, d. 7 Dec 1648; daughter of Anthony Cruttenden, of Burwash; and first wife of Thomas Collins, of Socknersh; no issue.

1. Formerly in sanctuary, now separated from the brass for her husband, see 39D.
2. Noted by Horsfield (*Sussex* I 567) and Davidson-Houston (*SAC* 76 96-7), with illustration and transcription.
3. Error in M.I., 'wth' for 'wch'.
4. For Cruttenden of Burwash see 45I, J, O and R.

Brightling, 39U Brasses for Thomas PYE, d. 1592 [Plate 29]

- Chancel, South wall, East end, at head height.
- Upper M.I.: 35(W) x 6.5(H); Figure and scrolls: 14(H); Lower M.I.: 47(W) x 12.5(H); Stone slab: 53(W) x 65(H) — Very good.
- 5 brasses mounted on a slab (Horsham stone?) with a moulded wooden frame; Upper M.I. records patron; Scrolls bearing mottos on left and right of a kneeling male figure; Lower M.I. (7 lines, engraved).
- Thomas Pye, d. 4 Jun 1592, an infant; only son of another Thomas Pye, D.D.; his virtues.

1. Noted by Horsfield (*Sussex* I 567), who gives the (incorrect) impression that this memorial is for Thomas Pye, D.D. See Davidson-Houston (*SAC* 76 93-96), with illustrations and transcription. Nairn & Pevsner (425) imply that this of Thomas Pye, D.D. as a boy.
2. Latin and English texts are combined.
3. The word 'pious' a play on the family name.
4. This Thomas Pye died as an infant. Thomas Pye the father was rector here 1590-1609, and vicar at Bexhill 1589-1610 (see 26F for his M.I.).

Brightling, 39V Mural monument for members of the BURRELL family, erected c.1790.

- Chancel, centre of South wall, above head height.
- 91(W) x 144(H) — Very good.
- Mainly in white marble; a draped urn in yellow freestone mounted on a cornice moulding; below, M.I. (many lines, final 2 added, engraved, black) on an unframed panel; below, small curved apron with fern and arms.
- Members of the extended family who d. 1708-89 include Rev. William Burrell, A.M., rector and prebendary of Brightling, buried 2 Aug 1708, son of William Burrell, Gent., of Chicknell St. James, Essex; his wife Honor, d. 6 Jan 1694, daughter of John Wotton, Gent., of Malton, Cambridgeshire; his mother, Dorothy Burrell, buried 5 Jan 1714; his

youngest daughter, Dorothea, buried 28 Feb 1741, aet 50, married to Richard Holmes, Esq., of Burnham; his eldest son Rev. William Burrell, chaplain to King George, rector of Brightling, vicar of Icklesham and rector of Burwash, d. 7 May 1737, aet 53, whose wife was Elizabeth, daughter of Laurence Noakes, of Brightling, d. 18 Jul 1769, aet 80, and their issue: elder daughter, Elizabeth, d. 8 May 1744, aet 32; elder son Rev. William Burrell, rector and prebendary of Brightling, d. 11 Jun 1746, aet 33; son John Burrell, A.B., succeeded his brother as rector and prebendary of Brightling, d 13 Jun 1752, aet 33; and younger daughter, Anne, d. 19 Oct 1776, aet 60, wife of Rev. William Hayley, A.M., rector and prebendary of Brightling and vicar of Preston with Hove, who d. 25 Oct 1789, aet 74; also, Rev. William Burrell Hayley, rector of Brightling, d. 1796, aet 41 and his wife Sophia, d. 1830, aet 77.

1. In situ, see Lambarde (*SAC* 68 221) noting arms.
2. 39V probably erected in early 1790s.
3. William Burrell, clerk, stood surety for a licence to marry dated 23 Apr 1696, see Dunkin (*Licences 1670-1729* 160).
4. JH notes that the three clergymen called William Burrell are all described as rectors and prebendaries of Brightling. This is not a Cathedral prebend, but a prebend in the free chapel in the castle of Hastings. See Horsfield (*Sussex* I 566).

(40) BRIGHTON, St. Nicholas of Myra

The 14th-century flint, parish church of Brighthelmstone (until 1873) set on a hill overlooking the ancient but transformed fishing village, was radically altered in 1853 - compare the ground plans in Clarke (*SAC* 32 36-40); the North aisle is completely new, the South aisle enlarged - Nairn & Pevsner (427-8); many monuments previously towards the East end were relocated to the West tower walls and the West ends of the North and South aisles, in 1892, when a clerestory was installed; the monuments record no prominent family dynasties and little recurrence of family name amongst the mass of wall tablets; there are many references to immigrants to the town; little remains in the floor (ledgers were replaced by tile flooring); a late 19th-century ledger in the choir commemorates earlier parishioners; in 1724, the condition was reported to be fine (Ford); Horsfield (*Sussex* I 141) calls it a tasteless and unsightly edifice for 1300 auditors, by then crowded with galleries ....

Brighton, 40A Mural monument for Anna Diana COXE, d. 1829

- Nave West wall, facing East, at head height.
- 105(W) x 84(H) — Dirty; broken edges.
- M.I. in 2 sections on marble tablet, unframed.
- Anna Diana Coxe, d. 11 Jan 1829, aet 84; daughter of Sir Charles Sheffield, Bart., of Normanby Hall, Lincolnshire; and wife of the late Major General Thomas Coxe, soldier; issue - youngest daughter, Julia, d. 19 May 1853, aet 66, widow of Major Richard Lothian Dickson; other(s) unnamed.

1. Formerly in the middle aisle - Horsfield (*Sussex* I 143).

Brighton, 40B Mural monument for Katherine BLAKER, d. 1809

- Nave West wall, very high.
- c.60(W); (H) inaccessible — Fine.
- M.I. (7 lines, engraved, black) on unframed marble tablet; engraved border with chamfered top.
- Katherine Blaker, d. 6 Sep 1809, aet 70; daughter of Nathaniel and Katherine Blaker, of Kingston by Sea.

1. One Nathaniel Blaker owned properties at Portslade in 1785 (R. Davey 171).

Brighton, 40C Mural monument for Henry KIPPING, d. 1785 and many other members of his family

- Nave West wall, immediately below 40B.
- c.180(W); (H) inaccessible — Fine.
- M.I. on marble tablet set portrait-wise.
- Henry Kipping, Snr, d. 8 Sep 1785, aet 59; his [first] wife, Elizabeth Kipping, d. 1 Dec 1756, aet 26; his [second] wife, Susannah Kipping, d. 15 Apr 1760, aet 26; their issue - John, d. 24 Sep 1760, infant; his [third] wife Anna, d. 12 Apr 1814, aet 74; their issue - John, d. 4 Mar 1774, aet 5; Anna, d. 26 Apr 1805, aet 35; Katherine, d. 11 Aug 1793, aet 18; Henry, d. 25 Mar 1803, aet 25; and William, d. 5 Apr 1855, aet 72; William's wife, Elizabeth, d. 20 Feb 1844, aet 53; their issue - William Henry Kipping, d. 3 Apr 1823, aet 15; and Thomas, d. 1 Dec 1869, aet 60; Thomas' wife, Mary Ann, d. 14 Dec 1867.

1. Formerly on the North side of the church - Horsfield (*Sussex* I 142).

Brighton, 40D Mural monument for Henry MICHELL, d. 1789

- Nave West wall, South of tower arch, at head height.
- 73(W) x 110(H) — Excellent; colour.
- M.I. (many lines, final 3 added; engraved and black) on white marble tablet; dark (blue?) baseplate; unframed; below, fluted decorative.
- Henry Michell, A.M., of Clare, Cambridge, rector of Maresfield, rector of Blatchington and vicar of Brighton, d. 1[?] Nov 1789, aet 75; his wife, [Faith], of 42 years, d. 12 Mar 1809, aet 82; their issue - 9 unnamed, 7 still living in 1790.

1. In situ in 1930 see Lambarde (*SAC* 71 158) noting arms.
2. Final 3 lines of M.I. added after 1809.
3. Henry Michell was born 1714, rector of Maresfield 1739-89, vicar of Brighton 1744-89, of Blatchington 1777-89; married Faith Reade 29 Dec 18 1747 (*Gent's Mag* 59/2 1789 1055); John Nichols' *Literary Anecdotes of the Eighteenth Century* IV 447, 867, etc.; Horsfield (*Sussex* I 145); Sawyer (*SAC* 29 207); A.F. Pollard rev. Philip Carter in *ODNB*; Wagner (*SAC* 97 35); Musgrave (1981). Classical scholar and socialite, famously an enemy of Dr Johnson and sometime tutor to the Duke of Wellington.
4. Patrons of 40D were Henry Michell's children.
5. The use of verb 'ago' for time passed is an unusual anachronism on a M.I.
6. NBI records the burials of Henry Michell on 6 Nov 1789, aet 74, and Faith Michell on 24 Feb 1809, aet 82, both at Brighton.

Brighton, 40E Mural monument for Humphry COTES, d. 1775

- Tower South wall, top left corner.
- 60(W) x 42(H) — Very good.
- M.I. (7 lines, engraved, black) on an unframed white marble tablet.
- Humphry Cotes, Esq., of Woodcote, Shropshire, d, Hove, 30 Apr 1775, aet 62.

Brighton, 40F Mural monument for Francis Milbourn MARSH, d. 1782

- Tower South wall, West of 40E.
- 69(W) x 52(H) — Very good.
- M.I. (6 lines, engraved, black) in upper 50% of an unframed white marble tablet.
- Francis Milbourn Marsh, Esq., Major (90th Regiment of Foot), d. 16 Sep 1782, aet 44.

Brighton, 40G Mural monument for Robert and Emma SWANTON, d. 1765 and 1822 and their daughter

- Tower South wall, West of 40F.
- 60(W) x 81(H) — Very good.
- M.I. (13 lines, engraved, black) on white marble tablet, unframed.
- Robert Swanton, Esq., Rear Admiral, d. 11 Jul 1765; his widow, Emma, d. 18 Jul 1822, aet 84; their daughter, Mrs Frances Swanton, 21 Feb 1841.

1. Originally in the middle aisle of the church - Horsfield (*Sussex* I 143).
2. Frances Swanton perhaps a daughter-in-law.

Brighton, 40H Mural monument for Wilhelmina PARR, d. 1827

- Tower South wall, West of 40G.
- 53(W) x 56(H) — Very good.
- M.I. (black) on an unframed white marble tablet.
- Wilhelmina Parr, d. 2 Sep 1827, aet 62; widow of Captain Parr, naval officer, of Langdown House, Hampshire; issue - 3 daughters (unnamed).

1. Patrons of 40H were Wilhelmina Parr's 3 daughters.

Brighton, 40I Mural monument for George HODGES, date unknown

- Tower South wall, West of 40H.
- Inaccessible — Dirty; faded; local losses.
- M.I. hardly legible.
- George Hodges, son of William Robert and Mary Hodges, date of death and other details illegible.

1. Looks early 19th century.

Brighton, 40J Mural monument for John PANKHURST, d. 1795 and his family

- Tower South wall, centre left.
- 87(W) x 70(H) — Very good.
- M.I. on unframed white marble tablet with scalloped edges; signed (lower left): 'WILLIAMS'.
- John Pankhurst, customs officer, d. 27 June 1795. aet 67; his wife, Sarah, d. 5 Dec 1760, aet 33; their issue - John Pankhurst, Esq., surgeon, d. 25 Nov 1804, aet 44, unmarried; Hannah Pankhurst, d. 20 Jan 1811, aet 72.

1. One of 5 tablets signed by Williams in this Survey (see Introduction).

Brighton, 40K Mural monument for Richard TIDY, d. 1788 and his family

- Tower South wall, West of 40J.
- 63(W) x 77(H) — Very good.
- M.I. on unframed white marble tablet.
- Richard Tidy, Esq., d. 27 Dec 1788, aet 69; his wife, Mary, d. 2 Feb 1760, aet 23; their issue - John, d. 11 Jul 1771, aet 12; Richard, d. 18 Jan 1760, aet 1.

1. Originally on North side of the church - Horsfield (*Sussex* I 142).

Brighton, 40L Mural monument for William RANDALL, d. 1796

- Tower South wall, West of 40K.
- 84(W) x 74(H) — Very good.
- M.I. (100%) on a white marble tablet, unframed, engraved border.
- William Randall, barrack master, d. 30 Nov 1796, aet 57; his wife, Phoebe, d. 25 Feb 1822, aet 77; their daughter, Mary, d. 21 May 1805, aet 34, wife of Lieut. Gerard Fletewood, R.N.

1. Originally on North side of the church - Horsfield (*Sussex* I 142).
2. William Randall was perhaps based at Preston barracks, see A Hudson, 'Napoleonic Barracks in Sussex' (*SAC* 124 267).

Brighton, 40M Mural monument for Richard ATKINSON, d. 1785

- Tower South wall, just West of 40L.
- 66(W) x 79(H) — Good; rust.
- M.I. on an unframed white marble tablet.
- Richard Atkinson, Esq., MP (New Romney), Alderman (London), d. 26 May 1785, aet 47.

1. Originally in the middle aisle - Horsfield (*Sussex* I 142).
2. JH notes that Richard Atkinson was Director of the East India Co. and said to be worth £300,000 at his death, see Namier & Brooke (2 32).

Brighton, 40N Mural monument for Charles PRICHARD, d. 1817
- Tower South wall, lower tier, East end.
- 45(W) x 30(H) — Edges damaged.
- M.I. on a white marble tablet, corners chamfered.
- Charles Prichard, Esq., d. 14 Feb 1817, aet 50.

Brighton, 40O Mural monument for Fanny COWLEY, dated 1830
- Tower South wall, lower tier, West of 40N.
- 20(W) x 25(H) — Dirty; faded.
- M.I. (engraved) on an unframed grey marble tablet.

1830

TO THE MEMORY

OF A POOR,

BUT EXEMPLARY PARISHIONER

NAMED

FANNY COWLEY

THIS STONE IS PLACED BY THE VICAR

BLESSED ARE THE DEAD

WHICH DIE IN THE LORD

....

1. A rare case of a monument erected to the memory of 'a poor but exemplary parishioner', by the vicar.

Brighton, 40P Mural monument for Elizabeth MICHELL, d. 1808
- Tower South wall, middle tier, towards West end.
- 48(W) x 67(H) — Very good.
- M.I. fills marble tablet.
- Elizabeth Michell, d. 31 Mar 1808, aet 33; eldest daughter of William Johnson, Esq., of Petworth; and wife of James Charles Michell; issue - Elizabeth Sarah, d. 2 Feb 1807, aet 2; John Eardley, d. 2 May 1807, aet 5.

Brighton, 40Q Mural monument for Rev. Radulph SNEYD, d. 1808, and his wife Penelope, d. 1820
- Tower South wall, lower tier, West of 40P.
- 47(W) x 63(H) — Fine: paint loss (border).
- M.I. in Latin (engraved) on white marble tablet, set portrait-wise; painted black border.
- Rev. Radulph Sneyd, LLB, vicar of Westham, rector of Jevington, d. 13 Jun 1808, aet 54; second son of Radulph Sneyd, armiger, of Keele, Staffordshire; his widow, Penelope, d. 20 Mar 1820, aet 62.

1. Originally in chancel - Horsfield (*Sussex* I 142).
2. JH notes that Rev. Ralph Sneyd, BCL from All Souls, Oxford, was sometime chaplain to the Prince of Wales. He was vicar of Rye 1781-93, of Westham 1793-1808, and rector of Jevington 1781-1808, see Foster (*Al. Ox.* 2 4 1326) and Hennessy (93, 129, 158). On 14 Dec 1780 he married Penelope Moore at St. Marylebone, London.

Brighton, 40R Mural monument for William GWYN, d. 1770
- Tower South wall, lower tier, East end.
- 51(W) x 35(H) — Very good.
- M.I. on white marble tablet, unframed.
- William Gwyn, A.M., principal of Brasenose College, Oxford, d. 17 Aug 1770, aet 35.

1. Originally in middle aisle - Horsfield (*Sussex* I 143).

Brighton, 40S Mural monument for James STANLEY, d. 1810
- Tower West wall, South of West door, very high.
- Inaccessible — Very good; colour.
- M.I. (engraved) on framed tablet of white marble, set landscape-wise; at top, escutcheon.
- James Stanley, armiger, d. 28 Sep 1810, aet 57; wife, brother and issue - all unnamed.

1. Originally in middle aisle - Horsfield (*Sussex* I 143).
2. In situ in Lambarde (*SAC* 71 158) noting arms.
3. Unusually powerful sentiments are expressed in the M.I.: '...uxor (nunc eheu! vidua)...'.
4. Proclamation of armigerous status confirmed by the escutcheon.

Brighton, 40T Mural monument for Thomas W. STEELE, d. 1796
- Tower West wall, South of West door, below 40S.
- c.50(W); (H) inaccessible — Very good; rust.
- M.I. on unframed, white marble tablet.
- Thomas W. Steele, of Trelawny, Jamaica, d. 28 Jan 1796, aet 12.

Brighton, 40U Mural monument for James HODGE, d. 1794
- Tower West wall, South of West door, below 40T.
- c.50(W); (H) inaccessible — Very good.
- M.I. on an unframed, white marble tablet.
- James Hodge, Esq., of Penryn, Cornwall, died at Brighton, 19 Oct 1794, aet 38.

Brighton, 40V Mural monument for Philip METCALFE, d. 1818
- Tower West wall, South of West door, below 40U, partly obscured by notice board.
- 57(W) x 70(H) — Fine; rust.
- M.I. (engraved, black) fills unframed white marble tablet. Final line (obscured) reads: '... made the scene of his residence'.
- Philip Metcalfe, Esq., F.R.S. F.S.A., of Hill Street, Berkeley Square, London and Hawsted, Suffolk, MP 1784-1807 (Horsham, Malmsbury, Plympton), died at Brighton, 26 Aug 1818, aet 85; regular visitor to Brighton for over 50 years.

1. Originally in middle aisle - Horsfield (*Sussex* I 141), perhaps then on Tower North wall. Lambarde (*SAC* 71 159) describes arms, which are no longer extant.
2. Philip Metcalfe was FRS and FSA.

Brighton, 40W Mural monument for Caroline Margaret THOMPSON, d. 1821
- Tower West wall, South of West door, low down.
- 48(W) x 37(H) — Very good.
- M.I. on an unframed, white, marble tablet.
- Caroline Margaret Thompson, d. 30 Mar 1821, aet 40; wife of Henry Thompson, Esq., late of Oporto.

Brighton, 40X Mural monument for William HALSTONE, d. 1809
- Tower West wall, North of West door, high up.
- c.50(W); (H) inaccessible — Very good.
- M.I. on an unframed white marble tablet.
- William Halstone, Esq., late of Bermondsey, Surrey, d. 20 Dec 1809, aet 63.

Brighton, 40Y Mural monument for Bridget BARNETT, d. 1816
- Tower West wall, North of West door, below 40X.
- c.50(W); (H) inaccessible — Very good.
- M.I. on an unframed white marble tablet.
- Bridget Barnett, d. 18 Sep 1816; widow of Charles Barnett, of Stratton, Bedfordshire.

Brighton, 40Z Mural monument for Thomas SMITH, d. 1823

- Tower West wall, North of West door, at head height.
- 36(W) x 45(H) — Very good.
- M.I. (engraved) on an unframed white marble tablet; chamfered corners.
- Thomas Smith, Esq., Alderman (London), d. 18 Apr 1823, aet 76.

Brighton, 40AA Mural monument for David BAILLIE, d. 1826

- Tower West wall, North of West door, near floor level.
- 41(W) x 36(H) — Very good.
- M.I. on an unframed white marble tablet.
- David Baillie, Esq., of West Moulsey Villa, Surrey, d. 4 Dec 1826, aet 66.

Brighton, 40BB Wall-mounted lead slab commemorating Edward LOWE and others, dated 1677 [Plate 30]

- Tower West wall, North of West door, standing on floor.
- 69(W) x 107(H) — Fine, blacked.
- M.I. (8 lines, relief) on a lead slab.
- Cites Edward Lowe, vicar; and John Scras, Henry Smith, Richard Herman, all three churchwardens, dated 1677.

1. Evidently, a slab commemorating work on the church roof and blown down in storms of 1703 (or 1705).
2. One John Scras (d. 1702) was master of a Brighton charity school in 1701 (Caffyn 334).
3. For others of this type see 40GG and HH.

Brighton, 40CC Mural monument for Walter MURRAY, d. 1826

- Tower North wall, West end, at head height.
- 55(W) x 33(H) — Very good.
- M.I. on an unframed white marble tablet.
- Walter Murray, Esq., of Jamaica, d. 25 May 1826, at Brighton, aet 53; his elder brother, William Murray, Esq.

1. Patron was William Murray.

Brighton, 40DD Mural monument for Charlotte MARYATT, d. 1816

- Tower North wall, East of 40CC.
- 39.5(W) x 42(H) — Good.
- M.I. on an unframed white marble tablet.
- Charlotte Maryatt, d. 7 Oct 1816, aet 23, daughter of Joseph and Charlotte Marryat, of Wimbledon, Surrey.

Brighton, 40EE Mural monument for Robert Home GORDON, d. 1826

- Tower North wall, East of 40DD.
- 56(W) x 35(H) — Fading.
- M.I. on an unframed, white marble tablet.
- Robert Home Gordon, Esq., of Embo, N[orth] B[ritain], d. 19 Dec 1826, aet 61; his widow, Susannah Harriot, d. 18 Jul 1839, aet 71.

Brighton, 40FF Mural monument for William TROUP, d. 1825

- Tower North wall, below 40CC-EE.
- 82(W) x 39(H) — Very good.
- M.I. on an unframed trapezoidal white marble tablet; space left for further lines.
- William Troup, surgeon in the East India Co., born, Brighton, 1801 - buried Bassadore, Persian Gulf, 30 Nov 1825, aet 23; son of George and Ann Troup, of St. James' Palace, she d. 31 Jan 1820, aet 50; also, her sister, Sarah Kent, d. 18 July 1829, aet 56.

Brighton, 40GG Wall-mounted slab commemorating Thomas FRILAND, etc., dated 16[7]5
- Tower North wall, centre, standing on the floor.
- 74(W) x 131(H) — Blacked.
- Escutcheon, then M.I. (relief) on a lead slab
- Thomas Friland, Thomas Roberds, Richard Rossum, all churchwardens; John Vandyke, Plum[b]er.

1. The John Vandyke named here is perhaps the author of 40 DD, II and JJ, all of them reportedly blown down from the roof in 1703/05.
2. A plumber named Thomas Vandyke, of Cliffe, Lewes, was still taking apprentices in 1733, see Rice (162).

Brighton, 40HH Wall-mounted slab commemorating Richard MASTERS, etc., dated 1705
- Tower North wall, alongside and East of 40GG.
- 69(W) x 114(H) — Blacked.
- 2 cherubim, an escutcheon, a M.I., all in relief on a lead slab.
- Richard Masters, Richard Tuppen, John Masters all three churchwardens, dated 1705.

1. See too 40BB and 40GG.
2. For licence to marry dated 2 May 1698 for Richard Masters, of Brighton, and Elizabeth Glover, of Brighton, see Dunkin (*Licences 1670-1729* 170).
3. Another dated 12 Feb 1717/8 for Richard Tuppen, of Brighton, carpenter, and Mary Smith, of Brighton, see Dunkin (*Licences 1670-1729* 219).
4. See too Brighton Additions.

Brighton, 40II Mural monument for Charlotte WILSON, d. 1782
- North aisle, West wall, facing East, South of window, above head height.
- (W) inaccessible; 34(H) — Very good.
- M.I. on an unframed white marble tablet, set portrait-wise.
- Charlotte Wilson, d. 8 Sep 1782, aet 18, daughter of Rev. William Worcester Wilson, D.D., vicar of Deptford, Kent.

Brighton, 40JJ Mural monument for Elizabeth Grace ROBINSON, d. 1830
- North aisle, West wall, facing East, towards South end.
- 51(W) x 54(H) — Fading.
- M.I. on a white marble tablet; moulded frame and black border.
- Elizabeth Grace Robinson, died at Brighton, 2 Jan 1830, aet 74; wife of George Robinson, Esq., formerly of Bath.

Brighton, 40KK Mural monument for Jane BATHURST, d. 1827
- North aisle, West wall, facing East, North of 40JJ.
- 48(W) x 29(H) — Very good.
- M.I. on an unframed white marble tablet.
- Jane Bathurst, died at Dieppe, 5 Jun 1827, aet 40; wife of Frederick Hervey Bathurst, Bart., of Clarendon Park, Wiltshire.

Brighton, 40LL Mural monument for Lady MANSFIELD, d. 1819
- North aisle, West wall, centre, facing East, below window, at head height.
- 91(W) x 69(H) — Fine.
- M.I. on an unframed white marble tablet; Grecian ornament in corners.
- Susan, Lady Mansfield, 22 Sep 1750 - 10 Nov 1819; wife of Rt. Hon. Sir James Mansfield, PC, etc., Chief Justice, etc.

1. Originally in middle aisle - Horsfield (*Sussex* I 143).

Brighton, 40MM Mural monument for Tobias ATKINSON, d. 1819

- North aisle, West wall, facing East, North of 40NN, above head height.
- 56(W) x 54(H) — Very good.
- M.I. on white marble tablet; border of chamfered corners; black baseplate.
- Tobias Atkinson, d. 19 Nov 1819, aet 75; his daughter, Elizabeth Jackson, d. 8 Jan 1821, aet 46.

Brighton, 40NN Mural monument for Elizabeth LEIGH, d. 1826

- North aisle, West wall, facing East, North end, above head height.
- Inaccessible — Faded; dirty.
- M.I. (engraved, black) fills unframed white marble tablet; black baseplate with pointed top; arms over moulded cornice.
- (Little legible) Elizabeth Leigh, d. 9 May 1826, aet 70; last daughter of Stratford Canning, Esq., of Carvagh, Ireland; her first husband, Captain Westly Percival, of Knight's Brook, Co. Meath; her second husband, Rev. William Leigh, of Rushhall, Hall, Staffordshire; issue - 3 daughters; her many virtues; quotes 1 Corinthians 15.22.

1. Originally in middle aisle - Horsfield (*Sussex* I 142).

Brighton, 40OO Mural monument for Mary ANGELO, d. 1823 [Plate 31]

- North aisle, North wall, high in North-West corner.
- Inaccessible — Very good.
- M.I. (engraved, black) on white marble tablet taking form of an open book; black baseplate.
- Mary Angelo, d. 16 Aug 1823, aet 21; eldest daughter of Captain George Frederick Angelo.

1. The M.I. shows biography on left and biblical text on right.

Brighton, 40PP Mural monument for John CLARKE, d. 1783

- North aisle, West wall, facing East, top left of group of 6.
- Inaccessible — Fine.
- M.I. on an unframed white marble tablet.
- John Clarke, of London, surgeon, d. 25 Aug 1783, aet 57; issue - an unnamed youngest son.

1. Erected by an unnamed son.

Brighton, 40QQ Mural monument for R[ichard] BRACKEN, d. 1830

- North aisle, West wall, facing East, top centre of group of 6.
- Inaccessible — Fine.
- M.I. on an unframed white marble tablet.
- R[ichard] Bracken, curate of Brighton, died in an alpine snowstorm, 13 Sep 1830.

1. Erected by the vicar Henry Michael Wagner.
2. JH notes that Richard Bracken was curate of Brighton from 1828.

Brighton, 40RR Mural monument for Elizabeth Harriet WAGNER, d. 1829

- North aisle, West wall, facing East, top right of group of 6.
- Inaccessible — Fine.
- M.I. on white marble tablet, unframed.
- Elizabeth H[arriet] Wagner, d. 1829, aet 32.

1. Original in middle aisle - Horsfield (*Sussex* I 143).
2. NBI records the burial of Elizabeth Harriet Wagner on 3 Dec 1829 at Brighton.

Brighton, 40SS Mural monument for Frances Crosbie FAIRFIELD, d. 1830 [Plate 32]

- North aisle wall, towards West end, at head height.

- 94(W) x 234(H) — Some local damage.
- Above, a relief with a shallow curved top; set portrait-wise; an angel embracing the subject as she is borne aloft; then, a moulded cornice; below, an unframed tablet with M.I. (9 lines, engraved, biography, script. quote) between 2 pilasters each with a digger in relief; supported by 2 corbels; signed (under lower base moulding): 'R WESTMACOTT JNR WILTON PLACE LONDON'.
- Frances Crosbie Fairfield, d. 28 Aug 1830, at Brighton; wife of Charles Fairfield, Esq.

1. In situ in Lambarde (*SAC* 71 158) noting arms.
2. Escutcheon below perhaps not originally associated with 40SS (Church Guide).
3. Cited by Nairn & Pevsner (428); by Gunnis (*Dict.* 427) as for Frances Crosbie.
4. Richard Westmacott, Jnr. (1799-1872), continued the practice of his father, Sir Richard Westmacott, who undertook few commissions after c.1830.
5. Not in Horsfield – presumably not erected when he carried out his survey.

Brighton Additions
Reported by S Clarke (*SAC* 32 71-2):
(1) Richard Masters, Gent., d. 27 Mar 1716, aet 77, his wife, Alice d. 25 May 1696, aet 56 (choir vestry floor).
(2) Captain Benjamin Masters, Gent., d. 28 Sep 1749, aet 47; his wife Hannah, d. 22 Jul 1755, aet 55 (ditto).
(3) Ann Hall, wife of Richard Hall, d. May 1728, aet 28; her sister Elizabeth, aet 22, also d. May 1728 (cloister leading to choir vestry, on East wall).
(4) Elizabeth and Mary Peircy, d. 1709, daughters of Cheeseman and Mary Peircy (as above West wall).
(5) George Pearce, d. 17 Aug 1817, aet 19, drowned (cloister East wall).
(6) Thomas Tuppen, bricklayer, d. 4 May 1712, aet 71 (ditto).
(7) William Marchant, d. 24 Dec 1780, aet 63 (ditto).
(8) Susanna Standing, d. 3 Feb 1803, aet 67 (ditto).
(9) Mary Marchant, wife of William, d. 4 Jun 1789, aet 63.
(10) David Jones, Esq., d. 16 Jun 1804, aet 83 (ditto).
(11) William Godfrey Hine, d. 29 Apr 1818, aet 28; Esther Hine, 14 Sep 1819, aet 19; her parents William and Mary Hine (ditto).
Noted in Horsfield (*Sussex* I 142-3).
(12) C. Scrase, 1792 - (North side).
(13) Robert Roberts Wilmot, 1822 - (middle aisle).
(14) Francis Biddulph, 1800 - (middle aisle).
(15) Mary Carter, 1781 - (middle aisle).
(16) Swan Downer, 1816 - (western gallery).

(45) BURWASH, St. Bartholomew
Much of the church is Early English; North arcade is Decorated, many windows renewed - Nairn & Pevsner (463); rebuilt in 1856 with wider aisles but reproducing ancient features, see *SNQ* (XI 167), Godfrey & Salzman (Pl. 33) views by Grimm 1784 (BL Add. MS 5670 f.10); in 1686 Mr John (or Anthony) Cruttenden had a South aisle gallery; in 1724, the condition was reportedly fine (Ford); there were c.400 communicants at Burwash in 1603, see Renshaw (*Ecclesiastical Returns*). Several memorials not mentioned in Horsfield (*Sussex* I 579).

Burwash, 45A Anonymous ledger, d. c.1700?
- Outer West porch floor, near church door.
- 70(W) x 140(L) — Very worn; part legible; cracks (West end).
- M.I. (engraved) in black slab; head to West.

[6 lines illegible]
...in th[e] year of ... Lord
God [1680?] he departed
this life the ..... v of

March .. 00

Burwash, 45B Mural monument for John CONEY, d. 1775

- Inner West porch, North wall, at head height.
- 80(W) x 133(H) — Very good.
- M.I. (7 lines, engraved) fill a slate panel with grey marble moulded base and cornice; flanking scrolls; above, part of a scrolled pediment; below, decorative apron.
- John Coney, of Burwash, Gent., d. 2 May 1775, aet 72.

1. Note the unusual mix of materials: slate, stone and marble.

Burwash, 45C Mural monument for Sarah ELLIS, d. 1800

- Inner West porch, North wall, at head height, East of 45B.
- 50(W) x 104(H) — Very faded.
- M.I. on oval white stone plaque with moulded border; on top, white marble ribbon decorative on a black baseplate.
- Sarah Ellis, d. 9 (or 19) May 1800, aet 28, eldest daughter of Thomas Johnson, of Framfield; and wife of James Ellis, Gent.

1. Unusual decorative ribbon work.

Burwash, 45D Mural monument for John POLHILL, d. 1689

- North aisle, West wall, high up, over 45E.
- 60(W) x 160(H) — Fine; faded; colour.
- M.I. (many lines, engraved, black) fill a white marble tablet; drapes flanking; 2 cherubim top left and right, another centre, below; above, an elaborate achievement.
- John Polhill, of Frenches, Burwash, Gent., d. 29 May 1689, aet 44; his wife, Frances, daughter of John Cason, Gent., of Woodnesborough, Kent; issue 6 sons, 7 daughters; 1 survives Mary.

1. Noted by Gunnis (*Dict.* 87) as being by Thomas Cartwright I (c.1617-1702).
2. Note the good quality cherubs.
3. Noted by Lambarde (*SAC* 67 155) describing arms.

Burwash, 45E Mural monument for John CASON, d. 1675

- North aisle, West wall, below 45D.
- 72(W) x 147(H) — Fine; colour.
- Oval cartouche filled by M.I. (Latin); within a wreathed frame; above and below, scroll decorative; at top, an achievement.
- John Cason, Gent., of Pelham, Hertfordshire, d. 14 Dec 1675, aet 65; his mother, Susan, daughter of Robert Oxenbridge, of Brede, wife of Thomas Blechende, of Woodnesborough, Kent; his first wife, Mary Brown; his second wife, Frances, only daughter of John Polhill, of Frenches; John Cason's virtues.

1. Noted by Nairn & Pevsner (463).
2. Note length and complexity of the Latin M.I..
3. JH notes that John Cason's father was Edward Cason of Furneux Pelham, Hertfordshire. Although described as being of Pelham, Herts, on the monument, John Cason is shown in the 1663-68 Visitation of Kent as 'of Allington, Kent', see Armytage (*Kent*, 32). He matriculated at Christ's, Cambridge in 1626, did not take a degree, and was admitted to Gray's Inn in Feb 1629, see Venn (1 1 304). See also Lambarde (*SAC* 67 155) for heraldry.

Burwash, 45F Mural monument for Elizabeth CASON, d. 1679/80

- North aisle, centre of West wall.
- 54(W) x 55(H) — Very good.
- Set diamond-wise; grey and white marble panel; unframed; M.I. (11 lines).
- Elizabeth Cason, 21 Jun 1614 – 14 Feb 1679/80; wife of John Cason.

1. Perhaps formed from an earlier monument? Note the spelling of 'Feburary'.
2. For John Cason see 45E.

Burwash, 45G Mural monument for Richard Still DYKE, d. 1761

- North aisle, West wall, North end.
- 74(W) x 153(H) — Very good; no colour.
- M.I. (engraved and black) on white stone tablet; arched top; moulded and decorative frame with yellow inlay in white; arch-topped cornice supports an urn; decorative course of quatrefoils on base moulding; below, apron with Baroque escutcheon.
- Richard Still Dyke, Esq., of Burwash, d. 2 Jun 1761, aet 45; his wife, Anne, d. 26 Sep 1794, aet 76, daughter of Rev. George Jordan, diocesian chancellor of Chichester.

1. Noted by Horsfield (*Sussex* I 579) who described heraldry, but it is now indecipherable.
2. Unusual colour combinations.
3. Patron was widow Anne.
4. Dating probably close to 1794 (quatrefoils).

Burwash, 45H Mural monument for Thomas DYKE, d. 1723

- North aisle, North wall, towards West end.
- 95(W) x 170(H) — Good; upper M.I. faded.
- White marble M.I. panel filled 60% from top in 2 equal parts; broken dark grey pointed pediment; Baroque achievement; decorative scrolls flanking; strong base mould; no apron.
- Thomas Dyke, d. 3[?] Nov 1723, aet 39; his wife, Mary, d. 16 Jun 1755, aet 66; her second husband Robert Streatfeild, Gent., of Delaware, Brasted, Kent; her father, Richard Still, Gent., of Cowden, Kent; Thomas and Mary Dyke's sole issue – Richard Still Dyke; Thomas Dyke is descended from the Polhills of Burwash.

1. For later Streatfeilds see 264M and O.
2. For Richard Still Dyke see 45G.
3. Lambarde (*SAC* 67 155) notes heraldry.

Burwash, 45I Ledger for Anthony CRUTTENDEN, d. 1686

- Nave floor, East end North of 45J.
- 125.5(W) x 166(L) — Very good; cut.
- Below an escutcheon, M.I. (12 lines, engraved) fills a black slab; head to West.
- Anthony Cruttenden, Esq., buried at Burwash, 24 Jun 1686; only son of Anthony Cruttenden, Esq.; his wife, Mary, buried 16 May 1681, aet unknown, second daughter of Herbert Hay, of Glyndebourne.

1. Noted - Horsfield (*Sussex* I 579).
2. For Hay of Glyndebourne see 114E-G.
3. Noted in A. Clarke (*Sussex* 33).

Burwash, 45J Ledger for Anthony CRUTTENDEN, d. 1716

- Nave floor, East end, South of 45I.
- 114(W) x 167(L) — Some shaling.
- An escutcheon, then M.I. (10 lines, engraving) fill visible surface of a black slab, cut at East end; head to West.
- Anthony Cruttenden, Esq., d. 21 May 1716; son of Anthony Cruttenden, Esq., and his wife, Mary.

1. Noted - Horsfield (*Sussex* I 579).
2. Patron appears to have been a son, also Anthony [the third?].
3. For licence to marry dated 23 Nov 1686 for Anthony Cruttenden of Burwash and Mary Cryer, of Burwash, see Dunkin (*Licences 1670-1729* 99).
4. Noted in A. Clarke (*Sussex* 33) and Lambarde (*SAC* 67 154) notes heraldry.

Burwash, 45K Mural for James PHILCOX, d. 1824
- South aisle, West end, South-West corner, above 45L.
- 70(W) x 60(H) — Stained; fading.
- White marble on black slate backplate; M.I. (8 lines, engraved, black) on tablet of sarcophagal form; small feet left and right; shallow pointed pediment with palmettes.
- James Philcox, of Burwash, Gent., d. 24 Jul 1824, aet 75; his wife, Mary, d. 3 Feb 1806, aet 58; buried in the churchyard at Burwash.

1. Unsigned but attributable to Parsons of Lewes.
2. One James Philcox owned and occupied lands at Burwash in 1785 (R. Davey 46).

Burwash, 45L Mural for Rev. John COURTAIL, d. 1806 [Plate 33]
- South aisle, West end, South-West corner, below 45K.
- 98(W) x 149(H) — Good; damaged cornice / pediment.
- Rectangular black marble baseplate; white marble panel set portrait-wise, with M.I. (11 lines); pointed pediment over; on apron, symbol of eternity (serpent); flanking allegory of Faith and Hope; M.I.; signed (lower right): 'FLAXMAN RA SCULPTOR'.
- Rev. John Courtail, M.A., archdeacon of Lewes, canon of Chichester, rector of Woodchurch, Kent and rector and vicar of Burwash for more than 51 years, d. 25 Feb 1806, aet 90.

1. Formerly on chancel North wall - Horsfield (*Sussex* I 579).
2. John Courtail owned and occupied lands at Burwash in 1785 (R. Davey 44).
3. Cited by Gunnis (*Dict.* 151) and Nairn & Pevsner (463).
4. JH notes that Courtail had also been rector of Great Gransden in Huntingdonshire; vicar of Ninfield and rector of Felpham (CCEd).

Burwash, 45M Mural monuments for William CONSTABLE, d. 1810 and his wife Barbara, d. 1799
- South aisle, centre of West wall, at head height and above.
- Lower: 103(W) x 137(H); Upper: inaccessible — Both fine.
- (Lower) a white & grey trapezoidal panel with M.I. (15 lines, engraved, black); base moulding & two feet; small cornice; shallow pointed pediment and palmettes supporting a draped urn; all on black slate backplate with point top.
  (Upper) white tablet with M.I. on a black slate baseplate; signed: 'PARSONS.LEWES'.
- William Constable, Esq., of Burwash, magistrate, etc., d. 6 Sep 1810, aet 65; his first wife Barbara, eldest daughter of Rev. George Strother, rector of Penton Mewsey and Grateley, [Hampshire], d. 1 Dec 1799, aet 59; buried on North side of church.

1. For the attribution of all or part of 45M to Parsons see Gunnis (*Dict.* 292); both parts of 45M probably by Parsons of Lewes but only one is signed.
2. Part (2) of 45M was perhaps erected in the later 1830s.

Burwash, 45N Ledger for Christian MACKENZIE, d. 1822, and her husband Rev. William Mackenzie, d 1840.
- South aisle, West end, on North buttress.
- Not measured — Excellent; fading; colour.
- Above, M.I. (engraved, black) on white marble obelisk; below, thistle decorative left and right; at foot, base moulding, drapes, escutcheon with mottoes; all on a grey oval baseplate; signed (at foot): 'R.BLORE PICCADILLY'.
- Christian Mackenzie, d. 17 Mar 1822; wife (42 years) of Rev. William Mackenzie, D.D.,

rector and vicar of Burwash for 19 years and rector of Smarden, Kent for 30 years, d. 4 Jun 1840, aet 82; issue - 2 daughters, both died infants.

1. Formerly on chancel North wall - Horsfield (*Sussex* I 579).
2. Erected after 1822 by Christian MacKenzie's widowed husband the Rev. William MacKenzie (who d. 1840).
3. Are the thistles a family crest?
4. For Robert Blore see Gunnis (*Dict.* 57).
5. Lambarde (*SAC* 67 155) describes the heraldry. The crest is 'a mountain in flames', see Fairbairn (310).

Burwash, 45O Mural monument for Nathaniel CRUTTENDEN, d. 1770 [Plate 34]

- Inner Porch, South wall, East end.
- 95(W) x 182(H) — Severe cracks and repairs; colour.
- M.I. (11 lines) on upper 50% of an unframed grey-veined marble panel; below, crude grey marble apron with 2 scrolled corbels; above, broken scrolled pediment and cornice with Baroque escutcheon.
- Nathaniel Cruttenden, Esq., of Hastings, d. 16 Jul 1770, aet 72, son of Anthony and Mary Cruttenden; his only daughter, [Mary], wife of Rev. John Bishop, rector of Sedlescombe.

1. The last Cruttenden, now 'of Hastings'.
2. JH also notes entry in A. Clarke (*Sussex* 33) and that NBI records burial of Nathaniel Cruttenden on 21 Jul 1770 at Burwash.

Burwash, 45P Mural monument for George JORDAN, d. 1737

- Inner porch, centre of South wall, above 45Q.
- 34(W) x 77(H) — Fine; some wear.
- M.I. (engraved) on grey and white stone slab; unframed.

GEORGIUS IORDAN
Reverendi .....
Huius Ecclesiæ Vicarii
Filius
Obiit XIX Novembris
Anno Dom^{ni} MDCCXXXVII
Ætatis 2do

Sicut Flos succiditur

1. George Jordan was the two year old son of George Jordan, vicar here 1717-54.
2. George Jordan, the father, was also vicar of Heathfield, 1713-31, and prebendary of Sidlesham 1723-45; he built the first proper vicarage at Burwash in 1724, see Heathfield Church Guide and Trower 'Burwash' (*SAC* 21 132) and supported local schools (Caffyn 75).
3. NBI records the burial of George Jordan on 24 Nov 1737 at Burwash.

Burwash, 45Q Mural monument for Obedience NEVITT, d. 1619 [Plate 35]

- Inner porch, centre of South wall, below 45P.
- 47(W) x 73(H) — Fine; some wear; restored.
- In freestone; M.I. (black); escutcheon (black) top left corner; 3 slabs of stone forming a rectangular panel with a domed top.
- Obedience Nevitt, b. 18 Apr 1587 – bur. 15 May 1619, aet 32, daughter of Robert Cruttenden, of Burwash; and wife (from 11 Mar 1604) of Thomas Nevitt, of London, Gent.; her virtues, piety; her husband's charitable bequest.

1. Noted (with transcription) in Trower (*SAC* 21 133).
2. Patron of 45Q was Thomas Nevitt.
3. Headed 'An Epitaphe'.

Burwash, 45R Mural for John CRUTTENDEN, d. 1727

- Inner porch, South wall, West end.
- Lower: 80(W) x 27(H); Upper: 62(W) x 80(H) — Stained; worn; losses at ends of baseplate.
- M.I. on the upper rectangular panel in grey-white marble; curved, ornamental apron in grey-white marble below.

M.S.

JOANNIS CRUTTENDEN
Antonii et Mariæ filii,
ex antiqua in hoc agro gente oriundi

QUI

cum cæteris suis ingenii dotibus
multifariam legum scientiam adjunxiſset,
Juvenis adhuc,
a Foro et urbe
in otium et rus hic se recepit,
ubi cum ſilentio latere maluit
quam in concursu et strepitu ſplendeſcere
et de penu suo utcumque parvo
aliorum neceſsitatibus hic inſervire:
quam illic alienis injuriis
et oppreſsionibus rem facere
quinus[?] aſsidue exercitatus virtutibus
ad cælum ſuis, heu cito nimium migravit

anno ætatis 32. Domini 1727

1. Noted - Horsfield (*Sussex* I 579).

(45) Burwash Addition
<u>Stephenson (p.505):</u>
(1) A brass M.I. to one Anthony Cruttenden, Esq., 1660, aged 87.

(47) BUXTED, St. Margaret the Queen

Church now isolated within the confines of the house which was noted by Milles as under construction (by Mr Medley) in 1743 (Farrant 98); originally 13th century; chancel of c.1300, with ceiling c.1600; generally much restored, probably pre-19th century - Nairn & Pevsner (465-6); views of church, etc. by Grimm, Lambert (BL Add. MS 5671 f.100); Turner (*SAC* 23 144) mentions 'late alterations' impacting on brasses; Gosset was supplying Buxted Park with portrait sculpture in 1779 but not, it seems, monuments for the church (Gunnis *Dict.* vid. Gosset 176).

Buxted, 47A Ledger for Edward CLARKE, d. 1786, and Anne his wife d. 1802

- Choir floor, North side, partly obscured by furniture.
- 92(L) — Fine.
- M.I. (Latin) fills a black slab; head to the West.

HIC CONDITVR
PRORE RELLIQVIAS AVI SVI CELEB..R..I GVILL.. WOTTON D D
QVOD SVPERIST
EDVARDI CLARKE A.M.
COLLEGII S IOHANNIS CANTABRIGIENSIS
...
... SALUTIS MDCCXXX DECESSI

... EODEM QVOQVE MARMORE
... EST ANNA AMANTISSIMA EIVS VXOR
.... MDCC.... NVPTA MDCCLXIII OBIIT MDCCCII

PATRI MATRIQVE
H M...S P
LIBERI SVPERSTIIES

.... CVRAVERVNT

1. Edward Clarke 1730-86, son of William, a previous rector of Buxted, and his wife Anne daughter of William Wotton. He was educated at St. John's College, Cambridge; diplomatic career Spain etc. 1760s. He was rector of Peper Harrow, Surrey, 1758-69; vicar of Willingdon and Arlington, and rector of Buxted, all 1768-86; prebendary of Hove Villa 1771-72, and Hove Ecclesia 1772-86, both in Chichester Cathedral, see Venn (1 1 341) and Hennessy (24, 44, 161); he died in November 1786. See Dunkin (*SAC* 26 20-1), biography by Robert T. Holtby in *ODNB*, and Horsfield (*Sussex* I 368).
2. Anne Grenfield, daughter of Thomas Grenfield of Guildford, married Edward Clarke in 1763.
3. See too 47K which commemorates his father, William Clarke.

Buxted, 47B Ledger for William WOTTON, d. 1726/7
- Choir floor, centre, partly obscured by furniture.
- 93(W) x 160(L) — Fine.
- M.I. (10 lines, engraved) on upper 75% of a black slab; head to the West.
- William Wotton, S.T.P., d. 13 Feb 1726/7, aet 61.

1. Transcribed in Horsfield (*Sussex* I 367).
2. JH notes that William Wotton was awarded a Lambeth doctorate, see Venn (1 4 467); For details of his interesting and scurrilous life, see biography by David Stoker in *ODNB*.

Buxted, 47C Anonymous Ledger, with a date 1719
- Choir floor, South side.
- 93(W) x 160(L) — Sound; worn.
- Hardly anything is now legible on a freestone slab.

1. Perhaps marking the place of Anne or Anthony Saunders' burials, see 47E.

Buxted, 47D Anonymous ledger, with a date of 1711
- Sanctuary floor, South side.
- Visible area: 89(W) x 114(L) — Sound; very worn.
- Hardly anything visible engraved in a freestone slab.

1. Perhaps to Catherine, d. 1711, aet 58, wife of Edward Wilson, d. 1728, aet 77, also buried at Buxted.
2. Daughter of Sackville Graves, of West Firle, see genealogy in A. Clarke (Sussex 56-7).

Buxted, 47E Mural cartouche for Anthony SAUNDERS, d. 1719 [Plate 36]
- Sanctuary, South wall, high.
- c.95(W) — Very good.
- Gilded white marble; 4 cherubs, top and bottom, support looping drapery with gilded fringes and tassels; displays M.I. (21 lines, engraved, Latin) above, an achievement, gilded trumpets and foliage.
- Rev. Anthony Saunders, S.T.P., rector of Buxted and Acton in Middlesex and chancellor of St. Paul's Cathedral, London, d. 7 Jan 1719, aet 76; his learning, virtues, charitable works.

1. In situ - Turner (*SAC* 12 19) - 'handsome'; transcribed in Horsfield (*Sussex* I 367).
2. Saunders was rector 1673-1719 and chancellor of St. Paul's, see Dunkin (*SAC* 26 20); he founded Uckfield Grammar School (Caffyn 77-8).
3. 47E is of very high quality, the heraldic elephant above is especially memorable.
4. Erected by Anthony Saunders' heir and nephew Timothy Dewell. .
5. See also Lambarde (*SAC* 67 163) describing arms.

Buxted, 47F Mural monument for Catherine, Countess of LIVERPOOL, d. 1827

- South chapel, South wall, East end, above head height.
- 106(W) x 97(H) — Excellent.
- Pendant to 47H; M.I. (13 lines, engraved) on a white marble tablet; on polished brown base; below, decorated apron with scrolls and foliage; above, decorated moulding, shallow pointed pediment; Countess' coronet.
- Catherine, Countess of Liverpool, d. 1 Oct 1827, aet 83; youngest daughter of Sir Cecil Bisshop, Bart., of Parham; her first husband, Sir Charles Cope, Bart., of Orton Longueville, Huntingdonshire; her second husband, Charles, 1st Earl of Liverpool – issue Cecil, Earl of Liverpool.

1. Formerly a Lady Chapel, the South chapel was enclosed on its West side in c.1807 for the family and household of Lord Liverpool, with burial vault below and known as the [Buxted] Park Pew (for ownership history see 47G).
2. Charles Cecil Cope Jenkinson, the patron of 47F, was 3rd Earl of Liverpool (1784–1851), politician, born on 29 May 1784. He was second son of 1st Earl, and only son of subject of 47F (see biography by W.A.J. Archbold, rev. H.C.G. Matthew in *ODNB*).

Buxted, 47G Mural monument for George MEDLEY, d. 1796, and his widow's parents [Plate 37]

- South chapel, South wall, centre, above head height.
- 127(W) x 175(H) — Very good; colour.
- Above, in semi-relief against a brown marble base, a draped female mourns at an urn; below, M.I. (18 lines), including rhyming verse, on a panel with cornice and base mouldings; decorated panels to sides; below, brackets decorative with acanthus; on apron, heraldry, foliage and swags of looping material; signed (on left bracket): 'C.Regnart Fecit Cleavland St' and (right) 'Fitzroy Square London'.
- George Medley, Esq., d. 1 Jun 1796, aet 77; his widow, Jane Medley and her parents, Sir Timothy and Catherine Waldo, the latter d. 19 Apr 1806, aet 95; rhyming epitaph.

1. Transcribed in Horsfield (*Sussex* I 367) who reports that Medley hatchments, amongst others, once hung in the South or Buxted Place Chapel.
2. Noted as by Regnart in Nairn & Pevsner (465-6).
3. The building of Buxted Place commenced in 1726 when the estate was purchased from the heirs of Stephen Penkherst (173K) by Thomas Medley (1645-1728); the estate passed to his grandson Edward, thence in 1751 to Edward's brother George Medley (47G), thence by a niece to the daughter of Sir George Shuckburgh Evelyn (1751-1804) whose daughter married Charles Jenkinson (1784-1851), later Lord Liverpool (see Farrant).
4. George Medley was MP for Seaford 1768-80, and East Grinstead 1783-90, see Namier & Brooke (3 127). He owned Highhurst Wood, Buxted in 1785 (R. Davey 49) and supported the charity schools at East Dean 1776-96, and at Friston (Caffyn 108); his portrait by Romney was reported to be at Buxted Park, see Hawkesbury 'Pictures at Buxted Park' (*SAC* 47 99); for other monuments of this family see Barcombe (16D, F, etc.).
5. For Charles Regnart, 1759-1844 (Gunnis *Dict.* 317).
6. For Jane Medley see 47H.
7. JH notes that Timothy Waldo was a solicitor, of Clapham. He was knighted on 12 Apr 1769, on the same day as Richard Hotham, the founder of Bognor.

Buxted, 47H Mural monument for Jane MEDLEY, d. 1829

- South chapel, South wall, West end.
- 106(W) x 97(H) — Excellent.
- Pendant with 47F; M.I. (13 lines, engraved).
- Jane Medley, d. 14 Dec 1829, aet 91; daughter of Sir Timothy Waldo; and widow of George Medley.

1. The Medley family were related to the family of Lord Liverpool by marriage (see 47G).

2. Erected by Jane Waldo, her executrix.
3. For George Medley see 47G.
4. JH notes that Jane was George Medley's second wife.

Buxted, 47I Mural monument for Rev. Matthias D'OYLY, d. 1815, and his daughter Henrietta, d. 1804

- South aisle, South wall, near East end, at head height.
- 73(W) x 117(H) — Very good.
- M.I. (11 lines) on a white marble tablet; grey marble base; foliage in flanking panels; signed (lower right): 'RICHARD WESTMACOTT'.
- Rev. Matthias D'Oyly, rector of Buxted for 26 years, vicar of Pevensey, prebendary of Ely and archdeacon of Lewes, d. 13 Nov 1815, aet 71; eldest son of Rev. Thomas D'Oyly, LLD, archdeacon of Lewes and chancellor of Chichester; Matthias' widow Mary; issue – Thomas, John, George, Henry and their only daughter, Henrietta Maria, d. 29 Oct 1804, aet 21.

1. Transcribed in Horsfield (*Sussex* I 367).
2. Cited by Gunnis (*Dict.* 426) and Nairn & Pevsner (466).
3. His father Thomas D'Oyly, LLD, was archdeacon of Lewes, chancellor of Chichester Cathedral and a tenant at Conyboro House, Barcombe (Farrant 154).
4. Rev. Matthias D'Oyly ; (Pevensey, from 1767, archdeacon of Lewes from 1806); biography account in Dunkin (*SAC* 26 22).
5. Very like 47J.
6. JH notes that Rev. Matthias D'Oyley, MA, was educated Christ's College, Cambridge and was vicar of Pevensey 1767-1815, Prebendary of Ely 1770-87, rector of Buxted 1787-1815, archdeacon of Lewes 1806-1815. On 22 May 1770 he married Mary, daughter of George Poughfer. See Venn (2 2 332), Horn (*Fasti 1541-1857* 7 25, and 2 19), Hennessy (44, 119) and biographical account in Dunkin (*SAC* 26 22).
7. Matthias D'Oyly did not live at Buxted as he preferred to live at Lewes (Farrant 187).

Buxted, 47J Mural monument for Sir Francis D'Oyly, d. 1815, and others

- South aisle, South wall, centre, at head height.
- 74(W) x 102(H) — Very good.
- Very similar to 47I ; M.I. (final 5 lines added); also signed.
- Lieut. Col. Sir Francis d'Oyly, K.C.B., 1st Regiment of Foot Guards, service in Holland, Peninsula War, etc., died at Waterloo, 18 Jun 1815, aet 38; third son of Matthias d'Oyly; also his mother, Mary d. 13 Aug 1827, aet 76; also his brother, second son of Matthias d'Oyly, Sir John d'Oyly, Bart., died at Kandy, Ceylon, 25 May 1824, aet 49.

1. For family links see 47I.
2. Gunnis (*Dict.* 426) cites 47I and 47J by Sir Richard Westmacott; Nairn & Pevsner (466) cite 47I & 47J as 'two very plain tablets' by Sir Richard Westmacott.
3. Francis D'Oyly was at Corpus Christi College, Cambridge in 1794; he received a gold cross and three clasps for the battles of Busaco, Fuentes de Onoro, Salamanca, Vitoria, the Nivelle, the Nive, and Orthes; made a KCB on the extension of the Order of the Bath and acted as assistant adjutant-general in the campaign of 1815 to Picton's division.
4. By Richard Westmacott (signed).
5. There is a graveyard inscription in his memory in Walton-on-Thames (biography by H.M. Stephens, rev. Katherine Prior *ODNB*).

Buxted, 47K Painting commemorating William CLARKE, d. 1771

- South aisle, South wall, near West end.
- 62(W) x 130(H) — Good.
- Painted lines fill surface of a painted, framed wooden panel.
- William Clarke, A.M., fellow of St. John's College, Cambridge; chaplain to bishop Simon Otley and Thomas Holles, Duke of Newcastle; rector of Buxted; born 1696, Shropshire, and died Chichester, 21 Oct 1771, aet 75; also reports a marble tomb at Chichester

for William Clarke, d. unknown, his wife Anne, daughter of William Wotton and Anne Hammond; their issue, 2, unnamed.

1. This is the father of Edward (47A).
2. JH notes that William Clarke was chancellor, prebendary and canon residentiary of Chichester, see Horn (*Fasti 1541-1857* II 13, 42, 78). He was buried in St. Peter the Great, Chichester – see NBI – hence the latter part of the text. See Venn (1 1 348) which confirms and adds to the above information. See also Horsfield (*Sussex* I 368) and a biographical account in M.Hobbs (ed.) *Chichester Cathedral. An Historical Survey* (1994) 197-198.

Buxted, 47L Brass commemorating Thomas SMITH, d. 1558
- South aisle, South wall, West end, in a glazed case.
- 42(W) x 11(H) — Fine.
- M.I. (engraved) in Latin on a brass plate.
- Thomas Smith, d. 27 Oct 1558; his wife, Anne.

1. Formerly on the North aisle floor between the North and South doors, see H.R. Hoare, 'Notes on the Church of St Margaret, Buxted', (*SAC* 9 215-6).
2. Stephenson (505) noted lost effigies for Thomas Smith, Esq. and wife Anne.
3. Turner (*SAC* 23 144-5) reports that 47L is lost but parts of it found at Buxted Rectory under some hay in the barn.

(47) Buxted Addition
Turner (*SAC* 23 144) reports:
(1) Christopher and Robert Savage, the latter rector [?] of Buxted, 1511-1530 (chancel).

(48) CATSFIELD, St. Laurence
Norman nave & Early English chancel; 13th-century North-East chapel - Nairn & Pevsner (468); North aisle of 1845, when chancel also restored, see Leeney (*SAC* 84 147); South view in Godfrey & Salzman (Pl. 35) (BL Add. MS 5670 f.33 & 5676 f.94); for plan see *SNQ* (V 145); the chancel was in need of repair in 1686 and the work done by 1724 (Ford); in 1603 Lady Montague was recorded as the protector of two households in the parish of non-church attenders although the patron of the living was John Ashburnham, see Renshaw (*Ecclesiastical Returns*).

Catsfield, 48A Mural monument for John FULLER, d. 1810 [Plate 38]
- Nave, West wall, facing East, high.
- 60(W) x 90(H) — Good; faded.
- In white marble; rectangular panel set landscape-wise with trophies in relief; above, inverted scrolls as pediment; below, M.I. (engraved, black) fills a panel flanked by more scrolls, with cornice and base mouldings; 2 brackets with foliage decoration and more mouldings at foot; signed (lower right): 'NOLLEKENS Ft'.
- John Fuller, Esq., of Catsfield House, magistrate for fifty years, d. 31 Mar 1810, aet 85; his nephew, also John Fuller, Esq., of Rosehill.

1. Formerly on the North wall - Horsfield (*Sussex* I 542) 'elegant'.
2. Cited in Gunnis (*Dict.* 279) and Nairn & Pevsner (468) noting military still-life, including oak-leaves.
3. John Fuller was taxed on land at Catsfield in 1785 (R. Davey 51).
4. Other Fuller monuments at Uckfield, Waldron, etc.
5. Patron was the subject's nephew, John Fuller of Rosehill also patron of monuments at Brightling (39).

Catsfield, 48B Mural monument for Edward STAPLEY, d. 1720
- North-East chapel floor, against South wall, facing North.
- 89(W) x 134(H) — Very worn.
- M.I. (engraved) fills a freestone dome-topped slab; squared bottom; ornamental shoulders.

- Edward Stapley, M.A., rector of Catsfield from 1708, and rector of Penhurst from 1707, d. 25 Dec 1720, aged 43; son of William Stapley, of Allington, yeoman, and his wife, Eleanor.

1. Perhaps formerly a headstone?
2. JH notes that Edward Stapley was curate of Uppingham, Rutland, in 1702, curate of Wartling in 1706, rector of Penhurst 1707-20, and of Catsfield 1708-20, each institution and induction made on his birthday in the relevant year. See Venn (1 4 151), and CCEd.

Catsfield, 48C Ledger for Lady [Jane] PELHAM, d. 1686
- Chancel floor, North of centre, partly obscured by furnishings.
- 60(W) x 150(L) — Worn; restored?
- M.I. (12 lines, engraved, English and Latin) in upper 80% of a black slab (marble?); head to West.
- Lady Pelham, d. 19 May 1686, daughter of James Huxley, Esq., of Dornford, Oxford and his wife, Elizabeth.

1. Noted - Horsfield (*Sussex* I 542).
2. JH notes that she was wife of Sir Nicholas Pelham of Catsfield Place, M.P. for Seaford 1671 and 1689.
3. Sussex 1679; Lewes 1702 and 1726; JP and DL. See Henning (3 219). He d. 1739.

Catsfield, 48D Ledger for Olive WARDROPER, d. 1766
- Chancel floor, South of centre, partly obscured by furnishings.
- 60(W) x 150(L) — Fine, diagonal crack.
- M.I. (21 lines, engraved) on upper 80% of black (marble?) slab); head to West.
- Olive Wardroper, died in childbed, 7 Jul 1766, aet 20; daughter of James Markwick, Esq., and Mary; and wife of Richard Wardroper, Gent.; issue - a daughter, [Mary], d. Jan 1767, infant; her virtues.

1. Noted - Horsfield (*Sussex* I 542).
2. Patron was husband Richard Wardroper.

Catsfield Additions
Horsfield (*Sussex* I 542):
(1) Mary Delitia Bedingfield, wife of F. P. Bedingfield, of Catsfield House, 3 Dec 1793 – 11 May 1828; also infant Daughter Philippa Rose d. 1828.
(2) James Markwick, Esq., 1782, aet 72; also his wife Mary.
(3) Rev. William Delves, rector, d. 4 May 1823, aet 36.
(4) Robert Fuller, Gent., d. 1729, aet 71; also Jane his wife, daughter of William Bishop of Sedlescombe, Gent., d. 1725, aet 52 – a slab.
(5) Thomas Fuller, 1720, aet 75.

(49) CHAILEY, St. Peter
Mostly 13th century, restored c.1845 (*SAC* 84 149ff); enlarged in 1878-9 with outer North aisle and fragmentary South aisle, see Nairn & Pevsner (469); walls mostly modern; for plan see *SNQ* (XII 6); for a view from South-East see Godfrey & Salzman (Pl. 36) (BL Add. MS 5671 f.45; 5677 ff.26, 53, 55); condition reported as fine in 1724 (Ford).

Chailey, 49A Iron slab for Richard PORTER, d. 1762
- On floor beneath West tower.
- 90(W) x 180(L) — Fine.
- A cast iron slab; M.I. (raised relief).

Here lieth the Body
of Richard Porter A.M.
Who was eight Years
Rector of this Parish.
He Died the third day
of February Anno Domini
1762

Aged 46 Years

1. Horsfield (*Sussex* I 227) says this was in the aisle.
2. This is the son of the Richard Porter who d. 1752- see 49E.
3. Richard Porter educated Jesus College, Cambridge, see Venn (1 3 382).
4. Instituted at Chailey, 1753, see Dunkin (*SAC* 26 71).

Chailey, 49B Mural monument for Richard BOURCHIER, d. 1770, and his wife Jane, d. 1771

- Vestry, South wall.
- 140(W) x 190(H) — Good; fading.
- In white marble; M.I. (12 lines [7+5]) flanked by scrolls, on rectangular panel; moulded top and bottom; above, a broken pediment and an urn in bas-relief on a pedestal; flanking, flaming lamps; below, an ornamental apron, fluted brackets, arms and a base finial.
- Richard Bourchier, Esq., of Ades, Chailey, formerly of East Indies Co. and governor of Bombay; d. 2 Dec 1770, aet 78; his widow, Jane, d. 10 Aug 1771, aet 32.

1. Originally on chancel South wall - Horsfield (*Sussex* I 227); later on North aisle, North wall, see Lambarde (*SAC* 71 146) noting arms.
2. Note remarkable disparity in ages of this couple.

Chailey, 49C Mural monument for John INGRAM, d. 1803, and his wife, Elizabeth, d. 1818

- Vestry, North wall.
- 85(W) x 160(H) — Fine; local losses (lower mouldings); faded.
- In white and grey marble in low relief; a fluted urn on a pointed pediment; below, a M.I. (12 lines) on a rectangular panel; grey frame; decorated roundels in corners; at foot, corbels and ornamental apron; signed: 'WILLIAMS. BRIGHTON'.
- John Ingram, Gent., d. 18 Dec 1803 aet 69; eldest son of Rev. James Ingram, rector of Sedlescombe and vicar of Westfield, by his second wife, Anne; John Ingram's wife, Elizabeth, d. 23 May 1818, aet 79.

1. Originally in South nave - Horsfield (*Sussex* I 227); later on North aisle, North wall, see Lambarde (*SAC* 71 146) noting arms.
2. For John Ingram's land tax in 1785 (R. Davey 52); for licence to marry dated 8 Oct 1772 for John Ingram, of Chailey, Gent., aged 22 and Elizabeth Willard, of Newick, spinster, see Dunkin & Penfold (*Licences* 234).
3. Last 2 lines of M.I. perhaps later.
4. Maker noted by Gunnis (*Dict.* 432).

Chailey, 49D Mural monument for Rev. Sir Henry POOLE, Bart., d. 1821

- Chancel North wall, West end, at head height.
- 86(W) x 99(H) — Very good.
- M.I. on white marble panel, black base; no decorative or figure work.
- Rev. Sir Henry Poole, Bart., rector of Chailey for more than 50 years, of Poole Hall, Cheshire and The Hooke, Sussex, d. 25 May 1821 aet 76.

1. Originally on chancel South wall - Horsfield (*Sussex* I 227).
2. William Poole (1696-1779) bought The Hooke in 1732.
3. For Rev. Sir Henry Poole's land tax in 1785 (R. Davey 53); he was the last of his line. see J. Brent

(*SAC* 114 69ff).

4. For the Pooles in Sussex see Farrant (188).

5. JH notes that despite the statement of 50 years on this memorial, Rev. Sir Henry Poole was in fact rector here for 37 years, 1784-1821, see Venn (2 5 154); Brent (op. cit. 80); Hennessy (45); CCEd. He was also rector of Waldron for the same period.

Chailey, 49E Mural monument for Rev. Richard PORTER, d. 1753, and other members of his family

- Chancel North wall, at head height.
- 72.5(W) x 152(H) — Good; local losses (top).
- In white marble; M.I. (13 lines, black) on a rectangular panel; moulded edge; above, chamfered shoulders and a now vacant pedestal; below, apron with floral relief and black base finial.
- Rev. Richard Porter, A.M., rector of Chailey for 40 years, d. 14 Aug 1753, aet 79; also Thomas Porter, d. Feb 1739, aet 64; his wife, Elizabeth, d. 25 May 1761, aet 73; also Catherine Porter, d. 11 May 1748, aet 71.

1. 49E commemorates the father of the other Richard Porter (see 49A).
2. Some of the M.I. details have perhaps been corrupted over time.
3. The tall, thin form of 49E suggests it was designed for its current space or one similar.
4. Noted in Horsfield (*Sussex* I 227).
5. JH notes that Richard Porter was rector of Thoresby, Lincolnshire, 1698-1715; curate of Brede 1702; rector of Chailey 1713-53. See Venn (1 3 382), and CCEd.

Chailey, 49F Mural monument for Frances DAY, d. 1769

- Chancel North wall, in centre, at head height.
- 98(W) x 170(H) — Excellent; fading; repaired (lower left).
- M.I. fills a white marble panel; brown marble frame; grey pilasters flanking with very pretty foliage relief; above, brackets support a layered entablature and broken pediment; flaming urn (gilded); below, a decorative base moulding; between corbels, a decorative apron with arms and base finial.
- Frances Day, d. 31 Jul 1769, aet 64; only daughter of John Middelton, Gent., and his wife, Frances, of Hurstbarns, Chailey; and wife of the late Robert Day, Gent.; and granddaughter of Ellyott Moor, Gent., of Moor House, Wivelsfield.

1. In situ - Horsfield (*Sussex* I 227) who gives date of death as 1767.
2. Mrs Day was the last of her lines on both sides (see 49G-H).
3. 49F is an elaborate and high quality monument erected by Mrs Day's executors.
4. For Ellyott Moor see Wivelsfield (303E,F,G,I and Additions).
5. JH notes that Lambarde (*SAC* 71 146) describes the heraldry, but the shield below the main inscription is now completely blank.

Chailey, 49G Mural monument for Francis MIDDLETON, d. 1673, his parents and descendants

- Chancel North wall, East end, at head height.
- c.100(W) x 170(H) — Fine; fading.
- M.I. (shallow engraved, gilded) fills a black slate panel; flanking, white pilasters; above, a grey frieze and white entablature; on cornice, flaming lamps (left and right); achievement in centre; below, a black base moulding and decorated apron between brackets.
- Francis Middleton, Gent., of Hurstbarns, Chailey, d. 23 May 1673, aet 53; son of Arthur Middleton, of Horsham, and Anne, who d. 1665 aet 70[?]; his son, John Middelton, Gent., of Hurtsbarns, d. 2 Feb 1750/1, aet 84.

1. Noted, not located, by Horsfield (*Sussex* I 227).
2. Perhaps erected after the death of John Middleton in 1750; in situ - Lambarde (*SAC* 71 146) noting arms, which are now indecipherable.

Chailey, 49H Mural monument for Thomas MYDDLETON, d. 1616
- Chancel, South wall, East end, at head height.
- 82(W) x 133(H) — Fine; faded.
- 2 abutting engraved stone panels; (1 upper): arms; (2 lower): M.I. and memento mori.

Memento Mori

In this chavncell lyeth bvryed the
body of Tho: Myddleton sone & heire
of William Myddleton of Vallence
in yᵉ parish of Westram in yᵉ covnty of
Kent esqᴿ : who dyed ye 11 day of Ivne
Anno Domini 1616.

et Ætatis Svæ 22ᴰᴼ

1. In situ - Horsfield (*Sussex* I 227) and Lambarde (*SAC* 71 146) noting arms.
2. Perhaps once floor-mounted.

Chailey, 49I Mural monument for George GORING, d. 1728, his wife and children [Plate 39]
- Chancel South wall, above head height.
- 75(W) x 155(H) — Good; colour losses.
- M.I. (13 lines, shallow engraved, black) on a rectangular, unframed panel; on base, foliate relief decorated; above, broken pointed pediment in grey; achievement.
- George Goring, Esq., of Eades, d. 3 Jan 1728, aet 58; his wife, Elizabeth, d. 17 Jun 1737, aet 63; daughter of Gabriel Egles, of Copwood, Esq.; their issue - Mary, d. 8 Aug 1745, aet 42; Elizabeth, d. 25 May 1705, infant; Martha, d. 8 Feb 1762, aet 55; (another) Elizabeth, d. 1 Jan 1733, aet 25; George, d. May 1711, infant; Dorothy, d. 14 Jul 1752, aet 39; no issue from any of them.

1. In situ - Horsfield (*Sussex* I 227) and Lambarde (*SAC* 71 146) noting arms.
2. 8 members of the family d. 1705-62; for licence to marry dated 30 Dec 1701 for George Goring and Elizabeth Egles, see Dunkin (*Licences 1670-1729* 313).
3. As is 49E, 49I is carefully shaped to fit its current location, or one similar.
4. Perhaps erected in the 1760s.

(50) CHALVINGTON, St. Bartholomew
Early English windows in nave; Decorated windows in chancel - Nairn & Pevsner (470); condition reported to be very good in 1724 report (Ford); view of church by Lambert BL Add. MS 5676 f.60.

Chalvington, 50A Mural monument for John Trayton FULLER, d. 1811 [Plate 40]
- Chancel, South wall, at head height.
- 67(W) x 80(H) — Generally excellent; 1 crack; faded.
- M.I. (6 lines, engraved, black, 1 corrected digit) on an unframed white marble tablet set landscape-wise; cornice and base mouldings in veined grey marble; 2 corbels with paterae decoration.
- John Trayton Fuller, Esq., of Ashdown House, d. 26 Mar 1811, aet 68.

1. The final engraved digit of '1811' has been corrected from '1812', reflecting uncertainty about the first day of the new year.
2. 50A is pendant with a slightly later monument in the same church to Fuller's wife, the Hon. Anne, daughter of Lord Heathfield, d. 24 Feb 1835, aged 81, for whom a hatchment also hangs in the church.
3. For Fuller's 1785 land tax payments at Chalvington, see R. Davey 53.

(56) CHIDDINGLY, Parish Church

Early English aisles; chancel, rebuilt in 1864 - Nairn & Pevsner (471); Vidal (*SAC* 18 186-7), see 46F. Engraved external views of church from North-West in Lower (*SAC* 14 207), (BL Add. MS 5671 ff.41-2; 5677 f.50). State of repair reported as fine in 1686; in 1724, it was reported that John Fuller of Rose Hill will repair the chancel ceiling and that the South wing windows belong to Mr Henry Pelham and need repair (Ford); 1724 report (Ford). The Sackvilles held the manor in our period, but were commemorated at Withyham (302). Chiddingly Place was not a prominent gentry residence for long, soon degenerating into a neglected tenanted farm. In 1634, the whole Jefferay inheritance in Sussex was sold for £8300 to Sir Thomas Pelham of Laughton (C Whittick in *ODNB* on Sir John Jefferay). However, the church contains a very distinguished set of 17th-century monuments to the Jefferays in their different branches, including those from Sir John Jefferay's two wives, e.g. 56L-M.

Chiddingly, 56A Ledger for Sara PILBEAM, d. 1692
- North aisle floor, just inside North porch.
- 50(W) x 99(L) — Pitted; worn.
- M.I. (engraved) on pale freestone slab; head to West.

HE[RE] LYETH

AT[...] EAM

... DIE[D] IUNE ...

1. Transcribed by Lower (*SAC* 14 245), in situ.
2. Sara Pilbeam, d. 2 Jun 1692, age unknown, her sister Wicks.

Chiddingly, 56B Ledger for James PILBEAM, d. 1728
- Nave floor, centre, opposite North door.
- 87(W) x 144(L) — Pitted; worn.
- M.I. (engraved) on black slab.

Here Lieth Interr'd ...

Body of IAMES PILBEA[M]

of this Parifh. Son of

[R]ICHARD & ELIZA PILBEA[M]

Late of Wiver[sfiel]d ...

... who De[parte]d

... ye ...

... 31 year ...

...d ... bo ...

ELIZABETH ...

aged ...

1. Transcribed by Lower (*SAC* 14 245): in situ.
2. James Pilbeam, d. 9 Apr 17-8, aet 31; his mother, Elizabeth d. 3 May 1757, aet 83.
3. Slab looks early 18th century?
4. For licence to marry dated 29 Apr 1690 for Richard Pilbeam, of Chiddingly, Gent. and Elizabeth Plummer, of Ripe, see Dunkin (*Licences 1670-1729* 123).
5. NBI records burial of James Pilbeam on 13 Apr 1728 at Chiddingly.

Chiddingly, 56C Mural monument for Richard JEFFERAY, d. 1600

- Nave, East end, on North-East pier, facing West, above head height.
- 72(W) x 100(H) — Fine; pigment traces.
- In alabaster; M.I. (engraved) on slate panel with arched top; above, a cherub; to sides, Death's heads and delicate ribbon work in relief; below, base mouldings and brackets; on the cornice, an achievement.

IN THE
CHANCELL OF THIS
CHVRCH LYETH BVRIED THE
BODY OF RICHARD IEFFERAY OF
SOVTH MALLING ESQ: SOLE BROTHER
TO Sʳ JOHN IEFFERAY LO: CHIEF BARON.
HE MARIED MARJERIE DAVGHTER OF IO:
HVMPHRY OF WARWICK ESQ & WIDOWE
OF RICHARD KEYME BY WHOME HE HAD
ISSVE FRA: HIS ONLY SONNE MARIED TO
ELIZ: MAYNEY ONE OF THE DAVGHTEʳˢ &
COHEIRES OF WALTER MAYNEY OF KENT
ESQ: & 2 DAVGHTʳˢ MARGARET MARIED TO
EDWARD MASCALL OF PLOMPTON GENT:
AND ALICE MARIED TO IOHN GARDINER
OF RATCLIFFE NEERE LONDON GENT: HE
DYED THE 13 DAY OF DECEMBʳ IN Yᴱ YEARE
1600: & THE 72 OF HIS AGE.
EXPECTO DONEC VENIAT IMMVTATIO MEA IOB..14
FRANCIS IEFFERAY FILIVS EIVS VNIC PATRI
SVO HOC MONVMENTVM POSVIT ANᴺᴼ 161[?]2

1. In situ - Lower (*SAC* 14 222 & 241) and in Lambarde (*SAC* 70 153) noting arms.
2. One Margaret Keymer, possibly daughter of Marjorie Jeffrey by her first marriage, licensed to marry on 15 Oct 1613, see Dunkin (*Licences 1586-1643* 88).
3. A ledger, perhaps for Richard Jefferay, was found during 1864 restoration, see Vidal 'Chiddingly Church' (*SAC* 18 187); Richard Jefferay was of nearby South Malling, a brother of the great Judge, Sir John Jefferay (see 56L); 56C was erected by Richard Jefferay's heir, is dated 1612 [?] and has decorative work of high quality; it is certainly London-made.
4. Esdaile (*SAC* 82 103) - often too optimistic on this point - suggests it is by E. Evesham (along with 56D and J).
5. For the undated monument of Elizabeth Jefferay, the patron of 56C see 212L at Ringmer.

Chiddingly, 56D Mural monument for Margaret JEFFERAY, dated 1620 [Plate 41]

- Choir, North wall, above head height.
- 141(W) x 99(H) — Fine; some local losses below; pigment traces remain.
- Alabaster; above, 2 angels seated on scrollwork, flank a very large urn with a wreath on top and bearing a motto; below, 2 very small slate M.I. panels; between them, a cherub's head and keys on a ring; to sides, bright blue inlaid lozenge decorative.

(On urn)
MARGARITA FVI
(left)
IN MEMORY OF MARGARITE ELDEST
DAVGHʳ OF RICHᴰ MOSELEY OF OVSDEᴺ:
HAIL IN Yᴱ COVʸ OF SVFFOLKE. ESQ
& WIFE VNTO THOˢ IEFFERAY SONE
& HEIRE OF WILLIAᴹ IEFFERAY OF THIS
PᴿISH GENT: TO WHOM (BEING 3 YEAˢ
MARRIED) SHE LEFT ISSVE TWO
DAVGHʳˢ LETTICE & MARGARITE
Fflesh is but fflesh: the fairest flowers do fall:
the strongest stoope: Death is the end of all.

(right)
...Gem[m]a jacet, prudens, pia, pulchra, pudica
Ante diemqᵉ cadens Inclyta Gemma iacet
Corporis Hæc quamqu[am]. cineres habet Vrna repostos
Maris super Astra tamen non peritura manet
OBIJT 8ᵛᵒ DIE SEPTEⁱˢ ANᵒ SALVT
1618 ÆTATIS SVÆ 25
Chariſsimæ Coniugis memoriæ pijqᵉ Amoris
ergo posuit mæstifsimus Maritvs
Anno 1620

1. In situ (despite rebuilding of chancel); noted by Horsfield (*Sussex* I 356-7) with poor transcription, describing as Mergerie; Nairn & Pevsner (471); Lower (*SAC* 14 221-2 & 243-4) with an account of Thomas Jefferay, d. 1663 and of 56D (inaccurate transcription); Lambarde (*SAC* 70 152) noting arms, which do not now exist.
2. Attributed by Esdaile (*SAC* 82 103) to E. Evesham (with 56C and 56J).
3. 56D, highly unusual for the urn in the centre of the composition and for the use of coloured inlaid hardstone, commemorates a daughter of Richard Mosley (d.1630), whose first wife, Laetitia (d. 1619) is commemorated in a monument at Ousden, Suffolk, similar in telling ways to 56D.

Chiddingly, 56E Mural monument for Stephen FRENCH, d. 1666 [Plate 42]
- Sanctuary, North wall.
- 80(W) x 180(H) — Fine; pigment lost.
- An oval panel in slate with M.I.; otherwise alabaster; wreathed border; base moulding; skulls in corners; above, broken pediment with highly ambitious scrolls and large coloured achievement.
- Stephen French, d. 23 Jun 1666, aet 41 (or 43); eldest son John French, Esq., of Stream, and Anne, eldest daughter of John Sackville, Esq., of Selscombe; his wife, Susan, second daughter of Sir Robert Foster, Knt., of Fosters, Egham, Surrey; their issue - Anne, Elizabeth, John (died and buried at Wadham College, Oxford), Mary, Susan, Charity and Katherine (died in infancy).

1. In situ Lambarde (*SAC* 70 153).
2. There was a ledger to Stephen French and his wife in the chancel; he was b 1623; his wife d. 16 Mar 1695, aet 76.
3. The French family had been ironmasters at Stream (at the North-East end of Chiddingly parish) since 1540, and were related by marriage to the Bromfields, see 56F and Lower (*SAC* 14 228).
4. Erected by widow and daughters after 1666.
5. The daughter Elizabeth is commemorated by 56G.

Chiddingly, 56F Wall monument for John BROMFIELD, d. 1735/6
- Sanctuary, against South wall.
- 188(W) x 308(H: including base) — Excellent.
- Marble; white panel with grey-veined surround of fluted Doric pilasters, a frieze with triglyphs and a broken pediment with escutcheon and an urn in centre and flaming lamps flanking; generous panelled basement; M.I. panel (engraved, black lines in 5 blocks, from top: (i) and (ii) commemoration of parents, (iii) patronage, (iv) commemoration of daughter, (v) commemoration of son; below M.I., base moulding.
- John Bromfield, d. 30 Jan 1735/6, aet 52; his wife, Elizabeth, d. 6 Nov 1734, aet 42, daughter of John Weekes, Esq., of Westfield, Sussex; their issue - Elizabeth d. Jan 1790, aet 62, buried St. Anne's, Lewes, and John d. 30 Jan 1792, aet 65.

1. In situ Lambarde (*SAC* 70 153) arms noted, but shield now blank.
2. Chancel was rebuilt in 1864 when 56F was moved West of the piscina, see Vidal (*SAC* 18 186).
3. Nairn & Pevsner (471) regard it as typical of architectural monuments of the 1730s, however, since the patrons were the orphaned Bromfield children, 56F was probably erected well after the deaths of the parents, perhaps even after John Bromfield (also buried here) acquired property locally.
4. The Bromfields were also of Udimore (see 265) and related by marriage to the French family (see

56E); see also Lower (*SAC* 14 229).

5. There is a hatchment in chancel for Thomas Bromfield (d.1710) and his wife Ann, eldest daughter of Stephen French. See Summers (136).

6. The flames of the flanking lamps might be additions, in another material [terracotta?].

Chiddingly, 56G Ledger for Elizabeth FRENCH, d. 1718

- Choir floor, East end, against altar rail.
- 101 square — Worn but legible, North side damaged.
- M.I. (7 lines, engraved) in upper part of a slab; head to West.
- Elizabeth French, d. 10 Sep 1718, aet 72; second daughter of Stephen French, Esq., of Stream and his wife, Susannah.

1. 56G-I commemorating issue of Stephen and Susanna French (see 56E).

Chiddingly, 56H Ledger for Anne and Thomas BROMFIELD, d. 1697/8 and 1710/1

- Choir floor, centre.
- 100(W) x 199(L) — Fine; cracks in East side.
- M.I.s (8 + 6 lines) either side of an escutcheon, fills surface of a black slab; head to West.
- Anne Bromfield, d. 19 Jan 1697/8; eldest daughter of Stephen French, Esq., and Susanna; and wife of Thomas Bromfield, Esq., of Lewes, d. 27 Jan 1710/1, aet 73, of Lewes; their issue - 2 sons.

1. 56G-I commemorating issue of Stephen and Susanna French (see 56E).

2. M.I. for Thomas Bromfield presumably added later, perhaps explaining the variant spellings of Lewes / Liwis?

3. JH notes the large coat of arms in centre of ledger – see Lambarde (*SAC* 70 153) for incomplete description. See also Summers (36-7).

Chiddingly, 56I Ledger for Mary FRENCH, d. 1695/6

- Choir floor, West end.
- 100(W) x 200(L) — Worn; legible.
- M.I. (6 lines, engraved) in upper 30% of a black slab; head to West.
- Mary French, d. 10 Mar 1695/6, third daughter of Stephen French, Esq., and Susanna, of Stream.

1. 56G-I commemorating issue of Stephen and Susanna French 56E. 56I noted in Lower (*SAC* 14 244), in situ.

Chiddingly, 56J Ledger for William JEFFERAY, d. 1611

- Nave floor, centre, extreme East end.
- 69(W) x 162(L) — Cracked; very worn.
- M.I. (6 + 6 lines, engraved, Latin) at ends of black slab with blank centre; engraved head to West.

Svb Hoc Marmore iacet ...
Gvlielimi Iefferay Generos.. vt
AMPLI ...
MONVMENTO ...
...IVI ECCLESI ...
Ivxta hoc ...
IACET ...VXOR
THO...HEREDIS
IPSI ... MONVMENTV^M
EXT ... ECCLESI[Æ]

.. PDICT .. THO. IEFFERAY POSV^T

1. For William Jefferay's monument see 56M, also set up by Thomas Jefferay, his son.

Chiddingly, 56K Ledger for Margaret SMITH, d. 1731

- Nave floor, centre, towards East end.
- 99(W) x 106(L) — Very worn; almost illegible.
- M.I. (8 lines, engraved) in upper part of very large freestone. slab; head to West.

<blockquote>
Here lies Interred the Body
of Margarett Smith widdow
late of Thunders Hill in
this parifh, fifter to the
faid Thomas and William
Thunder, who departed
this life the 31st day a [sic] March
1731 in the 76 year of her Age
</blockquote>

1. In situ; transcribed by Lower (*SAC* 14 245).

Chiddingly, 56L Wall monument for Sir John JEFFERAY, d. 1578, and descendants, dated 1612 [Plates 43 & 44]

- South transept, South wall, facing North.
- 332(W); (H) inaccessible — Recently (1996) restored; local losses to figures.
- In alabaster and other decorative stones; standing effigies in arched niches, the female figure (right) with 1 foot on a skull, flanking recumbent figures above a kneeling figure; above, a semi-circular hood over a M.I. on slate; at top, arms; flanking, personifications of Toil and Rest; beyond, more arms; railing now raised on a wooden plinth.
- Sir John Jefferay, Knt., Lord Chief Baron of the Exchequer, d. 23 May 1578; his first wife Alice Apsley (dates not given), sole daughter of John Apsley, Gent., of London; their only issue - Elizabeth, d. 6 Dec 1611; Elizabeth's husband Sir Edward Montagu, Knt., of Boughton, Northamptonshire; their issue - also Elizabeth, wife of Rt. Hon. Sir Robert Bertie, Lord Willoughby; their issue - Montagu, Roger, Peregrine and Katherine.

1. In situ; noted in Lower (*SAC* 14 222-4 with engraving p.227); Sperling 'Jefferay Monument, Chiddingly' (*SAC* 18 193-4, arms); Lambarde (*SAC* 70 153-4) noting arms; J.G. Mann, 'English Church Monuments, 1535-1625', (Walpole Society XXI 1932-3 17); Nairn & Pevsner (471), for the rarity of standing figures.
2. In poor condition by 1812 (Horsfield *Sussex* I 357), remaining so until recently (Esdaile *ECM* 106).
3. The South transept was rebuilt to receive this massive monument erected by John Jefferay's son-in-law, at the request of his (late) daughter. The patronage explains the prominence of the younger generation with John Jefferay's grand-daughter at the very front (in Horsfield's day the child's effigy was broken in two – see illustration In 1835 I 356-7). Standing figures on 17th-century monuments are rare (c.f. with that in the Willoughby chapel, at Spilsby, Lincolnshire).
4. The 19 lines on the M.I. of 56L must always have been very hard to read.
5. The authorship of 56L is uncertain; Esdaile (*ECM* 106 *EMS* 42) suggests both William Cure II on the grounds of the similarity of its figure carving to Cure's signed and documented Queen Anne of Denmark at Trinity Great Gate (Cambridge) and Garret Johnson, comparing it with Lady Lucy Stanley, c.1630, Walthamstow; Sir Edward Montague, part-patron of 56L, later employed Cure on the documented monument to Bishop Montague at Bath (1618); White rejects the attribution of 56L to Cure (45, 65-70) and to Garret Johnson II (73).
6. There were IPMs for John Jefferay, late Chief Baron of the Exchequer, one at Battle in Jan and another at Lewes in Aug an. reg. 22 Elizabeth I; his daughter and heir was Elizabeth Jefferay, aet 15 at his death (Salzman *Inquisitions* 118ff, Holgate 18).
7. 56L has been the subject of gossip and superstition: Mosse (pp. 47-51) notes that it was abused because ignorant individuals thought it commemorated the infamous Judge Jefferies, scourge of Protestants, a reflection of local sensitivities about the protestant martyrs of the 16th century.
8. By way of reaching a ridiculous explanation for the flanking figure pedestals, some have described the family as so proud that they should walk on cheeses not on the ground. See Lower (*SAC* 14 243).
9. JH notes that Sir John Jefferay was MP for Clitheroe, Lancashire, 1563; East Grinstead 1571; and Sussex in 1572. His first wife was Alice Apsley (d. 1570) and his second wife (married c.1576) was Mary, daughter of George Goring of Ovingdean. See biography by Christopher Whittick in *ODNB* and Hasler (2 374-5).

Chiddingly, 56M Mural monument for William JEFFERAY and his wife Awdray, dated 1612

- South aisle, South wall, near South transept, at head height.
- 92(W) x 186(H) — Restorations to left pilaster and elsewhere; gilding remains.
- In alabaster, marble and slate; an achievement on a cornice; below, a pair of shallow arches with a prayer-desk and male and female kneeling figures to left and right (2 adults, 2 sons, 2 daughters); framed M.I. panel between heavy moulded shelves.
- William Jefferay, Gent., d. 29 Oct 1611, aet 68; his wife, Awdray, sole daughter of Thomas Harvey, of London; their issue - 2 sons and 7 daughters living; first son Thomas.

1. Originally located on right of chancel arch, opposite 56D. See Lower (*SAC* 14 221).
2. In situ by 1928 Lambarde (*SAC* 70 154) noting arms; noted by Mosse; Nairn & Pevsner (471) and Esdaile (*SAC* 82 103) as by Evesham (together with 56C-D).
3. The contrast in scale with 56L is telling.
4. William Jefferay's family were a parallel, Peaks, branch of the Jefferays of 56L; William Jefferay was brother to Thomas, see 56D and Lower (*SAC* 14 221).
5. The patron of 56M seems to been the son and heir, Thomas Jefferay (see 56D).
6. Figures of some daughters have perhaps been lost?

Chiddingly, 56N Ledger for Thomas THUNDER, d. 1710

- Centre of nave floor, towards West end.
- 93(W) x 186(L) — Extremely worn.
- M.I. (11 lines, engraved) fill freestone slab; head to West.
- Illegible.

1. 56N is in situ and transcribed by Lower (*SAC* 14 24); noted in Horsfield (*Sussex* I 356-7).
2. Thomas Thunder, late of Thunder's Hill, d. 3 Mar 1710, aet 60; his brother William, d. ?? Dec 1703, age unknown; Thomas Thunder was presented for non-payment of church tax in the mid 1670s, see Johnstone (6).

Chiddingly, 56O Ledger for Rev. Thomas BAKER, d. 1795

- Centre of nave floor, towards West end, West of 56N.
- 101(W) x 169(L) — Very good.
- M.I. (7 + 8 lines, engraved) biography and epitaph, fill black slab, head to West.
- Rev. Thomas Baker, vicar of Chiddingly and Alciston, d. 29 Dec 1795, aet 62.

1. Baker was a poet (*Poem on the Winter Season*), cited by Lower (*SAC* 14 252) who transcribed the M.I.
2. A splendid ledger, similar to 56P.
3. JH notes that Rev. Thomas Baker was vicar of Chiddingly 1777-95, and of Alciston 1781-95, see Hennessy (20, 29).

Chiddingly, 56P Ledger for Thomas EADES, d. 1717

- Centre of nave floor, far West end.
- 103(W) x 199(L) — Very worn.
- M.I. (10 lines, engraved) in upper 30% of black slab; head to West.

The body of Mr Thomas Eades lies here.
A faithful shepherd that did not pow'rs fear;
But kept old Truth, And would not let her go,
Nor turn out of the way for Friend or foe.
Who was Suspended in the Dutchman's days,
Because he would not walk in their Strang ways.
Dæmona non armis sed morte subegit Iefus.
As Christ by death his Rampant foes troddon.
So must all those who doe expect a crown.
He Died 1717, Aged about 80 Years

1. Eades refused the Oath of Allegiance to William and Mary and was deprived of his living Lower (*SAC* 14 251).
2. Similar to 56O. .
3. NBI records burial of Thomas Eades on 13 Feb 1718 at Chiddingly.

Chiddingly, 56Q Mural monument for Rev. John HERRING, d. 1776
- North Porch, West wall, facing East, at head height.
- 99(W) x 79(H) — Fine; moss staining.
- In grey-white marble; M.I. (4 lines, engraved) in upper 30% of grey freestone slab with a moulded top; 2 simple corbels.
- Rev. John Herring, vicar of Chiddingly for 28 years, d. 28 Dec 1776, aet 67.

1. Noted by Lower (*SAC* 14 251).
2. John Herring introduced the potato into this part of Sussex (Church Guide).

Chiddingly Additions
Reported by Lower (*SAC* 14 245), using Burrell notes taken Jun 1783:
(1) French Bromfeild, Esq., first son of Thomas Bromfeild, of Lewes, d. 11 Nov 1719, aet 52 (chancel).
(2) Ann Bromfeild, d. 19 Jan 1697, wife of Thomas, first daughter of Stephen French and Susannah (chancel).
(3) Thomas Bromfeild, of Lewes, d. 27 Jan 1710, aet 73; his wife Ann, daughter of Stephen and Susanna French (chancel), also in Lambarde (*SAC* 70 153).
(4) Elizabeth French, d. ?? Sep ????, second daughter of Stephen French (chancel).
(5) Susanna, d. 21 Jun 1709, aet 56, fourth daughter of Stephen French (chancel).
Church Guide following Lower (*SAC* 14 207-258).
(6) Brasses for 16th-century members of Jefferay family, e.g. William, of Peke's House, father of William d. 1611, perhaps marked by matrices under sanctuary carpet and near sanctuary step.

(61) CLAYTON, St. John the Baptist
11th-century core; chancel largely 19th century - Nairn & Pevsner (472-3); see plan in *SNQ* (III 187) with monuments marked; views of church in BL Add. MS 5672 f.33; 5677 f.48; condition reported to be fine in 1724 (Ford); floor slabs now inaccessible due to carpeting.

Clayton, 61A Ledger for John PARKER, d. 1691
- Nave floor, East end, at chancel step, inaccessible beneath carpet.
- 84(W) x 163(L) — (Assumed) fine.
- (Reported) M.I. (engraved) in a freestone slab.

> Hic requiescit in Spem Poelæ
> [R]esurrectionis per D. g. Christum
> Depositum Johannis Parker. A.M.
> Hujus Ecclesiæ Rectoris
> Liberalib. Parentibus nati
> In maritimis Septentrion
> Lancastriæ
> munus susceptum exercuit
> Strenue & adornavit
> Atrophia tandem languescens
> Probis & eruditis charus,
> Sancte animam Deo
> resignavit Decembr. 28. 1691
> Ætatis Suæ 49

1. Cited by Horsfield (*Sussex* I 241): as before the Communion Table; in situ on plan in *SNQ* (III 187).
2. John Parker was incumbent at Keymer/Clayton 1683-91 and also vicar of Ditchling 1674-1691 (Church Guide).

Clayton, 61B Mural monument for Samuel BETHELL, d. 1803
- Sanctuary, East wall, North of East window, above head height.
- 94(W) x 140(H) — Very good; discolouring.
- Backplate, formerly painted black; an oval tablet set portrait-wise; urn on top; below, moulded corbels.
- Samuel Bethel, A.M., rector of Clayton, d. 5 Apr 1803, aet 47; his virtues.

1. In situ - Horsfield (*Sussex* I 241), SNQ (III 187), see photograph in Leeney (*SAC* 87 190).
2. Lettering suggests that engraved marks were filled first with red ground, then blacked.

Clayton, 61C Mural monument for Ann LUXFORD, d. 1729 [Plate 45]
- Chancel, South wall, above head height.
- 73(W) x 210(H) — Fine; fading.
- A scrolled frame; moulded plaster garlands; (double) cartouche painted in ochre; M.I. (painted not engraved); above, achievement; above that, painted escutcheon; at foot, cherub carved in freestone.
- Ann Luxford, d. 21 Oct 1729, aet 67; daughter of John Luxford of Ockley.

1. In situ - Horsfield (*Sussex* I 241), Lambarde (*SAC* 71 149) noting arms and SNQ (III 187).
2. A moulded version of the stylish London-made cartouche starting to appear in Sussex in the 1720s, e.g. at Streat.
3. Luxfords are prominent elsewhere in East Sussex.
4. JH notes that Horsfield (*Sussex* 1 241) says that she married John Watson, then Lawrence Price, both rectors of this parish. There are entries in the Sussex Marriage Index (1689 and 1715) to confirm this. It seems odd that the memorial is in her maiden name.

Clayton Additions
Located on plan in SNQ (III 187) and/or cited in Horsfield (*Sussex* I 241):
(1) Elizabeth Salter, 1765, centre nave, towards West.
(2) Mrs Ellen Morris, sister of James (see 7), 4 Feb 1785,aet 62, centre nave, East of (1).
(3) Rev. Lawrence Price, rector, 18 Jun 1752, chancel floor, against North wall.
(4) Rev. John Watson, rector, 22 Jul 1715, aet 55, chancel floor, South-East corner.
(5) Slab for Rev. Samuel Bethell, rector, 1803, chancel floor, North-East corner.
(6) Susanna Bethell d. 8 Oct 1804, aet 85, mother of Samuel Bethell see 61B.
(7) Rev. James Morris, d. 23 Jul 1793, aet 74.
(8) Sarah Morris, wife of James, d. 21 Nov 1777, aet 65.
Also, in Horsfield (*Sussex* I 241).
(9) Richard Idon, parson of Clayton and Pykeen (Pyecombe), d. 1573.

(69) CRAWLEY, St. John
For a view of the old church seen in rural isolation from the North-East see Godfrey & Salzman (Pl. 49) (BL Add. MS 5673 f.58); in 1724 it was reported that the condition of the church was poor (Ford) and except for the tower it was thoroughly restored and the North aisle added in 1879-80 - Hannah (*SAC* 55 4-11) and Nairn & Pevsner (202); Horsfield (*Sussex* I 263-5) does not cite any post-medieval M.I.s at Crawley.

Crawley, 69A Mural monument for Robert GALLUP, d. 1815 and Henry GALLUP, d. 1823
- Nave, West wall, North of tower arch, above head height.
- 63(W) x 51(H) — Very good.
- M.I. (10 lines, engraved, black) fill an unframed, oval white marble plaque, metal clasp above; tiny stone corbel.
- Robert Gallup, naval officer (East India Company), d. 8 Dec 1815, aet 22; son of Robert

and Sarah Gallup, of Poynings, Sussex; his brother, Henry, surgeon, d. 5 Mar 1823, aet 24.

1. Noted as located in the nave by Ellman (*SAC* 24 301).

Crawley, 69B Mural monument for John BROADWOOD, d. 1812

- Nave, South wall, near chancel, high.
- 115(W) x 180(H) — Very good.
- M.I. (engraved, black) on a white marble tablet set portrait-wise; moulded cornice and escutcheon on pointed pediment; decorated corbels; black baseplate with point top; signed (right corbel): 'PATENT WORKS / ESHER ST. WESTMINSTER'.
- John Broadwood, Esq., 6 Oct 1732 - 17 Jul 1812; his wife, Mary, 17 Feb 1752 - 15 Jun 1839; their son, Thomas Broadwood of Holmbush.

1. Noted in the nave by Ellman (*SAC* 24 301).
2. An enormous ledger of the 1840s[?] in the chancel near to 69B commemorates its patron, Thomas Broadwood, and many other family members (the piano makers).
3. The biography by Charles Mould in *ODNB* makes no mention of 69B or the Broadwood ownership of the Holmbush estate.
4. John Broadwood was from a Scottish family of cabinet makers; working as an apprentice in London in the 1760s; first marriage was to Barbara Shudi (d. aet 27 in 1776), leaving three children to be brought up; second marriage, in 1781, was to Mary Kitson; a further six children between 1782 - 1793.
5. In 1795, Broadwood took his son James Shudi Broadwood (1772–1851) into partnership, making the firm John Broadwood & Son (by this time devoted wholly to the pianoforte); and when another son, Thomas, entered the partnership in 1807, it became John Broadwood & Sons.
6. The makers of 69B have also signed the nearby monument to Rev. Spencer James Lewin who was rector of Ifield and Crawley.
7. See Lambarde (*SAC* 69 209) noting arms.

Crawley Additions
Noted by Ellman (*SAC* 24 301-2):
(1) Michaell Martin d. 15 Dec 1642, buried 21 Dec 1642 (floor slab), see too Hannah (*SAC* 55 11).

(70) CROWBOROUGH - no monuments found

(71) CROWHURST, St. George
A late 13th-century church in fine condition in 1724 (Ford) largely rebuilt by Teulon in 1794 - Nairn & Pevsner (476-77), Horsfield (*Sussex* I 434) and views BL Add. MS 5676 f.25-6; 5670 f.32; Crowhurst, St. George was the site of an ancient Pelham manor; 71B-C are from the old church.

Crowhurst, 71A Mural monument for Anne HARDINGE, d. 1819
- Over North door, behind organ, above head height.
- 55(W) x 95(H) — Very good.
- M.I. (17 lines, engraved, black) on white marble panel of scrolled parchment form, thin black slate baseplate with pointed top; signed (lower right): 'T.SHARP. SC / 50 CONNAUGHT TERRACE / HYDE PARK, LONDON'.
- Anne Hardinge, d. 1819, aet 26; eldest daughter of Thomas Papillon, Esq., of Acrise, Kent and Anne, daughter of Henry Pelham, Esq., of Crowhurst Park; in 1815 she married her husband, Richard Hardinge, Esq., Royal Artillery, brother of 1st Viscount Hardinge; issue (2) – Henry, Frances Anne.

1. In situ; see Gunnis (*Dict.* 349) - by Thomas Sharpe (1805-?).
2. Patron - probably Henry Pelham, for a granddaughter.
3. See Foster (*Peerage* 308).

Crowhurst, 71B Ledger for Elizabeth MARTEN, d. 1706
- On nave floor, against wall, near North door, behind the organ.
- 55(W) x 95(L) — Worn; restored.
- M.I. (6 lines, engraved and black) in upper 50% of a freestone slab; head to East.

> Here lies yᵉ body
> of Eliza yᵉ daugh
> ter of Mʳ Thomas
> Marten who died
> Feb 17ᵗʰ 1706
> *Aged 19 months*

1. Perhaps formerly in the nave where Horsfield (*Sussex* I 434) noted Marten slabs.

Crowhurst, 71C Anonymous ledger, 18ᵗʰ century?
- Nave floor, near North door, next to 71B, partly obscured by flooring.
- 82(W) x 179(L) — Very worn.
- M.I. (engraved) on black slab of oolitic freestone; head to East.

> ... of his age ...

1. Horsfield (*Sussex* I 434): notes on a flat stone 'Hic jacet Matthæus ... Hujus Ecclesiæ rector obit Sept. 1705, æt 70' which seems not to reconcile with 71C as found.
2. JH notes that Matthew Wing was vicar here from 1666 until 1705, when he died - Hennessy (55) and NBI.

Crowhurst, 71D Mural monument for Jeremiah DYSON, d. 1813 [Plate 46]
- Chancel, South wall, above head height.
- 92(W) x 48(H) — Very good; fading.
- A striking mottled grey rectangular baseplate; M.I. (7 lines, engraved, centred, black, English and Latin) in marble, in the form of a draped cloth with tasselled fringes; signed (lower right): 'HENRY WESTMACOTT LONDON'.
- Jeremiah Dyson, Esq., Junr., of Twickenham, Middlesex, died at Hastings, 6 Jan 1813, aet 31.

1. In situ - Horsfield (*Sussex* I 434); cited by Gunnis (*Dict.* 422).
2. Henry Westmacott was the brother of the better-known Sir Richard Westmacott.
3. Was Dyson buried at Crowhurst through a link with the Pelhams?

(72) CUCKFIELD, Holy Trinity
Mostly c.1330, restored by Bodley in 1855-56, Nairn & Pevsner (477-78); views of church and Sergison monument in BL Add. MS 5677 f.56; 5672 ff.31-5; 12555.a-f; groundplan and monuments list see *SNQ* (IV 15-17); the spaces without the rails and in the middle aisle were newly paved in 1715, see J. Cooper (*SAC* 50 17) and the church flooring was relaid in 1927, see J. Cooper 'Notes and Queries - Cuckfield' (*SAC* 69 231); a church report of 1724 noted that the building was in good condition (Ford); the Sergisons of Cuckfield (see 72A, etc.) were Tory opponents of the Pelham/Newcastle Whig faction in the 1730s; for the Sergison/Warden pedigree see Lower (*SAC* 25 84); Horsfield (*Sussex* I 254) notes the Burrell monuments in the South aisle.

Cuckfield, 72A Mural monument for Mary Ann SERGISON, d. 1804
- High over North door.
- 90(W) x 180(H) — Very good; fading.
- Against a tall unframed trapezoidal white baseplate, a female figure mourns over an urn on a pedestal; above, a shallow pointed pediment with a small escutcheon and palmettes flanking; below, a M.I. (engraved) tablet set landscape-wise with a moulded border, on 2

acanthus brackets; signed (on underside): 'WESTMACOTT A.R.A. SCULPTOR'.
- Mary Ann Sergison, d. 11 Sep 1804, aet 36; eldest daughter of William Kerr, Esq., M.D., of Northampton; and wife of Warden Sergison, Esq., of Butlers Green, Cuckfield, Lt. Col. (Horse Guards).

1. In situ - Horsfield (*Sussex* I 254), *SNQ* (IV 15-17), cited in Lower (*SAC* 25 226), Gunnis (*Dict.* 426) and Nairn & Pevsner (478).
2. Warden Sergison was taxed on Butler's Green in the East of the parish in 1785 (R. Davey, 62).
3. Patron of 72A was presumably Mary Ann's husband, Warden Sergison d. 1811.
4. Richard Westmacott was 'A.R.A.' only 1805-11.

Cuckfield, 72B Mural monument for Daniel WALTER, d. 1761
- North nave aisle, near North door.
- 110(W) x 278(H) — Very good; local losses (base moulding left).
- M.I. tablet (Latin, engraved) set portrait-wise; flanked by grey Doric pilasters; above, an entablature, cornice and scrolled achievement; below, a thick, dark base mould, then scrolled brackets flanking another M.I. tablet in apron with winged cherub as finial.
- Daniel Walter, A.M., vicar of Cuckfield, etc., d. 8 Apr 1761, aet 81; his wife, Dorothy, daughter of Thomas Manningham, bishop of Chichester, buried Holborn.

1. Appears to be in situ - *SNQ* (IV 15-17); noted and part-transcribed by J. Cooper (*SAC* 50 15-17); Lambarde (*SAC* 69 203, noting arms.
2. A ledger commemorating Daniel Walter, formerly behind the altar at Cuckfield, was taken to Chichester and installed in the cloister there in 1861.
3. Patrons of 72B were the 3 children Daniel, Elizabeth and Mary.
4. Note the good quality carving of the cherub.
5. JH notes that Daniel Walter was vicar of Cuckfield 1713-61; prebendary of Wisborough in Chichester Cathedral 1713-46; precentor of the Cathedral 1719-61; and canon residentiary 1751-61.

Cuckfield, 72C Mural monument for Francis WARDEN, d. 1785
- North nave aisle, East of 72B, partly obscured by wooden ceiling.
- 180(W) x 330(H) — Generally good; fading; local losses to upper garlands.
- M.I. on a white rectangular marble tablet within acanthus pilasters with rosette capitals and skulls as corbels; below, narrow base moulding; above, gadroon moulding and moulded cornice supporting a dark grey obelisk on 2 ball finials; on the obelisk, a white achievement with festoons and an urn.
- Francis Warden, Esq., of Butler's Green, Cuckfield, magistrate, d. 1785, aet 84.

1. In situ - Lambarde (*SAC* 69 203) noting arms; *SNQ* (IV 15); transcribed in Lower (*SAC* 25 83).
2. Francis Warden was only son of John Warden, and his second wife Hopestill, his property, Cuckfield Place, passed to Francis Sergison (see Cuckfield Additions 3) in 1785 (R. Davey 59).
3. High quality carving of skulls.
4. NBI records burial of Francis Warden on 6 Jan 1785 at Cuckfield.

Cuckfield, 72D Mural monument for Michael and Sarah SERGISON, d. 1784 and 1771
- North aisle wall, near East end, above head height.
- 88(W) s 208(H) — Generally very good; some fading.
- M.I. on an oval white marble tablet on black baseplate with upper parts in obelisk form with escutcheon; base moulding in grey marble; below, white apron.
- Michael Sergison, Esq., of Cuckfield Place, d. 16 Jul 1784, aet 74; his wife, Sarah, d. 4 Apr 1771, aet 55; erected by their issue - Ann.

1. In situ - Horsfield (*Sussex* I 254); Lambarde (*SAC* 69 203) noting arms; transcribed in Lower (*SAC* 25 83).
2. Sarah was daughter of John Deane; Michael and Sarah Sergison were married in 1738; Michael was fourth son of Thomas Warden but succeeded to the estate of his brother Thomas (d.1766), who had taken the surname Sergison in 1732. Michael also took the name and arms of Sergison. Patron

of 72D was their daughter Anne.
3. For what looks like a pendant to 72D see Addition (10).
4. NBI records burial of Sarah Sergison on 15 Apr 1771 at Cuckfield.

Cuckfield, 72E Mural monument for John WARDEN, d. 1766

- North chapel (vestry), South wall, facing North, high up.
- 95W x c.200(H) — Very good.
- A white marble tablet set portrait-wise; lettering blacked; pink inlaid border; grey base moulding; scrolled brackets with ornate apron with crossed ferns and blank escutcheon; ball finial at foot; above, a cornice then broken scrolled pediment with urn in relief.
- John Warden, Esq., naval officer, 10 May 1702 - 23 Oct 1766, aet 64; second son of Thomas and Prudence Warden; his wife, Anne, widow of John Madgwicke, Esq.; their issue - one son, Thomas Sergison Warden, d. 22 Jun 1739, aet 4, buried at Cuckfield.

1. See Lower (*SAC* 25 83) for transcription.
2. John was third son and predeceased his brother Thomas by a few weeks, which allowed Michael (72D) to succeed. For John's wife, Anne, see Addition (2).
3. Patron of 72E was Michael Sergison, Esq., the subject's brother.
4. See 72EE for a monument by Burnell (Gunnis *Dict.* 72) to an earlier John Warden.

Cuckfield, 72F Mural monument for Mary INGRAM, d. 1726

- North chapel (vestry), South wall, facing North, East of 72E, high up.
- 94(W) x c.200(H) — Very good.
- Description as for 72E.
- Mary Ingram, d. 30 Apr 1726, aet 26; second daughter of Thomas and Prudence Warden; and wife of James Ingram, clerk, A.M., rector of Cuckfield and Sedlescombe; and niece of Charles Sergison, Esq., of Cuckfield Place; their issue - eldest son, Thomas, d. 25 Jun 1751, aet 28; second son, Arthur, d. 15 Dec 1748, aet 23, (buried in the Temple Church, London); youngest son, Charles, d. 5 May 1727, infant.

1. Transcribed, J. Cooper (*SAC* 49 100-101) some details incorrect.
2. Patrons of 72F were John and James, sons of Mary Ingram's widowed husband by his second wife.

Cuckfield, 72G Mural monument for Guy CARLETON, d. 1628 and his nephew and niece [Plate 48]

- North-East chapel, South wall, at head height.
- 79(W) x 119(H) — Fine; some colour.
- Rectangular slate(?) tablet within an alabaster surround decorated with gilded foliate pattern; escutcheons top & bottom; M.I.s fill tablet; a heart-shaped central border, within a border of symbols - (1 top left) heart with eye & M.I.: 'OYME BΛEΨON ANΩ'; (2) an angel pointing to the right; (3) a flaming heart on a book with motto 'COR RECTUM INQUIRIT SCIENTIAM'; (4) anchor within strapwork border, with motto: 'ANCHOR SPEI CRUX CHRISTI'; (5) winged skull on hourglass with motto 'MORS VITÆ INITIUM'; (6) the motto 'MY LORD & MY GOD'; (7) flying putto with snake (Eternity) & motto 'FINIS AB ORIGINE PENDET'; and (8) anchor with strapwork and cross, without an upper arm, with a serpent entwined around it and the citation 'JOHN III XIV'.
- Guy Carleton, died at Lewes, 11 Apr 1628 and buried on 13 Apr [Easter Day]; son of George Carleton, bishop of Chichester; also George Vicars, d. 24 Nov 1627, and his sister, Anne Vicars, d. 28 Feb 1624/5, children of Thomas Vicars, B. of D., vicar of Cuckfield and Anne, his wife, daughter of George Carleton, bishop.

1. In situ.
2. See the account of the families (Carleton, Vicars) by J. Cooper (*SAC* 45 12-20): there were two Bishops of Chichester called Carleton, George (bishop 1619-28) and his distant relative Guy, (bishop 1678-85). Guy Carleton (1602-28), main subject of 72I, was one of five children of George and was third son.

3. Ann (1605-) was youngest child, married Thomas Vicars, from Carlisle, an associate of the bishop's and a scholar. Vicars penned punning verses attached to a portrait engraving of the bishop, after Boissard, and designed the title-page of a book written by the bishop, *A Thankful Remembrance of God's mercie* (first ed. 1624), which was signed 't/vic.inv' and engraved by Crispin Van de Passe. Vicars was also a Fellow of and associated with other members of Queens' College, Oxford and the subject of verses by Drayton; he was collated vicar of Cuckfield in 1622 and the publisher in 1624 of a book by Bishop Carleton called, *The madnesse of Astrologie*.

4. The patron of 72G was perhaps Bishop Carleton, commemorating his son and grandchildren at his son-in-law's church, in a manner that reflected their circle's scholarly and emblematic interests.

5. Esdaile (ECM 93) attributed 72G to Epiphanius Evesham by comparison with the latter's work at Marsworth, Bucks, signed and dated 1618 (see Esdaile's article 'An incised slab at Cuckfield' *SAC* 82 96-103).

6. White (51, 58, 86) proposes an attribution to Edward Marshall rather than Evesham, comparing the distinctive cursive script on 72G with Marshall's signed brasses for Sir Edward Filmer at East Sutton, Kent (before 1638) and for Sir Thomas Playters (d.1638), Sotterley, Suffolk.

7. JH notes that Lambarde (69 202) describes the heraldry and some unusual 'Latin' numerals on this monument – e.g. XXIIX for 28.

Cuckfield, 72H Standing wall monument for Charles SERGISON, d. 1732

[Plate 47]

- Sanctuary, against North wall.
- 220(W) x 395(H) x 55(depth of base) — Generally very good: colour gone.
- A generous basement of grey-veined marble with a panelled front and engraved tablet (biography left; virtues right); this supports a sarcophagus and backplate in obelisk form, both in dark grey marble; escutcheon tops the obelisk; on the sarcophagus, in white marble, a seated draped figure of Truth with mirror and portrait roundel supported by a putto; the edge of mirror signed: 'Th.º ADEY SCULPT. IT'.
- Charles Sergison, Esq., Lord of the Admiralty, of Cuckfield Place, d. 26 Nov 1732, aet 78; issue - none; his many virtues - intellect, integrity, fidelity, diligence, patriotism, neighbourliness, pacivity and kindness.

1. In situ; Horsfield (*Sussex* I 254); Lambarde (*SAC* 69 202) noting arms.

2. In his will (Apr 1732, PCC Bedford. 296), Charles Sergison left £200 for a monument to be erected on North side of the chancel within 12 months of his death; cited by Gunnis (*Dict.* 15); Nairn & Pevsner (478).

3. Mr Stapley, of Hickstead (see 263) attended a vestry meeting at Cuckfield on 9 Jun 1734, that 'was held ... by Mr Sergison, concerning the setting up a Monument in the Chancel on the North Wall, the Vicar opposed him but the Vestry decided it should be erected', see Turner (*SAC* 23 68-9).

4. A full biography of Charles Sergison by Lower (*SAC* 25 62-84) with full transcription of M.I.s, 78-9 and by J.C. Hattendorf in *ODNB* (monument mislocated, maker's name misspelled); Charles Sergison retired from his Admiralty post in 1719 and lived at Cuckfield; and see Cruikshanks, vol. 5, 401.

5. There are passages of brilliant carving on 72H by Adey, fl. 1730-53, for whom see Whinney (248 and Pl. 179).

6. Adey's trademark was the portrait medallion of the subject, held by a cherub or allegorical figure.

Cuckfield, 72I Mural monument for Sir Thomas HENDLEY, d. 1656/7, and others

- North-East buttress of South-East chapel, facing South, above head height.
- c.160(W) x c.340(H) — Generally very good.
- Very large; alabaster; designed round M.I.s on 3 slate tablets (once gilded) in a vertical arrangement; flanking the upper 2 panels, a pair of black attached Corinthian columns supporting a complex entablature with a panel inscribed 'memoriae/sacrum' and a curved, broken pediment with an achievement; on the outside, swags; the upper panel has a decorative curving top; centre panel with moulded rectangular frame; lower panel set in the basement beneath base mouldings and between scrolled brackets with escutcheons; below, scrolled, draped ornament.
- Sir Thomas Hendley, Knt., of Cuckfield, d. 28 Jan 1656/7, aet 76; son of Thomas Hendley,

Esq., of Courshorne, Cranbrooke, Kent; his wife, Elizabeth, d. 1634, aet c. 53, buried at Cranbrooke, daughter of [John] Wilford, Esq., of Enfield, Middlesex; their issue - sons: Bowyer, Thomas, Walter, and John; daughters: Jane, Elizabeth, Rachell, Anne, Constance, Margaret and Frances; monument erected by Walter Hendley.

1. In situ - see Lower (*SAC* 25 82) and J. Cooper (*SAC* 42 49-51) with transcriptions; Lambarde (*SAC* 69 204) with arms but wrongly dated 1675; *SNQ* (IV 15-17) also notes a monument to Francis and Elizabeth Hendley, 1649 in East chapel, of South aisle, North-East corner.
2. Patron of 72I is Walter, later Sir Walter Hendley, Bart. (d.1675), third son of Thomas Hendley, himself commemorated by a M.I. at bottom, added afterwards; erected before the patron was created Baronet in 1661.
3. For burials of Sir Thomas Hendley on 6 Feb 1657 and Walter Hendley on 17 Jul 1675, see Renshaw (*Cuckfield Registers* 171 & 191).
4. 72I is attributed to Joshua Marshall (1628-78), of London, on grounds of similarity with documented works - distinct surround, panel on arched top of panel, small segmented pediment, see White (96).

Cuckfield, 72J Mural monument for Henry BOWYER, undated

- North-East buttress of the South-East chapel, facing South, at head height, below 72I.
- 99(W) x 145(H) — Sound; worn; M.I. damaged.
- In alabaster and freestone; centred panel supporting a wall-mounted brass plaque, with husband and wife and their children at a prayer-desk, setting within an interior; touchstone columns flanking; M.I. (engraved, gilded); above, a cornice with escutcheon framed by strapwork; below, 6 lines, engraved and black on the apron.

> HENRY BOWYER ESQVYER HAD TO WYFE
> ELIZABETH VAVX DAUGHTER AND HEYRE
> OF THOMAS VAVX OF K...DRO ... CLARKE
> CONTROLLER TO KINGE HENRY THE
> EIGHT BY WHOME HE
> HAD THREE SONNES
> THOMAS FRANCIS
> HENRY AND TWO
> DAVGHTERS ANNE
> AND MARIE

1. Probably in situ; Horsfield (*Sussex* I 254) notes this as a M.I. on the East wall, on the South side of the Communion Table.
2. 72J has often been misdated and misidentified: see Lower (*SAC* 25 82), with full transcription, where 72J is discussed as if an element of 72I.
3. Stephenson (506) notes both a brass M.I. and 72J, noting that Thomas Vaux was of Keterlen Hall (Caterlen, Penrith), Cumberland and was clerk controller to Henry VIII.
4. Noted by Lambarde (*SAC* 69 204) noting arms.
5. *SNQ* (IV 15-17) also locates a slab for Henry Bowyer, 1588 and Sir Thomas Hendley in centre of South aisle floor towards East end.
6. A notice in the church records that there is a brass to Henry Bowyer (d. 1589) beneath the Lady Chapel carpet and Davidson-Houston (*SAC* 77 157-60) notes that this brass comprises a standing armoured figure on floor of South aisle, with Bowyer arms and a lost M.I.
7. Lower (*SAC* 25 82) noted that an inscription had read that this armoured figure represented Sir Thomas Hendlie, Knt, son of another Thomas Hendlie and his wife Ann, who was daughter of Henry Bowyer.
8. In his will of 1656, Thomas Hendlie directed to be buried under the stone where his grandfather is buried.
9. Nairn & Pevsner (478) note 72J as a brass plate in a stone surround for Henry Bowyer, d. 1589.
10. Bowyer (*SAC* 42 36) pedigree gives date of death as 1587 and his daughter Ann as wife of Thomas Hendley (72I).
11. Renshaw (*Cuckfield Registers* 134) records the burial on 25 May 1606 of a Sir Henry Bowyer, Knt - son (3) of subject of 72J[?].

Cuckfield, 72K Mural monument for Gerard BURRELL, d. 1508, perhaps erected or re-erected in late 18ᵗʰ century

- South wall of South-East chapel, in far South-East corner, above head height.
- 82(W) x 188(H) — Very good.
- A squared, unframed, white marble M.I. tablet (engraved) and a curved ornamental apron dropping to a corbel finial; above, gilded in grey and black, an ogival arch with crocket ornament and a panel, perhaps brass, now illegible (but see below) and an escutcheon.
- Gerard Burrell, D.D., vicar of Cuckfield and archdeacon and residentiary of Chichester, d. 17 Apr 1508; youngest son of Sir John Burell, of Devonshire; his grandparents Ralph Burell, of Northumberland and Sirmonda, daughter of Sir Walter Woodland, of Devon.

1. In situ - see Lambarde (*SAC* 69 203) noting arms; *SNQ* (IV 15-17).
2. It commemorates Gerard Burrell who died in 1508 but the dating of the monument is uncertain. A Burrell drawing (BL Add. MS 5698 f.36) reputedly shows the tablet with brasses inserted; Cooper (*SAC* 43 1) gives year of death as 1509, notes that Horsfield (*Sussex* I 254) described the brass as discovered under pews and by then fixed to a tablet (72K) and argues that Sir William Burrell inserted it into the Gothick revival tablet c.1780, by which time the Burrells were non-resident owners in Cuckfield - J. Cooper (*SAC* 43 1ff) and R. Davey (59-64); Davidson-Houston (*SAC* 77 156-7) says that the brass was mentioned in a Visitation of 1634, see Bannerman (*Sussex* 165).
3. JH notes that in addition to being vicar of Cuckfield 1483-1509, Gerard Burrell was archdeacon of Chichester 1495-1509, a prebendary of Chichester Cathedral 1496-1509, and rector of Hartfield. See Emden (73-4) and Horn (*Fasti 1300-1541* 13 & 15).

Cuckfield, 72L Mural monument for Walter BURRELL, d. 1671

- South wall of South-East chapel, South-East corner, above head height.
- 160(W) x 270(H) — Very good; M.I. illegible; gilding lost.
- A large black M.I. (20 lines, engraved, Latin) tablet set portrait-wise, within a moulded white marble frame; flanked by free-standing black Corinthian columns, supporting an entablature with frieze and cornice; breaking into the cornice, an achievement with coloured arms; below, base mouldings and the order supported by thick fluted and scrolled brackets flanking a plain black apron with winged cherub below; beyond, scrolls set sideways against the wall; above, festoons of foliage.

GVALTERVS BVRELL Armiger
NINIANI (cujus ossa
Vicinum hinc ab laeva Marmor tegit)
Filius natu Maximus
Heic[?] juxta situs,
ex FRANCISCA
IOANNIS HOOPER Armig: Cantuarii
Filia
(Quacum 42 plus minus annos
Pie ac prospere conjugio vixit)
Numeroſam prolem, vizᵗ
GVALTERVM, NINIANVM, THOMAM, IOANNEM,
TIMOTHEVM, RICHARDVM, ALEXANDRVM,
RADVLPHVM et PETRVM Filios;
Filiasq: FRANCISCAM et binas IANAS
Suscepit.
Septuagenarius tandem Naturae ceſsit.
Primo die Martij Anno salutis reparatæ
1671
Et desiderium sui apud omnes bonos
reliquit

1. In situ - Horsfield (*Sussex* I 254); *SNQ* (IV 15-17).
2. Walter Burrell, Esq. buried on 4 Mar 1671, see Renshaw (*Cuckfield Registers* 188); see J. Cooper (*SAC* 43 14-16) with reproduction of a portrait of Walter Burrell who was b.1600, son of Ninian and Jane Burrell (72M).
3. For his sons see 72O and 72Q.

Cuckfield, 72M Mural monument for Ninian BURRELL, d. 1614 [Plate 49]

- South-East chapel, centre of South wall, above head height.
- 103(W) x 186(H) — Good; top of brass worn.
- A rectangular brass, set landscape-wise, engraved and black; within an alabaster frame; engraved images of Ninian Burrell and wife kneeling over a prayer-desk with children behind them; motto: 'IESU ESTO MIHI JESUS'; flanked by panelled pilasters with escutcheons; below, a base moulding, then a black M.I. panel (English and Latin) flanked by escutcheons; above, a large, moulded cornice supporting 2 slender obelisks flanking an achievement.
- Ninian Burrell, Esq., d. 2 Sep 1614, aet 74; his widow (married 16 years), Jane, buried Aug 1655, aet 77, daughter of Henry Smith, Gent., and later, wife of Peter Courthope, of Danny, Hurstpierpoint, Esq.; their issue - (5 sons): Walter, Ninian, Alexander, Thomas and John; and (6 daughters): Timothie, Jane, Anne, Dorothie, Elizabeth and Judeth.

1. In situ - Horsfield (*Sussex* I 254), *SNQ* (IV 15-17), noted by J. Cooper (*SAC* 43 9-10) and in Lambarde (*SAC* 69 203) noting arms.
2. Ninian Burrell, married at 58, when bride was 20, buried on 4 Sep 1614, see Renshaw (*Cuckfield Registers* 143); Peter Courthope d. 1657, was purchaser of Danny in 1652; Jane was buried 26 Sep 1655 (Parish register); Ninian Burrell's first wife was Agnes Esterfelde of Wivelsfield, widow, in Jan 1591, see Dunkin (*Licences 1586-1643* 12); for the daughter, Anne, see 139/1T.

Cuckfield, 72N Mural monument for Elizabeth BURRELL, d. 1682

- Very high in North arcade of South-East chapel, pair to 72O.
- Inaccessible — Very good.
- Cartouche in form of a banner; curtained drapes; M.I. (11 lines, Latin); escutcheon over; below, a cherub.
- Elizabeth Burrell, d. 24 Oct 1682; daughter of Henry Goring, Bart., of Highden, and wife of Timothy Burrell, armiger.

1. In situ - Horsfield (*Sussex* I 254), Lambarde (*SAC* 69 204) noting arms, *SNQ* (IV 15-17).
2. 72N is noted and transcribed by J. Cooper (*SAC* 43 24-5).
3. Patron is widowed husband Timothy Burrell (see 72O).
4. Elizabeth Burrell was not buried at Cuckfield, see Renshaw (*Cuckfield Registers* 143), her widowed husband later married Mary (d.1694), daughter of Sir Job Charlton, then Elizabeth Chilcott (d.1696).

Cuckfield, 72O Mural monument for Timothy BURRELL, d. 1717 [Plate 50]

- South-East chapel. arcade, below 72N, its pair.
- c.70(W) x c.160(H) — Very good.
- Convex cartouche in white marble; foliate surround to cartouche; M.I. (engraved, black and reddened, Latin, 100% filled); 2 cherubim at foot; above, a flaming lamp.
- Timothy Burrell, d. 26 Dec 1717, aet 75; his wife, Elizabeth.

1. In situ - *SNQ* (IV 15-17); transcribed by Blencowe (*SAC* 3 171).
2. Timothy Burrell was known as 'Councillor Burrell', see J. Cooper (*SAC* 43 24); born 1643, lawyer; first wife was Elizabeth Goring, second wife Mary Charlton, third wife Elizabeth Chilcott, only offspring was a daughter born 1696, married at 19 to Lord Trevor; in 1706 Timothy Burrell contributed £5 towards a monument for his Cambridge tutor John Ray (151); he administered a bequest in support of the charity school at Cuckfield (Caffyn 101).
3. Patrons of 72O were Walter and Peter Burrell.
4. See Lambarde (*SAC* 69 204) noting arms.

Cuckfield, 72P Mural monument for Ninian BURRELL, d. 1628 [Plate 51]

- Above head height on South wall of South-East chapel, towards West end.
- 114(W) x 240(H) — Very good.
- In alabaster and coloured marbles, a male kneeler, in armour, with cape and sword, on a cushion, facing East before a prayer-desk; flanked by standing angels holding back curtains; all on a base moulding supported on moulded brackets flanking a framed slate

M.I. tablet (11 lines, Latin and English); above, a Doric frieze and another slate lettered tablet and triglyphs, an entablature supporting finials flanking an achievement on a broad, fluted pedestal.
- Ninian Burrell, of Wadham College, Oxford and Middle Temple, died of consumption, 10 Nov 1628, aet 27; second son of Ninian Burrell, Esq., of Cuckfield; his brother and first son Walter.

1. In situ - Horsfield (*Sussex* I 254) but with incorrect date and age; *SNQ* IV (15-17); transcribed by J. Cooper (*SAC* 43 13-14).
2. Ninian Burrell died in London, see Renshaw (*Cuckfield Registers* 157) for his burial by torchlight on 13 Nov 1628).
3. Mosse noted that M.I. claims that it rehearses Ninian Burrell's own death-bed speech.
4. Nairn & Pevsner (478) note the high quality carving of the angels holding back the curtains.
5. This Ninian Burrell is third child and second son of the Ninian Burrell commemorated by 72M.
6. Patron of 72P is Ninian's brother.

Cuckfield, 72Q Mural monument for Walter BURRELL, d. 1650
- Very high over West arch of South-East chapel.
- Inaccessible — Fine; worn.
- M.I. (engraved, gilded, black) on cartouche; above, an over-large scrolled frame and escutcheon; much gilding, some colour visible; freestone surround; crude flattened corbel.
- Walter Burrell, of Trinity College, Cambridge and Inner Temple, buried 24 Mar 1650, aet 21; eldest son of Walter Burrell, Esq., of Holmested.

1. J. Cooper (*SAC* 43 19) transcription; in situ *SNQ* (IV 15-17).
2. This Walter Burrell was first son of another Walter Burrell and Frances Hooper (see 72L).
3. Modest quality of 72Q c.f. other Burrell commissions.

Cuckfield, 72R mural monument for Walter BURRELL, d. 1683/4
- Above head height on South wall of South nave aisle, South-East corner.
- 90(W) x c.240(H) — Very good; faded.
- In white marble; M.I. (13 lines Latin, English) fills 60% of an oval lettered cartouche framed by scrolls and garlands of hops(?); initial capitals in red, otherwise black; above and below, winged cherubs; above, a curving cornice with coloured and gilded escutcheon.
- Walter Burrell, Esq., 8 Mar 1660/1 - 21 Feb 1683/4, died of smallpox; eldest son of Ninion Burrell, Esq., and Anne, daughter of Sir William Culpeper, of Wakehurst, Baron.

1. Arms noted by Lambarde (*SAC* 69 205), in situ *SNQ* (IV 15-17), transcribed by J. Cooper (*SAC* 43 21) and views of 72R in BL Add. MS 5677 f.56; 5672 ff.31-5; 12555.a-f.
2. See pedigree in Attree & Booker (*SAC* 48 98) and Blaauw (*SAC* 10 154) for marriage of Anne Culpeper (1634-97) and Ninian Burrell (1631-74), son of Walter Burrell and Frances Hooper (see 72L); this Walter Burrell was their first son.
3. Note the high quality of the cutting of 72R.

Cuckfield, 72S Mural monument for John BURRELL, d. 1690/1
- South aisle wall, above head, between central windows.
- 89(W) x 184(H) — Very good.
- Moulded white marble frame with small pointed pediment; encloses a black M.I. tablet (engraved and gilded); below, base mouldings, a curved scrolled apron with ferns and other foliage and a distraught, winged cherub acting as corbel.
- John Burrell, Gent., d. 15 Jan 1690/1, aet 76; youngest son of Ninion Burrell, Esq., of Holmsted; his wife, Bridgett, daughter of Thomas Short, Gent., of Tenterden, Kent; their issue - 8: only Mary still living, wife of William Board, eldest son of William Board, Esq., of Board Hill.

1. In situ - *SNQ* (IV 15-17); carving of good quality.
2. M.I. suggests that William Board, son-in-law, might be patron of 72S; John Burrell was not buried at

Cuckfield, Renshaw (*Cuckfield Registers* 157); for John's parents see 72M, for his brothers Walter 72L and Ninian 72P, see J. Cooper (*SAC* 43 18).

3. Mary Burrell was baptised 5 Oct 1645, see Renshaw (*Cuckfield Registers* 50).

4. For the Boards, proprietors of the Board Hill estate, see 164G.

5. NBI records burial of John Burrell on 17 Jan 1691 at Cuckfield, Holy Trinity.

Cuckfield, 72T Mural monument for William FETEPLACE, d. 1656

- South nave aisle, very high in arcade, opposite 72S.
- c.80(W) x c.140(H) — Generally good; cornice damaged.
- In freestone, around a black M.I. tablet (engraved and gilded), set landscape-wise; radically broken pediment around an achievement; below, a generous base moulding, then volutes and gilded foliate ornament; scrolled bracket in centre.
- William Feteplace, Gent., d. May 1656, aet 71, at Cuckfield; youngest son of Bessells Feteplace, Esq., of Bessells Lee, Berkshire; also, Walter Burrell, Esq., of Holmested, near kinsman.

1. In situ - Lambarde (*SAC* 69 205) noting arms and *SNQ* (IV 15-17).

2. Patron was William Feteplace's near kinsman Walter Burrell of Cuckfield.

3. Note extraordinary and naive proportions of this composition.

Cuckfield, 72U Mural monument for Peter BURRELL, d. 1775

- East of South nave / aisle door, above head height.
- 88(W) x 122(H) — Very good; fading.
- White marble M.I. tablet (engraved and black), set portrait-wise; mid relief border of foliage; on 2 corbels.
- Peter Burrell, Esq., of Beckenham, Kent, Crown Officer, d. 6 Nov 1775; his wife Elizabeth, eldest daughter of John Lewis, Esq., of Hackney, Middlesex; their issue - Peter, b. 16 Jun 1754, husband of Priscilla Barbara Elizabeth, baroness Willoughby de Eresby, eldest daughter of Perigrine Bertie, Duke of Ancaster and Kesteven; Elizabeth Amelia, b. 28 Jan 1749/50, wife of Richard Bennet, Esq.; Isabella Susannah, b. 19 Dec 1750, wife of Algernon, Earl of Beverley; Frances Julia, b. 21 Dec 1752, wife of Hugh, Duke of Northumberland; Elizabeth Anne, b. 10 Apr 1757, wife of Douglas, Duke of Hamilton and Brandon; and Charlotte Maria, 31 Aug 1761 - 5 Jun 1762; Peter Burrell's surviving brother William.

1. In situ in *SNQ* (IV 15-17).

2. Patron is brother William (72V).

3. Noted and transcribed with biographical details by J. Cooper (*SAC* 43 35-6).

4. JH notes that Peter Burrell was MP for Launceston 1759-68 and Totnes 1768-74, see Namier and Brooke (2 160-1).

Cuckfield, 72V Mural monument for Sir William BURRELL, d. 1796

- Above South door.
- 150(W) x 90(H) — Very good.
- White marble M.I. tablet (engraved and black), set landscape-wise; flanked by panels with friezes of Greek key ornament and symbols in relief; below, two plain brackets; above, a shallow, plain, pointed pediment.
- Sir William Burrell, Bart., LL.D., politician, public servant, etc., died at Deepdene, Dorking, Surrey, 20 Jan 1796, aet 63, buried at West Grinstead, Sussex; third son of Peter Burrell, Esq., of Beckenham, Kent and Amy, daughter of Hugh Raymond, Esq.; his wife, Sophia, eldest daughter of Sir Charles Raymond, Bart.; their issue - Charles Merrick, b. 24 May 1774; William Raymond, 23 Dec 1775 - 24 Aug 1777; Walter, b. 15 Apr 1777; Percy, b. 6 Jul 1779; Juliana, b. 11 Jul 1782; Peter Algernon, 4 Aug 1787 - ?? Sep 1787; and Elizabeth Amelia, b. 5 Oct 1789.

1. In situ - Horsfield (*Sussex* I 254) and *SNQ* (IV 15-17); see Gomme (171) and J. Cooper (*SAC* 43 38-

40); Nairn & Pevsner (478) - Flaxman of average quality; Gunnis (*SAC* 97 84-5 & *Dict.* 150) agrees: patron was William Burrell's widow, who commissioned John Flaxman and he went to see the sites at West Grinstead, where there was very little space and at Cuckfield where he found space above the door.

2. For William Burrell's biography see Horsfield (*Lewes* 328-9) and now J.H. Farrant 'The family circle and career of William Burrell, antiquary' (*SAC* 138 169-85) and biography by John H. Farrant in *ODNB*: giving death date as 20 Jan 1796 and buried on 28 Jan 1796 in the family vault at West Grinstead.

3. William Cole, a fellow antiquary, described Burrell as 'an active, stirring, man, and a good antiquary. He is rather low, and squints a little; but very ingenious, and scholar-like' (BL Add. MS 5864 f. 69).

4. JH notes that William Burrell was MP for Haslemere from 1768-74, as well as holding other public offices, see Namier & Brooke (2 163).

Cuckfield, 72W Mural monument for Peter BURRELL, d. 1756, and others

- South aisle, West of 72V.
- 94(W) x 173(H) — Very good; fading.
- White marble unframed M.I. (engraved, black and reddened) fills upper 60%; set portrait-wise on 2 scrolled corbels; above, modest moulded cornice.
- Peter Burrell, Esq., of Beckenham, Kent, d. 16 Apr 1756, buried Beckenham; his wife Amy, eldest daughter of Hugh Raymond, Esq., of Saling Hall, Essex and Langley, Kent; their issue - Peter (died after 1756); William (died after 1756); Amelia, wife of Tobias Frere, Esq., no issue; Raymond (died in infancy); Issabella (died in infancy); and John (died in infancy); he was the eldest son of Peter Burrell, d. 13 Sep 1718, aet 69, lived at Beckenham from 1684, ninth son of Walter Burrell, Esq., of Holmsted Place, Cuckfield; and Isabella, second daughter of John Merrick, Esq., of Stubbers, North Ockenden, Essex; his siblings - Sir Merrick Burrell, Bart., of West Grinstead Place, Sussex; Francis, wife of Richard Wyatt, Esq., of Egham, Surrey; Issabella, wife of Thomas Dallison, Esq., of Hamptons, Kent; Ann, wife of Richard Acland, Esq., of Devonshire; four other sons died in infancy; one other daughter died in infancy.

1. In situ - Horsfield (*Sussex* I 254) and *SNQ* (IV 15-17).
2. Transcribed with biographical details by J. Cooper (*SAC* 43 33-34).
3. JH notes that Peter Burrell was MP for Haslemere 1722-54, and Dover 1755-56, see Namier & Brooke (2 160).

Cuckfield, 72X Mural monument for Percy BURRELL, d. 1807

- South aisle, West end, South wall.
- 154(W) x 310(H) — Very good.
- An idealised military figure group of 3 males, within a shallow niche with arched top; above, an entablature with a curved top and an urn; below, M.I. tablet set landscape-wise, flanked by squared blocks and on block corbels; a curving apron below with a decorative escutcheon, the upper parts against a black baseplate; signed (lower right corbel) : 'J. BACON, Jun' Sculptor, / LONDON, 1810'.
- Percy Burrell, Captain (6th Dragoon Guards), 5 Jul 1779 - 5 Jul 1807 at Buenos Aires; fourth son of Sir William Burrell, Bart., and Sophia, daughter of Sir Charles Raymond, Bart.; 2 surviving brothers, unnamed.

1. In situ - Horsfield (*Sussex* I 254) and *SNQ* (IV 15-17); dated by Gunnis (*Dict.* 30) as by Bacon 1807; Nairn & Pevsner (478) note the brawny arms of supporting soldier; transcribed with biography details by J. Cooper (*SAC* 43 42-3); Lambarde (*SAC* 69 205) noting arms.
2. For patrons see 72V.
3. Bacon first used this figure composition in his monument for Captain Edward Cooke (d.1799) at Westminster Abbey; his design for 72X is at the V&A (E.1562-1931), see Physick (177).

Cuckfield, 72Y Ledger for Thomas WARDEN, d. 1695

- Nave floor, opposite South door.
- 54(W) x 78(L) — Cracked; damage and losses upper right.

- M.I. (9 lines, engraved) showing white in upper 60% of a slate slab; set head to West.
- Thomas Warden, b. 10 Jul 1695, buried 28 Aug 1695; son of John and Hopestill Warden.

1. For Thomas Warden's immediate family see 72Z and 72EE; John Warden was an attorney; Thomas and Matthew not in Lower pedigree (*SAC* 25 84); for Matthew Warden see J. Cooper (*SAC* 49 92) & 72Z.

Cuckfield, 72Z Ledger for Matthew WARDEN, d. 1697/8
- Nave floor, alongside 72Y.
- 54(W) x 78(L) — Sound; damaged edges.
- M.I. (9 lines, engraved) in a black slab; set head to West.
- Matthew Warden, d. 4 Jan 1697/8, aet 1; son of John and Hopestill Warden.

1. For Matthew Warden's immediate family see 72Y and 72EE; John Warden was an attorney, see Renshaw (*Cuckfield Registers* 209).

Cuckfield, 72AA Anonymous ledger, d. 1735
- Nave floor, West end, partly obscured by door into tower.
- 75(W) x 136(L) — Very worn.
- Engraved lines in centre of a freestone slab; head to West.

Un[der] ...

Body of ...

Relict of John C...

...

Departed this life

May the 26 1735

Aged 73 years

Cuckfield, 72BB Mural monument for James WILLETT, d. 1795, and his daughter
- North nave aisle, North wall, North-West corner, top left, very high.
- 50(W) x 70(H) — Fine; faded; local damage.
- Unframed, white marble tablet; M.I. (engraved and black) in upper 50%; cornice over.
- James Willett, d. 6 Dec 1795, aet 32; his widow, Elizabeth; their issue - Louisa Elizabeth Willett, d. 9 Feb 1795, aet 4.

1. In situ - *SNQ* (IV 15-17).
2. Patron is Elizabeth Willett, the widow.
3. NBI records burial of James Willett on 12 Dec 1795 at Cuckfield, Holy Trinity.

Cuckfield, 72CC Mural monument for Jane and Lashford WILLETT, d. 1790 and 1794
- North nave aisle, North wall, East of 72BB, top obscured by wooden ceiling.
- 50(W) x 100(H) — Fine; pigment fading.
- Unframed white marble tablet set portrait-wise; M.I. (9 lines) in upper 75% of tablet; cornice over; grey marble pointed pediment with coloured escutcheon; below, a base moulding on two scrolled brackets; curving apron.
- Jane Willett, d. 23 Oct 1790, aet 60; wife of Lashford Willett, Esq., of Brighthelmston, d. 3 Mar 1794, aet 60.

1. In situ - *SNQ* (IV 15-17).
2. Datable 1791-3.
3. Arms noted in Lambarde (*SAC* 69 203).

Cuckfield, 72DD Monument for Mercy MICHELL [HURST], d. 1706
- North nave aisle, North wall, below 72BB and 72CC.
- 113(W) x 136(H) — Fine; local damage to cornice.

- A slate(?) panel, set portrait-wise, M.I. (7 + 6 lines, engraved); within a freestone surround; cornice breaking forward of panelled pilasters on bases and moulded blocks.
- Mercy Michell, of Cuckfield, d. 5 Jun 1706, aet 42; daughter of John Monlos, of Withyham; and wife of John Hurst; their issue - also John Hurst, d. 11 May 1726, aet 42.

1. Crude local work, called Mercy Michell and in situ in *SNQ* (IV 15-17).
2. JH notes that NBI records burial of Mary Mitchell on 14 Jun 1706 at Cuckfield and (IGI) John Hurst, son of John and Mary Hurst, baptised at Hurstpierpoint 1685.

Cuckfield, 72EE Mural monument for John and Hopestill WARDEN, d. 1730 and d. 1749

- High in the South nave aisle.
- 95(W) x c.180(H) — Generally very good; fading.
- M.I. (14 lines, engraved, black) white marble tablet; set portrait-wise; within a grey veined marble frame; above, entablature with broken pointed pediment and urn; below, squared base moulding, then block corbels against a darker grey apron with the escutcheon and motto 'Guardez le foy'; signed (underneath): 'Thos. Burnell Londini fecit'.
- John Warden, of Butler's Green, d. 30 Apr 1730, aet 79; his wife, Hopestill, d. 22 Jul 1749, aet 92; their only son - Francis Warden, Esq.

1. In situ - *SNQ* (IV 15-17); transcribed in Lower (*SAC* 25 82).
2. Patron was only son.
3. The new generation has acquired esquire status.
4. Thomas Burnell, b c 1740, founded a London firm of monument makers which operated 1761-1841, see Gunnis (*Dict.* 72). .
5. Arms not in Lambarde (*SAC* 69 203).

Cuckfield, 72FF Mural monument for Sir Henry and Jane RYCROFT, d. 1846 and d. 1797

- Very high in North nave aisle arcade, facing North.
- 90(W); (H) unknown — Fine.
- M.I. (8 + 4 lines) on a white marble tablet set landscape-wise with part-fluted Doric pilasters; rosette corbels below and a grey apron with crossed ferns and an escutcheon; above, a moulded entablature supporting 2 lamps, an urn and festoons against a broad dark grey obelisk as backplate; unsigned.
- Sir Henry Rycroft, Knt, of Butler's Green, died at Brighton 3 Oct 1846, aet 80; his wife, Jane, d. 21 Apr 1797, aet 31.

1. In situ - *SNQ* (IV 15-17).
2. JH notes that for arms, see Lambarde addenda (*SAC* 75 188) but genealogical details incorrect, Jane having been confused with her sister in law. Jane was daughter of Ferdinando Travell, of Upper Slaughter, Glos., and widow of William Lennox Dutton Naper (they married in 1787, he died in 1791). Henry, son of 1st Baronet Rycroft, went to Cambridge and was awarded BA in 1788, MA in 1792. He married Jane in 1794. He was knighted on his appointment as Knight-Harbinger to the King in 1816. (The office was abolished at his death). See Foster (*Peerage* 514) and Venn (2 5 393).

Cuckfield Additions

Transcribed by Lower in (*SAC* 25 82-3):
(1) Thomas Warden, of Cuckfield, d. 5 Oct 1713, aet 47; his wife of 22 years, Prudence Sergison; issue - 4 sons, 4 daughters (taken by Lower from Burrell MS).
(2) Anne Warden, d. ?? Feb 1781, aet 81; parents Thomas and Elizabeth Ives, of Westup.
(3) Francis Sergison, Esq., of Cuckfield Place, d. 4 Apr 1793, aet 57 ; his widow Anne (patron).
From J. Cooper (*SAC* 50 12) and heraldry given in Lambarde (*SAC* 69 203), mural monument in North aisle.
(4) Robert Middleton, vicar of Cuckfield, ?? May 1713, aet 70; his wife Mary d. 1 Nov 1708, sister of Simon Patrick, Bishop of Chichester and Ely (ledger, North chancel aisle) for a letter by Robert Middleton on the 1695 election in Sussex see *SAC* 106 145f-57. Also located here in *SNQ* IV 15-17.

Noted in Lambarde (*SAC* 75 188).

(5) William Board 1697 and wife Jane, daughter of And. Wall, 1704 (ledger in South aisle), located there also in *SNQ* IV 15-17.

Noted in *SNQ* (IV 1932-33 15-17).

(6) Ledger for Archdeacon Tobias Henshawe, 1680, between North aisle, East chapel and chancel.

(7) Francis Baker, 1653, between South aisle, East chapel and chancel.

(8) Sir Walter Hendley, 1675, just West of (7).

(9) Rev. Joseph and Jane Fearon, 1816, extreme North-West corner of North aisle.

ALSO.

(10) A mural monument, now almost completely obscured by the organ in the North choir aisle, on the wall North of 72D and identified by the present incumbent as very like 72D. On the apron is just visible the M.I.: '.. AND HER HUSBAND THE REV.D WILLIAM SERGISON / WHO BOTH DIED IN 1848, ARE INTERRED IN THIS CHURCH'.

(73) DALLINGTON, St. Giles (also St. Margaret)

Condition reported to be fine in 1724 (Ford) but the church was largely rebuilt in 1864 - Nairn & Pevsner (479); for views see BL Add. MS 5676 f.2; 5670 f.66-67; the mural monuments from the old church were repositioned as a group in the North aisle, the ancient Randoll pew and burial place – Horsfield (*Sussex* I 569), having been found under the belfry; monuments at Dallington have been heavily cleaned.

Dallington, 73A Wall-mounted brass for Ann CRAUFURD, d. 1771 [Plate 52]

- North aisle, North wall, far West end.
- 37(W) x 50(H) — Good.
- M.I. on a decorated brass lozenge; raised ornamental edging.
- Ann Craufurd, d. 10 Sep 1771, aet 61; widow of Col. George Craufurd.

1. Horsfield (*Sussex* I 569) noted what he called 73A's horizontal hatching.
2. Is this a coffin plate relating to monument 73H? For her son see 73E.

Dallington, 73B Mural monument for Ann NORTH, d. 1780

- North aisle, North wall, uppermost, grouped with 73C-D.
- 61(W) x 45(H) — Sound; very cleaned.
- M.I. (12 lines, engraved) fills an unframed white marble panel, with veining.
- Ann North, d. 22 Feb 1780, aet 53; wife for 28 years of Rev. William North, vicar of Dallington; daughter of Thomas Wakeham, Gent., of Worth; her piety.

1. Noted by Horsfield (*Sussex* I 569).

Dallington, 73C Mural monument for Mary MACKENZIE, d. 1770

- North aisle, North wall, with 73B and D.
- 60(W) x 39(H) — Very cleaned; rust (top left and lower right).
- M.I. (10 + 2 lines, engraved) fills a white marble panel; engraved, moulded edge.
- Mary Mackenzie, d. 6 Apr 1770, buried in vault of Robert Randoll, Esq. (see 73I); wife of Gen John Mackenzie, d. 6 Oct 1791.

1. Noted by Horsfield (*Sussex* I 569).
2. The final 2 lines, added later, commemorate the patron and widower, for whom see 73D.
3. For Mrs Mackenzie's relatives see 73 I & J.
4. 73C was erected pre-1791.

Dallington, 73D Brass for John MACKENZIE, d. 1791

- North aisle, North wall, with 73B and C.
- 31(W) x 41(H) — Fine.
- Escutcheon, then M.I. (5 lines, engraved) on a brass plate; Motto: 'SIC ITUR AD ASTRA'.
- Lieut. Gen. John Mackenzie, d. 6 Oct 1791, aet 79.

1. Noted by Horsfield (*Sussex* I 569).
2. See 73C for MacKenzie's death and burial.
3. JH notes that the Brass is not noted by Stephenson and Arms not listed by Lambarde.

Dallington, 73E Mural monument for Patrick George CRAUFURD, d. 1804, and his son

- North aisle, North wall, with 73F and G.
- 98(W) x 74(H) — Very cleaned; repaired.
- M.I. (14 lines, engraved) on unframed white marble panel; moulded cornice over; below, brackets and Grecian decorative.
- Patrick George Crauford, Esq., 19 Jan 1741 – 3 Feb 1804; only son of George Crauford, Lt. Col. (53rd Regiment of Foot), of Herrings Place; his first son George Crauford, Esq., 1 Oct 1779 – 9 Mar 1804.

1. Noted by Horsfield (*Sussex* I 569).
2. Patrick George Craufurd acquired the estate in 1791 (see 73J); he and his first son died within days of one another; for his widow see 73F; for his mother see 73A.
3. Very close to 73H in design.

Dallington, 73F Mural monument for Jane CRAUFURD, d. 1811

- North aisle, North wall, with 73E and G.
- 68.5(W) x 29(H) — Very cleaned.
- M.I. (7 lines, engraved) in an unframed. undecorated white marble panel.
- Jane Craufurd, 2 Feb 1753 – 4 Jul 1811; eldest daughter of Donald Macdonald, Lieut-Col. 84th Regiment of Foot and Brigadier-General in America; widow of P. G. Craufurd, of Herrings Place, Esq.

1. Noted by Horsfield (*Sussex* I 569).
2. For her husband see 73E.
3. See 73G, probably a burial marker.
4. JH notes that the date of 4th July conflicts with 5th on 73G.

Dallington, 73G Wall-mounted brass for Jane CRAUFURD, d. 1811 [Plate 53]

- North aisle, North wall, with 73E and F.
- 30.5(W) x 41(H) — Fine.
- M.I. (5 lines, engraved) fills brass plate.
- Jane Craufurd, d. 5 Jul 1811, aet 58.

1. Noted by Horsfield (*Sussex* I 569), perhaps marking the burial place in the floor.
2. JH notes that the date of 5thJuly conflicts with 4th on 73F.

Dallington, 73H Mural monument for Anne CRAUFURD, d. 1771

- North aisle, North wall, now within the vestry, with 73I-J.
- 89(W) x 58(H) — Fine; cracked (lower right).
- M.I. (7 lines, engraved) in an unframed white marble panel; above, a flat moulded cornice (no pediment); below, a fluted base with rosettes left and right.
- Anne Craufurd, 20 Aug 1710 – 8 Sep 1771, widow of Lt. Col. George Craufurd (53rd Regiment of Foot).

1. For another monument [coffin plate?] to her see 73A; for her son see 73E.
2. Very close to 73E in design.

Dallington, 73I Mural monument for Robert RANDOLL, d. 1783, and his daughter, d. 1759 [Plate 54]

- North aisle, North wall, now within the vestry, with 73H and J.
- 67(W) x 47(H) — Very cleaned; 3 repairs; rust stains.

- M.I. (10 lines, engraved) on a panel cut in the form of a scroll.
- Robert Randoll, Esq., of Herrings, d. 5 Jul 1783; his daughter, Margaretta, 6 Jun 1757 – 19 Apr 1759.

1. Noted by Horsfield (*Sussex* I 569).
2. The scroll is an ingenious and rare conceit.
3. Mrs Mary Randoll was owner of Herrings in 1785 but not in occupation (R. Davey 65); the estate was sold to Craufurd in 1791.

Dallington, 73J Wall-mounted brass for Margaretta RANDOLL, d. 1791
- North aisle, North wall, now within a vestry, with 73H-I.
- 31(W) x 41(H) — Fine.
- M.I. (6 lines, engraved) fill a brass plate; above, an escutcheon.
- Mrs Margaretta Randoll, d. 4 Nov 1791, aet 65.

1. A view of Herrings Place in 1784 shows funeral hatchments hanging for Robert Randoll (Farrant 201).
2. Margaretta Randoll is his widow who died childless; estate passed to Patrick George Crauford (73E).
3. See comments on 73G.
4. JH notes that the brass, with engraved arms, in not mentioned in either Stephenson nor Lambarde.

Dallington Additions
Horsfield (*Sussex* I 569):
(1) M.I. for Robert Randoll, Esq., d. 1815.
(2) Mary wife of Francis Bodell, d. 1727, aet 75. Also Francis Bodell, d. 1736 aet 86.
(3) Wm Weller, 1743, aet 63.
(4) Ann Barton 1708.

(74) DANEHILL - no monuments found

(75) DENTON, St. Leonard
Early English and Decorated with Victorian restorations - Nairn & Pevsner (480); views in BL King MS 42 f.42 and BL Add. MS 5676 f.78; paving reported poor in 1686, but generally fine in 1724 (Ford); parish had only 24 communicants in 1693, see Renshaw (*Ecclesiastical Returns*).

Denton, 75A Mural monument for Henry BATES, d. 1826, and descendants
- Choir, South wall, above head height.
- 98(W) x 160(H) — Very good condition; colour.
- Black frame round M.I. on white marble tablet, set portrait-wise; below, 2 small black corbels support grey marble base mouldings; above, grey marble broken pediment & white marble achievement; signed (lower moulding): 'WILLIAMS. BRIGHTON'.
- Henry Bates, Esq., d. 6 Aug 1826, aet 72; his son, John Henry Bates, Esq., deputy-lieutenant of the county, d. 21 Mar 1828, aet 50; and John Henry Bates' wife, Harriet Eliza, d. 20 Oct 1826, aet 41; and their son, Francis Edward, d. 13 Nov 1824, aet 13.

1. Horsfield (*Sussex* I 272) notes that the major landowner in the parish is William Henry Bates but does not note the monument, so perhaps it was erected after c.1835.
2. In situ Lambarde (*SAC* 70 150) noting arms.
3. The additional space below the final lines on the M.I. was never used.
4. John Henry Bates married Harriett Eliza Smith on 15 Mar 1806 at St. Mary's, Marylebone, London, see IGI.

Denton Addition
Horsfield (*Sussex* I 273):
(1) Dorothy Tillingham 16 Apr – 26 Jul 1633, daughter of John Tillingham, on the chancel South wall, on parchment and framed; a beautiful Latin monody on the death of Dorothy Tillingham.

(77) DITCHLING, St. Margaret

12th-13th-century aisles, North transept rebuilt 1863, South chapel 14th century - Nairn & Pevsner (481-2) and plan in *SNQ* (III 186); external view of church, see Farrant (205; BL Add. MS 5672 f.14; 5677 f.49); paving reported to be fine in 1724, with exception of South or Abergavenny chancel, see Ford (129); the parish had 200 communicants in 1603, see Renshaw (*Ecclesiastical Returns*); two branches of the Turners are commemorated here by ledgers: for one family see 77B-C, E-H, for the other 77D.

Ditchling, 77A Ledger for [Edwar]d POWELL, d. 1746

- Crossing floor, North side, mostly obscured by organ console.
- 90(W) x 182(L) — Worn.
- M.I. (6 lines, engraved) in upper 30% of surface of pale, freestone slab; head to North.
- [Edwar]d Powell of Ditchling, d. ?? May 1746, aet 33.

1. NBI records burial of Edward Powell on 16 May 1746 at Ditchling.

Ditchling, 77B Ledger for Richard TURNER, d. 1748

- Choir floor, near North wall, West of rail, partly obscured by radiator.
- 87(W) x 170(L) — Worn; water staining.
- M.I. (16 lines, engraved) fill surface of freestone slab; head to West.
- Richard Turner, Gent., of Oldland, d. 14 May 1748, aet 59; eldest son of Richard and Sarah Turner; his wife, Jane, d. 21 Sep 1728, aet c. 37, daughter of Thomas and Amy Gratwick, of Angmering, Sussex.

1. In situ, *Gent's Mag* 1812 in Gomme (241); see pedigree in Arnold (*SAC* 25 216).
2. This Richard Turner is son of Richard Turner of 77C and grandson of Thomas Turner (77E), for his son, also Richard Turner and his wife Jane see 77B, for his grandchildren see 77F, G and H.

Ditchling, 77C Ledger for Richard TURNER, d. 1720

- Choir floor, alongside and South of 77B.
- 84(W) x 170(L) — Fine.
- M.I. (7 lines, engraved) in upper 50% of freestone slab; head to West.
- Richard Turner, Gent., of Oldland, Keymer, d. 2 Oct 1720, aet 68.

1. In situ, *Gent's Mag* 1812 in Gomme (241).
2. Men of this name stand surety for licences to marry in 1681 and 1693, see Dunkin (*Licences 1670-1729* 147).
3. See pedigree in Arnold (*SAC* 25 216); see further family members in note to 77B.

Ditchling, 77D Ledger for William TURNER, d. 1733

- Choir floor, alongside and South of 77C.
- 79(W) x 170(L) — Good (recut?).
- M.I. (7 lines, engraved) in upper 50% of a pale grey freestone slab; head to the West.
- William Turner, apothecary, d. 11 Oct 1733, aet 33; no issue.

1. Roughly in situ, *Gent's Mag* 1812 in Gomme (241).
2. William Turner is not a Turner of Oldland (see 77B-C, E-H, etc.) but is commemorated alongside them at Ditchling; one Thomas Turner, son of Richard Turner, of Keymer, Gent. was apprenticed to Charles Chatfield of Cuckfield, apothecary, on 25 Feb 1741 and William Turner, son of Richard Turner, of Clayton, Gent. was apprenticed to Walter Dobell, citizen and apothecary on 3 Jul 1717, see Rice (194).

Ditchling, 77E Ledger for Thomas TURNER, d. 1671/72

- Choir floor, alongside and South of 77D.
- 83(W) x 144(L) — Good (recut?).

- M.I. (8 lines, engraved) in upper 40% of a grey freestone slab; head to the West.
- Thomas Turner, of Keymer, d. 8 Feb 1671/2, aet 84.

1. Roughly in situ, *Gent's Mag* 1812 in Gomme (241).
2. This Thomas Turner was grandfather of Richard Turner in 77C and his wife's maiden name was Smyth.
3. Pedigree in Arnold (*SAC* 25 216).

Ditchling, 77F Ledger for Richard TURNER, d. 1754
- Sanctuary floor, now installed as part of the altar plinth.
- 67(W) x 66(L) — Worn.
- Richard Turner, Gent., of Oldland, d. 17 Apr 1754, aet 36; eldest son of Richard and Jane Turner.

1. In situ, *Gent's Mag* 1812 in Gomme (240).
2. Measurements of 77F-G show that these ledgers have been cut to form the altar plinth.
3. This Richard Turner is son of Richard Turner 77A and brother of Thomas Turner 77G and William 77H; see pedigree in Arnold (*SAC* 25 216) and comments on 77B for family interrelations.

Ditchling, 77G Ledger for Thomas TURNER, d. 1745
- Sanctuary floor, alongside 77F, now inaccessible.
- 68(W) x 66(L) — Fine.
- Close in type to 77F.

HERE LIES
the Body of THO^S TURNER
Youngeſt ſon of
RICH^D AND JANE his Wife
who Departed this Life
the 26th of Feb^{ry} 1745
AGED 21

1. See comment under 77F.
2. Reported as in sanctuary in *Gent's Mag* 1812, see Gomme (240).
3. See pedigree in Arnold (*SAC* 25 216), Thomas Turner is son of Richard Turner 77A and brother of Richard 77F and William 77H.

Ditchling, 77H Ledger for William TURNER, d. 1786
- Sanctuary floor, forming South end of the altar plinth.
- 91(W) x 140(L) — Fine; faded.
- M.I. (18 lines, engraved) fill a slab; head to East.
- William Turner, Gent., of Oldland, Keymer, d. 26 Jun 1786, aet 65; last surviving son of Richard and Jane Turner; his wife, Sarah, d. 3 May 1802, aet 77; daughter of late Rev. Edward Wilson, rector of Westmeston.

1. In situ, *Gent's Mag* 1812 in Gomme (240).
2. See comments under 77F.
3. This William Turner is son of Richard Turner 77A and brother of Richard 77F and Thomas 77G.

Ditchling, 77I Mural monument for Henry POOLE, d. 1580
- South-East (Abergavenny) Chapel, North wall, facing South.
- 150(W) x 180(H) — Fine; restorations.
- In freestone; flat cornice over a frieze with M.I. (engraved and black); entablature mouldings; centre of monument comprising 4 niches; upper pair with arches carried on fluted pilasters; lower pair comprising framed escutcheons; mouldings between the arches; dividing pilasters with lozenge decorative.
- Henry Poole, Esq., d. 28 Mar 1580.

1. Formerly in the centre of the North Transept North wall; in Oct 1810 described as decayed, injured and whitewashed, see Gomme (241-2); seen there by Horsfield (*Sussex* I 238) – decayed and part-concealed by pews; moved in 1863 and damaged by heating pipes (lower left shield removed).
2. Attree (*SAC* 28 134), reporting Burrell (BL Add. MS), notes Aubrey's account of an inscription for Henry Poole's son Thomas d. 13 Feb 1609; still in North transept in 1930 - Lambarde (*SAC* 71 147) noting arms; decorative vocabulary noted in Nairn & Pevsner (482); see line drawing in *SNQ* (III 204-5); re-erected in present position and restored in 1947.
3. Henry Poole married Margaret Neville, a daughter of Lord Abergavenny in 1560 and she was given the manor of Ditchling as part of her jointure. They lived at Wing's Place South of the church (Church Guide); Henry Poole's sons were John, Francis (married Anne Covert), Henry (of Fisherton Anger, Wilts, will proved 1604), George, William, Thomas (the eldest, married to Elizabeth Wingfield and d. 1609).
4. Typical freestone monument for its date, without figurative work and originally highly decorated.
5. JH notes that Henry Poole was MP for Wootton Bassett in 1553. Margaret Neville was a daughter of George Neville, 5th Lord Bergavenny and Mary, daughter of Edward Stafford, Duke of Buckingham. She was also widow of John Cheyne. See Bindoff (3 130).

Ditchling, 77J Ledger for Sarah PRICE, d. 1764

- Crossing floor, South side, near South wall.
- 93(W) x 194(L) — Very worn.
- M.I. engraved in upper parts of a brown freestone slab; head to East.

...

of M^r .... r of

Mr N.....e of

B.....ark

who ...1764

A[ged] ... Years

1. Cited in *Gent's Mag* as Sarah Price, widow of Nathaniel, late of Bermondsey, Southwark, she d. 29 Dec 1764, aet 75, see Gomme (241).

Ditchling Additions

Gent's Mag see Gomme (240):
(1) In the chancel, slab to Richard Turner, of Oldland, Keymer, son of Thomas Turner, d. 1 Jul 1681, aet 64.
(2) Sanctuary, Dr James Hougham, d. 2 Nov 1700 and wife Mary Culpeper, d. 5 Oct 1688 - confirmed by Horsfield (*Sussex* I 238) and Attree (*SAC* 28 133).
(3) South chancel, 1598 Constance Hause, widow, d. 3 Jan - also in Horsfield (*Sussex* I 238);
(4) South chancel, Ann, d. 2 Jun 1790, aet 90, wife of James Wood, also Mary, their daughter d. 8 Jan 1736, aet 1;
Horsfield (*Sussex* I 238).
(5) 2 slabs with lost brasses in South chancel.
(6) Slab with lost brass for Marchant, of Ditchland, d. 1 May 1661.

(82) EAST BLATCHINGTON, St. Peter

With an Early English chancel - Nairn & Pevsner (482-3) and for plan see *SNQ* (XV 232); floor paving is reported missing in 1686, see Ford (54); condition described as generally fine in 1724, Ford (164); for Lambert's view from South-East of 1770 and one of a ruined chapel, see BL Add. MS 5766 f.76 & 5677 f.28; Horsfield (*Sussex* I 274-5) cites no monuments here.

East Blatchington, 82A Mural monument for Mary KING, d. 1822

- Chancel North wall, above head height.
- 107(W) x 177(H) — Excellent.
- Dark grey baseplate with shouldered, domed top; M.I. (10 + 6 + 3 + 3 + 4 lines, engraved) on a grey unframed marble tablet; flanked by Doric half-columns; over the capitals, an entablature with foliate decoration; base mouldings and corbels with roundel motifs;

above the cornice, an escutcheon.

- Mary King, d. 13 May 1822, aet 34, second daughter of Thomas Rogers, of Kingston near Lewes, Sussex; her husband, John King, Esq., of East Blatchington, d. 5 Jul 1853, aet 78; their issue - Henry, d. 22 Nov 1818, infant; John, d. 30 Jul 1821, aet 4; Mary, wife of Lieutenant George Watson, R.M., d. 12 Jan 1836, aet 25, at Stonehouse, Devon; and Elizabeth, d. 12 Feb 1908, aet 94, at Paignton, Devon, wife of Rev. Robert Nathaniel Dennis d. 17 Feb 1892, rector of East Blatchington.

1. In situ; see part transcription by Dennis (*SAC* 13 302) and Lambarde (*SAC* 71 134) noting arms.
2. John King was patron of the living here; Kings were resident at Blatchington Court; for licence to marry dated 3 Jun 1809 for John King, then of Wilmington, Gent., bachelor, age 30 and Mary Rogers, of Kingston near Lewes, spinster, aged 21, see Dunkin & Penfold (*Licences* 252); Elizabeth, his second daughter, was his heiress and married Robert Dennis, the rector 1844-80.
3. Lines were being added to 82A into the 20th century.
4. The pierced-through contrast of the grey on the black is unusual and interesting.

East Blatchington, 82B Mural monument for William CHAMBERS, d. 1808
[Plate 55]
- Sanctuary North wall, above head height.
- 87(W) x 180(H) — Very good; fading.
- A black obelisk, unadorned, rises above & behind an altar topped by a course of fluted decoration; volutes left and right; on the altar, the initials 'WC'; below, base moulding & apron with M.I. (7 lines, engraved); signed (lower left): 'L & C PARSONS / LEWES'.

WILLIAMS CHAMBERS Esq.,
died May 7 1808, aged 57 Years
He was a sincere Friend and an honest Man
His Widow
erected this Monument
as a Tribute of her
Affection

1. In situ; transcribed by Dennis (*SAC* 13 302).
2. William Chambers paid land tax in 1785 (R. Davey 22); for licence to marry dated 22 Oct 1782 for William Chambers, of East Blatchington, Gent., bachelor, age 25 and Susanna Brook, of Blatchington, spinster, 25, see Dunkin & Penfold (*Licences* 80).
3. 82B is the most ambitious work from the Parsons shop in Lewes included in this catalogue, cited by Gunnis (*Dict.* 292).

East Blatchington Additions
Dennis (*SAC* 13 302).
Rough stone slabs then beneath the chancel floor, inscribed: 'Anne, wife of Nicholas Gilbert, gent., died 8th March, 1652' and 'Nicholas Gilbert, gent., died Febry. 25th, 1677'.

(83) EAST CHILTINGTON - No monuments found

(85) EAST DEAN (East Sussex), St. Simon & St. Jude
Norman; nave lengthened in 1885 & again in 1961 - Nairn & Pevsner (491); for views see BL Add. MS 5671 f.79; 5676 f.75; repairs were needed in 1686 (Ford); the parish had 70 communicants in 1603, see Renshaw (*Ecclesiastical Returns*).

East Dean (East Sussex), 85A Mural monument for Nicholas WILLARD, d. 1762, and his wife Sarah, d. 1761
- Chancel North wall, at head height.
- 90(W) x 196(H) — Very good; stain (top); faded.
- In white, dark grey, pinkish and black marbles; a broken scrolled pediment flanking an urn; beneath, a cornice; in the centre, M.I. (7 lines, engraved, black) in upper 30% of a tablet;

pink decorative strips as pilasters; below, a base moulding, pair of corbels with scrollwork between; at foot, black ball finial.
- Nicholas Willard, Gent., d. 8 Feb 1762, aet 60; his wife, Sarah, d. 14 Jul 1761, aet 56.

1. The space for arms on the scrolled apron was perhaps never completed, neither was the M.I., which appears to have been written after Willard's death, although his wife pre-deceased him.
2. Other Willards are commemorated at Eastbourne (see 80G, 80H, 80L, 80DD).
3. In 1785, James Dippery (see 85B) owned land occupied by one Nicholas Willard, perhaps this Nicholas' successor; Dippery himself lived on George Medley's land (see R. Davey 67).
4. Horsfield (*Sussex* I 285) reports a slab in the sanctuary for Nicholas Willard, either in error, or a lost item.

East Dean (East Sussex), 85B Mural monument for James DIPPERY, d. 1791
- Chancel North wall, at head height, to East of 85A.
- 65(W) x 102(H) — Very good; faded.
- In white and column marbles; at top, a broken scrolled pediment flanking an urn; in centre, M.I. (6 lines, engraved, black) fills unframed panel; flanking, coloured strip pilasters; below, 2 square corbels with a concentric decoration and a rounded apron on a ball finial.
- James Dippery, Gent., d. 11 Sep 1791, aet 88.

1. The upper section perhaps designed to fit with 85A.
2. James Dippery seems to have co-owned lands with Nicholas Willard (see 85A).
3. As with 85A, Horsfield (*Sussex* I 285) reports a slab in the sanctuary for James Dippery, either in error, or a lost item.

(86) EAST GRINSTEAD, St. Swithun

Early monuments were relocated after a fire, c.1684 – see Horsfield (*Sussex* I 390-1), Leeney (*SAC* 88 165-168); Nairn & Pevsner (491-2) and again after the collapse of the church tower (on 12 Nov 1785) and the consequent rebuilding of the church (see 86B); for early views see Godfrey & Salzman (pls. 56-7), one showing the ruined interior; in 1724 state of church reportedly fine (Ford); North and South chancels were parish owned; in 1724, central chancel belonged to Mrs Payne and Thomas Medley; the Paynes were prominent at East Grinstead throughout the 16th-17th centuries, see Crawfurd passim; Stephenson (509) noted a brass loose in 1895 [now lost?] to Katherine, daughter of John Michelburne, Gent., 1617.

East Grinstead, 86A Mural monument for Sir John MAJOR, d. 1781
- South aisle wall, West of South door, above head height.
- 120(W) x 175(H) — Very good.
- M.I. (engraved) on a grey marble tablet, set portrait-wise; curved top and low relief foliage in spandrels; darker grey decorated border; flanking, plain pink pilasters; modest cornice moulding with achievement; enriched base moulding and 2 flattened corbels decorated with acanthus.
- Sir John Major, Bart., of Worlingworth Hall and Thornham Hall, Suffolk, High Sheriff of Sussex in 1755, d. 16 Feb 1781, aet 82; his wife, Elizabeth, of the family of Dale in Yorkshire, d. 4 Sep 1780, aet 76, both buried at Worlingworth; their grandson, Hon. John Henniker Major.

1. Dated 1801, patron is grandson, John Henniker, who later took the name and arms of Major. (See biography by Gordon Goodwin, rev. R.H. Sweet in *ODNB*).
2. JH notes John Major was MP for Scarborough 1761-68. He was an elder brother of Trinity House (1741) and a director of the South Sea Company, see Namier & Brooke (2 99). For heraldry see Lambarde (*SAC* 67 182).

East Grinstead, 86B(i) Wall-mounted brasses reputedly for Katherine LEWKNOR, d. 1505, and her two husbands

- South aisle wall, centre, mounted on stone, at head height.
- 95(W) x 121(H) — Good.
- On the upper freestone slab; 3 standing brass figures; on lower marble slab, on scrolled corbels, top M.I. (9 lines, engraved in English) on brass, lower brass (4 lines, Latin).
- Katherine, d. 1505, daughter of 7th Lord Scales, supposedly in centre; left, first husband, Sir Thomas Grey; right, second husband, Richard Lewknor.

1. The Latin M.I. carved on the lower, marble section of this memorial explains that when the tower fell in 1785, Thomas Wakeman recovered these brasses and had them refixed in 1798.
2. Described by Horsfield (*Sussex* I 390-1).
3. JH notes that, in fact, the centre figure is not of Katherine, but is a male figure, see Davidson-Houston (*SAC* 78 68-70), who also gives fuller details of Katherine and her husbands; and see Stephenson (509). A further complication is that there is doubt about Katherine being the daughter of Lord Scales, see Cockayne (*Peerage* XI 504-7) and Lambarde (in *SNQ* 3 234-5).

East Grinstead, 86B(ii) Wall-mounted brass for Robert CHRISTIAN, d. 1660

- South aisle wall, centre, below 86B(i).
- 31(W) x 22(H) — Good.
- M.I. (9 lines, engraved, English) on brass on a wooden mount.
- Robert Christian, buried 1660, aet c. 9; only son of John and Anne Christian of St. Gregory's by Paul's, London, citizens of London.

East Grinstead, 86C Mural monument for Charles ABBOT, Baron COLCHESTER, d. 1829

- South aisle wall, towards West end, above head height.
- 120(W) x 80(H) — Very good.
- Simple composition; M.I. (13 lines, engraved) on unframed white marble tablet; black baseplate; signed (lower left): 'WILLSON, SCULP.t / LONDON'.
- Rt. Hon. Charles Abbot, 14 Oct 1757 - 8 May 1829, Speaker of the House of Commons for more than 15 years; Baron Colchester from 3 Jun 1817.

1. One of few monuments at East Grinstead cited by Horsfield (*Sussex* I 390-91), so erected pre-1835.
2. Daniel William Willson (fl.1824-34) had a yard at Bath Place, New Road, see Gunnis (*Dict.* 433).
3. *ODNB* gives death of Charles Abbot as 7 May 1829 and buried at Westminster Abbey on 17 May; lawyer; speaker of commons 1802-1817 (see his diary and correspondence for this period, published in 3 volumes by John Murray, London, 1861); married Elizabeth (1760/61–1847) on 29 Dec 1796, the daughter of Sir Philip Gibbes, first Bart., of Spring Head, Barbados, and his wife, Agnes Osborne; issue - 2 sons (biography of Charles Abbot by Clare Wilkinson in *ODNB*).
4. JH notes that Charles Abbot was MP for Helston 1795-1802, New Woodstock 1802-06 and Oxford University 1806-17. He purchased Kidbrook, near East Grinstead, as his private residence in September 1802. He became Lieut-Col. of the East Grinstead Volunteers in 1803. See Thorne (3 1-8) and Farrant (232).

East Grinstead, 86D Undated fragment of an anonymous mural monument

- South aisle wall, West end, at head height.
- 153(W) x 45(H) — Mostly sound; vertical crack in centre.
- M.I. (engraved, English) on a freestone frieze; competent mouldings.

> In the Cold Gound she now is laied, itts for a debt she now hath payd
> it is a debt none can out stand, but must be payed upon demand

1. A curious fragment, its survival presumably explained by the dramatic history of the building.

East Grinstead, 86E Wall-mounted iron slab for Thomas WICKERSHAM, d. 1713

- Nave, West wall, North-West corner.
- 53(W) x 150(H) — Very pitted.
- M.I. (5 lines, cast relief) in upper 20% of a rectangular iron slab.

HERE LYETH THE BODY

OF THOMAS WICKERSHAM

WHO DIED MAY THE 11

AS AGED 78 YEAR

AN DOMINI 1713

1. 86E was dug out of the churchyard in 1931, see Willatts (*SAC* 125 107), perhaps buried there since the tower collapse of 1785; Willatts (*SAC* 125 102) lists 3 of the 4 extant cast iron slabs at East Grinstead; another iron fragment is parked nearby, probably unrelated, showing the Royal Arms.
2. The eccentric wording and orthography of 86E results from casting errors.
3. For William Wickersham, close in date, see 86Z.
4. Willatts misdates 86E to 1714.
5. Thomas Wickersham had been churchwarden.
6. NBI records burial of Thomas Wickersham on 15 May 1714 at East Grinstead.

East Grinstead, 86F Wall-mounted slab for Robert PICKNALL, d. 1712

- Nave West wall, North-West corner.
- (Irregular) 44(W) x 57(H) x 15(D) — Sound.
- M.I. (8 lines, engraved) on a freestone slab.

Here Lyeth

The Body of

ROBERT PICKNA

LL who Departed This

Life The 21 Day of

Febru. in The year of

our LORD GOD

[1]71½ Aged 37 year[s]

1. A remarkably thick slab, perhaps formerly built into the mediaeval wall of the collapsed church.

East Grinstead, 86G Mural monument for John and Catherine CRANSTON, d. 1781 and 1823

- North aisle wall, towards West end, above head height.
- 101(W) x 99(H) — Very good.
- Thin black baseplate with pointed top; M.I. (9 lines, engraved) on an unframed white marble tablet, set landscape-wise; cornice with lamp in relief; signed (lower right): 'W.PISTELL, NEW ROAD'.
- John Cranston, Esq., of East Court, Sussex, d. 26 Mar 1781, aet 44; his wife, Catherine, d. 13 Feb 1823, aet 80.

1. Style and consistency of lettering suggest a date after 1823.
2. Mrs Cranston owned lands in East Grinstead in 1785 (R. Davey 90 ff).
3. Noted by Gunnis (*Dict.* 306) as by William Pistell, fl. 1814-44.

East Grinstead, 86H Wall-mounted iron slab for Anne FORSTER, d. 1591

[Plate 56]

- North aisle wall, centre, at head height.
- 122(W) x 72(H) — Fine; some wear; repairs (below).
- M.I. (8 lines, cast relief) set landscape-wise on an iron slab; complex patterned border with beading on outer edge.

HER LIETH ANE FORST

R DAVGHTER AND

HEYR TO THOMA

GAYNSFORD ESQVIER

DECEASED XVIII OF

IANUAREI 1591 LEAVING

BEHIND HER 11 SONES

AND

V DAUGHTERS

1. 86H was discovered in 1850, after a house fire, used as a fire-back.
2. It is a duplicate, see Lower 'On Miscellaneous Antiquities discovered in ... Sussex' (*SAC* 5 203) citing Manning & Bray (*History and Antiquities of the County of Surrey* II 369); Willatts (*SAC* 125 109 and figure 3) notes that 86H derives from the original slab at Crowhurst, Surrey; others were at Ardingly (see 8F) and Anne of Cleves House, Lewes.
3. There is a trend at East Grinstead of M.I.s in cast iron slabs, set landscape-wise, see Lower (*SAC* 5 202-3).

East Grinstead, 86I Mural monument for Nathaniel MOORE, d. 1746, and family members

- North aisle wall, West of North door, above head height.
- c.94(W); H inaccessible — Very good; faded.
- M.I. (10 lines, in English) on a cartouche within a draped border; below, a large scrolled and fluted bracket; above, an urn.
- Nathaniel Moore, Gent., buried 7 Dec 1746, aet 92; his wife, Dorothea, buried 21 Nov 1752, aet 81; their son, also Nathaniel Moore, Gent., buried 31 Aug 1768, aet 72.

1. Consistency of lettering suggests a date after 1768.

East Grinstead, 86J Mural monument for Rev. John and Hester STAPLES, d. 1732 and 1746

- North aisle wall, immediately West of North door, above head height.
- c.92(W); H inaccessible — Very good.
- M.I. (15 lines, engraved, black) on an oval tablet; escutcheon over; broad black marble surround with ornate scrolled white border; above, part of a curved pediment topped by a flaming lamp.
- Rev. John Staples, vicar of East Grinstead for 44 years, buried 4 Aug 1732, aet 70; his wife, Hester, buried 27 Aug 1746, aet 77; daughter of George Elfred, Esq., of Hooe.

1. Consistency of lettering suggests a date after 1746.
2. For their sons see 86K.
3. JH notes that for heraldry see Lambarde (*SAC* 67 182). Rev. Staples was vicar of East Grinstead 1690-1731 and rector of Brede 1702-1732, see Venn (1 4 150).

East Grinstead, 86K Mural monument for Elfred and John STAPLES, d. 1784 and 1789

- North aisle wall, East of North door, above head height.
- 120(W); H inaccessible — Fine; local losses (garland from basement).
- Dark grey baseplate with pointed top; escutcheon over; cornice on very unusual fluted pilasters with narrow bottoms, ending in foliage (missing on right); M.I. on tablet set portrait-wise, base mouldings; black apron with palmettes in corners; broad corbel with acanthus, shells and grapes. Signed (lower left) 'E. PEIRCE fecit' and (lower right) 'DEPTFORD'.
- Elfred Staples, lawyer (Middle Temple, etc.), d. 5 Mar 1784, aet 86; John Staples, lawyer (Middle Temple, etc.) d. 15 May 1789, aet 87; both sons of Rev. John Staples, A.M., vicar of East Grinstead and his wife, Hester.

1. Consistency of lettering suggests a date after 1789.

2. For their parents see 86J.

3. See Gunnis (*Dict.* 304) on Edward Peirce, fl. 1770-90.

East Grinstead, 86L Mural monument for Francis and Edward GREEN, d. 1754 and 1763

- North aisle wall, at North-East chapel screen, above head height.
- Inaccessible (very large) — Fine; faded.
- Broken pointed pediment; a lamp on each slope; in centre above, an escutcheon; M.I. on tablet set portrait-wise within grey Doric pilasters; blank apron between black scrolled brackets.
- Francis Green, Gent., of Sevenoaks, Kent and East Grinstead (50 years), d. 1 Apr 1754, aet 73; his 8 siblings, all older, all unnamed; his wife Anne, family unnamed; his youngest son Edward Green, Gent., 16[?] Oct 1719 - 21 Aug 1763, aet 43.

1. See Lambarde (*SAC* 67 182) for heraldry.

2. NBI records burial of Francis Green on 5 Apr 1754 at East Grinstead.

East Grinstead, 86M Ledger for George GURNETT, d. 1746

- North-East chapel floor, towards North wall, partly obscured by furnishings.
- 74(W) x 193(L) — Worn.
- M.I. (engraved) in upper 50% of a freestone (perhaps Horsham?) slab; head to West.

Here ly ...
of the Reverend
Mr GEORGE GURNETT
who was Vicar of this
Parish near 11 Years
And Rector of West
Chiltington in this
County 18 Years
He departed this life
August ye 2nd[?] 174[?]6 in ye
51 year of his Age

1. JH notes that George Gurnett was BA and MA from Trinity College, Cambridge and chaplain to the college 1723-46, see Venn (1 2 276).

2. NBI records burial of George Gurnett on 4 Aug 1746 at East Grinstead.

East Grinstead, 86N Anonymous ledger, undated

- North-East chapel floor, East of 86M, mostly obscured by furnishings.
- Inaccessible — Unknown.
- Traces of an escutcheon, then a M.I. on a black slab; head to North.

East Grinstead, 86O Mural monument for Gibbs CRAWFURD, d. 1793

- Sanctuary North wall, West end, above head height.
- 123(W); H inaccessible — Very good.
- Black baseplate in obelisk form; rises above a draped urn over a tablet set landscape-wise with cornice; flanking a small M.I., 2 braziers; below, an ornamental row of outsize droplets; signed (lower left): 'C.ROSSI. Sculptor. London'.
- Gibbs Crawfurd, Esq., J.P. (30 years), M.P. for Queenborough, Clerk of Ordnance, d. 13 Oct 1793, aet 61; his wife, Anna, family unnamed.

1. Noted by Nairn & Pevsner (492).

2. 86O is pendant to 86V.

3. Patron was widow, Anna.

4. Gibbs Crawfurd owned taxable lands in East Grinstead in 1785 (R. Davey 90 ff); for a map of his seat at Sainthill, West of the centre of East Grinstead [1776?], see Steer (19); Sainthill was acquired by John Crawfurd in 1733 and replaced by Gibbs Crawfurd in 1788 with a larger building (Farrant 233).

5. 86O is by J.C.F. Rossi (1762-1839), Gunnis (*Dict.* 328). 86O and 86V were early works by Rossi,

who was employed early in his career by the Coade stone factory but whose promising start as a Royal Academy Gold Medallist was not sustained, see Whinney (304, 367).

6. JH notes that Anna Crawfurd was daughter of Charles Payne of Newick and East Grinstead. (see 86P and 86R).

East Grinstead, 86P Ledger for Charles PAYNE, d. 1734

- Sanctuary floor, North side, partly obscured by furnishings.
- 96(W) x 205(L) — Very good.
- Escutcheon, then M.I. (4 lines) in upper 40% of a black slab; head to West.

Here lyeth the Body of

CHARLES PAYNE Efq.

Obiit AUGUST 18TH 1734

Ætatis 28

1. For Payne's monument see 86R.

East Grinstead, 86Q Ledger for Henry PAYNE, d. 1708

- Sanctuary floor, North-East corner, East of 86P.
- 92(W) x 195(L) — Worn.
- M.I. in upper end of a cretaceous freestone slab; head to West.

UNDERNEATH LIES HENRY PAYNE

GENT. WHO DIED IUNE 5TH

1708

1. For Payne's mural monument see 86S.
2. The discrepant dates of death are curious, see 86S.

East Grinstead, 86R Mural monument for Charles PAYNE, d. 1734

- Sanctuary East wall, North-East corner, above head height.
- 120(W); H inaccessible — Very good.
- A pointed pediment in grey marble enclosing an escutcheon; broken cornice; M.I. fills tablet with domed top, flanked by Corinthian pilasters with foliate decoration and scrolls; all on a large gadrooned base moulding, over a curved apron with inverted acanthus brackets and a skull.
- Charles Payne, Esq., of Newick, d. 18 Aug 1734, aet 28; surviving son of Edward Payne, Esq., of East Grinstead and third wife Anne; his uncle, John Payne, of Newick; his daughters, Anna (still living); Mary, d. 5 Jun 1734, an infant; his wife, Mary, family unnamed.

1. For Charles Payne's ledger see 86P.
2. 86R was erected soon after his death, by his widow Mary.
3. An earlier wife of Charles Payne's father Edward, was Hannah Hickman, of East Grinstead, licence to marry 28 Jan 1705-6, see Dunkin (*Licences 1670-1729* 193).
4. JH notes that both the ledger (86P) and this monument have coats of arms, but neither are mentioned in Lambarde.

East Grinstead, 86S Mural monument for Robert and Henry PAYNE, both d. 1708 [Plate 57]

- Sanctuary East wall, South-East corner, above head height.
- 102(W); H inaccessible — Very good.
- Grey marble frame; a deep, broken curved pediment encloses a large urn in relief; on a cornice; below, M.I. (engraved) on a white marble tablet, set portrait-wise; below, base moulding with 2 cherubs as corbels flanking an escutcheon on the apron adorned with palms and other foliage.
- Robert Payne, Gent., of Newick, d. 7 Dec 1708, aet 74; his brother, Henry Payne, Gent., of Newick, d. 5 Jul 1708, aet 67; their father, Edward Payne; Robert and Henry Payne were domestic partners 40 years; virtues - monarchy, episcopacy, piety and charity.

1. An unsigned work of a very high class.
2. For Henry Payne's ledger see 86Q.
3. Discrepancies of death date for Henry Payne are curious.
4. JH notes that NBI records burial of Henry Payne on 10 July 1708 at East Grinstead, so death on 5th July rather than 5th June (see 86Q) seems likely. See Lambarde (*SAC* 67 181) for heraldry. Robert Payne left money in his will to support the local charity school, see Caffyn (109).

East Grinstead, 86T Ledger for George HORNE, d. 1738

- Sanctuary floor, South side, partly obscured by furnishings.
- 106(W) x 198(L) — Very good.
- Escutcheon, then M.I. (4 lines, engraved) on upper 50% of a black slab; head to West.

M[R] GEORGE HORNE
OF LONDON BANKER
DIED DECEM[R] 31 1738
AGED 44 YEARS

1. JH notes that George Horne married Philadelphia Payne daughter of Edward Payne of East Grinstead and his 2nd wife Elizabeth, daughter of Sir Nicholas Toke, see Comber (*Ardingly* 287). For heraldry, see Lambarde (*SAC* 67 181).

East Grinstead, 86U Floor monument for Margaret and John PAYNE, d. 1723 and d. 1730

- Sanctuary floor, South-West corner.
- 105(W) x 195(L) — Very good.
- M.I. (11 lines, engraved) in upper 80% of a black slab; head to West.
- Margaret Payne, d. 11 Dec 1723, aet 44; wife of John Payne, Esq., of Newick, d. 31 Mar 1730, aet 65.

1. For heraldry, see Lambarde (*SAC* 67 181).

East Grinstead, 86V Mural monument for John and Anna ANTROBUS, d. 1794 and d. 1793

- Sanctuary, South wall, above head height.
- 122(W); H inaccessible — Very good.
- Pendant with 86O.
- John Antrobus, Esq., of London, banker, d. 27 Apr 1794, aet 32; his wife, Anna, d. 18 Jun 1793, aet 23, daughter of Gibbs Crawfurd, Esq., of Saint Hill.

1. Not signed by Rossi but pendant to 86O.
2. The patron of 86V was probably Anne Crawfurd, who was bereaved of her husband, her daughter and her son-in-law between June 1793 and April 1794.

East Grinstead, 86W Mural monument for Samuel JEFFRIES, d. 1819

- Nave East wall, towards South-East chapel, at head height.
- 80(W) x 56(H) — Very good.
- A rectangular black baseplate; a white unframed trapezoidal tablet; straight cornice on 2 ball feet; below, a supporting shelf; M.I. (11 lines, engraved).
- Samuel Jeffries, Esq., of Westmoreland, Jamaica and Pixton, East Grinstead, d. 19 Dec 1819, aet 74.

1. One of a number of Sussex monuments commemorating residency in the West Indies.

East Grinstead, 86X Mural monument for Lord William ABERGAVENNEY, d. 1744

- South aisle wall, South-East corner, above head height.
- 140(W); H inaccessible — Fine; scaling achievement.

- A remarkable composition; sarcophagus with a decorative edging; gadrooned top; M.I.
  (Latin) on face of sarcophagus; a huge achievement.

Hic juxta depositæ sunt Reliquiæ
Honoratissimi Domini
GULIELMI *Domini* ABERGAVENNY
Baronis Angliæ Primatii
Qui Dignitatem, a longa traditam Majorum Serie
Gerendo vere illustrem,
Merendo fecit suam
Obiit 21 Septembris 1744 Suæq. Ætatis 47

1. One of few monuments at East Grinstead cited by Horsfield (*Sussex* I 390-91); noted by Nairn &
   Pevsner (492).
2. Abergavenny's name stands at the head of the town land tax return in 1785 as owner and occupier
   (R. Davey 89); sometimes he is given as d. 1745, see pedigree in J. Cooper 'The Manor of Cuckfield
   from the fourteenth to the nineteenth centuries' (*SAC* 41 80).

East Grinstead, 86Y Floor stone for John TILT, d. 1778

- Nave floor, near entrance to South-East chapel.
- 60(W) x 115(L) — Very worn.
- Winged cherub, then M.I. (engraved) on freestone slab; head to West.

In Memory of
IOHN TILT..
who died April 7
177[?].
Aged 34[?] Years ...

1. From the churchyard.
2. NBI records burial of John Tilt on 11 Apr 1778 at East Grinstead.

East Grinstead, 86Z Floor stone for William WICKERSHAM, d. 1766

- Nave floor, alongside and South of 86Y.
- 57(W) x 103(L) — Fine.
- Crossed bones, then M.I. (engraved) on a freestone slab; head to West.

In Memory of WILL
Son of John & Ann
WICKERSHAM
who died June yᵉ 12ᵗʰ
1766 Aged 24 Years

1. From the churchyard.
2. For a possible relative of William Wickersham see 86E.

East Grinstead, 86AA Iron floor slab for Anne BARCLEY, d. 1570

- Nave floor, near South door.
- 148(W) x 58(H) — Fine.
- M.I. (2 diagonal lines in relief; 3 lines in relief), all set landscape-wise on a rectangular cast
  iron slab; head to East.

HERE LYETH ANNE BARCLEY SOMETYME
WYFE VNTO HENRY BARCLEY DOCTOR. OF
LAWE DECEASED THE 12 OF MAY 1570

1. Noted in Nairn & Pevsner (492); Willatts (*SAC* 125 102, 104 and 110) notes that 86AA was returned
   to the church in 1881 having been used upside down as scullery step in the vicarage.
2. Slabs with the M.I. set landscape-wise are extremely unusual.
3. JH notes that Anne must have been first wife of Henry Berkeley, MP for East Grinstead in 1571.
   He was awarded DCL by New College, Oxford, in 1567, where he was Fellow 1554-68. No trace of
   marriage, which must have taken place after he left, as Fellows had to be unmarried, see Hasler (1
   430). See also Bolney 33C, for monument to Berkeley's second wife.

East Grinstead, 86BB Iron floor slab for Francis HASELDEN, d. 1616 [Plate 58]

- Nave floor, alongside and East of 86AA.
- 134(W) x 46(H) — Fine; 2 of 4 corners lost.
- M.I. (in relief) on a rectangular slab; lower corners removed; head to East.

HERE LYETH BVRYED FRANCIS HASELDEN LATE. WYFE
VNTO IOHN HASELDEN OF HAY DAFTER VNTO HUMFREY
..VERT ESQVYRE WHO DYED AVGVST 26 ANNO 1616

1. Noted by Nairn & Pevsner (492); Willatts (*SAC* 125 102, 104 & 100 & figure 4) notes that 86BB was used as hearthstone in vicarage; after a fire of 1908 it was returned to church, the corners having been cut to fit a hearth.
2. One John Haselden, of East Grinstead, yeoman, stood surety for a marriage licence in July 1621, see Dunkin (*Licences 1586-1643* 126); parish register notes burial on 26 Apr 1616 of Francis Haselden; John Haselden was buried 3 Mar 1627, see Crawfurd (166, 174) and in dispute about access to a pew in the church in 1623, see Renshaw (*SAC* 55 272-3).

East Grinstead, 86CC Floor monument for Tobias SHEWEN, d. 1730

- Nave floor, alongside and North of 86BB.
- 49(W) x 75(H) — Very worn.
- M.I. (engraved) on a freestone slab; curved top, head to West.

In
Memory of
TOBIAS SHEWEN
who *Died* the 12th of
March 1730 Aged
48 years
And also SUSANNA [?]
his wife ...

1. Probably from the churchyard.
2. NBI records burial of Tobias Shewen on 14 Mar 1730 at East Grinstead.

(87) EAST GULDEFORD, St. Mary

On the Kent border; the church was constructed after the draining of the marsh and consecrated in 1505 under the patronage of Sir Richard Guldeford who died the following year while on a pilgrimage to the Holy Land; the Guldeford seat was at Hemsted, Kent (baronetcy extinct in 1740) and his are the arms mounted on a freestone block (61 x 95) towards the East end of the North wall; the pavements were described as in 'indifferent good order' in 1686 (Ford); the parish had 26 communicants in 1603, see Renshaw (*Ecclesiastical Returns*); Nairn & Pevsner (495-6) note that the interior was remodelled in c.1820 (see box pews) but is now aisleless, though formerly with timber posts.

East Guldeford, 87A Mural monument for Stephen IEWHURST, d. 1782

- Nave, South wall, above head height, embedded in plaster.
- 61(H); (W) inaccessible — Fine; local losses (edges).
- In marble, an unframed, M.I. (8 lines, engraved, black) on upper 80% of surface of an oval plaque.
- Stephen Iewhurst, of East Guldeford, d. 3 Nov 1782, aet 84; his issue, a son Stephen.

1. Noted by Horsfield (*Sussex* I 502).
2. The space left available for further lettering was never used.

(88) EAST HOATHLY, Parish Church

Some Perpendicular details; mostly 1856 - Nairn & Pevsner (496); fabric reported in 1724 to be fine (Ford); there is also an external tablet for Samuel Atkins (d.1742), gardener to Duke of Newcastle.

East Hoathly, 88A Ledger stone for John MITTELL, d. 1734

- Centre of nave floor, far West end.
- 120(W) x 200(L) — Badly worn; pitted.
- Escutcheon and M.I. (5 lines, engraved) in upper 60% of dark grey freestone slab; head to the West.

Here Lieth Interrd y Body of
Iohn M[ittell] Esq. Late of y
Moat [in this] Pariſh who Died
November 1.. 1734
Aged 6 Years

1. See Horsfield (*Sussex* I 359), Lambarde (*SAC* 70 154) - noting arms, Nairn & Pevsner (496).
2. For the inaccessible mural monument associated with 88A see Addition (2).
3. JH notes that NBI records him as John Mittell, buried on 18 Nov 1734 at East Hoathly.

East Hoathly, 88B Mural monument for Rev. Thomas PORTER, d. 1794, his wife, d. 1792, and 5 infant children

- Choir, South wall, near West end, at head height.
- 90(W) x 210(H) — Excellent.
- Against a grey baseplate of obelisk shape, an urn, in high relief; below, a cornice over an unframed rectangular M.I.; below that, a base moulding and 2 corbels.
- Rev. Thomas Porter, M.A., rector of East Hoathly and Ripe, d. 30 Sep 1794, aet 74; his wife Mary, d. 1 Aug 1792, aet 67, daughter of Christopher and Mary Coates, of Wensley, Yorkshire; their issue - five of their children died in infancy - Catherine, d. 22 Aug 1753, aet 3; Christopher, d. 18 Dec 1753, infant; Thomas, d. 8 Mar 1760, infant; Elizabeth, d. 8 Jan 1761, aet 4; Thomas, d.14 Sep 1761, infant; surviving children unnamed.

1. Noted by Horsfield (*Sussex* I 359).
2. Other rectors of Ripe were commemorated there (see 213).
3. JH notes that Rev. Thomas Porter was vicar of West Hoathly 1750-53; rector of East Hoathly 1752-94; and rector of Ripe 1757-94, see CCEd, Hennessy (84, 125) and Venn (1 3 382).

East Hoathly Additions

Horsfield (*Sussex* I 359).
(1) Slab for M Haworth, rector, 1718. The rector 1693-1718 was Richard Haworth - see Hennessy (84) and CCEd.
Nairn & Pevsner (496).
(2) To John Mittel d. 1734, and his wife, Martha, d. 1738, with an urn before an obelisk, by Edward Pierce of Deptford (fl. 1770-90); inaccessible in locked room beneath tower; Gunnis (*Dict.* 304) notes that this monument is signed and datable c.1780; for the related ledger see 88A. Why was this erected some 50 years after Mittel's death?

(93) EASTBOURNE, St. Mary

Arcades and most of the remainder c.1200, aisle windows a little later, late 14th-century remains of Easter Sepulchre in chancel - Nairn & Pevsner (483-4); this area was altered to accommodate 93A - Horsfield (*Sussex* I 296-7); sympathetic restorations took place between 1844-1873, see Leeney (*SAC* 88 157ff); for a plan see *SNQ* XV 18; for a view from South-East see G.F. Chambers 'Eastbourne' (*SAC* 14 127); in 1686 it was reported that paving was required - Ford (51); the chancels belonged at that date to Mr Alcorn [centre?], Sir William Wilson (South-East) and the Gildredges (North-East); by 1724, the repairs [centre?] belonged to Mr Thomas Worge - Ford (167); in Horsfield's day the North-East chapel was for Gildredge and Gilbert and the South-East for Cavendish; the parish was always populous: there were 500 communicants in 1603, see Renshaw (*Ecclesiastical Returns*).

Eastbourne, 93A Wall monument for Henry LUSHINGTON, d. 1763 [Plate 59]

- South nave aisle, South wall, near West end, at head height.
- 147(W) x 287(H) — Very good; cracks (arms).
- Portrait bust in civil dress on moulded pedestal against grey marble backplate contained within moulded ogival arch; over the subject's head, an escutcheon flanked by garlands; below, straight base moulding, then M.I. (many lines, engraved, black) filling an unframed white marble panel set landscape-wise; at foot, 2 scrolled corbels.
- Henry Lushington, soldier (East India, Calcutta, etc.), from 1754, died Patna, India, 1763, aet 26; eldest son of Henry Lushington, D.D., vicar of Eastbourne, and Mary his wife.

1. Originally on chancel North wall, in Easter sepulchre alcove, adjacent to present 93KK (*SNQ* XV 18); in its present location since 1851 - Lambarde (*SAC* 70 140) noting arms; Nairn & Pevsner (484) and St. Mary's (*Inscriptions* 27-30); probably moved here when 93K was moved.
2. The present ogival arch must have been built to accommodate the monument on its removal from the sanctuary and there are other signs of disruption to 93A.
3. The M.I. correction 'PERSIAN' is curious, perhaps a reflection of the patron, the Rev. Henry Lushington's, scholarly and personal interest in the commemorative project.
4. The quality of the portrait bust 93A is notably high.
5. For more Lushington patronage (of the local sculptor Morris) see 93K.

Eastbourne, 93B Mural monument for John MORTIMER, d. 1824

- South aisle, West wall, high up.
- c.102(W); (H) inaccessible — Very good.
- M.I. (22 + 22 lines, engraved, black) on a white marble panel; thick black baseplate; below, base mould, 2 squared corbels with rose decorative; above, decorative frieze, cornice moulding and pointed pediment with blank lozenge.
- John Mortimer, late of Lewisham, Kent, d. 6 Oct 1824, aet 49; second son of Charles Smith and Elizabeth Mortimer, of Eastbourne; John Mortimer's eldest son, John Russell, d. 27 Oct 1810, aet 4; and his youngest son, John, of Redhill, Surrey, d. 18 Nov 1876, aet 65, buried at Norwood; also Charles and Elizabeth Mortimer's youngest daughter, Maria d. 17 Jan 1866, aet 81.

1. See St. Mary's (*Inscriptions* 27-30).
2. Final 11 lines added.
3. JH notes that the father of John Mortimer (d. 1824) was Charles Smith Mortimer whose burial is recorded on 5 Apr 1803 at Eastbourne.

Eastbourne, 93C Mural monument for Joseph FILDER, d. 1818

- South nave aisle wall, West end, at head height.
- 118(W) x 107(H) — Very good.
- M.I. (6 lines, engraved, centred, black) on a panel of trapezoidal form; moulded frame flanking; cornice moulding, then scrolled pediment with rosettes and foliage; below, apron with small escutcheon with motto and ferns, flanked by 2 decorative corbels; all on a thin black baseplate; unsigned.
- Joseph Filder of Eastbourne, d. 28 Dec 1818, aet 61; his wife, Mary, d. 21 Mar 1795, aet 37.

1. In situ in Lambarde (*SAC* 70 140) noting arms.
2. See St. Mary's (*Inscriptions* 9-10).

Eastbourne, 93D Mural monument for Rev. Alexander BRODIE, d. 1828

- Nave, South wall, West end, very high, above 81C.
- 85(W) x (H) inaccessible — Very good.
- M.I. (engraved, Latin) fills a white marble panel in pedestal form; thin, black baseplate; above, a frieze of volutes, drapes and a rose; on top, a flaming urn on base mouldings; below, in relief on the apron, the symbols of a pastor's office; decorative corbel signed (lower right, only partly legible): '... [SQUARE?] / LONDON'.
- Rev. Alexander Brodie, D.D., vicar of Eastbourne for 18 years, d. 18 Jun 1828, aet 53; his widow, Anna, d. 6 Oct 1864, aet 85; issue - 11 children; eldest son Alexander, d. 9 May 1815, aet 6.

1. See St. Mary's (*Inscriptions* 27-30).
2. Final 4 lines perhaps added in the 1860s.
3. JH notes that Alexander Brodie had been private chaplain to George IV when Prince of Wales. He married Anna, daughter of John Walter, founder of *The Times* (*BLG* 1952 267).

Eastbourne, 93E Grave marker for Alexander BRODIE, d. 1815

- Nave floor, far West end.
- 46(W) x 46(H) — Good.
- M.I. (engraved) in a diamond-shaped slate panel.

MEM
ALEX: BRODIE
ÆTAT 7
1815

1. Alexander Brodie is mentioned in M.I. of 93D which commemorates his father; Alexander was aged either 6 or 7 (81D-E).
2. See St. Mary's (*Inscriptions* 9-10).

Eastbourne, 93F Mural monument for Arthur PIGGOTT, d. 1819

- Nave, North wall, far West end, at head height.
- 105(W) x c.145(H) — Very good.
- M.I. (engraved, black) fills white marble oval panel; thin black baseplate; below, small scrolled corbels for both panel and frame; unsigned; top 6 lines original, remainder added.
- Sir Arthur Piggott, Knt, d. 6 Sep 1819, aet 69; his wife of 46 years, Jane, d. 3 Jul 1841, aet 89.

1. Noted but not located by Horsfield (*Sussex* I 296-7).
2. See St. Mary's (*Inscriptions* 9-10).
3. The later M.I. was left short of space in the final lines.
4. The alignment of corbels for both panel and backplate is highly unusual.
5. JH notes that Arthur Leary Piggott was solicitor general to the Prince of Wales 1783-92; knighted 1806; MP to various Sussex constituencies 1806-19; Attorney General 1806-07. He married Jane Dunnington. See Thorne (4 803).
6. For a contemporary courtier see 93D.

Eastbourne, 93G Mural monument for Thomas WILLARD, d. 1794, his wife, 3 children and ancestors

- North aisle, North wall, far West end, above head height.
- c.90(W), (H) inaccessible — Good; staining.
- M.I. (many lines, engraved, black, centred) fills a white oval plaque with light black inlay border; above, an escutcheon on a stand; below, white base moulding and partial black backplate; below that, black apron with engraved M.I. in slate (11 lines, engraved); at foot, small ball finial; unsigned.
- Thomas Willard, Esq., of Eastbourne, d. 21 Jan 1794, aet 64; his widow, Harriot, d. 14 Dec 1807, aet 68; their eldest son, Thomas George Willard, d. 2 Feb 1794, aet 34, buried St. Bride's, Fleet Street, London; second son, William Davis Willard, d. 18 May 1778, aet 16;

and fourth daughter, Louisa, d. 13 Jan 1777, aet 4; also, George Willard, of Eastbourne, buried 24 Feb 1559, aet 75; his widow, Sisley Willard, buried 26 Apr 1559, aet 71.

1. In situ - Lambarde (*SAC* 70 140) arms noted; See St. Mary's (*Inscriptions* 14-17).
2. For other Willard commemoration, see 93H, L and DD, and at nearby East Dean (85A); at Hailsham (119) there is a tablet dated 1839 setting out the pedigree of the family; since the lettering seems to have been completed in a single stage, 93G probably postdates Harriot's death in 1807; Thomas Willard was taxed on lands in Eastbourne in 1785 (R. Davey 70); Willard's wife was Harriot Davies.
3. The composition of 93G is unusually flat.
4. George Willard, d. 1559 and his wife Sisley, d. 1559 were the ancestors of John Willard (1632-1680) whose three children were Thomas (1654-1733) see 93DD, John (1663-1716) see Friston Addition 3, and Nicholas (1666-1728) see Friston Addition 3. One of Nicholas' sons was Thomas (1699-?) who married Mary Smythe (1700-1774) see 93L and they had three children - Katherine (1727-1735) see 93DD, Thomas (1729-1794) commemorated on this monument and Nicholas (173-?). This Thomas married Harriet Davis (1740-1807) see 93G and they had Thomas George Willard (1760-1794), William David Willard (1762-1778), Louisa Willard (1770-1774), Nicholas Willard (1774-1852) see 93H, and others. See J. Willard, *Willard Memoir; or Life and Times of Major Simon Willard*, published 1858.

Eastbourne, 93H Mural monument for Mary Ann WILLARD, d. 1812, and later members of the family

- North aisle, North wall, East of 81G, above head height.
- 102(W); (H) inaccessible — Very good; colour.
- M.I. (many lines, engraved, black) on a rectangular white panel set portrait-wise; flanking, black Doric pilasters, breaking forward on scrolled and fluted corbels; below, curved apron with additional M.I. and pink inlay border; above, entablature mouldings supporting a white marble obelisk with achievement.
- Mary Ann Willard, d. 22 Feb 1812, aet 30; daughter of Nathaniel William Thomas, Esq., of Cobcourt, Selmeston; and first wife of Nicholas Willard, Esq., of Eastbourne, d. 12 May 1852, aet 77, sixth son of Thomas Willard, Esq.; second wife was Barbara Bean Willard, d. 30 Apr 1817, aet 28, daughter of Captain George Bayly, of Storrington, Sussex; and third wife was Louisa, d. 21 May 1866, at Paris; also, Charles Willard, Esq., of Eastbourne, fourth son of Thomas Willard, d. 22 May 1843, aet 80, buried Sevenoaks, Kent; also Maria Ann Cole, third daughter of Thomas Willard and widow of Rev William Cole, d. 12 Apr 1844, aet 75, buried Brighton; also Harriott Willard, spinster, eldest daughter of Thomas Willard, d. 30 Jan 1846, aet 80.

1. In situ - Lambarde (*SAC* 70 140) noting arms; See St. Mary's (*Inscriptions* 14-17).
2. For other members of the family see 93G.
3. 93H is an ambitious and expensive monument and pendant with 93K which is signed by Morris.
4. 93H must date from the 1770s, not the 1810s, perhaps as part of a commemorative campaign launched by the Willards after the death of some of Thomas Willard's children in the 1770s.

Eastbourne, 93I Ledger for Jane MARCHANT, d. 1762?

- North aisle floor, towards West end.
- 65(W) x 192(L) — Very worn.
- M.I. (few lines, shallow engraved) in upper 30% of a cream freestone slab; head to West.

In Memory of

*J*ANE wife of

H*ENRY* M*ARCHANT*

..

She died ... March[?]

...

...

...

1. Identified as H. Marchant 1762 in St. Mary's (*Inscriptions* 14-17).

2. JH notes that NBI gives burial of Henry Marchant 16 Oct 1762, and Jane Marchant 12 Oct 1789, both at Eastbourne. See later inscriptions on 93J which tend to confirm these details, given period between death and burial.

Eastbourne, 93J Mural monument for Nicholas VENTRIS, d. 1734, and others

- North aisle, North wall, to West of North door, at head height.
- c.97(W) — Very good.
- A black backplate in obelisk form; a white unframed oval panel with M.I. (25 lines (16+9) engraved); below, grey base moulding, then a curved ornamental apron, blank, with black ball finial at foot.
- Nicholas Ventris, Gent., d. 16 Jun 1734, aet 66; his wife Mary, d. 12 Jan 1743/4, aet 73; eldest son John, d. 29 May 1710, aet 7; youngest son Nicholas, d. 1 Nov 1765, aet 59; also Henry Marchant, Gent., d. 11 Oct 1762, aet 66; his wife Jane, d. 7 Oct 1789, aet 90; also Mary Mayfield, widow, d. 26 Dec 1805, aet 92; also Jane, daughter of William and Mary Russell, d. 2 Apr 1768, aet 32.

1. See St. Mary's (*Inscriptions* 14-17).
2. Status of the final 7 lines of the M.I. is unclear, they were probably added later, but in a very similar lettering hand, to commemorate individuals apparently unrelated to the Ventris family, i.e. Marchant (see 93I), Mayfield and Russell.
3. JH notes that Nicholas Ventrice and Mary Verrell were granted an Archdeaconry of Chichester marriage licence, 24 Oct 1699, see E.H.W. Dunkin *Calendar of Sussex Marriage Licences ... for the Archdeaconry of Chichester, 1575-1730* (*SRS* vol. 9 133).

Eastbourne, 93K Mural monument for Mary LUSHINGTON I, d. 1775, and Mary Lushington II, d. 1811 [Plate 60]

- North aisle, North wall, centre, high.
- 106(W) — Very good; colour.
- 81 K is pendant with 81H; signed 'MORRIS invenit & sculpsit'.
- Mary Lushington, d. 24 Jul 1775, aet 66; first wife of Henry Lushington, D.D., vicar of Eastbourne; and daughter of Roger Altham, D.D., archdeacon of Middlesex, etc.; issue unnamed; another Mary, second wife of Henry Lushington, d. 17 Apr 1811, aet 78.

1. Cited by Gunnis (*Dict.* 265); See St. Mary's (*Inscriptions* 14-17); formerly in sanctuary (with 93A); moved here in 1851; in situ in Lambarde (*SAC* 70 139) noting arms and assuming one single Mary Lushington, not 2.
2. 93K commemorates both wives of Henry Lushington; husband is patron (M.I.), so likely to be datable c.1776.
3. 93K and 93H are pendant (93H is not signed).
4. Morris worked through the mid 1770s.
5. JH notes the reference to 93LL for Henry's second wife.

Eastbourne, 93L Ledger for Jane WILLARD, d. 1739, and Mary Willard, d. 1774

- North aisle floor, East end.
- 65(W) x 122(L) — Pitted; damaged edges.
- Empty space for arms, then M.I. (14 lines engraved) filling surface of freestone slab; head to West.

Here under lies the body
of Jane Willard the wife of
Thomas Willard of this
Place Gent. who Departed
this Life the 26 of March
1739 Aged 78 years.
Likewise of Mary Widow
of Thomas Willard and
Mother of Thomas Willard

Esq[r] of this Parish She
departed this Life the
26 day of March 1774
in the 74 Year of her Age

1. See St. Mary's (*Inscriptions* 14-17).
2. Thomas Willard, 1654-1733 (see 93DD) married Jane Westbourne 1660-1739 (see above). Their son Nicholas married Jane (see Friston addition 3) and had, with other issue, Thomas Willard 1699 -? who married Mary Smythe 1700-1774 (see above). For their son Thomas Willard 1729-94, mentioned above, see 93G. See J. Willard *Willard Memoir; or Life and Times of Major Simon Willard*.

Eastbourne, 93M Mural monument for William and Herbert MORTIMER, d. 1808 and d. 1810
- North choir aisle, North wall, between windows, above head height.
- c.80(W) x 109(H) — Very good; faded, local loss (upper right).
- A flat, moulded cornice; below, M.I. (7+6 lines, engraved) on an unframed panel; below, base mouldings and 2 small corbels with low relief acanthus decorative.
- William Mortimer, d. 24 Aug 1808, aet 27; fifth son of Charles Smith and Elizabeth Mortimer; also their sixth son, Herbert Mortimer, sailor (East India Co.), died circa 5 Sep 1810, aet 25, lost at sea off the coast of China.

1. Commemorating 2 sons of parishioners.
2. See St. Mary's (*Inscriptions* 20-26).

Eastbourne, 93N Mural monument for Charles Davies GIDDY, d. 1813
- North-East chapel, North wall, towards West end, at head height.
- 44(W) x 38(H) — Excellent; faded.
- M.I. on polished cream marble panel; dark grey cretaceous limestone backplate; above, in centre, in relief, an escutcheon.
- Charles Davies Giddy, 15 Apr 1810 - 16 May 1813, eldest son of Davies and Mary Ann Giddy.

1. In situ - Horsfield (*Sussex* I 296-7); Lambarde (*SAC* 70 139) noting arms and claiming wrongly that Charles Davies Giddy was married to Mary Anne, daughter of Francis Gilbert of Eastbourne.
2. See too St. Mary's (*Inscriptions* 20-6).
3. For Charles Davies Giddy's father, Davies Gilbert, formerly Davies Giddy, see biography by David Philip Miller in *ODNB* (q.v. 'Giddy'); The children's names were changed from Giddy to Gilbert in Jan 1818, a TAQ for 93N.
4. JH notes the reference in Thorne (4 18-21) for Davies Gilbert.

Eastbourne, 93O Mural monument for Nicholas GILBERT, d. 1774, and family
- North-East chapel, against North wall, West end, resting on the floor.
- 111(W) x 89(H) — Fine; fading; leeching.
- M.I. (20 lines [15+5], engraved, centred, black) on simple unframed cream marble panel set landscape-wise; grey marble frame; no mouldings.
- Nicholas Gilbert, Gent., d. 29 Jul 1774, aet 67; his wife Susanna, d. 20 Jun 1767, aet 56; issue - Susanna, d. 16 Mar 1816, aet 73; Mary Anne, wife of Davies Giddy, of Tredrea, Cornwall; eldest son, Nicholas, d. 7 Apr 1797, aet 62; Nicholas' wife, Catherine, d. 4 Jul 1782, aet 40; Nichoas and Catherine's daughter, also Catherine, died an infant; second son Charles, d. 1 Feb 1816, aet 79, patron of 93O; third son John, d. 3 Nov 1757, aet 19; youngest son, Thomas, d. 15 Apr 1782, aet 41, husband of Ann, d. 1807.

1. In 1785 tax was paid on lands in Eastbourne by Nicholas Gilbert's son, also Nicholas (R. Davey 70); See St. Mary's (*Inscriptions* 20-6); the younger Nicholas Gilbert, lord of the manor of Eastbourne Gildridge, made a gift of plate to the church dated 1775, see Couchman (*SAC* 55 145-6).
2. All Nicholas Gilbert's children were dead by 1816 except for Mary Ann, wife of Davies Giddy (M.I.); her husband's interest in Cornwall was political - he was MP for Bodmin, etc. (see *History Today* Nov 2005 4-5).

3. 93O is close to 93P in design.

4. JH notes that Mary Ann, wife of Davies Giddy (M.I.) was the daughter of Thomas (d. 1782) and grand-daughter of Nicholas Gilbert. See also Thorne (4 18-21).

Eastbourne, 93P Mural monument for Ann GILBERT, d. 1807, and her daughter Mary Ann, d. 1845

- North-East chapel, North wall, beneath the window, resting on the floor.
- 126(W) x 88(H) — Fine; faded.
- M.I. (7+13 lines, engraved) fills shallow cream panel set landscape-wise; simple grey-black frame; no mouldings.
- Ann Gilbert, d. 12 Jul 1807, buried London, widow of Thomas Gilbert; her daughter, Mary Ann, 29 Feb 1776 - 26 Apr 1845; wife from 18 Apr 1808, of Davies Giddy (later, Davies Gilbert), who d. about 1840; issue - 4 children survive Mary Ann.

1. See St. Mary's (*Inscriptions* 20-6).
2. The patron of 93P is Ann's daughter, Mary Ann, whom it also commemorates.
3. See 93O also for Ann's son-in-law and Mary Ann's husband, Davies Gilbert (named thus from 1808), scientific administrator and applied mathematician, born Davies Giddy (see *ODNB* q.v. 'Giddy; for political interests and diary', see *History Today* Nov 2005 4-5); he d. 24 Dec 1839, although the M.I. of 93P is vague on that point; their eldest son was Charles Davies Giddy as in 93N.
4. 93P is close to 93O in design.

Eastbourne, 93Q Mural monument for Katherine GILDREDGE, d. 1629

- North-East chapel, North wall, North-East corner, at head height.
- 150(W) x 290(H) — Very good; local losses; colour.
- M.I. (53 lines, engraved) on a large composite slate panel, set portrait-wise; flanking, attached Corinthian columns with gilded capitals; on their tall pedestals, escutcheons and masks on the outer returns, with scrolled corbels at foot; main M.I. within a moulded alabaster setting; above, a cherub, then, open broken segmented pediment with 2 angels reclining on upper cornice; achievement on very top with blank black panel below; below the main M.I., another M.I. (11 lines) in part dedicated to the patron 'Nicholas Gildredge'; at the very foot, another cherub, as corbel supporting a bulging black panel with additional M.I. (3 lines, gilded).
- Katherine Gildredge, d. 2 Oct 1629, buried 4 Oct; one of four daughter of Edward Burton, of Eastbourne, Knt, and his wife, Mary; Katherine's husband (since 15 Aug 1627), Nicholas Gildredge, of Eastbourne; issue - Thomas, died in infancy; Katherine, d. 18 Mar 1635.

(1 at top):
Solvs Christvs
MIHI
SOLA SALVS
(on lower moulding);
Mihi vivere Christvs est et mori lvcrvm. Obmvtesco qvia tv domine fecisti
Melivs est nomen bonvm qvam vngventa prætiosa
et dies mortis die nativitatis
memoria ivstus benedicta

1. In situ Lambarde (*SAC* 70 139) noting arms; Nairn & Pevsner (484) with date of death as 1625; See St. Mary's (*Inscriptions* 20-6).
2. 93Q commemorates Katherine née Burton, see 93NN for others of the Burton family.
3. Probably erected prior to Nicholas Gildredge's later wedding, see licence issued on 10 Apr 1640 for Nicholas Gildredge of Friston, Esq. and Anne Thorpe of Friston - Dunkin (*Licences 1586-1643* 263).
4. An ambitious monument and M.I. of a kind rare in Sussex at this date.

Eastbourne, 93R Wall-mounted brasses commemorating Nicholas GILDREDGE, d. 1605

- North-East chapel, East wall, North of East window, at head height.
- Shield: 15(W) x 18(H); M.I.: 42(W) x 20(H) — Fine.

- An escutcheon above M.I. (8 lines, engraved).
- Nicholas Gildredge, Esq., d. Nov 1605, aet 26; his wife, Mary, eldest daughter of Ralph Pope, Esq., of Hyndale, Buxted; issue - son, also Nicholas.

1. Burrell records in 1776 that these were on Gildredge chapel floor, though in part removed and 'laid in the window', see Davidson-Houston (*SAC* 77 162); Stephenson (507); in situ in Lambarde (*SAC* 70 139), arms noted; See St. Mary's (*Inscriptions* 20-6).
2. This Nicholas Gildredge was son of James and Frances Gildredge; for another Nicholas Gildredge, son of this Nicholas, see 93Q.

Eastbourne, 93S Wall-mounted brasses commemorating Mary FOSTER, d. 1616
- North-East chapel, East wall, South of East window, at head height.
- Arms: 19(W) x 21(H) — Highly polished. M.I.: 46(W) x 43(H) — Part stained.
- On the lower brass M.I. (19 lines, engraved).
- Mary Foster, d. 6 Dec 1616, aet 31; daughter of Ralph Pope; her first husband, Nicholas Gildredge; issue - a son Nicholas; her second husband, John Foster, issue 4 sons, 2 daughters.

1. Noted by Stephenson (507); in situ in Lambarde (*SAC* 70 139), noting arms and Davidson-Houston (*SAC* 77 163-4).
2. For Mary Foster's first marriage, to Nicholas Gildrege, see 93R.
3. Lambarde (*SAC* 70 139) names her Gildredge, not Foster.

Eastbourne, 93T Ledger for William ALLEN, d. 1719 [Plate 61]
- North choir aisle floor, centre, entrance to North-East chapel.
- 50(W) x 95(L) — Edges fine; M.I. worn.
- M.I. (9 lines, engraved) in upper 50% of a pale yellow freestone slab; head to West.
- William Allen, d. ?? Mar 1719, aet 27; son of another William and Phyllis Allen.

1. See St. Mary's (*Inscriptions* 20-6).

Eastbourne, 93U Ledger for Frances WIER, d. 1795
- North choir aisle floor, South side, East end.
- 93(W) x 186(L) — Very good.
- M.I. (4 lines, engraved) in upper 30% of a black slab; head to West.

THE REMAINS OF FRANCES WIER
LATE OF MORPETH
WHO DIED THE 15TH DAY
OF SEPTEMBER 1795

1. See St. Mary's (*Inscriptions* 20-6).
2. Since Morpeth is in Northumberland it is unclear why Frances Wier is buried at Eastbourne.

Eastbourne, 93V Ledger for Elizabeth WRIGHT, d. 1721
- North choir aisle floor, North of 93U.
- 95(W) x 172(L) — Scratched; worn.
- M.I. (engraved) in upper 25% of cretaceous limestone slab; head to West.

Here
lies interrd ye body of Elizabeth
Wright Widdow of this Parish who
departed this life March ye 19th
Anno Dom. 1721 in ye 80th year
of her Age

Eastbourne, 93W Ledger for Anne LANGSTAFF, d. 1742

- North choir aisle floor, North of 93V.
- 89(W) x 177(L) — Very worn.
- M.I. engraved in freestone slab.

Here lieth the Body
of ANNE the relict
of Capt. THO LANGSTAFFE
of the Royal navy
who departed this Life
Sept. the 3ᵈ 1742 Aged 37 Years

1. Identified as 'T Langstaffe, 1742' in St. Mary's (*Inscriptions* 20-30).
2. Very close to 93V in type.
3. Is this a relatively early reference to the 'Royal' Navy?.
4. JH notes that Thomas Langstaff married Ann Frankwell on 8 Aug 1738 at Jevington - see Sussex Marriage Index.

Eastbourne, 93X Anonymous ledger probably for [John CROWH]URST?, d. 1754, and his wife Elizabeth, d. 1763

- North choir aisle floor, South side, largely obscured by furnishings.
- 83(W) x 179(L) — Worn.
- M.I. (engraved) in upper 75% of cream freestone slab; head to West.
- [Crow]hurst, d. 3 ??? 1754[?], aet 67; his wife Elizabeth, d. 7 Apr 1763, aet 77.

1. St. Mary's (*Inscriptions* 20-26) notes M.I.s on slabs to E. Crowhurst 1727 and J Crowhurst 1754, the latter beneath the organ, which probably refer to 93X.
2. NBI gives John Crowhurst, bur. 11 Jan 1754, and Elizabeth bur. 15 Apr 1763.

Eastbourne, 93Y Ledger for Catherine MORTIMER, d. 1746, and relatives

- North choir aisle floor, centre.
- 91(W) x 195(L) — Fine; very worn in places.
- M.I. (7+7+7+5 lines, centred, engraved) on a cream freestone slab; head to West.
- Catherine Mortimer, d. 6 Oct 1746, aet 44; wife of Thomas Mortimer, Gent.; also, her sister, Frances Smith, spinster, d. 10 May 1750, aet illegible; also, their mother, Catherine, widow, d. 20 Oct 1750, aet 80; also, Thomas Mortimer, d. 31 Oct 1774, aet 78.

1. See St. Mary's (*Inscriptions* 20-26).
2. The original patron was probably Thomas Mortimer d. 1774, husband of Catherine.

Eastbourne, 93Z Ledger for Susanna EVERSFIELD, d. 1689

- North choir aisle floor, centre, North of 93Y.
- 82(W) x 166(L) — Fine; local losses (upper).
- M.I. (12 lines, engraved) in upper 60% of black slab; head to West.
- Susanna Eversfield, d. 2 Aug 1689, aet 63; widow of John Eversfield, Esq.; her first husband was Thomas Foster.

1. See St. Mary's (*Inscriptions* 20-6).

Eastbourne, 93AA Ledger for Nicholas GILBERT, d. 1713

- North choir aisle floor, South side, now obscured by an organ.
- (W) inaccessible; 180(L) — Worn.
- End parts of M.I. visible (10 lines, engraved) in upper 30% of a cream freestone slab; head to West.
- Nicholas Gilbert, d. ?? May ????, aet 39; and his wife, Mary, d. 20 Aug ????

1. See St. Mary's (*Inscriptions* 20-6), citing a ledger to Nicholas Gilbert dated 1713.
2. NBI records burial of Nicholas Gilbert on 24 May 1713 and Mary Gilbert on 13 Aug 1722, both at Eastbourne.

Eastbourne, 93BB Ledger for Thomas GILBERT, d. 1704/5
- North choir aisle floor, centre, North of 93AA.
- 100(W) x 192(L) — Fine; faded.
- M.I. (6 lines, engraved) in upper 30% of pale cream freestone slab; head to West.
- Thomas Gilbert, Gent., d. 14[?] Mar 1704/5, aet 70.

1. See St. Mary's (*Inscriptions* 20-6).
2. NBI records burial of Thomas Gilbert on 17 Mar 1705 at Eastbourne.

Eastbourne, 93CC Ledger for Jane MORTIMER, d. 1824
- North choir aisle floor, centre, North of 93BB.
- 92(W) x 102(L) — Damaged (East end and sides); very worn.
- M.I. (8 lines centred, engraved, gilded?).
- Jane Mortimer, d. 24 Mar 1824, aet 86; relict of John Hamilton Mortimer, Esq.

1. See St. Mary's (*Inscriptions* 20-26).
2. NBI records burial of Jane Mortimer on 31 Mar 1824 at Eastbourne, aet 86.

Eastbourne, 93DD Ledger for Thomas WILLARD, d. 1733
- North choir aisle floor, against South wall, partly obscured by furniture.
- 97(W) x 198(L) — Good.
- Escutcheon then M.I. (17 lines) fills surface of black slab (slate?); head to West.
- Thomas Willard, Gent., of Eastbourne, d. 16 Jun 1733, aet 77; his great-niece, Katherine,
  d. 13 Aug 1735, aet 8, daughter of another Thomas Willard and Mary Willard; also Thomas
  Willard's nephew, also Thomas Willard, d. 6 Jan 1735/6, aet 36.

1. In situ in Lambarde (*SAC* 70 141) arms noted; see St. Mary's (*Inscriptions* 20-26).
2. For the family see 93G.

Eastbourne, 93EE Ledger for Susanne WEEKES, d. 1705
- North choir aisle floor, North of 93DD.
- 85(W) x 182(L) — Cracks; rust.
- M.I. (11 lines, engraved) in upper 50% of pale cream freestone slab; head to West.
- Susanne Weekes, d. 28 Aug 1705, aet 12; third daughter of John Weekes, Gent., late of
  Westfield, Sussex; and his wife, Mary, daughter of Thomas Gilbert, Gent., of Eastbourne.

1. See St. Mary's (*Inscriptions* 20-6).
2. For Thomas Gilbert see 93BB.

Eastbourne, 93FF Ledger for [?] a daughter of Anna PHILCOX, date unknown
- North choir aisle floor, centre.
- 54(W) x 100(L) — Worn; local damage (lower corners).
- M.I. fills surface of a cut down cretaceous freestone slab; head to East.
- Illegible.

1. Close in type to 93GG.

Eastbourne, 93GG Ledger for [Samuel] PILBEAM, d. 1737
- North choir aisle floor, centre, towards North wall.
- 64(W) x 76(L) — Poor; cracked; edges damaged.
- M.I. (engraved) fill upper 60% of surface of cut down shelly slab; head to North.
- Samuel Pilbeam, d. 16 Sep 1737, aet 40; wife and issue unnamed.

1. St. Mary's (*Inscriptions* 20-26) reports a floor slab for S. Pilbeam, 1737 which can be identified with
   93GG.
2. Very close in type to 93FF.
3. Mrs N. Pilbeam of the SRS confirms this identification, citing Budgen (*Eastbourne*).
4. NBI records burial of Samuel Pilbeam on 19 Sep 1737 at Eastbourne.

Eastbourne, 93HH Ledger for Elizabeth DUTTON, d. 1758

- North choir aisle floor, centre, towards West end.
- 66(W) x 76(L) — Very worn; edges damaged.
- M.I. (8? lines, engraved) in upper 75% of surface of cream cretaceous freestone slab; head to North.
- Elizabeth Dutton, d. 20 Apr 1758, aet illegible; also illegible.

1. St. Mary's (*Inscriptions* 20-6) notes a M.I. to B. Dutton, 1758.
2. Benjamin Dutton, of Eastbourne, married Elizabeth Pilbem on 13 Mar 1738/9 at Hooe, see Sussex Marriage Index. NBI records burial of Elizabeth Dutton on 24 Apr 1758 and Benjamin Dutton on 9 Dec 1764, both at Eastbourne.

Eastbourne, 93II Mural monument for Major General WORGE, d. 1774

- Choir North wall, West end, above head height.
- 90(W) x 198(H) — Very good; fading.
- M.I. (6 lines, engraved) on cream marble panel with scrolled cornice; dark grey border; above, in centre, an urn in relief; below, decorated apron and ball finial at foot.
- Major General Worge, d. 4 May 1774, aet 69.

1. In situ - Horsfield (*Sussex* I 296-7).
2. Subject identified as one R. Worge in St. Mary's (*Inscriptions* 11-13), which also cites additional monuments to M Worge (1739) and E Worge (1721).
3. In 1735, one Thomas Worge had acted as steward to the Earl of Wilmington (Caffyn 105); Gen. Worge commanded the forces sent against Goree in 1758 and remained as Governor of Senegal, his daughter Mary later married Sir Arthur de Capell Brooke, Bart.
4. Final lines of lettering never added to M.I.
5. JH notes the reference in Berry (*Sussex* 274) and biography by Elizabeth Baigent in *ODNB* under Sir Arthur de Capell Broke [sic].

Eastbourne, 93JJ Wall-mounted brass for James GRAVES, d. 1647

- Sanctuary, North wall, far East end, near floor and modern steps.
- 31 square — Fine.
- M.I. (12 lines, engraved) in crude Latin lettering on rectangular brass plate.

SECVNDVM CHRISTI REDEMPTORIS
ADVENTVM SVB HOC TVMVLO EX
PECTANT CINERES IACOBI GRAVES
VIRI DOCTI, CONCIONATORIS EX
IMII, IN ARTIBVS M^{RI} ET HVIVS
ECCLESIÆ OLIM SACERDOTIS QVI
CVM CONCIONATORIO SVO MVNE
RE, PAVCIS AB HINC MENSIBVS, FVNGI
NON LICERET, MORI MALVIT OBIIT & RE
LICTIS VXORE, ET DVPLICI PROLE
ÆTATIS SVÆ ANNO 43 FVRORVM
CIVILIVM 7 ANNOQE DOMI, 1647
IAN 12

1. Noted by Stephenson (507); in situ in Davidson-Houston (*SAC* 77 164-5); See St. Mary's (*Inscriptions* 11-13). .
2. JH notes that James Graves was vicar of Eastbourne 1638-1647. See Hennessy (61) and CCEd.

Eastbourne, 93KK Ledger for Henry LUSHINGTON, d. 1779

- Sanctuary floor, towards North wall, partly built over by modern steps.
- 99(W) x 194(visible L) — Worn.
- M.I. (16 lines, engraved, centred) on a black (marble?) slab; head to East.
- Henry Lushington, D.D., vicar of Eastbourne for 44 years, d. 13 Jan 1779, aet 68; his wife, Mary, d. 24 Jul 1775, aet 65; their issue, Henry Lushington of Bengal and 7 others.

1. In situ; original alongside 93A (since moved); see St. Mary's (*Inscriptions* 27-30).
2. Henry Lushington's burial in the chancel noted by Gomme (172).
3. For Henry Lushington of Bengal (his son) see 93A.
4. JH notes that Rev. Henry Lushington, DD, was vicar of Eastbourne 1734-79. See Hennessy (61) and Foster (Al. Ox, pt. 2 3 883).

Eastbourne, 93LL Ledger for Mary LUSHINGTON, d. 1811

- Sanctuary floor, alongside and South of 93KK, partly built over by modern steps.
- Exposed area: 109(W) x 148(L) — Fair.
- M.I. (10 lines, engraved) on a black slab.
- Mary Lushington, widow, d. 17 Apr 1811, aet 78.

1. See St. Mary's (*Inscriptions* 27-30).
2. This Mary Lushington was the second of that name, see 93K.

Eastbourne, 93MM Mural monument for Thomas ALCHORNE and others, dated 1735 [Plate 62]

- Choir South wall, West end, high up.
- 110(W) x 260(H) — Excellent; local damage (lower left); colour.
- In a variety of marbles and coloured stones; M.I. (11 lines) in upper 75% of a black rectangular panel set portrait-wise; flanking, decorative panels and scrolls; above, cornice mouldings, flaming lamps left and right, large central achievement on a stand; below, thick dark base moulding on 2 scrolled corbels; between, the apron formed by a voluted cap on an acanthus corbel.
- Thomas Alchorne, Esq., and his wife, Frances, d. 10 Sep 1735, daughter of John De La Chambre, son of Sir Laurence De La Chambre, of Rodmell, Sussex; issue - three daughters, two of whom, Anne and Judith, died as infants; also her sister, Anne De La Chambre.

1. In situ, see photograph in Budgen (*SAC* 51 124).
2. The Alchorne family controlled one of the chancels in 1686 (Ford); Lambarde (*SAC* 70 135) notes arms; See St. Mary's (*Inscriptions* 11-13).
3. The anomalies in the M.I. are curious: the name of the wife is left blank as if unknown, as is her date of death, and Thomas Alchorne's date of death; the only date given is that of a daughter 1735; for licence to marry dated 2 Aug 1677 for Thomas Alchorne, of Hailsham, Gent., and Frances De La Chambre, of Lewes, see Dunkin (*Licences 1670-1729* 43).
4. 93MM shows a striking combination of colours and patterns.
5. JH notes that Thomas and Frances married 16 Aug 1677 at St. John sub Castro, Lewes - see Sussex Marriage Index. Thomas was Sheriff of Sussex in 1701, see Berry (*Sussex* x). NBI records the burials of Thomas Alchorne on 12 Oct 1703, Fran Alchorne on 13 Jun 1694; Anne Alchorne on 2 Mar 1687 and Judith on 16 Feb 1690, all at Eastbourne.

Eastbourne, 93NN Wall-mounted brasses for the BURTON Family, dated 1586, 1631, etc.

- South-East chapel, North wall, against the wall.
- Base stone: 76(W) x 99(H); Top left brass shield: 18.5(W) x 21(H); Top right brass shield: 18(W) x 21(H); Upper brass M.I.: 38.5(W) x 18(H); Lower brass M.I.: 43.5(W) x 21(H) — All fine.
- A shallow, grey freestone slab; squared bottom end; gabled top; supporting 4 brasses; above, 2 escutcheons; in the centre, a M.I.; below, another M.I.
- Mary Burton, buried 19 Apr 1631, only daughter of Henry Perient, Esq., of Birch, Essex; her husband, Sir Edward Burton, Knt; issue - 15 unnamed.

1. Davidson-Houston (*SAC* 77 161 & 164) found these brasses on the chancel wall; however, they were in situ in Lambarde (*SAC* 70 136); noted but not located by Stephenson (507); see St. Mary's (*Inscriptions* 31ff).
2. Brass (iv) commemorates John (d.1586), son of James Burton, and John's wife Grace Capell, the

parents of 10 children, the eldest of whom was Sir Edward Burton; Grace was daughter of Sir Edward Capell of Little Hadham, Herts.

3. See Berry (*Sussex* 333) for genealogy.

Eastbourne, 93OO Ledger for Lady Rechard WILSON, d. 1686/7 and her daughter Rechard EXETER, d 1755

- South-East chapel floor, towards North wall, partly obscured by altar rail.
- 83(W) x 169(L) — Very good; minor pitting.
- Escutcheon, then M.I. (6+7 lines, engraved) in centre and at lower end of a black marble slab; head to West.
- Lady Rechard Wilson, buried 1 Mar 1686/7, wife of Sir William Wilson; their daughter Rechard Exeter, relict of William Exeter, Gent., d. ?? Jun 1755.

1. In situ in Lambarde (*SAC* 70 135); see St. Mary's (*Inscriptions* 31ff) with date 1686.
2. See pedigree in Blencowe (*SAC* 12 241).
3. Rechard was second daughter of Richard Peacock of North End, Middlesex.
4. NBI records burial of Richard Wilson on 1 Mar 1687 at Eastbourne.
5. JH notes that Rechard was wife of Sir William Wilson, 2nd Bart. the eldest son of Sir William Wilson, 1st Bart., see 93PP. See also Berry (*Sussex* 210).

Eastbourne, 93PP Ledger for Sir William WILSON, Bart., d. 1685, and his wife Mary, d. 1681

- South-East chapel floor, centre.
- 113(W) x 153(visible L) — Good; damaged edges.
- Very large escutcheon then M.I. (6? lines, engraved) on a black slab (marble?); head to West, other lines perhaps now obscured by altar.
- William Wilson, d. 9 Dec 1685, aet 77; rest obscured by furnishings.

1. In situ in Lambarde (*SAC* 70 135); see St. Mary's (*Inscriptions* 31ff); see pedigree in Blencowe (*SAC* 12 241).
2. William Wilson was created Baronet in an. reg. 13 Charles II, d. 1685; his wife was Mary, d. 1681, daughter of Thomas Haddon, of London, merchant.
3. NBI records burial of William Wilson on 12 Dec 1685 at Eastbourne.
4. See also Berry (*Sussex* 210).

Eastbourne, 93QQ Ledger for William WILSON, d. 1713

- South-East chapel floor, towards South wall.
- 95(W) x 196(L) — Good.
- M.I. (engraved, centred) on a black marble slab; head to East.
- William Wilson, Esq., d. 15 Jul 1713, aet 31; only son of Sir William Wilson, Bart.; William Wilson's wife Jane, only daughter of the late Nicholas Townley, Esq.

1. In situ in Lambarde (*SAC* 70 135) noting arms; see St. Mary's (*Inscriptions* 31 ff); see pedigree in Blencowe (*SAC* 12 241).
2. This William Wilson was second son of William Wilson, the 2nd Bart. and his wife Rechard (see 93OO).
3. NBI records the burial of William Wilson on 18 Jul 1713 at Eastbourne, aet 32.
4. See also Berry (*Sussex* 210).

Eastbourne, 93RR Ledger for an anonymous female, d. 1743

- South aisle floor, East end, near door into South-East chapel, now partly obscured by a prayer desk.
- 97(W) x 200(visible L) — Fine.
- M.I. (3 lines engraved) at West end of a black slab (marble?) mostly unlettered; head to West.

.... she exchanged this life for a better
on the 28ᵗʰ Day of December 1743
in the 36ᵗʰ year of her age

Eastbourne, 93SS Mural monument for Anne Colden NEVILLE, d. 1798
- South choir aisle, South wall, towards West end, above head height.
- 51.5(W) x 91(H) — Very good; faded.
- M.I. (10 lines, engraved, centred) on a panel; arched top; engraved dark border.
- Anne Colden Neville, d. 21 Aug 1798, aet 33; her husband, Major Neville, (Royal Artillery).

1. See St. Mary's (*Inscriptions* 31ff).
2. 93RR is like a churchyard headstone in form.
3. NBI records burial of Ann Neville on 24 Aug 1798 at Eastbourne.

Eastbourne, 93TT Mural monument for James RANKING, d. 1827, and John RANKING, date of death unknown [Plate 63]
- South choir aisle, high on South wall, towards West end.
- 79(W) x 97(H) — Excellent.
- In white marble on a black baseplate with curved profile, top and bottom; M.I. (13 lines, engraved, black) on a panel of sarcophagus form, on legs, on a ledge; above, moulding; at top, in low relief, a three-masted ship under sail; unsigned.
- James Ranking, Commander of the SS Vittoria, d. 12/13 Feb 1827, aet 44, drowned in the Bay of Biscay; also John Ranking, died Surinam, dates unknown, aet 14; admonitory text.

1. See St. Mary's (*Inscriptions* 31ff).
2. James and John were perhaps brothers; both died unexpectedly.

Eastbourne, 93UU Mural monument for Jane-Eliza WAKE, d. 1823
- South aisle, South wall, East of main door, at head height.
- 109(W) x 73(H) — Very good; fading.
- A shallow, black baseplate; M.I. (14 lines, engraved) on white marble tablet, unframed, with 2 corbels with acanthus decoration; cornice over; at top, pointed pediment with flames left and right; signed (lower right): 'WHITING, Sculp. NORTHAMPTON'.
- Jane-Eliza Wake, d. 8 Jun 1823, aet 44, buried Eastbourne; her husband, Richard William Wake, rector of Courteenhall, Northamptonshire; no issue mentioned; her many virtues.

1. See St. Mary's (*Inscriptions* 27-30).
2. Patron was Jane-Eliza Wake's husband, a Northants rector, who employed John Whiting (1782-1854) a local Northants maker; Jane-Eliza Wake seems to have died at Eastbourne.
3. JH notes that Jane-Eliza was daughter of Sir William Dunkin, a judge of the Supreme Court of Calcutta see Venn (2 6 308).

Eastbourne, 93VV Mural monument for Lucy WRAY, d. 1824
- South aisle, South wall, East of main door, at head height.
- 65(W) x 91(H) — Very good.
- Black baseplate; 2 grey marble corbels; grey marble panel set landscape-wise; raised central section, with cusped corners; M.I. (9 lines, engraved, centred).
- Lucy Wray, d. 14 Nov 1824; daughter of Rev. Sir William Ulithorn Wray, Bart., of Darley, Derbyshire, and his wife, Frances, daughter of Rev. Francis Bromley, D.D.; Lucy Wray's virtues and piety.

1. See St. Mary's (*Inscriptions* 27-30).

Eastbourne, 93WW Ledger stone for Charles BALDWYN, d. 1801
- South aisle floor, West of South door, East of 93XX.
- 82(W) x 180(L) — Very worn centre.

- M.I. (12 lines, engraved, centred) in upper 50% of a pale yellow freestone slab; head to West.

HERE LIE[TH TH]E BODY
[OF]
CHARLES B....N ESQ^R
LATE OF ... O... LATE
IN THE CO[UNTY] O[F] STAFFORD
AND FOR ... [Y]EARS
ONE OF THE ....ATIVES
IN P[ARLIAM]ENT
FOR THE [COUNTY] OF SALOP.
HE DEPA[RTED THI]S LIFE
ON THE 28 [DAY OF] ...BER 1801
N.... ARS

1. See St. Mary's (*Inscriptions* 27-30).
2. JH notes that Charles Baldwyn was born in 1729. He was MP for Shropshire 1766-80, who at the end of his parliamentary career was described in the Public Ledger as 'A puzzle-headed country gentleman'. At one time he was in receipt of a secret service pension. He married Catherine Childe, daughter of another MP, and died 28 Sep 1801. See Namier & Brooke (2 44).

Eastbourne, 93XX Ledger stone for Elizabeth ...., d. 1819

- South aisle floor, West of South door, West of 93WW.
- 83(W) x 178(L) — Very worn.
- M.I. (13 lines, engraved, centred) on a pale yellow freestone slab; engraved border, cusped corners; head to West.

S[AC]RED
TO THE M[EM]ORY OF
ELIZ[ABETH] WIFE OF
S^R JOHN .... BAR^T
OF C....ELL
IN THE C[OUNTY OF] LIMERICK
WHO DIED 7 1819:

H.... [BO]DY
EL[IZABETH] ... OX
DAUGH[TER] ... ILLE
EIGHT .... THANET
WHO DIED S.... 16 1849

1. JH notes that this is Elizabeth, née Hall, first wife of John Allen De Bourgh (spelled variously) the 3rd Baronet of Castle Connell, in Co. Limerick. She was bur. 12 Aug 1819. He died in 1839, and is probably the person named in Eastbourne Additions 11. See Cockayne (*Baronetage* 5 417-8).

Eastbourne Additions

St. Mary's (*Inscriptions*) reports a number of additional items:
(1) R. Adams (1734) pp. 9-10.
(2) Th. Morton (1765) pp. 9-10.
(3) H. Sandys (1736) pp. 9-10.
(4) M. Smith (1773) recorded by Sir William Burrell but lost, pp. 11-13.
(5) N. Townley (1712), very worn, pp. 11-13.
(6) M. Worge (1744), recorded by Sir William Burrell but lost, pp. 11-13.
(7) H. Fairway (1703), very worn, pp. 20-26.
(8) J. Faulkner (1695), lost, pp. 20-26.
(9) Franckwell (1711), lost, pp. 20-26.
(10) E.A. (1771), pp. 20-26.
(11) J.A. Bourch (1819), pp. 27-30 (see note to 93XX).
(12) William Exeter (1738), pp. 31 ff.
(13) A. Calverley (17433), pp. 31 ff.

(98) ETCHINGHAM, The Assumption & St. Nicholas

14th century throughout, but pre-Perpendicular, including collegiate chancel - Nairn & Pevsner (496-7), plan in *SNQ* (XV 155) and external view, see BL Add. MS 5670 ff.59-62; pavement reported missing in 1686, otherwise fabric was fine (Ford); Horsfield (*Sussex* I 588) notes nothing post-medieval.

Etchingham, 98A Mural monument for John SNEPP, d. 1823, and descendants
- Just West of South door, above head height.
- 90(W) x 165(H) — Fine; 1 bracket lost (right).
- On an irregular, decorative slate base; below, a white marble low relief portrait roundel (with quote from Horace); above, on a trapezoidal panel with a fan decoration over and 2 brackets below (1 lost), a M.I. (engraved); at top, an escutcheon; signed (neck of portrait): 'G.B. BIRCH, Sc LONDON 1859'.
- John Snepp, gent., of Haremare, d. 18 Aug 1823, aet 69; his wife, Hannah, d. 11 Oct 1832, aet 66; only issue - John, d. 25 Nov 1857, aet 68; his wife, Martha, d. 6 Jul 1873.

1. Nairn & Pevsner (497): note the profile medallion.
2. Haremare (or Haremore) was nearby.
3. John Snepp previously occupied lands owned by Sir John Lade (273C) (R. Davey, 73, who spells Ladds); for licence to marry dated 28 Oct 1833 for John Snepp [the son], of Etchingham, Gent. and Martha Noakes, of Etchingham, spinster, see Dunkin & Penfold (*Licences* 393).
4. Dated 1859.
5. See Lambarde (*SAC* 67 153) for heraldry.

Etchingham, 98B Ledger for Thomas CONSTABLE, d. 1773
- North aisle floor, by side chapel.
- 92(W) x 178(L) — Lettering very good; edges worn.
- M.I. (6 lines, engraved) in upper parts of a freestone slab.
- Thomas Constable, Gent., of Ticehurst, d. 1 Jan 1773, aet 29.

1. Perhaps set up by a successor, William Constable, who occupied lands at Etchingham in 1785 (R. Davey, 73).
2. NBI records burial of Thomas Constable on 5 Jan 1773 at Etchingham.

Etchingham, 98C Ledger for Thomas RAWLIN, d. 1655
- South aisle chapel floor.
- 74(W) x 179(L) — Very worn; partly illegible.
- Freestone slab with M.I. (engraved).

HERE.....ER AWAITS
Y^E TRUMPET OF Y^E
GREAT IVDG^{AND}IVBLE
Y^E BODY OF MR THOM
AS RAWLIN SON OF
MR ALEXADER RAW
LIN CLERGY MAN
SERVAT TO Y^E WO..
GEORGE STRODE KN
LORD OF ETCHNGHAM
HE FEL ASLEP OCT 14
[1]655 ON Y^E LORDS DAY
AND SHAL AWAKE .. A
DAY OF Y^E LORD.

1. JH notes that Thomas Rawlin(g)s, son of Mr Alexander Rawlings, clergyman, was manservant to the worshipful Sir George Strode, lord of the manor of Etchingham, and died 30 Jul 1655. For George Strode, see W. Cooper (*SAC* 19 110).

Etchingham, 98D Ledger for Samuel FARNDEN, d. 1660
- South chapel, against East wall, behind altar.
- 48(W) x 85(L) — Lettering good; edges very worn.
- M.I. (6 lines, engraved) in upper 40% of a slate slab.
- Samuel Farnden, d. 16 Nov 1660; son of Peter Farnden and Ann, eldest daughter of John Busbridge, Esq.

1. One Peter Farnden of Sedlescombe was a prominent ironmaster, see Vivian (133).

Etchingham, 98E Engraved brasses for anonymous son of Sir Gyfford THORNHURST, dated 1626
- South aisle floor, to West of side chapel.
- Base: 49(W) x 96(L); Escutcheon: 19.5(W) x 17.5(H); M.I.: 30(W) x 19(H) — Fine.
- 2 brass plates towards the East (top) end of freestone slab; escutcheon over M.I. (7 lines).
- Anonymous son of Sir Gyfford Thornhurst, Bart. and Susan, still living, only daughter of Sir Alex Temple, Knt; dated 1626.

1. Apparently in situ; noted by Stephenson (507) and Davidson-Houston (*SAC* 77 173) with illustration and transcription citing entry in Burrell manuscript (BL Add. MS 5697 f.52).
2. See also Lambarde (*SAC* 67 152-3) for heraldry.

Etchingham Additions
Davidson-Houston (*SAC* 77 167-171), Horsfield (*Sussex* I 588), Lambarde (*SAC* 67 151), Nairn & Pevsner (497) and Stephenson (507).
Brasses to various members of the Echingham family.

(99) EWHURST, St. James-the-Great
South arcade 12th century; North arcade is later - Nairn & Pevsner (498); a view from North-East - Godfrey & Salzman (Pl. 62) (BL Add. MS 5670 f.12; 5677 f.62); a plan - VCH (9 267); condition reported to be fine in 1724 (Ford); no monuments cited in Horsfield (*Sussex* I 518-520).

Ewhurst, 99A Mural monument for Mary Catherine Gilbert COOPER, d. 1806
- Chancel, against North wall, West end.
- 61(W) x 87(H) — Fine.
- M.I. (engraved, black and red) on a rectangular freestone panel, unframed.
- Mary Catharine Gilbert Cooper, d. 22 Jun 1806, infant; daughter of Rev. Godfrey Gilbert Cooper and Elizabeth; quotes II Samuel 12. 23.

1. If the present colouring is original, rather than a restoration, it is unusual.
2. Possibly, but not certainly, once a floor slab.
3. JH notes that Rev. G.G. Cooper was vicar of Bodiam 1803-9, and rector at Ewhurst Green 1803-24, see Venn (2 2 126).

Ewhurst addition
Davidson-Houston (*SAC* 77 173-4), Horsfield (*Sussex* I 520), Nairn & Pevsner (498) and Stephenson (508).
Brass for William Crysford.

(100) FALMER - No monuments found

(107) FLETCHING, St. Andrew & St. Mary

13th-century nave arcades and transepts, mausoleum added in late 18th century, chancel in Early English style added as part of 1880 restoration - Nairn & Pevsner (501) and for external view see BL Add. MS 5671 ff.43-44; 5676 ff.49 & 97); generally in fine condition in 1724 although a chancel owned by T. Newnham Esq. was then poor, see Ford (169).

Fletching, 107A Mural monument for Mary FIELD, d. 1779

- North nave arcade, almost opposite South door, high.
- c.65(W) x c.130(H) — Fine; faded.
- M.I. (9 lines, engraved) in upper 60% of a white marble oval panel; coloured surround; on top, garlanded urn; below, strapwork corbel.
- Mary Field, d. 9 Dec 1779, in childbirth, aet 33; wife of Thomas Field, Esq., of Woodgate, Fletching.

1. JH notes that there is an almost obliterated coat of arms on a small escutcheon below the oval, not mentioned by Lambarde, and there is a hatchment in the church for Field impaling Hunt, see Summers (139).

Fletching, 107B Mural monument for Elizabeth HUTCHINSON, d. 1824

- Nave arcade, North side, near East end, high.
- c.80(W) x c.68(H) — Good.
- Black backplate with pointed top; M.I. (engraved) in upper 60% of a white marble tablet, unframed, pointed top; 2 white block corbels.
- Elizabeth Hutchinson, 15 Jun 1783 - 29 Mar 1824; wife of G.P. Hutchinson, Esq., of Woodgate, Fletching.

1. As with 107F, the family owned Woodgate, in this case as early as 1785 (R. Davey 79).

Fletching, 107C The SHEFFIELD Mausoleum, late 18th century [Plates 64 & 65]

- In an enclosed area to the North of the North transept.
- c.450 max (W) — Very good.
- Confronting the viewer is a Decorated screen, carrying M.I.s on tablets, reaching up through 2 stories of blank arcades into the vaulted spaces of the church; lit by the original North transept window; at top, a cornice supporting an achievement and a M.I. in a frieze.
- From top, left to right, M.I.s for:
  (i) Dorothy, wife of Isaac Holroyd, born 1704, died aet 73;
  (ii) her husband, Isaac, born 1708, died aet 70, son of John and Sarah Holroyd, and father of John Baker Holroyd;
  (iii) John Baker Holroyd, Earl of Sheffield, d. 20 May 1821, aet 86;
  (iv) Abigail Way, his first wife, d. 1793;
  (v) Lucy Pelham, his second wife, daughter of the Earl of Chichester, d. 1797;
  (vi) Anne, his third wife, daughter of Lord North, 1764 - 1832;
  lower storey, from left to right, M.I.s for:
  (vii) Dorothy, daughter of Isaac and Dorothy Holroyd [see (i) - (ii)], d. 1770, aet 25;
  (viii) Daniel, son of Isaac and Dorothy Holroyd [see (i) - (ii)], brother of John Baker Holroyd, killed in action 30 Jul 1762;
  (ix) John William Holroyd, son of John Baker Holroyd and Abigail, d. 1772, infant;
  (x) Frederick Henry Stuart, Viscount Pevensey, 1827 - 1829, eldest son of George, 2nd Earl;
  (xi) Edward Gibbon, historian, family friend, lived 56 years, 7 months and 28 days and d. 17 Feb 1794.

1. Noted in Gomme (253) from *Gent's Mag* 1805 ii 601, identifying the author of M.I.s for Gibbon and Holroyd himself as Dr Parr and Rev. Hugh James Rose.
2. Unique amongst Sussex monuments, the mausoleum was erected by John Baker Holroyd, first Earl of Sheffield (1741- 20 May 1821), for whom see John Cannon's biography with bibliography in *ODNB* and Horsfield (*Sussex* I 380).
3. The family gallery or pew was located in the East end of the North wall of the North aisle (corbels still visible).
4. 107C should be understood as a product of the antiquarian and social circle occupied by John Baker Holroyd who hosted Burrell and Grose on their antiquarian tour of Sussex in 1777 - see Farrant (*SAC* 131 153).
5. John Baker Holroyd massively improved the estate which he purchased in 1769 for £31,000.
6. JH notes that the mausoleum is listed in Lambarde (*SAC* 67 185) with details of the heraldry. There are also three hatchments in the church, for the first Earl of Sheffield.
7. And for his first two wives – see Summers (138-9).

Fletching, 107D Standing wall monument for Richard LECHE, d. 1596, and his wife Charity [Plate 66]

- South transept, East wall, in a recess.
- 247(W) x 256(H) x 129(D); effigies - 186(L) male; 180(L) female — Heavy restoration to superstructure and effigies.
- A large canopied altar-tomb; alabaster tomb-chest, effigies and walling; grey marble columns flanking; grey marble and raunce panels and mouldings behind and below; M.I.s (engraved and gilded) on black panel, much of it in wood, on tomb-chest and back wall; a flat superstructure of entablature, frieze and cornice; achievement, perhaps separated; 2 effigies with hands clasped, feet to the North, he forward of her.
- Richard Leche, Esq., High Sheriff of Sussex, Surrey etc., d. 22 Dec 1596, aet 66; his wife, Charitye, daughter of Robert White, Esq., late of Christchurch, Hampshire; no issue.

1. Noted by Grose as 'an ancient monument of the reign of James I' (Farrant 117).
2. In situ - Horsfield (*Sussex* I 381).
3. Badly damaged in 1783 by the collapse of the columns and canopy.
4. Nairn & Pevsner (501) note that the widow 'of her owne accorde and herself livinge [is] to be pictured lyinge by him'; she married as her second husband the second Earl of Nottingham.
5. Transcribed in Mosse (89).
6. JH notes that Richard Leeche was an ironmaster, JP for Sussex and Kent, and MP for Camelford in 1593, see Hasler (2 451-2). Lambarde (*SAC* 67 185) mentions heraldry.

Fletching, 107E Mural brasses for members of the WILSON family from our period, erected in the 19th century: (a) Sir William Wilson, d. 1685; (b) John Wilson, d. 1640 and (c) Sir Thomas Wilson, d. 1581

- South transept, West wall.
- (a) 46 square ; (b) 46(W) x 36 (H) ; (c) 46(W) x 36 (H) — All fine.
- Each with M.I. engraved in rectangular brass plate, 3 forming a set.

(a)
In Memoriam
Sir William Wilson Bart.
of Compton Place Eastbourne
obit 1685 aged 77
Mary his wife obit 1661
Rochard his wife obit 1680
William their son obit 1713
aged 32
Rochard their daughter
obit 1755 aged 72
Interred in the Chancel
of that Parish Church

(b)
In memory of
John Wilson, Esquire,
died 1640:
and Edward Wilson his son,
died 1621:
who resided at Sheffield Park
in this Parish.
and were interred in
this Churchyard.
(c)
In Memoriam
Sir Thomas Wilson, L.L.D.,
Secretary of State and Foreign
Ambassador to Queen Elizabeth,
obit 1581, Buried at S. Catharine's.
Also Charles Wilson, Grandson
of the above, Major of House in
the Kings Service, who fell in
the Battle of Naseby 1645

1. Perhaps erected by later members of the family since there are two other brasses nearby which commemorate Wilsons who died in the 1890s; for their lands in the Barkham Quarter of Fletching in 1785 see R. Davey 79-80; members of this immediate family are also commemorated at Eastbourne (see 93OO-QQ and pedigree in Blencowe (*SAC* 12 240-1), suggesting that William and Mary Wilson had additional progeny.
2. JH notes that Sir Thomas Wilson (d. 1581) had a distinguished career in politics, the Church, the Diplomatic Service, the Law, and in literature, see biography by Susan Doran and Jonathan Woolfson in *ODNB* and Hasler (3 629-631).

Fletching Additions
Noted in Church Guide.
(2) Floor stone for Michael Baynes possibly in the belfry, slate, from nave floor after 1880 restoration. Malcolm Baynes was rector of Fletching from 1760-86 and vicar of Ringmer from 1754-86 and was buried under the nave at Fletching, see Venn (2 1 197).

(108) FOLKINGTON, St. Peter
The nave of the mediaeval building runs directly into the chancel - Nairn & Pevsner (503); state of repair in 1686 reported to be fine, as it was in 1724 (Ford); the parish had 125 communicants in 1603, see Renshaw (*Ecclesiastical Returns*); in 1706, a group of manors owned by Sir William Thomas of Folkington (see 108E) passed under the terms of his will to William Dobell, d. 1752, see Streat (250A,B), who moved to Folkington, see Crawfurd (1 ff.); after the death of Dobell's daughter, Mary (1796), the property passed to Lancelot Harrison of Seaford (108G) see Radcliffe (*SAC* 66 129).

Folkington, 108A Ledger for Catherine THOMAS, d. 1678
- Nave floor, centre of East end, without the sanctuary.
- 95(W) x 178(L) — Fine.
- M.I. (8 lines, engraved) almost fills surface of a black slab; head to West.
- Catherine Thomas, d. 11 Nov 1678; daughter of Squire Rose, of Woodmancourt; and widow (23 years) of William Thomas, Esq.; issue: 1 son and 4 daughters surviving.

1. Noted in Lambarde (*SAC* 70 147) arms.
2. For Catherine Thomas' husband see 108B; for licence to marry of Catherine Rose and William Thomas, Jnr, of West Dean, Gent., 24 Dec 1631, see Dunkin (*Licences 1586-1643* 194).
3. See 108B for different number of children.

Folkington, 108B Ledger for William THOMAS, d. 1655

- Nave floor, near North wall, without the sanctuary.
- 95(W) x 178(L) — Fine.
- Arms, then M.I. (8 lines, engraved) fill upper 75% of a polished black slab; head to West.
- William Thomas, Esq., d. 1655; his wife, Catherine, daughter of Squire Rose of Woodmancourt, Sussex; issue: 4 sons and 2 daughters.

1. Noted in Lambarde (*SAC* 70 147) arms.
2. For William Thomas' widow see 108A; for licence to marry of Catherine Rose and William Thomas, Jnr, of West Dean, Gent., 24 Dec 1631, see Dunkin (*Licences 1586-1643* 194); William Thomas' heir was, his son, another William Thomas, Bart., see Budgen (*Dobell* 43). See 108E and 108H.
3. See 108A for different number of children.

Folkington, 108C Mural monument for Lady Barbara THOMAS, d. 1697 [Plate 67]

- Sanctuary, North wall, above head height.
- 110(W) x 240(H) — Very good; recent restoration.
- A white marble cartouche; M.I. (17 lines, engraved, black) below a shield of arms supported by 2 putti and more arms below, resting on a cherub; on top, a fluted, decorated urn; surround decorated with drapery and foliage.
- Lady Barbara Thomas d. 25 Oct 1697, aet 56; daughter of Sir Herbert Springett, Bart., of Sussex; and wife of Sir William Thomas, Bart.

1. In original location - noted as 'handsome' by Horsfield (*Sussex* I 324-5), arms noted in Lambarde (*SAC* 70 147) and noted by Nairn & Pevsner (503).
2. For Sir Herbert Springett, Bart, see Ringmer 212V, W, X, Z, AA; for her husband see 108E; for marriage settlement of William Thomas and Barbara Springett of Broyle, Ringmer, dated Jul 1676, see Budgen (*Dobell* 175-6); biographic outline of Barbara Springett in 'Notes & Queries' *SAC* 22 222.
3. 108C is of very high quality, almost certainly London-made.

Folkington, 108D Brass for Herbert STAPLEY, d. 1687

- Sanctuary floor, near North wall.
- 42(W) x 21(L) — Fine.
- M.I. (8 lines, engraved) and arms fill surface of a brass plate; head to North.
- Herbert Stapley, d. 28 May 1687, aet 2; fourth son of (another) Herbert Stapley, Esq. and an unnamed daughter of Sir Richard Colepepyr, of Aylesford, Kent.

1. In situ - Horsfield (*Sussex* I 324-5).
2. Herbert Stapley and Alice Colepeper marriage licence dated 26 Mar 1675 at Canterbury (Sussex Marriage Index).
3. Arms not noted by Lambarde.

Folkington, 108E Ledger for Sir William THOMAS, d. 1706 [Plate 68]

- Sanctuary floor, North of centre.
- 94(W) x 190(L) — Fair.
- Arms and M.I. (6 lines, engraved) fill upper 75% of surface of polished black slab; head to West.
- Sir William Thomas, Bart., d. 18 Nov 1706, aet 64.

1. Arms noted in Lambarde (*SAC* 70 147).
2. 108E is ledger to 108H.
3. William Thomas (1641-1706) must have been the builder of Folkington Place; at his death, the estate passed to his nephew William Dobell (d.1752); for William Thomas' wife see 108C; he left provision for a charity school at Folkington, see Caffyn (116).
4. The style of lettering of 108E differs from that on 108 A, B and F.
5. JH notes that William Thomas, son of William and Catherine (see 108 A and B) attended Oriel College, Oxford, but did not graduate. He was created a baronet in 1660 at the surprisingly young age of 19, and entered parliament the following year. He was MP for Seaford and Sussex alternately

from 1661 until his death in 1706. See Cruikshanks (5 621).

Folkington, 108F Ledger for Lady Barbara THOMAS, d. 1697

- Sanctuary floor, centre, partly obscured by the altar.
- 97(W) x 190(L) — Good.
- Arms and M.I. (5 lines, engraved) visible on a polished black slab; head to West.

> Heere Lyeth the true Exemp
> lar of piety the Lady Barbara
> Thomas in whose memory her
> most indulgent Husband yᵉ Honʳ
> Sʳ William Thomas Erected this ...

1. Noted in Lambarde (*SAC* 70 147) arms.
2. Patron of 108F (as in 108C) was Barbara Thomas' widowed husband Sir William Thomas.
3. She supported the charity school in her home village, Ringmer, see Caffyn (219).

Folkington, 108G Ledger for Lancelot HARISON, d. 1816, and his wife Catherine, d. 1812

- Sanctuary floor, South of centre, partly obscured by altar and carpeting.
- 92(W) x 192(L) — Fine; scratched.
- M.I. (11 lines, engraved) fills upper 50% of surface of polished black slab, head to West.
- Lancelot Harison, Esq., d. 29 Dec 1816, aet 81; his wife, Catherine, d. 28 Dec 1812, aet 74.

1. Lancelot Harrison came into possession of the Thomas estate at Folkington from 1796, Farrant (222-3), under the terms of the will of William Dobell; he was an associate of Francis Grose (Diary in Farrant); Caffyn (116); baptised at Seaford 1735; for Lancelot Harrison's own will dated 1804, proved 1817, see Lower (*SAC* 7 132).
2. No arms on 108G.
3. Another Harrison ledger at West Dean, 280B.

Folkington, 108H Wall monument for Sir William THOMAS, d. 1706 [Plate 69]

- Standing against sanctuary South wall.
- 123(W) x 330(H) — Excellent; restored (in 2002).
- In white, cream, grey and black marbles of exceptional quality; in pedestal form, on a black plinth; M.I. on a convex, oval panel; acanthus, scroll-work and other decoration in spandrels and frieze; above, a cornice; a black backplate supports fluted base with an elaborate achievement; flanking are standing, mourning putti, supporting arms.
- Sir William Thomas, Bart.; his nephew William Dobell.

1. In situ - noted as 'handsome' by Horsfield (*Sussex* I 324-5), Lambarde (*SAC* 70 147) noting arms and Nairn & Pevsner (503): with date c.1720.
2. William Dobell was patron of 108H and came into Folkington on death of William Thomas on 18 Nov 1706, see Radcliffe (*SAC* 66 129); the relevant ledger is 108E (see 108E for biography).
3. The quality of materials and carving of 108H is exceptionally high and can be linked to the Dame Katherine Nutt monument at Willingdon (297R) and indicative of the later Dobell commissions at Streat (250A-B); Dobell employed the mason Blownupp in 1714 (see 250B).

(110) FRAMFIELD, St. Thomas à Becket

Mostly built after the fire of 1509 - Nairn & Pevsner (506); the East end again rebuilt in 1842, necessitating the relocation of ledgers noted by Horsfield (*Sussex* I 364) from the North-East or Hempstead or Smith Chapel (see 110O) and the North side of the chancel (110D-F, J and K, etc.); a Harmer terracotta in churchyard to Ann Leadner, d. 1825.

Framfield, 110A Mural monument for Robert DURRANT, d. 1799

- Nave, East wall, North of chancel arch, high above pulpit.
- 102(W); (H) inaccessible — Very good; local damage (cornice).
- M.I. on white marble tablet; tall dark grey backplate in obelisk form; above, a decorative urn on cornice; at foot, 2 corbels; signed (lower right): 'PARSONS. Sculp. LEWES'.
- Robert Durrant, Esq., d. 13 Dec 1799, aet 84; his nephews/heirs William, Thomas, John and Henry Woodward; his virtues.

1. Formerly on nave North wall - Horsfield (*Sussex* I 364); noted by Gunnis (*Dict.* 292) and Nairn & Pevsner (506).
2. Another monument by Parsons in the church commemorates Mary Wright, 1831, see 110R.
3. Robert Durrant was the last of the family, his heirs were his Woodward nephews - Hoare (*SAC* 4 303) - the patrons of 110A (for William Woodward see 110L).
4. Parsons is working here in the manner of Bacon (Gunnis), c.f. to 82B at East Blatchington.

Framfield, 110B Mural monument for Francis WARNETT, d. 1622

- North-East or Hempstead Chapel (now an inaccessible vestry), on East wall, above furnishings.
- 74.5(W) x 138(H) — Condition unknown.
- (Reportedly) in alabaster; scrolled top with escutcheon; tablet flanked by pilasters; scrolled decoration under.
- M.I. reported as:

> here lyeth the body of
> frances warnet esquie.r
> who married the daugh-
> ter, of sir edward boys
> knight and had by hir 2
> sonnes and 2 daughters
> and died the 18 daye of
> march 1622

1. Noted in Nairn & Pevsner (506) and in Hoare (*SAC* 4 298).
2. Francis Warnett's wife was Anne Boys; his seat was at Hempstead.
3. NBI records burial of Francis Warnett on 21 Mar 1622 at Framfield.

Framfield, 110C Mural monument for Josias SMITH, d. 1827

- North-East or Hempstead Chapel (now an inaccessible vestry), on South wall.
- 91.5(W) x 90(H) — Condition unknown.
- (Reportedly) M.I. on white tablet; black marble baseplate; pointed top/pediment.

> in the vault
> beneath are deposed the remains of
> josias smith esq
> who was born at hemsted place in this parish
> on the 27th day of december 1736 o.s.
> and died at his house in lewes
> on the 22nd day of march 1827
> where he practised more than 60 years
> with unimpeached integrity
> and consequent success as an
> attorney at law

1. Parsons of Lewes?
2. NBI records burial of Josias Smith on 29 Mar 1827 at Framfield, aet 90.

Framfield, 110D Ledger for Thomas STONE, d. 1811

- Chancel floor, next to altar rail.
- 104(W) x 192(L) — Dented.
- M.I. (engraved) in upper 60% of a black slab; head to West.

- Thomas Stone, Gent., of Stone Bridge, d. 7 Jul 1811, aet 80; his widow, Martha, d. 18 Mar 1833, aet 72.

1. For licence to marry dated 19 Apr 1788 for Thomas Stone, of Framfield, Gent., bachelor, age 50 and Martha Stone, of Framfield, spinster, age 26, see Dunkin & Penfold (*Licences* 407).

Framfield, 110E Ledger for William STONE, d. 1744, and others
- Chancel floor, immediately West of 110D.
- 116(W) x 203(L) — Very good, damaged edges.
- M.I. (engraved; sections added) in upper 75% of a black slab; head to West.
- William Stone, Gent., of the Gatehouse, Framfield; d. 30 Jul 1744, aet 71; his wife, Mary, d. 2 Feb 1745/6, aet 66; their descendant, David Stone, Gent., of New Place, d. 23 Mar 1826, aet 82; his parents William and Frances Stone, of Stonebridge.

1. 110E was erected after 1745; lines were added in the later 1820s.
2. JH notes that William Stone married Mary Everest on 2 Jun 1696 at Framfield, see Sussex Marriage Index. For David Stone's parents see 110F.

Framfield, 110F Ledger for Mary STONE, d. 1725
- Chancel floor, immediately West of 110E.
- 99.5(W) x 201(L) — Very good.
- M.I. (engraved) in upper 60% of a black slab, head to West.
- Mary Stone, d. 8 Jun 1725, aet 30; her husband, William Stone, Gent., called Jnr., of Stone Bridge, Framfield, d. 4 Sep 1757, aet 59; also his second wife and widow, Frances, d. 27 May 1786, aet 75.

1. JH notes that William Stone is the son of William and Mary Stone, see 110E. He married his first wife Mary Godly on 18 Apr 1723 at Framfield and his second wife Frances Palmer on 14 Jul 1730 at East Hoathly, see Sussex Marriage Index.

Framfield, 110G Anonymous [perhaps Harriet STONE?], undated ledger
- Chancel floor, South of 110D, partly obscured by altar rail.
- 49(W) x 65(L) — Very worn.
- M.I. (7? lines in English + 6 lines Latin, engraved) on a freestone slab; head to West.
- Illegible.

1. In style and type early 18th century.

Framfield, 110H Mural monument for Rev. John THOMPSON, d. 1830
- Sanctuary South wall, above head height.
- 115(W) x 90(H) — Excellent.
- M.I. (15 lines, engraved) on an unframed white tablet; 2 scrolled corbels; plain moulded cornice; shallow pointed pediment; signed (lower centre): 'PARSONS. LEWES'.
- Rev. John Thompson, vicar of Framfield, d. 29 Aug 1830, aet 75; his widow, Mary Thompson, d. 6 Dec 1835, aet 78; his charitable acts.

1. For licence to marry dated 21 May 1796 for John Thompson, of Streat, clerk, bachelor, age 40 plus and Mary Hall of Portslade, spinster, age 30 plus, see Dunkin & Penfold (*Licences* 419); John Thompson was educated at Queens' College, Oxford; brother of previous vicar, George Thompson, see Dunkin (*SAC* 26 46), which cites source as M.I. in 'churchyard'.
2. JH notes that John Thompson was previously curate at Framfield and vicar 1808-30, see CCEd and Hennessy (72).

Framfield, 110I Mural monument for the GAGE family, dated 1595 [Plate 70]
- South-East chapel (Bentley / Gage), South wall, at head height.
- 99(W) x 95(H) — Fine; faded; local damage (cornice).
- Engraved on a brass with a decorative alabaster surround: Edward and Margaret Gage kneel opposite to each other at a table. Behind Edward kneels one son; behind Margaret

kneel five daughters. Above them, engraved in the stone surround is the inscription:
HEERE LYETH Y^E BODIE OF EDWARD GAGE ESQVIRE & MARGARETT
HIS WIFE (DAVGHTER OF IOHN SHELLIE OF MICHELGROVE) & HAD 3 SONNES
& SEAVEN DAVGHTERS. ANNO DO^[M]NI 1595
and below five further lines of Latin:
DOMINE SECVNDVM ACTIVM MEVM NOLI ME IVDICARI : NIHIL DIGNVM
IN CONSPECTV TVO EGI : IDEO DEPRECOR MAIESTATEM TVAM VT
TV DEVS DELEAS INIQVIATEM MEAM. AMPLIUS LAVA ME
DOMINE, AB INIVSTITIA MEA, ET A DELICTO MEO MVNDA ME VT
TV DEVS DILEAS INIQVITATEM MEAM.

1. In situ - Horsfield (*Sussex* I 364); Hoare (*SAC* 4 296); Turner (*SAC* 23 159); Lambarde (*SAC* 70 158) - noting arms; Stephenson (509); Davidson-Houston (*SAC* 77 190) - noting similarity to the John Shelley brass, at Clapham, West Sussex; Nairn & Pevsner (506).
2. For the Gages in general see *SNQ* XV 102; descendants of the Gages of Firle, these Gages were settled at Bentley by 1539 (Church Guide); see IPM for James Gage of Bentley, d. 12 Jan an. reg. 15 Elizabeth I, naming Edward Gage, aged 27, as his son and heir (Salzman *Inquisitions* 81ff).
3. Several of Edward Gage's issue appear not to be shown on 110I; the M.I. includes a quotation from the Latin Office for the Dead, perhaps an indicator of the family's determined recusancy; as White (65) reminds us, Edward Gage was executor to the Earl of Southampton commemorated by a documented tomb of c.1594 at Titchfield, Hants by Garret Johnson and 110I must be close in date to Garret Johnson's documented set (1595-6) of Gage brasses at West Firle (281B-G) and is perhaps from the same workshop?

Framfield, 110J Ledger for William STONE, d. 1717
- Nave floor, East end of centre aisle, at chancel arch.
- 99.5(W) x 196(L) — Very good.
- M.I. (7 lines, engraved) in upper part of a slab; head to West.
- William Stone, Gent., d. 22 Dec 1717, aet 68; his wife, Margaret, d. 29 Oct 1710, aet 66.

1. For licence to marry, dated 18 Jan 1672-3, for William Stone and Margaret Austin, both of Framfield, see Dunkin (*Licences 1670-1729* 292).

Framfield, 110K Ledger for David and Martha STONE, d. 1731 and d. 1782
- Nave floor, centre aisle, West of 110J.
- 93(W) x 71 and 89(L) — Good.
- In 2 parts; M.I. fills upper part; another M.I. in upper 50% of lower part; heads to West.
- David Stone, Gent., of Blackboys, d. 21 Apr 1731, aet 55; his wife, Martha, d. 24 Aug 1782, aet 83.

1. The Thomas Stone who owned lands at Framfield in 1785 was perhaps a descendant (R. Davey 83).
2. JH notes that David Stone married Martha Hay on 2 Jul 1717 at Little Horsted, see Sussex Marriage Index.

Framfield, 110L Ledger for Rev. William WOODWARD, d. 1786
- Nave floor, centre, West end.
- 100(W) x 200(L) — Good; some wear.
- M.I. (7 lines, engraved) in upper 25% of a black slab; head to West.
- Rev. William Woodward, B.A., rector of Plumpton, d. 26 Feb 1786, aet 43.

1. Plumpton was not William Woodward's chosen burial site perhaps because he leased out extensive properties at Framfield in 1785 (R. Davey 82); these properties perhaps came via his wife Sarah Peckham (110N).
2. The Woodwards were heirs to Durrant see 110A. .
3. JH notes that William Woodward was rector of Plumpton 1771-86 and had been curate of Maresfield.

Framfield, 110M Mural monument for Rev. Thomas WHARTON, d. 1767
- South nave arcade, facing North, high.
- c.80(W) x c.60(H) — Very good.

- M.I. (engraved) on a tablet, with revetment; above, broken pediment with escutcheon.
- Rev. Thomas Wharton, M.A., vicar of Framfield for over 40 years, family seats in Westmorland, d. 21 May 1767, aet 67; his virtues and charitable acts.

1. In situ, at Thomas Wharton's burial place - Horsfield (*Sussex* I 364), Lambarde (*SAC* 70 158) noting arms and Church Guide.
2. Rev. Thomas Wharton was rector of Framfield 1726-67 and left money to educate the Framfield children, see Caffyn (117); charitable bequests were often noted on Framfield monuments (see 110O).

Framfield, 110N Mural monument for William PECKHAM, d. 1770
- South nave arcade, facing North, West of 110M, high.
- 61(W) x 91(H) — Very good.
- M.I. on an unframed oval slate (?) plaque; above, a decorated escutcheon.
- William Peckham, Gent., of Arches, d. 27 Aug 1770, aet 50; his wife (from c.1741), Sarah, d. 11 Jan 1776, aet 63, daughter of William Durrant, Gent., of Streele; their issue - Sarah, wife of Rev. William Woodward, A.M., rector of Plumpton, Sussex; and Mary, wife of Rev. Henry Courthope, A.M., vicar of Brenchley, Kent.

1. In situ - Lambarde (*SAC* 70 158) noting arms.
2. For Sarah Peckham's second husband see 110L.
3. Patrons - the 2 daughters.

Framfield, 110O Mural monument for John and Robert SMITH, d. 1718
- South aisle, North wall, facing South, West of South-East chapel.
- 70(W) x c.90(H) — Very good.
- M.I. (engraved) fills upper 75% of slate tablet; grey freestone surround.
- John Smith, of High Cross, Framfield, d. 10 Apr 1718, aet 79; his brother Robert Smith, also of High Cross, d. 5 Oct 1719, aet 78.

1. Robert Smith was tenant, then owner of Hempstead House at Framfield, Farrant (224), and left money to educate the village children, Caffyn (117).
2. For related charitable bequests at Framfield see 110M.

Framfield, 110P Mural monument for Thomas WOODWARD, d. 1830
- South aisle, South wall, facing North.
- 92(W) x 133(H) — Very good.
- White on black; M.I. (engraved) on white tablet (engraved), set portrait-wise; above, a pointed pediment; below, base mouldings and block corbels.
- Thomas Woodward, Esq., of Highlands, Framfield, d. 19 Apr 1830, aet 52; his widow, Mary Elizabeth Woodward, d. 29 Sep 1876, aet 82; their issue - Ellen and Julia, died in infancy; eldest daughter, Mary Elizabeth, d. 3 Apr 1835, aet 20; eldest son Thomas Mason Woodward, Esq., 18 Mar 1819 - 13 Sep 1850, Ehrenbreitstein, Prussia; and youngest son, Alfred Walter Woodward, ensign (40th Regiment), died at Landour, East Indies 30 Sep 1843, aet 18.

1. For licence to marry, dated 14 Apr 1813 for Thomas Woodward, of Framfield, Esq., bachelor, age 21 plus and Mary Elizabeth Mason of Hellingly, spinster, age 18 plus, see Dunkin & Penfold (*Licences* 480).
2. For Thomas Woodward as patron see 110A.

Framfield, 110Q Mural monument for Sarah WOODWARD, d. 1823, and others
[Plate 71]
- South aisle, South wall, facing North, near font.
- 83(W) x 145(H) — Very good.
- White on dark grey; curved top; M.I. (engraved, final lines added) on a tablet; above, a fan-shaped pediment and cornice.

- Sarah Woodward, of Arches, Framfield, d. 1 May 1823, aet 79; daughter of William and S. Peckham; and widow of Rev. W[illiam] Woodward, rector of Plumpton, d. 26 Feb 1786, aet 43; their issue - Sarah, d. 6 Jun 1804, aet 29; youngest son, Henry, d. 30 Nov 1858, aet 77.

1. Nairn & Pevsner (506), noting the Grecian decoration, follow Gunnis (*Dict.* 427) in attribution of 110Q to Sir Richard Westmacott (1775-1856).
2. Lines added for Henry Woodward d. 1858.
3. Sarah Peckham, daughter of William and Sarah, was baptised at Framfield on 10 May 1744.
4. For Rev. William Woodward see 110L.

Framfield, 110R Mural monument for Joseph WRIGHT, d. 1802
- South aisle, South wall, facing North, near West end.
- 77(W) x 128(H) — Excellent.
- White on black; M.I. (engraved) on tablet; above, a pediment; signed (lower left): 'PARSONS / LEWES'.
- Rev. Joseph Wright, of Chorley, Lancaster, rector of Litlington, vicar of Alfriston and rector of Fulbeck, Lincolnshire, died at Fulbeck, 14 Dec 1802, aet 73; his widow, Mary Wright, died at Uckfield, 29 Jul 1831, aet 89; their daughter Mary Wright, died at Uckfield, 28 Aug 1817, aet 47.

1. See too a slate ledger in the nave for Mary Wright, d. 1831.

Framfield, 110S Mural monument for William John DUGDELL, d. 1823
- North nave aisle, facing South, near North door, high.
- Inaccessible — Fine; dirty; faded.
- White on black; M.I. (5 lines, engraved) on upper 50% of a tablet; 2 corbels; signed (lower centre): 'PARSONS. LEWES'.
- William John Dugdell, Esq., d. 22 May 1829, aet 50.

Framfield Additions
Horsfield (*Sussex* I 364):
(1) John Smith, of Hempsted, d. 1 Jul 1777, aet 79, his wife, Mary, d. 20 Jan 1766, aet 64.
Church Guide citing Ayloffe MS.
(2) Ledger in side chapel: 'Here lyeth the body of Henry Gage Esquire of Bentley, son of Thomas Gage Esquire of Bentley, born the 26th day of July 1648, deceased March the 10th, 1717, aged 69 years'.
(3) Other damaged ledgers at West end of church.

(111) FRANT, St. Alban
A report of 1724, Ford (170) noted that East chancel was adequate although the North chancel belonging to Lord Abergavenny was in a poor state; church was rebuilt with donations from local worthies (the vicar, the son of the Earl of Abergavenny, the Marquis of Camden who had a family pew built into his South aisle) from 1819 and reopened 14 Jul 1822 - Horsfield (*Sussex* I 408-9); Nairn & Pevsner (507) follow Horsfield in citing the antiquarian expertise of the designer John Montie; monuments from the old church were reinstalled; for the earliest slabs in the church (not found) for the Fowles, local ironmasters, one to Sybil, d. 1631, the third wife of William Fowle, of Riverhall, and one to 'EF', perhaps Elizabeth Fowle, d. 1606, the first wife of William Fowle, see Eeles (253-4). See too Horsfield (*Sussex* 1 409); Willatts (*SAC* 125 102-4) reports 3 iron slabs here, one with the Fowle arms, which recur at Wadhurst.

Frant, 111A Mural monument for William DELVES, d. 1784

- West wall, near North-West corner, at head height.
- 100(W) x 60(H) — Fine; faded.
- M.I. on unframed grey marble tablet, moulded cornice, simple curved apron.

SACRED

TO THE MEMORY OF REV° WILLIAM DELVES M.A.

WHO WAS 42 YEARS VICAR OF THIS PARISH

HE DEPARTED THIS LIFE ON THE 19 DAY OF APRIL 1784

AGED 66 YEARS.

ALSO OF ELIZABETH DELVES HIS WIFE

WHO DEPARTED THIS LIFE

ON THE 9 DAY OF JANUARY 1822

AGED 86 YEARS.

1. Reported by Horsfield (*Sussex* I 409) as in Chancel and damaged in the move [c.f. with 111B, suggests loss of upper backplate and escutcheon?] probably soon after 1784, with the final lines, added in a consistent hand.
2. JH notes that William Delves was installed as vicar at Frant in 1741, see CCEd and Hennessy (72).
3. On West wall in Eeles (249).

Frant, 111B Mural monument for Daniel CROFTS, d. 1785

- North aisle wall, near North-West corner, at head height.
- 100(W) x 87(H) — Fine; rust, crack on right side.
- Description as for 111A; added is a thin baseplate in dark marble above the cornice and an escutcheon; final 3 lines added later.
- Daniel Crofts, Esq., d. 2 Sep 1785, aet 45; his wife, name unknown, d. 11 Dec 1799, aet 52.

1. See Lambarde (*SAC* 67 179) for heraldry. Daniel Croft's wife is probably Catherine as NBI has entry for Catherine Croft, with anomalous burial date of 18 Oct 1799, aged 52.
2. See also Eeles (248).

Frant, 111C Mural monument for Catherine Erskine ROWLAND, d. 1829 [Plate 72]

- North aisle wall, centre, at head height.
- 114(W) x 128(H) — Fine; colour.
- In freestone; Perpendicular frame; M.I. (engraved, black) in upper 75% of marble tablet; below, additional epitaph; above, Tudor arch decorated with trefoils; then, mantling and escutcheon carried by 2 winged angels; below, decoration.
- Catherine Erskine Rowland, d. 10 Dec 1829, aet 52; daughter of Pelham Maitland, Esq., and Charlotte Helen, of Belmont, near Edinboro'; and wife of Daniel Rowland, Esq., of Saxonbury Lodge, Frant; their son, Erskine Knightley Rowland, d. 31 Jan 1819, an infant.

1. Daniel Rowland was the agent to the Eridge estate and in 1830 donated the school building, to the village, in memory of his wife, see Wright (75 and 79).
2. 111C was praised by Horsfield (*Sussex* I 409): 'a very beautiful gothic structure ... much and deservedly admired'.
3. Have the lower elements been incorrectly reassembled?
4. See Lambarde (*SAC* 67 179) for heraldry and Eeles (248).

Frant, 111D Mural monument for Charles BROWN, d. 1754 [Plate 73]

- Sanctuary, North wall, above head height.
- 114(W) x 268(H) — Excellent.
- White marble tablet, unframed; 2 decorative corbels with an ornate acanthus urn; flanked by decorative scrolls; above, a moulded cornice and an urn, festooned, in relief against a dark grey backplate in obelisk form; towards the top, a wreathed escutcheon; signed (on urn base): 'Peirce Fecit Deptford.'.

- Charles Brown, Esq., of Bay Hall, Pembury, Kent, d. in 1754, aet 36, his wife, Elizabeth, d. 6 Dec 1789, aet 89.

1. The heraldic device at the top stands proud of the backplate and may not be of stone; the signature is unusually prominent; cited by Gunnis (*Dict.* 304) and Nairn & Pevsner (507).
2. Edward Pierce, fl. 1770-90.
3. 111D can be dated post-1789 [?].
4. See Lambarde (*SAC* 67 177) for heraldry and Eeles (246).

Frant, 111E Mural monument for Henry WELLER, d. 1720/1
- Sanctuary, South wall, above head height.
- 100(W) x 236(H) — Excellent; colour.
- M.I. (engraved and black) fills a cartouche; revealed by putti holding back tasselled curtains with gilded edges; below, centre, 2 cherubs; a moulded pedestal and an ambitious achievement.
- Henry Weller, d. 2 Mar 1720/1, aet 81; son of Thomas, [grandson] of Richard Weller; also Robert Weller, of Rochester, son of Thomas and brother of Henry, his heir.

1. In situ - Horsfield (*Sussex* I 408-9) and Nairn & Pevsner (507).
2. Note the high quality of the cherubs and the marble carving throughout 111E.
3. See Lambarde (*SAC* 67 178) for heraldry and Eeles (245) for transcription.

Frant, 111F Ledger for Robert DYKE, d. 1644
- Nave floor, near chancel steps, (beneath carpet), alongside and North of 111G.
- 64(W) x 149(L) — Fine; damage to left side.
- An escutcheon, then M.I. (engraved; Latin, 14 lines concluding with 6 lines of elegiac couplets) in black slab; head to West.

IN MEMORIAM ROBERTI DYKE QVI ERAT
FILIUS GVILIELMI DYKE HVIVS ECCLESIÆ
MINISTRI VXOREM DVXIT PRIMAM
MARIAM FARNDEN DEFVNCTAM EX
QVA GVILIELMVM VNICVM FILIVM
SVVM SVSCEPIT ALTERAM FRANCISCAM
PETTER ADHVC SVPERSTITEM OBIIT
25 DIE AVG ANNO DNI 1644
ANNOQ. ÆTATIS SVAE 2[4?]

Hic iacet in chaos pietas spectata paterne
Hic iacet in bina conivge nota fides
In prolem pater indulgens devotus Amicis
Et vero summi raptus Amore Dei
Dicitur Absumpti iecoris periisse ruina
Nec mirum est tantus si iecur hausit Amor

1. Formerly in South aisle - Horsfield (*Sussex* I 408-9).
2. Robert Dyke, and his wife Mary, née Farnden. Robert was son of William Dyke who was vicar 1603-59 and owned extensive properties in the parish and had 12 children; all his sons were highly acquisitive, only one survived him, see Wright (27, 44).
3. NBI records burial of Robert Dyke on 27 Aug 1644 at Frant.
4. See Lambarde (*SAC* 67 178) for heraldry and Eeles (252).

Frant, 111G Ledger for Emmerline Champneys GARNAR, d. 1807
- Nave floor, near chancel steps (beneath carpet), alongside and South of 111F.
- 89.5(W) x 185(L) — Very worn in parts.
- Grey-veined marble slab; head to the W; pigment originally red?

EMMERLINE CHAMPNEYS
GARNAR
of Grantham in Lincolnshire
Died at TUNBRIDGE WELLS
29th October 1807
In her 19th YEAR.
While living she desired to be buried wherever
Life departed

1. Emmerline Champneys Garnar was probably a patient or spa-tourist at Tunbridge Wells.
2. See also Eeles (253).

Frant, 111H Ledger (and brass) for Richard DYKE, d. 1635

- Nave floor, West of 111G, beneath nave carpet.
- 66.5(W) x 154(L) — Cracked; (always) in 2 parts.
- On a brown freestone slab, above - oval brass and engraved escutcheon [33W x 45H]; below, another brass with M.I. (engraved) [43W x 18H].

HERE LYETH INTERRED THE BODIE
OF RICHARD DYKE, MARCHANT
OF LONDON, WHO DEPARTED THIS
LIFE THE 22 OF AVGVSTE, ANNO
DONI 1635

1. Formerly in South aisle - Horsfield (*Sussex* I 408-9) who mentions inscription to his wife, d. 1638.
2. Davidson-Houston (*SAC* 77 192) noted, illustrated, transcribed in situ.
3. For Dyke, see 111F.
4. NBI records burial of Richard Dyke on 24 Aug 1635 at Frant.
5. See Lambarde (*SAC* 67 178) for heraldry and Eeles (253).

Frant, 111I Ledger for Jane WEEKES, d. 1768

- Nave floor, West of 111F, beneath carpet.
- 114(W) x 202(L) — Bad cracks; part-illegible.
- M.I. (6 lines, engraved) in upper 15% of a black slab.

In Memory of
M[rs] IANE WEEKES Relict of
WALTER WEEKES Gent[n]
of Tunbridge in Kent
She departed this Life Aug[st] the 11th 1768
Aged 55 Years

1. See Eeles (253).

Frant Additions

Nairn & Pevsner (507):
(1) 3 iron slabs at West end of nave, one dated 1631 – Lambarde (*SAC* 67 178) identifies the heraldry as that of Fowle and related families.
Horsfield (*Sussex* I 408-9).
(2) A stone with 4 brass escutcheons in corners and Fowle arms in centre.
(3) A stone with 2 escutcheons and a crest, M.I. reads 'EE'.

(112) FRISTON, St. Mary the Virgin

Norman with 14th-century chancel - Nairn & Pevsner (508); in Horsfield's day (*Sussex* I 283), folding doors separated the nave from the Selwyn chapel; state of church never less than fine in 1686 and 1724 (Ford); in 1777, Grose thought the Selwyn monuments at Friston fine (Farrant 118); the parish had just 20 communicants in 1603, see Renshaw (*Ecclesiastical Returns*).

Friston, 112A Floor slab for Edward READING, d. unknown

- Porch floor.
- 39(W) x 37(L) — Fine.
- M.I. (3 lines, engraved) on a pale brown freestone slab; head to North.

EDWARD

READING

M OF MVSIC

1. Appears to be 17th century.
2. Grove notes several musicians surnamed Reading active in Restoration and early Georgian England.
3. JH notes that there are none of this name in Venn or Foster (*Al. Ox.*).

Friston, 112B Mural monument for Thomas SELWYN, d. 1613/4, and Elizabeth his wife [Plate 74]

- North chapel, West wall.
- 170(W) x 325(H) — Good; repairs; losses.
- In alabaster; Thomas Selwyn (to left) and his wife kneel at a prayer desk; below, 3 infants in chrisoms; below that, a ledger stone with chamfered edge, on a chest with 6 daughters, in relief, who kneel and face North; flanking, 2 black polished Corinthian columns; on back wall, an arch over strapwork; M.I. (engraved, gilded) on a black panel with lozenged ends, set portrait-wise; above, a straight gilded entablature, 3 achievements, the central one very large; all stands on a moulded plinth.
- Thomas Selwyn, armiger, d. 16 Mar 1613/4, aet 67; his wife, Elizabeth, daughter of Sir Henry Goring, of Burton; issue – 3 sons, two died in infancy; Mary, wife of Thomas Woodward; Elizabeth, wife of Thomas Parker; Alice, wife of John Woodward; Dorothy; Anne; and Beatrice.

1. Formerly on the North side of the chancel - Horsfield (*Sussex* I 283); moved when the new transept was built to receive it in the mid 19th century.
2. In situ - Lambarde (*SAC* 70 145) noting arms; *SNQ* (II 15-17); Mosse (92); Nairn & Pevsner (508).
3. Patron of 112B was Thomas Selwyn's widow, after his death.
4. For licences to marry of Thomas Selwyn's daughter Elizabeth (1596, Thomas Parker of Willingdon) and Anne (1620, Roger Gratwicke of Tortington) see Dunkin (*Licences 1586-1643* 25 & 122).
5. The antiquity of the Selwyns is stressed in the M.I. because the Selwyns' sons did not survive infancy.
6. Repairs probably followed 19th-century relocation of 112B.
7. The subsidiary kneelers are large relative to the main kneelers; 112B is attributed by White (62) to the distinguished tomb-maker Isaac James (fl.1600-living 1625/6), of St. Martins-in-the-Fields, Westminster, on the grounds that aspects of Thomas Selwyn's effigy resembles that on the documented Norris tomb at Westminster Abbey.
8. Whoever made 112B also made the Bunce tomb of c.1614 at Otterden, Kent.
9. NBI records burial of Thomas Selwyn on 17 Mar 1614 at Friston.

Friston, 112C Wall monument for Edward SELWYN, d. 1704/5, and family

- North Chapel, East wall.
- 240(W) x 380(H) — Good.
- White and grey marbles; M.I. (engraved) in English on a slate panel set landscape-wise on a broad grey marble base; a segmented pediment with an achievement over its centre; in the middle, a serliana comprising 3 additional M.I.s (Latin) on panels; 2 escutcheons left and right; vertical scrolls at sides; a rectangular basement with a 4th M.I.
- Left panel - William Thomas Selwyn, 11 Aug 1684 – 9 Feb 1704/5, aet 20, son of Edward Selwyn.
  Central panel - Edward Selwyn, Esq., 19 Sep 1638 - 9 Dec 1704, son of Francis Selwyn, armiger, and Penelope daughter of George Shurley, Esq., and Mary; and grandson of Edward Selwyn, armiger, and Alicia, daughter of Edward Burton, Esq.; Edward's wife, Mary Garret, widow, daughter of Sir Robert Smith, Bart., of Westham (Essex); issue – William Thomas Selwyn and Penelope.

Right panel - Francis Selwyn's seventh daughter Judith Meddlicote, 15 Jun 1637 – 18 Dec 1707.

Lower panel - Francis Selwyn, d. 20 Aug 1661 and his wife, Penelope, d. 13 Jan 1664/65, daughter of Sir George Shurley, of Isfield, Lord Chief Justice of Ireland; issue of Francis & Penelope – 7 sons: George, Francis (d. in Holland), Thomas (d. in London), Nicholas, Edward, John and another John (d. in Spain) and 8 daughters: Mary (d. in Ireland), Charity (d. in London, aet 63), another Mary, Philadelphia, Penelope (d. in London), Alice, Judith (living), Elizabeth (d. in London).

1. Formerly on South side of chapel - Horsfield (*Sussex* I 283); in situ Lambarde (*SAC* 70 145) noting arms.
2. The Selwyns died out on the male side and the property descended via Judith, eleventh child of Sir Francis Selwyn, to the Medleys of Buxted Place (47), hence the fact that the Earl of Liverpool was a later descendant and hence Judith's patronage of this monument in 1706.
3. The lower M.I. panel in slate is perhaps a survival from an earlier monument; the survey includes only a small number of these reredos-type standing monuments, with M.I.'s but no figures (e.g. a more provincial version for the Richbells of Wivelsfield [303H]).
4. Sir Edward Selwyn, son of Francis and Penelope Selwyn, d. 1704; William Thomas Selwyn, also d. 1704; Judith Meddlicote, d. 1707.
5. JH notes that Edward Selwyn [b. 1638] was MP for Seaford 1681 and 1685, Sheriff of Sussex and knighted 1683, see Berry (*Sussex* 114-5), A. Clarke (*Sussex* 97-8) and Shaw (2 258). NBI records the following burials at Friston - Edward Selwyn on 11 Dec 1704, his father Francis Selwyn on 3 Aug 1661 and mother Penelope Selwyn on 16 Jan 1665 and grandfather Edward Selwyn on 16 Aug 1618. Judith Selwyn married Richard Medlicott on 22 Apr 1666 at East Dean, see Sussex Marriage Index.

Friston Additions
Horsfield (*Sussex* I 283); Lambarde (*SAC* 70 146); Davidson-Houston (*SAC* 77 192-3); Nairn & Pevsner (508):
(1) Thomas Selwyn, d. 22 Sep 1539 and wife Margery, d. 18 [28?] Oct 1542 (2 brass figures, 15 inches, on nave slab), see Mosse (92).
(2) Alice, d. 1624, wife of Edward Selwyn, daughter of John Burton of Borne.
(3) John Willard, d. 1716; Nicholas Willard, d. 1728 and his wife Jane, d. 1747, all of Crowlink.

(114) GLYNDE, St. Mary
The demolition of the old church commenced on 1 Aug 1763; the inscribed stones were removed for replacement; see account entry for recutting inscriptions, 'afresh upon the tombstones and setting them to rights', and another for 'Paving the aisle and before the altar with tombstones'; the mason's and bricklayers were managed by John Morris of Lewes; the present building was completed by 1 Jul 1765: '... the walls neatly floated, the Monumental Stones and Pavements Laid and the Marble Font ... etc.' (Register entry) at the expense of Richard Trevor of Glynde Place, Bishop of Durham - see Salzman (*Glynde Registers* 61), S. Berry (*SAC* 142 109ff) and plan in *SNQ* (XIII 248); the present building covers parts of the foundations of the mediaeval building; earlier ledgers were relocated to the new nave aisle and given uniform width measurements and the sanctuary floor became the memorial ground for the bishop's family, the Trevors of Glynde Place; the identity of the architect of the new church is disputed (ESRO MS Glynde 2770); it was perhaps Sir Thomas Robinson (no reference to Glynde in his biography by Giles Worsley in *ODNB* entry); the builders were Hodgson and Morris; original 18th century fittings are still in place and there are Harmer terracottas in churchyard (e.g. Marianne New, d. 1811); elaborate monuments were planned, or indeed built in the original church, see the request in his will made by Robert Morley, dated 10 Apr 1514, see Rice & Godfrey (42 210); see De St. Croix (*SAC* 20 47-90) for parish history; the

estate passed from Morley to Trevor when Elizabeth, the widow of William Morley, married John Trevor son (2) of Sir John Trevor, Secretary of State to Charles II (see *SNQ* I 56-7); some of the original, longer M.I.s may have been recut in abbreviated form, see note on the inscription of Elizabeth Polhill (114L); Horsfield (*Sussex* I 345) comments on the M.I.s for the Trevors, Hampdens, Hays and Morleys. See too De St. Croix, 'Names from the Register Books of Glynde' (*SAC* 24 99ff).

Glynde, 114A Ledger for Henry JOHNSON, d. 1716
- Porch floor, East side.
- 80(W) x 134(L) — Very worn.
- M.I. (engraved) in upper parts only of grey freestone slab.

Here Lieth the body of
Henry Johnson
who departed this life
the 25th Day of March 1716
aged 65 Years

1. See De St. Croix (*SAC* 20 86) for transcription - Henry Johnson, d. 25 Mar 1716, aet 65.

Glynde, 114B Anonymous ledger, date unknown
- Nave central aisle floor, far West end.
- 84(W) x 183(L) — Very worn.
- Nothing now visible on a freestone slab.

1. Possibly one of the slabs transcribed in De St. Croix (*SAC* 20 86).

Glynde, 114C Ledger for William ROSE, d. 1844
- Nave central aisle floor, towards West end.
- 83(W) x 182(L) — Very worn.
- M.I. visible in upper parts only of freestone slab; head to West.

here rest
in humble hope of
a blessed resurrection
the ... remains of ... ose
... vicar
...

1. Transcribed in De St. Croix (*SAC* 20 86): William Rose, 2 Dec 1765 - 3 Jun 1844. He was vicar of Glynde for 20 years, 1824-44, and had previously been curate of Maresfield, Little Horsted and Uckfield.
2. His wife, Susannah Wade Rose, , 16 Aug 1762 - 21 Apr 1839.

Glynde, 114D Ledger for Ciceley HAY, d. 1663
- Nave, central aisle floor, towards West end.
- 63?(W) x 167(L) — Very worn; cracked.
- M.I. engraved in grey freestone alabaster; head to West.

Here Lieth the Body of
Ciceley the daughter of
Sr John Rouphe of Boughton
under the Blean in Kent
Knt and wife of John Hay
[of] Glynd Esq.r who died [the]
30 Day of October 1663

1. Probably the Mrs Cecilia Hay, buried 6 Nov 1663, wife of John Hay, Esq. - see Salzman (*Glynde Registers* 47).
2. Transcribed in De St. Croix (*SAC* 20 86).

Glynde, 114E Ledger for Elizabeth HAY, d. 1671
- Nave, central aisle floor, West of 114F.
- 82(W) x 184(L) — Worn.
- M.I. fills surface of a brown freestone slab; head to West.

> Here Lieth the Body of
> that Pious and Virtuous
> Gent[w] M[rs] ELIZABETH H[AY]
> Second Wife of JOHN HAY
> of GLYND Esq[r] and Eldeſt
> *daughter* of RICH[D] BURDET
> of *Southover* Gent. She had
> Five Sons JOHN HARBERT
> HENRY WILLIAM AND WILL[M]
> *Henry* and the first *William*
> departed this Life
> Before Her being Twins
> She deceased the 19th of
> January Anno Dom 1671

1. Elizabeth Hay was buried 22 Jan 1671, see Salzman (*Glynde Registers* 48).
2. John Hay seems also to have presented plate to the church in this same year, 1671, see Couchman (*SAC* 55 163).
3. The gender implications in line 3 are unusual, a small 'w' appearing to form the word 'gentlewoman'.
4. See A. Clarke (*Sussex* 58).
5. John Hay, Esq. of Glyndebourne married Elizabeth Burdett, daughter of Richard, on 19 Jul 1664 at Ringmer, see Sussex Marriage Index.

Glynde, 114F Ledger for Frances HAY, d. 1643
- Nave, central aisle floor, West of 114G.
- 82(W) x 179(L) — Very worn.
- M.I. in upper parts of a brown freestone slab; head to West.

> Here lieth Frances
> Cilpiper the wife of
> Hirbirt H[ay] Esq[r] who died
> June the 16th 1643

1. M.I. is transcribed in De St. Croix (*SAC* 20 86).
2. For Frances Hay's spouse Herbert see 114G; on 6 Mar 1633 Frances Hay was granted licence to eat flesh during Lent and subsequently, on account of her sickness; however, she survived another 10 years, Salzman (*Glynde Registers* 81).
3. JH notes that Frances Hay was daughter of John Colepeper of Folkington – see Comber (*Ardingly* 133).

Glynde, 114G Ledger for Herbert HAY, d. 1652
- Nave, central aisle floor, East end.
- 82(W) x 70(L) — Very worn; cracked.
- M.I. in upper parts of a dark freestone slab; head to West.

> Here Lieth the Body o[f]
> Herbert Hay of Glynde[bourn]
> Esq[r] who departed [this]
> Life the 3[d] of Febuary
> Anno Dom 1652 Aged 6[1] Y[ears]

1. For Herbert Hay's spouse see 114F.
2. Herbert Hay was buried 4 Feb 1652 - see Salzman (*Glynde Registers* 24); transcribed in De St. Croix (*SAC* 20 86); for his daughter see 45I.
3. See A. Clarke (*Sussex* 58).

Glynde, 114H Ledger with mounted brass for Henry TREVOR, Baron DACRE, d. 1853, for his wife Pyne, d. 1844, for Victoria BRAND, d. 1865, for John Morley TREVOR, d. 1719 and his wife Lucy, d. 1720

- Sanctuary floor, West side, centre.
- 77(W) x 175(L) — Fine.
- Escutcheon, M.I. on brass plate (engraved) and M.I. (engraved) fill surface of a black slab (marble?); head to West.
- Henry Trevor, General, and Colonel of 31st Regiment, 21st Baron Dacre, 27 Jul 1777 - 2 Jun 1853; his wife, Pyne, d. 11 Jan 1844, aet 67, sister of William, 4th Baron Brandon; also, Victoria, d. 20 Jul 1865, aet 23, wife (from 21 Jan 1863) of Henry R Brand, first son of Hon. Henry Brand, of Glynde, MP, and daughter of S. Van De Weyer, Belgian Ambassador; also, John Morley Trevor, d. 7 Apr 1719, aet 37, buried 12 Apr 1719; and his wife Lucy, d. 12 Jul 1720, aet 42, buried 16 Jul 1720, daughter of Edward Montague of Horton, Northamptonshire.

1. All transcribed by De St. Croix (*SAC* 20 87), brasses to John Morley Trevor and his wife Lucy cited by Croix as if grouped with that to Bishop Trevor (see 114L).
2. Brasses on 144H postdate the ledger by many years.
3. For licence to marry dated 23 Mar 1701/2 for John Morley Trevor and Lucy Montague of East Hoathly, see Dunkin (*Licences 1670-1729* 187); his daughter, Elizabeth, was buried 10 Mar 1720, see Salzman (*Glynde Registers* 38).

Glynde, 114I Ledger with 2 mounted brasses for John TREVOR, d. 1686, for Jane Maria, Viscountess HAMPDEN, d. 1833, for Catherine, Viscountess HAMPDEN and for Elizabeth SPENCE, d. 1764

- Sanctuary floor, West side, North of centre.
- 81.5(W) x 175(L) — Fine.
- M.I. (engraved) on black slab; also M.I.s on 2 brasses (engraved); escutcheon at foot.
- John Trevor, of Glynde, d. 30 Sep 1686, aet 34; also, Jane Maria, Viscountess Hampden, d. 27 Jun 1833, aet 59, daughter of George Brown of Ellistoun, second wife of Thomas Trevor Hampden, Viscount Hampden; also, Catherine, Viscountess Hampden, d. 24 May 1804, aet 53, only daughter of General David Graeme of Braco; also, Elizabeth Spence, d. 15 Oct 1764, aet 70, daughter of John and Ann Spence of Malling, (Ann was sister to John Trevor of Glynde).

1. All transcribed in De St. Croix (*SAC* 20 87), who groups the brass M.I.s to John Trevor (d. 1743) and Elizabeth Spence (d. 1764, buried 21 Oct 1764), see Salzman (*Glynde Registers* 59).
2. Spence arms noted by D'Elboux (*SAC* 86 122), as in situ.

Glynde, 114J Ledger stone for Col. Herbert MORLEY, d. 1667, with brasses for Thomas, d. 1824, and John, d. 1824, Viscounts HAMPDEN

- Sanctuary floor, North-West corner.
- Ledger: 80(W) x 177(L) — Fine.
- Escutcheon and M.I. (engraved) on the upper surface of a black slab (marble?); head to West; below, 2 brass plates with arms and M.I. (engraved). Motto: 'nec aspera terrent vestigia nulla retrorsum'.
- Herbert Morley, d. 29 Sep 1667, aet 51; eldest son of Robert Morley, of Glynde, deceased; also, Rt. Hon. Thomas Trevor-Hampden, Viscount Hampden, Baron Trevor, of Bromham, (MP for Lewes 1768-74), d. 20 Aug 1824, aet 78 ; also, Rt. Hon. John Trevor-Hampden, Viscount Hampden, Baron Trevor, of Bromham, d. 9 Sep 1824, aet 76.

1. Brasses added later.
2. The younger Viscount succeeded but only survived his brother by 2 weeks. Col. Morley's wife, Mary, was buried 18 Sep 1656; his daughter, Anne, was baptised in Oct 1654 and an anonymous daughter was buried late in Sep 1649, see Salzman (*Glynde Registers* 24-5, 45); transcribed in De St. Croix

(*SAC* 20 87).

3. Brasses for Thomas and John Trevor, Viscounts Hampden, and Col. Morley's ledger, noted for their heraldry in Lambarde (*SAC* 70 160).

4. For the correspondence of Col. Morley, staunch Parliamentarian, see Blencowe (*SAC* 10 5ff) and De Beer 'Evelyn and Colonel Herbert Morley 1659 and 1660' (*SAC* 78 177-183); for biography of Herbert Morley see J.T. Peacey in *ODNB*; he was baptised 2 Apr 1616; his guardian was Sir Thomas Pelham, a prominent political independent during first Civil War and only a hesitant supporter of the restoration of Charles II.

5. See *ODNB* biography by William Carr, rev. P.J. Jupp of John Trevor, 3rd Viscount Hampden (1748-1824), diplomatist; second son of Robert (1706-83), 4th Baron and 1st Viscount; succeeded his brother as Viscount for just a few weeks; his wife, Harriet, 1751-1829.

6. For heraldry of Thomas and John (both d. 1824) see Lambarde (*SAC* 70 160).

Glynde, 114K Floor-mounted brasses for Hon. John TREVOR, d. 1743, and his wife Betty, d. 1742, and for the Right Hon. Harriet, Viscountess HAMPDEN, d. 1829

- Sanctuary floor, North-East corner.
- Brass 1: 25(W) x 35.5(L); Brass 2: 31(W) x 41(L); Brass 3: 23.5(W) x 32.5(L) — Good; local losses to brasses 2-3.
- Three rectangular engraved brass plates mounted on a black slab (marble?).

(Brass 1)
the Hon[ble]
Iohn Trevor,
of Glynd, in the County
of Sussex Esqr
Died the 9th Sep[r] 1743
in the 27th year of his age
(Brass 2)
Sacred
To the Memory of
The Right Honourable Harriet Viscountess [Hampden]
Widow of the Right Honourable John Viscount Hampden
and Daughter of the Revd Dr Burton. Canon Christch
She Died on the 26th day of June 1829
(Brass 3)
Betty Trevor
Wife of the Honble
John Trevor Esqr of this plac..
Eldest Daughter of Sr Thoma..
Frankland of Thirkleby i..
the County of York, Bart. Ob., 28 December, 1742, aetat 25

1. John Trevor, one of the Lords of the Admiralty, was buried 29 Sep 1743; his wife, Betty, was buried on 5 Jan 1743, see Salzman (*Glynde Registers* 52).

2. The text of the M.I., as above, was completed from De St. Croix (*SAC* 20 87).

3. Brass for John Trevor noted for its heraldry in Lambarde (*SAC* 70 160) and in situ.

4. *ODNB* biography by William Carr, rev. P.J. Jupp of John Trevor, 3rd Viscount Hampden 1748-1824, diplomat; second son of Robert 1706-83, 4th Baron and 1st Viscount; succeeded his brother as Viscount for just a few weeks then died; his wife Harriet 1751-1829.

5. JH notes that John Trevor was MP for Lewes 1738-43.

Glynde, 114L Ledger for Elizabeth POLHILL, d. 1708, and mounted brass for Bishop Richard TREVOR, d. 1771

- Sanctuary floor, South-East corner, partly obscured by furnishings.
- 51.5(W) x 129(L) — Fine.
- M.I. (engraved) on a black slab; later brass.
- Elizabeth Polhill, 4 Jun 1708, aet 25; eldest daughter of John Trevor; and wife of David Polhill, of Otford, Kent; also, Richard Trevor, bishop of Durham, son of Thomas Lord Trevor, 30 Sep 1707 - 9 Jun 1771.

(1 on slab):
H.I.
Elisabetha, Johannis
Trevor Arm Filia,
& Davida Polhill
Conjux
Ob. 4.to Kal. Junii
Anno Aetat. 25.o
Dom: 1708
(2 on brass):
... sce mori moriture
...ard Trevor, ...hop of Durham.
...Son of Tho. L. Trevor,
...n Sep. 30.. 1707.
...d June 9.. 1771.

1. An anonymous portrait of Richard Trevor, 1707-71 at Glynde Place shows the Bishop of Durham seated, reproduced in Caffyn (120 and Pl. 6); he inherited Glynde in 1743, provided charity schooling in Glynde and Beddingham and was also a benefactor of Mayfield School.
2. Elizabeth Polhill's M.I. is transcribed in De St. Croix (*SAC* 20 87) with additional lines stressing her virtues.
3. Richard Trevor's M.I. also transcribed in De St. Croix (*SAC* 20 87) and grouped with other brasses to John Morley Trevor and his wife Lucy (see 114H).
4. See *ODNB* for biography by F. Deconinck-Brossard of Richard Trevor (1707-71); he was Bishop of Durham from Nov 1752; unmarried; a statue by J. Nollekens was erected to him in the Bishop's Chapel at Bishop Auckland, Durham in 1775, Gunnis (*Dict.* 277); buried at Glynde 19 Jun 1771 see Salzman (*Glynde Registers* 64).

Glynde, 114M Ledger for Susanna MORLEY, d. 1667, William, d. 1679, and Frances, d. 1712

- Sanctuary floor, South-West corner.
- 86(W) x 198(L) — Worn.
- Escutcheon, then M.I. (engraved) on a black slab (marble?).
- Susanna Morley, d. 19 Apr 1667, aet 71; daughter and heir of Thomas Hodgson, Gent., of Pounslow; and wife of Robert Morley, Esq., of Glynde; also, William Morley, Esq., of Glynde, d. 20 May 1679, aet 25; also, Frances Morley, d. 1712, daughter of Robert Morley, Esq.

1. Salzman (*Glynde Registers* 29, 48) reads the parish register as suggesting that Susanna Morley was buried on 15 Apr 1667; William Morley's daughter Anne was born on 17 Jan 1678; he was a son of Col. Herbert Morley (see 114J).
2. Transcribed in De St. Croix (*SAC* 20 86-7).
3. Susanna Morley's ledger noted for its heraldry in Lambarde (*SAC* 70 160).

Glynde, 114N Ledger for John Morley TREVOR, d. 1706, his brother Thomas, d. 1707, and sister Elizabeth, d. 1722

- Sanctuary floor, West side, South of centre.
- 68(W) x 175(L) — Good.
- Escutcheon and M.I. (engraved) on a black slab (marble?).
- John Morley Trevor, d. 24 May 1706, aet 2, son of another John Morley Trevor; also, Thomas Morley Trevor, d. 16 Dec 1707, aged 2 months, second son of John Morley Trevor; also, Elizabeth Morley Trevor, d. 7 Mar 1722, aet 19, daughter of John Morley Trevor and Lucy his wife.

1. Salzman (*Glynde Registers* 49) reads the parish register as suggesting that John, son of John Morley Trevor was buried on 27 May 1705.
2. M.I.s transcribed in De St. Croix (*SAC* 20 87).
3. John Morley Trevor arms noted in Lambarde (*SAC* 70 160).

Glynde, 1140 Wall-mounted ledger for Abraham COO[PER], d. 1657

- Porch, against South wall.
- 80(W) x 120(H) — Worn; local losses.
- M.I. on rectangular panel set portrait-wise; arched top; curved base.

> HERE LYETH THE BODY OF
> ABRAHAM COO ... D
> MARCH ... 1657 AGED 71
> YEERES WHO APPOINTED
> THIS EPITAPH VPON HIM
> SELFE
> CHRISTS DEATH ...
> MY DEATH TO LIFE IS PORTAL
> SO BY TWO DEATHS
> I HAVE ONE LIFE IMMORTALL

1. Abraham Cooper, of Glynde, yeoman, was licensed to marry Elizabeth Rowe of Lewes 10 Oct 1640, see Dunkin (*Licences 1586-1643* 270); he d. 23 Mar and buried 26 Mar 1657; issue of Abraham Cooper [the same?] and his wife Elizabeth were baptised 28 Nov 1641, see Salzman (*Glynde Registers* 13, 28, 46).

(118) GUESTLING, St. Laurence (or Lawrence)

Norman; enlargements to North side c.1200; arcades and Ashburnham or South chapel c.1300; Rector's chancel dilapidated in 1686; some Victorian replacements - Nairn & Pevsner (513); a 'heavy' restoration in 1886; a serious fire in 1890; view from South-East, see Godfrey & Salzman (Pl. 68); plan in *SNQ* 5 55; North chancel taken over & repaired by Sir Denis Ashburnham in 1686, see Ford (44); further repairs by his successor Sir William to North and South chancels - 1724 report in Ford (97); the parish had 109 communicants in 1603, see Renshaw (*Ecclesiastical Returns*); unusually, the only monuments at 118 are of the Renaissance period, both in a very battered state [fire of 1890?].

Guestling, 118A Mural monument for John CHEYNEY, d. 1603, and his wife Elizabeth

- Chancel, North wall, at head height.
- 145(W) x 179(H) — Poor; restored and reassembled; many losses.
- In various coloured marbles, slate and alabaster; 2 adult kneelers on cushions; in civil dress (he is armoured); no prayer desk; a restored colonette; female figure on right with daughter behind her; flanking, squared pillars; above, entablature with pillowy frieze; ribbon work; below, base moulding, gadroon ornament, M.I. on a framed slate panel set landscape-wise; at foot, plaque with a winged death's head relief.
- John Cheyney, Esq., d. 20 Sep 1603; his wife, Elizabeth, daughter of John [P]alme[r], Esq., of Lincoln's Inn; their issue, 1 son and 1 daughter (unnamed).

1. In situ (North side of the rector's chancel, within sanctuary rail) - Horsfield (*Sussex* I 468); Nairn & Pevsner (513); damaged in 1890 fire, see Mosse (100); for its earlier state see photograph in H.C.G. Colborne 'Guestling Church' (*SCM* 2 408); significant losses perhaps include, effigies' hands, the figure representing Cheyney's son, an achievement-of-arms on the entablature and a cradle (Church Guide).

Guestling, 118B Mural monument for Adam ASHBURNHAM, d. 1597

- South (Lady) Chapel, West wall, above head height.
- 85(W) x 140(H) — (Upper) Fine; (lower) damaged; colour.
- M.I. on rectangular, black marble panel; flanking, alabaster pilasters (damaged), ribbon work; above, achievement on black panel; below, motto on alabaster panel (damaged on left).

- Adam Ashburnham, Esq., d. 5 Jun 1597, aet 40; son of Laurence Ashburnham and Eve Adames; his wife, Elizabeth Twisden; issue (still living 1597) - Elizabeth, Laurence, John, Roger, Charles and Edward.

1. In situ - Horsfield (*Sussex* I 468); in pieces in early 20th century - Colborne (*SCM* 2 408); an ancient Ashburnham burial site which they promised to extend and repair in the 17th century, see churchwarden's presentments in Johnstone (48-9).
2. For his son John see 11A; for marriage licence for his son Lawrence Ashburnham of Guestling and Sibbel Goringe of Hurstpierpoint, gentlewoman, maiden 2 Sep 1610, see Dunkin (*Licences 1586-1643* 75); for IPMs of Adam Ashburnham's father, Lawrence Ashburnham, d. 30 Oct an. reg. Elizabeth I, son and heir Adam, aged 10 in Mar an. reg. 9 Elizabeth I, see Salzman (*Inquisitions* 44) and for Adam Ashburnham himself see Holgate (50), his son and heir being Lawrence.
3. Did they adopt the dedicate name of the church and make a play (Adam and Eve) on Adam Ashburnham's mother's name?.
4. JH notes that the achievement of arms in poor condition is not mentioned by Lambarde. Beneath the inscription is the family motto 'Will God and I Shall', see Elvin (229).

(119) HAILSHAM, St. Mary the Virgin

Perpendicular; South aisle of 1870 - Nairn & Pevsner (513-14); in 1686, paving was needed; condition reportedly fine by 1724, see Ford (172): Hailsham had c.400 communicants in 1603, see Renshaw (*Ecclesiastical Returns*); Gunnis (*Dict.* 188) and Nairn & Pevsner (514) report works in terracotta by Harmer in the yard South-West of the church.

Hailsham, 119A Mural monument for Edward LUXFORD, d. 1746, his wife Jane, d. 1768, and several descendants including members of the LAUGHAM and PLUMER families

- North aisle, North wall, East of North door, at head height.
- 154(W); (H) unknown — Excellent; crack (pediment); faded.
- In grey marble, a pointed pediment with a broken entablature on fluted brackets; enclosing an escutcheon with a Baroque frame; behind, a secondary order; below, M.I. (21 + 5 lines) on white marble tablet; irregular moulded frame; decorative border in raunce; below, base moulding and another M.I. (7 lines); flanking, squared pilasters and base moulding on scrolled corbels; at foot, another escutcheon in a Baroque frame; corbel decoration with ferns.
- Edward Luxford, d. 3 Mar 1745/6, aet 66; his wife, Jane, d. 6 Sep 1768, aet 86; issue - eldest son, John, d. 13 May 1775, aet 64; eldest daughter, Mary, d. 11 May 1763, aet 50; fourth daughter, Ann, d. 16 Mar 1742/3, aet 23; youngest son, Edward, d. 7 Dec 1770, aet 47; Edward's wife, Frances, d. 7 Oct 1796, aet 72, and their issue, Frances, d. 26 May 1763, aet 9.
  also, Abraham Laugham, d. 12 Jun 1793, aet 76; his wife, Jane, d. 15 Apr 1805, aet 90, daughter of Edward and Jane Luxford; and their issue, Ann, d. 11 Apr 1757, aet 4.
  also, Richard Plumer, Esq., of South Sea House, London, d. 3 May 1813, aet 58; and his wife, Elizabeth, d. 16 Dec 1798, aet 41, daughter of Abraham and Jane Laugham.

1. In situ - Lambarde (*SAC* 70 135) noting arms; described as 'splendid' in Horsfield (*Sussex* I 318) and cited in Salzman (*Hailsham* 119) with transcription.
2. Probably erected after the death of Jane Luxford in 1768; for licence to marry dated 24 Nov 1709 for Edward Luxford and Jane Burgis, of Wadhurst, see Dunkin (*Licences 1670-1729* 318).

Hailsham, 119B Mural monument for Philip VAN CORTLANDT, d. 1814 [Plate 75]

- North aisle, North wall, between windows, above head height.
- 69(W) x 113(H) — Very good.
- M.I. (14 lines, engraved, black) fills a marble tablet; moulded ogival arched top; flanking,

polished Doric half columns in black marble, flecked with white; straight base moulding; corbels with pointed bottoms; signed (under base moulding): 'H.W.DODD, EASTBOURNE'.
- Colonel Philip Van Cortlandt, of the Manor of Cortlandt, royalist in the American War of Independence, died at Hailsham, May 1814, aet 74; quotes Prov x vii.

1. Cited in Salzman (*Hailsham* 119) with transcription.
2. In a style later than 1814.
3. Philip Van Cortlandt fought on the British side; the progenitors of the Van Cortlandts arrived in the New Netherlands in 1637; in 1694 Jacobus Van Cortlandt purchased a property in what is now New York state; the family were prominent in New York throughout the 18th century and Washington used the Van Cortlandt house as a military HQ in 1776, indeed, the family generally were active on the Revolutionary side; the estate was sold to the city of New York as a public park in 1889 and still so functions.
4. The maker of 119B, HW Dodd, seems to be otherwise unknown.

Hailsham, 119C Mural monument for Ann BRISTOW, d. 1800 and her husband John, d. 1803

- North aisle, North wall, near North choir aisle, very high.
- 50(W) x 150(H) — Fine, fading.
- M.I. (11 lines, shallow engraved) fills an unframed marble panel with scalloped corners; set portrait-wise; below, freestone corbel; above, finial.

Near This Place
Lie the Remains of ANN
Wife of Mr JOHN BRISTOW,
And only surviving Child
Of Mr JOHN MILLER
Late of this Pariſh
She died on the 29th of April 1800
in the 76th Year of her Age
THE MEMORY OF THE JUST IS BLESSED
Mr JOHN BRISTOW
died Octr 17th 1803. Aged 81 Years.

1. Cited in Salzman (*Hailsham* 118) with transcription.
2. NBI records burial of Ann Bristow on 8 May 1800 and John Bristow on 21 Oct 1803, both at Hailsham.

Hailsham, 119D Mural monument for Rev. Thomas HUBERSTY, d. 1793 [Plate 76]

- Choir, North wall, above head height.
- 70(W) x 152(H) — Excellent; local loss (drapery on right).
- A shallow dark grey baseplate with pointed top; M.I. (12 lines, engraved, black) on white marble oval panel; above, a painted escutcheon; decorative drapery in white marble low relief; below, a white and pink corbel.
- Rev. Thomas Hubersty, curate of Hailsham, d. 31 Oct 1793, aet 25.

1. In situ - Lambarde (*SAC* 70 134) noting arms and cited in Salzman (*Hailsham* 118) with transcription.
2. Markedly tall and narrow in its composition, an unusually elegant late Rococo; pink marble below being used in the manner of pietra dura.
3. JH notes that the surname is also spelled Hubbersty, see Venn (2 3 470) and NBI.

Hailsham, 119E Mural monument for Elizabeth HOOPER, d. 1810

- Sanctuary East wall, North-East corner, at head height.
- 85(W) x 193(H) — Fair; local damage (crossed ferns).
- Close in design to 119F; M.I. (12 lines, engraved, gilded) on an unframed, black oval panel, set portrait-wise; a shallow, grey marble base; over, a moulded entablature; at top, achievement on a pedestal; below, a second M.I. (15 lines, engraved, black) on marble;

flanked by scrolls; below, 2 corbels with roundel decoration; black apron with crossed ferns decoration; a corbel.

(Upper M.I.):

Sacred
to the Memory of
ELIZABETH HOOPER
who resided the whole of her Life
in the Vicarage House
in this Parish
and
who died Novr ye 8th 1810.
Her remains are deposited
with her family in the Chancel
at Beckley.
(Aged 84.)

(Lower M.I.):

She left by her Will
respectively to the Parishes of
Hailsham and Beckley
300L of old South Sea Annuities
directing the Dividends to be given
to the Poor.
at the discretion of each
Incumbent
She also left 300L five pr Cents
Bank Annuities
To the Vicar & Churchwardens of
this Parish
The Dividend to be applied for ever
towards the Support of the Charity School
established here in the Year 1812

1. In Horsfield's day (*Sussex* I 318) in the vestry, formerly a chapel North of the chancel; in situ in Lambarde (*SAC* 70 135) noting heraldry and cited in Salzman (*Hailsham* 117) with transcription and notes that the Charity school was formed in 1802.
2. Minor differences between 119E and 119F perhaps reflect later additions to 119E, e.g. the second M.I.
3. Gunnis (*Dict.* 361) notes a letter of 1749 associating Richard Spangen of Camberwell with three monuments at Hailsham for Mr Hooper, a commission possibly linked to 119E-F.
4. Miss Hooper owned the Parsonage and the Vicarage at Hailsham in 1785 (R. Davey 97); her charitable interests were reflected in the gift to the church of an alms plate in 1807, see Couchman (*SAC* 55 153); for the theme of a long life spent in the rectory see 213A (Ripe); Elizabeth Hooper is commemorated by other monuments at Beckley (21D & 21I).

Hailsham, 119F Mural monument for Odiarne HOOPER, d. 1769 [Plate 77]

- Sanctuary, East wall, South-East corner, at head height.
- 72(W) x 170(H) — Good; local losses (decoration below).
- Close in design to 119E; on top, achievement on pedestal; cornice; M.I. (13 lines, engraved, gilded) on a black oval panel, on a rectangular white marble base; narrow base moulding; 2 corbels with roundel decoration; between, crossed fern decoration (now lost); below, decorated centred corbel.
- Odiarne Hooper, M.A., 'faithful and truly pastoral vicar' of Hailsham for 46 years, d. 29 Aug 1769, aet 68, buried Beckley.

1. Despite the statement on this monument, although Odiarne Hooper had been curate of Hailsham since 1726/7, he was vicar from only 1753 – i.e. 16 years. He is shown as MA, although elsewhere he is given as LLB. Cited by Salzman (*Hailsham* 117) with transcription and notes that the 46 years mentioned on the monument should read 16 years.
2. Gunnis (*Dict.* 361) notes a letter of 1749 associating Richard Spangen of Camberwell with three monuments at Hailsham for Mr Hooper, a commission possibly linked to 119E-F.

3. Caffyn (417) notes that Odiarne Hooper attended Rev. Thankful Frewen's school at Northiam as a boarder 1712-20; for Thankful Frewen see 186G.
4. Odiarne Hooper was educated at University College, Oxford. He was vicar of Mayfield 1730-33/4, rector of East Guldeford 1736-53 and vicar of Hailsham 1753-69, see Dunkin (*SAC* 26 70); His father Thomas Hooper of Beckley had been the previous incumbent, instituted in 1701 (Ford); Odiarne Hooper is also commemorated by 21E, at Beckley.
5. JH notes that Lambarde does not mention the heraldry, although he does on 119E, which is the same.

Hailsham, 119G Mural monument for Anthony TRUMBLE, d. 1733 [Plate 78]
- South-East chapel, South wall, above head height.
- c.85(W) x 200(H) — Very good.
- M.I. (7 lines, centred, engraved, black) on an unframed white rectangular panel set portrait-wise; flanked by pairs of dark grey fluted Ionic pilasters; entablature over, its centre breaking forward; above, a pyramid with decorated ball finial; achievement flanked by flaming torches; below, a cherubim flanked by scrolls, then death's head; at foot, a tiny bearded male face.
- Anthony Trumble, Gent., d. 1 Sep 1733, aet 63.

1. In situ - Lambarde (*SAC* 70 135) noting that arms, if ever painted on monument, are now worn off; and cited in Salzman (*Hailsham* 118) with transcription.
2. For licence to marry dated 5 Oct 1716 for Anthony Trumble, of Hailsham, Gent., and Jane Wilson, of Eastbourne, widow, see Dunkin (*Licences 1670-1729* 213): the meaning of the bearded male at the foot of 119G is unclear.
3. The texture, variety and colour of 119G is characteristic but it is not signed.

Hailsham, 119H Mural monument for Thomas Bonell WEBB, d. 1805
- South aisle, East end, on pier facing South, above head height.
- 55(W) x 153(H) — Very good; fading; local loss (top urn).
- M.I. (10 lines, engraved, gilded) filling black oval unframed tablet; engraved border; below, scrolled corbel; above, in relief, urn on pedestal.
- Lieut. Thomas Bonell Webb, 39th Regiment, d. 7 Feb 1805, aet 26.

1. Cited in Salzman (*Hailsham* 118) with transcription.
2. Perhaps moved - South aisle was rebuilt in the 1870s.
3. Datable after 1805.

Hailsham, 119I Mural monument for the WILLARD family, d. 16th century
- On the Choir, South wall
- Not measured — Very good
- White marble tablet, with inscription in Gothic lettering and coat of arms, a chevron between two fish-wheels.
- The family of Willard, Lords of the Manor of Ersham, since 1341. Amongst many members buried are Christopher Willard, d. 1500; Robert Willard, d. 1528, Nicholas Willard, d. 1543, and William Willard, d 1595. Erected by Lt-Col John Harry Willard on 25 Dec 1839.

1. Mentioned by Lambarde (*SAC* 70 135) and cited by Salzman (*Hailsham* 118) with transcription.
2. The Willards are prominently buried and commemorated at Eastbourne (see 81G, 81H, 81L, etc.).

(120) HAMSEY, St. Peter
The medieval importance of Hamsey, as a burial place, was maintained in our period, despite the slow depopulation of the village and the rise of Offham; parish had 120 communicants in 1603, see Renshaw (*Ecclesiastical Returns*), 52 families in 1724 and a population of 367 in 1801; Norman nave and chancel redone c.1300 - Nairn & Pevsner (516), for plan see *SNQ* (II 53) and views in BL Add. MS 5677 ff.22-25); the church avoided nineteenth-century restoration; in 1724 it was reported

in Ford (131) that the fabric was fine; there had been recent repairs to chancel; by later 19th century, the church was dilapidated and fit only as a cemetery chapel, see Chapman in 1865 (*SAC* 17 93) and there were modest repairs, see G.C.Shiffner 'Hamsey Church' (*SAC* 25 227); Horsfield (*Sussex* I 221) noted several floor slabs near altar with lost brasses (see Additions).

Hamsey, 120A Mural monument for Sir John Hutton COOPER, d. 1828

- Nave, North wall, above the former North door.
- 100(W) x 84(H) — Very good.
- M.I. on simple white panel; on slate baseplate with pointed top; moulded cornice and consoles; signed (lower right): 'STOREY.LONDON'.
- Sir John Hutton Cooper, Bart., M.D., F.R.S., F.S.A., of Walcot, Somerset, Lt. Colonel, (2nd Regiment Somerset Militia), born 7 Dec 1765, Sleaford, Lincs; died Brighton, 24 Dec 1828; his widow, Maria Charlotte, 7 Mar 1774 - 7 Feb 1842, only daughter of Sir George Baker, Bart., M.D., F.R.S.

1. In situ - Chapman (*SAC* 17 99) with transcription.
2. Final 5 lines added after 1842. .
3. JH notes that Sir John Hutton Cooper was MP for Dartmouth in 1825, see J. Burke (*Baronetcies* 130).

Hamsey, 120B Wall monument for Dame Rebecca BRIDGER, d. 1803

- Nave, East wall, North-East corner, at head height.
- 124(W) x 236(H) — Good.
- Under earlier arch; M.I. on white marble rectangular tablet; chamfered corners and red hardstone border; flanking, grey marble decorated panels within dark grey Doric half columns; above, a decorated frieze; on cornice, an achievement and a metal helm (painted); below, a grey marble plinth and white consoles.
- Dame Rebecca Bridger, d. 25 Dec 1803, aet 79; heiress of John Elliot, Esq., of Croydon, Surrey; and wife of Sir John Bridger, of Combe, Hamsey, d. 15 Dec 1816, aet 83.

1. In situ - Chapman (*SAC* 17 98) with transcription and Lambarde (*SAC* 71 145) noting arms.
2. See 120J for vault of the Bridgers of Coombe Place (also called Combers, see 1785 tax return in R. Davey 98-99); Bridger hatchment still hangs in the nave, see Summers (141-2); Bridgers settled at Coombe near Lewes, temp Charles II, see Chapman (*SAC* 17 89).

Hamsey, 120C Mural monument for John SHORE, d. 1722

- Chancel, West wall, North-West corner, above head height.
- 109(W) x 188(H) — Good; staining; very faded.
- M.I. (9 lines?, gilded) on rectangular panel; flanking, fluted Doric pilasters with subsidiary order behind; above, a broken pediment and urn in relief; decorated corbels in support; below, apron with cherub in mid relief.

HSE
Dep
Iohannes Shore per XLVII annos
Hujus Ecclesiæ rectoris.
De quo plurima dicenda sint
Et multa dicta essent -
Ne vivus prœceperat nil aliud
Marmori inscribi
Prœter
Ως δαλος εξεσπασμευος εκ πυρος
probably quoting Zech. III 3.

1. In situ - Chapman (*SAC* 17 97) with transcription and Lambarde (*SAC* 71 145) noting arms.
2. Shore was admitted as the rector in 1674, serving (perhaps intermittently) until his death in 1722.
3. The style and composition of 120C is unusual for early 18th-century Sussex.

4. JH notes that John Shore was also rector of St. John sub Castro in Lewes and NBI records burial of John Shore on 9 May 1722 at Hamsey.

Hamsey, 120D Mural monument for Frances GUY, d. 1826, her sister and parents

- Chancel North wall, North-West corner, above head height.
- 56(W) x 75(H) — Very good; faded.
- M.I. (19 lines, engraved) on a rectangular white marble panel; set portrait-wise on a slate backplate.
- Frances Guy, d. 13 Jan 1826, aet 14; her sister Elizabeth Guy, d. 30 May 1840, aet 30; daughters of Henry Guy, d. 16 Sep 1845, aet 58, and Dorothy, d. 25 Feb 1874, aet 85, of Hamsey Place Farm, Hamsey.

1. In situ - Chapman (*SAC* 17 99) with part-transcription.
2. Some dates added after 1874.

Hamsey, 120E Mural monument for Henry SHIFFNER, d. 1795

- Chancel North wall, centre, above head height.
- 80(W) x 138(H) — Good; faded.
- Black slate backplate with pointed top; M.I. on white marble trapezoidal panel with pointed pediment; plain pedestal with 2 consoles; signed (below): 'PARSONS. LEWES'.

IN THE TOMB
TO THE NORTH OF THIS CHURCH
LIE THE REMAINS OF
HENRY SHIFFNER, ESQ.
LATE OF PONTRYLASS, HEREFORDSHIRE,
AND FORMERLY
M.P. FOR THE BOROUGH OF MINEHEAD,
OB: MAY 30TH. 1795, AET: 74
ALSO
OF MARY HIS WIFE
DAUGHTER AND CO HEIRESS OF
JOHN JACKSON, ESQ.
GOVERNOR OF BENGAL, IN 1747,
AND OF ELIZABETH BELLENDEN HIS WIFE,
OB: MARCH 12TH. 1814, AET: 78.
ALSO
OF THOMAS SHIFFNER, ESQ.
YOUNGEST SON OF THE ABOVE
HENRY AND MARY SHIFFNER,
OB: FEBRUARY 28TH. 1800, AET: 32
ISABELLA HANNAH SHIFFNER RELICT
OF THE ABOVE THOMAS SHIFFNER, ESQ.
DIED AT BUDLEIGH SALTERTON MAY 22 1845.
AGED 74 YEARS AND WAS BURIED
IN THE PARISH CHURCH OF BUDLEIGH, DEVON

1. In situ - Chapman (*SAC* 17 91 and 98) with faulty transcription and death date of 1775.
2. Mary Shiffner left plate to the church in 1801, see Couchman (*SAC* 54 227); Shiffner family hatchments still hang in the nave.
3. The shape of 120E, unusual from the Parsons shop, was perhaps dictated by the restricted space.
4. JH notes that Henry Shiffner was born in St. Petersburg son of Matthew, a Russian merchant and Agnata, governess of the Duchess of Courland, niece of Peter the Great. He was MP for Minehead 1761-68. See Namier & Brooke (3 434). The family hatchments in the nave are for Henry's son Sir George d. 1842, and his wife Mary, née Bridger, d. 1844, see Summers (142).

Hamsey, 120F Mural monument for John Bridger SHIFFNER, d. 1814

- Chancel, North wall, North-East corner, above head height and is above 120G.
- 92(W) x 124(H) — Very good.
- M.I. (engraved) on a white marble panel; base mouldings; 2 consoles; above, cornice with pointed pediment and ornamental palmettes.
- Captain John Bridger Shiffner, (3rd Regiment of Foot Guard), died (with Wellington's army) at Bayonne, 14 Apr 1814, aet 25; eldest son of George and Mary Shiffner of Combe, Hamsey.

1. In situ - Chapman (*SAC* 17 98) with transcription.
2. George Shiffner gave plate to the church in 1801, see Couchman (*SAC* 54 227) and was a successful Parliamentary candidate at Lewes in 1812, see L. Davey (13); Shiffner hatchments still hang in the nave.
3. For the Coombe Place vault see 120J.
4. 120F was erected by John Bridger Shiffner's parents for a hero of the Peninsula Wars.
5. Wellington's title was conferred on 4 May 1814.

Hamsey, 120G Wall monument for Edward MARWICK, d. 1538 [Plate 79]

- Chancel, in a niche against North wall, North-East corner.
- 181(W) x c.250(H) — Fair.
- Of freestone; a tomb-chest faced with 3 cusped quatrefoils and blind niches; over the recess, a very flat arch; diamond-patterning in vault; above, cresting with leaf decorated; quatrefoils in frieze; naturalistic decorated in arch spandrels.
- No M.I.

1. In situ - Horsfield (*Sussex* I 221) who notes excessive whitewashing with identification to Say family.
2. Chapman (*SAC* 17 95-6) quotes Elliott's antiquarian account of 120G, made to Sir William Burrell on 30 Mar 1777 with an engraving after a drawing by Lambert Jnr. showing railings protecting the monument; Chapman correctly rejects Elliott's conjecture that 120G is a Rivers monument.
3. Line drawing in *SNQ* II 54-5.
4. Nairn & Pevsner (516) noting decoration.
5. Godfrey identified the subject of 120G as Marwick citing the will dated 12 Nov 1534 and proved 22 May 1538, *SNQ* (II 54) and Rice & Godfrey (2 254), that requested 'one Tombe of Stone to be leyde oppon me with an Image and scripture there graven whereuppon the Sepulcre may be sett on'.
6. No figure carving or M.I.s survive, neither does any original colour.
7. A monument close in type to 120G, but probably earlier, survives at Selmeston (also prestigiously located at or near the position of the Easter sepulchre).

Hamsey, 120H Mural monument for Rev. [John] WENHAM, d. 1773

- Chancel, South wall, South-East corner, at head height.
- 104(W) x 215(H) — Excellent; some fading.
- Above an obelisk bearing an achievement; then, a moulded cornice with blank frieze; below, Doric pilasters frame M.I. (engraved, black) on a rectangular panel; at foot, apron and corbels.
- Rev. [John] Wenham, A.M., rector of Hamsey, d. 12 Aug 1773, aet 33: quotes Rev. XIV 13.

1. In situ - Chapman (*SAC* 17 98) and Lambarde (*SAC* 71 145) noting arms - which are now indecipherable.
2. Rev. John Wenham was rector of Hamsey 1766-73 and noted for his educational work (Caffyn 123).

Hamsey, 120I Vault stone for Thomas W. PARTINGTON, d. 1791

- Chancel floor, centre.
- 90(W) x 54(L) — Worn.
- M.I. (engraved) on surface of a freestone slab; head to West.
- Thomas W. Partington, Esq., 1791.

1. Later Partingtons are commemorated by a mural monument on the North nave wall.
2. For Thomas Partington's land tax record in 1785 see R. Davey (99); he signed the Town Book of

Lewes in 1800 (Smith 142).
3. NBI records burial of Thomas Walley Partington on 15 Mar 1791 at Hamsey.

Hamsey, 120J Vault stone for COOMBE Place, in the parish, date unknown.
- Nave floor, centre, opposite South door.
- 110(W) x 116(L) — Worn.
- M.I. (engraved) on a freestone slab; head to West.

COMBE VAULT

1. For the masters of Combe see 120B, 120E and 120F.

Hamsey, 120K Vault stone for Sir John Hutton COOPER, d. 1828
- Nave floor, centre, West end.
- 87(W) x 184(L) — Very worn.
- M.I. (3 lines, engraved) on a freestone slab; head to West.
- John Hutton Cooper, Bart., d. 24 Dec 1828.

1. For John Hutton Cooper see 120A.

Hamsey Additions
Reported by Chapman (*SAC* 17 97):
(1) Sir Thomas Rivers, d. 8 Dec 1657 (sanctuary).
(2) Charity Rivers, d. 2 May 1655 (sanctuary).

(121) HANGLETON, St. Helen
The latest extant part of the mediaeval church is the 14th-century chancel - Nairn & Pevsner (457-8); the oldest building in the City of Brighton and Hove is now surrounded by a post-WW2 estate, c.f. the view in Clayton (*SAC* 34 167); the 1724 report was that the fabric was fine but the chancel needed roof repairs, see Ford (132), perhaps relevant for the condition of 121B.

Hangleton, 121A Grave marker for Ann NORTON, d. 1749
- Nave floor, centre aisle.
- 53(W) x 69(H) — Worn; cracked (lower right).
- M.I. (engraved) fills surface of a freestone grave marker; head to East.

Here Lieth
Buried the Body of
ANN NORTON
(Daughter of
JOHN NORTON
of Portslade and
ANN his wife)
- 1749

1. In situ, see Clayton (*SAC* 34 177) with transcription.
2. Ann Norton died aet 21; probably a sister or niece of Robert Norton, rector 1755-57 (Church Guide).
3. NBI records burial of Ann Norton on 12 Dec 1749 at Hangleton.

Hangleton, 121B Mural monument probably for Richard BELLINGHAM, d. 1592
- Sanctuary, South wall, South-West corner.
- 174(W) x 143(H) — Worn; water damage; local losses (columns).
- In soft freestone; above, straight entablature; triglyphs in frieze; in centre, moulded panels; flanking columns now lost; kneelers (male to right), he armoured; captions lost; prayer desk; 5 sons (right); 4 daughters (left); below, flowers, vase, 5 dead infants in chrisoms; at foot, base mouldings, in the antique manner, relief masks on pedestals.

- No M.I.

1. In situ, but formerly 121B was dilapidated, plastered over and its identity lost - Horsfield (*Sussex* I 162-3); uncovered c.1880 in Clayton (*SAC* 34 177-78), when its 'debased classic style' was dated to early 18th century!; Nairn & Pevsner (458) - still not identified.
2. Richard Bellingham was grandson of the builder of Hangleton Manor (to the South-East); by the early 17th century, the family seems to have moved to Newtimber 1622, see Dunkin (*Licences 1586-1643* 101, 110, 133); see C.G.S. Foljambe 'Extracts from the parish registers of Newtimber ... relating to the Families of Bellingham and Woodcock' (*SAC* 38 206-9) and Comber (*Lewes* 12) for his place in the family pedigree.
3. The designer of 121B is following in the antique manner patterns, perhaps learned from woodcuts, with some accuracy.

(123) HARTFIELD, St. Mary

North side is late Early English; South side is Decorated - Nairn & Pevsner (517); church plan *SNQ* (VII 189); repairs needed in 1686 and completed in 1724, see Ford (41 172); there were 300 communicants in 1603, see Renshaw (*Ecclesiastical Returns*); Horsfield (*Sussex* I 392-3) noted numbers of iron slabs and stone slabs for brasses. An unusually high percentage of signed or attributed works at Hartfield.

Hartfield, 123A Mural monument for Thomas and Mary ELLIOTT, d. 1815 and 1817
- Nave, South-West corner, against South wall, at head height.
- 90(W) x 112(H) — Very good; rust.
- M.I. (14 lines, engraved, black) on an unframed trapezoidal tablet; moulded cornice; below, a black moulded base; 2 corbels with guttae decoration.
- Thomas Elliott, of Newbridge, Hartfield, d. 21 May 1815, aet 86; his wife, Mary, d. 30 Jul 1817, aet 83; second son, Obadiah Elliott, F.S.A., coach builder, of Westminster Bridge, London.

1. Dated 1826.
2. Patron was their son Obadiah, a coachbuilder in Westminster, Fellow of the Society of Antiquaries and landowner at Hartfield in 1785 (R. Davey 100); an earlier 'Obediah' Elliott was born c.1740 at Hartfield, perhaps the grandfather of the patron of 123A, see Dunkin & Penfold (*Licences* 136).

Hartfield, 123B Mural monument for Frederica Louisa MAITLAND, d. 1822
- Nave, West wall, South of tower arch, high.
- c.80(W); (H) inaccessible — Good.
- A thin black square baseplate; in centre, unframed white marble disk with M.I. (20 lines, engraved, black); signed (lower right): 'COLES PORT.D ROAD LONDON'.
- Frederica Louisa Maitland, 10 Mar 1805 - 24 Aug 1822, buried at Hartfield, 1 Sep 1822; daughter of Lieut. Gen. Frederick Maitland.

1. Noted by Horsfield (*Sussex* I 392-3) and Nairn & Pevsner (517) dated 1823.
2. For a sister (Harriet) see 123C.
3. Cited by Gunnis (*Dict.* 110) as by John Coles (fl. 1790-1833).
4. For biography of General Maitland see *ODNB*.
5. 123B must pre-date 1825, when he was promoted full General.

Hartfield, 123C Mural monument for Ellinor Jane MAITLAND, d. 1823
- Nave, West wall, North of tower arch, high.
- 136(W); (H) inaccessible — Very good.
- In pale grey marble; a pointed pediment, with escutcheon, over a frieze of garlands on Doric columns on fluted, scrolled corbels; M.I. (many lines, engraved, black); below, another small panel in the same material (52W x 34H) with a raised and chamfered centre; roses in corners.

- Ellinor Jane Maitland, d. 15 Oct 1823, aet 21, buried 23 Oct 1823; daughter of late Gilbert Ansley, Esq., and Susannah, daughter of Sir Henry Blackman, Kt., of Lewes; and wife of Captain John Madan Maitland, Esq., married 24 Oct 1822; issue, one daughter, unnamed; On a separate tablet: Ellinor Jane Maitland's sister, Harriet Maclean, 10 May 1801 - 20 Sep 1830, died at Castelamare, Italy, buried at Naples, second daughter of General Frederick Maitland and wife of Donald Maclean, Esq.

1. Noted by Horsfield (*Sussex* I 392).
2. Ellinor Jane Maitland's grandfather, Sir Henry Blackman, a wine-merchant, was a prominent supporter of Sunday schools, see J. Caffyn 'Sunday Schools in Sussex in the late 18th century' (*SAC* 132 156), and resident in Lewes; he was High Constable there in 1795 (L. Davey 43).

Hartfield, 123D Mural monument for Samuel SLADE, d. 1829
- Nave, West wall, high.
- 100(W); (H) inaccessible — Very good.
- Against a black base plate, a trapezoidal grey marble tablet on guttae corbels; straight moulded cornice; M.I. (13 lines, engraved, black); signed (lower right): 'R. GAFFIN, / REGENT St. LONDON'.
- Samuel Slade, D.D., rector of Hartfield, vicar of Staverton, Northamptonshire, dean of Chichester, etc., 11 Apr 1771 - 29 Dec 1829.

1. For the related grave marker see 123G.
2. JH notes that Samuel Slade was vicar of Staverton, Northants, rector and vicar of Hartfield 1815-29, dean of Chichester 1824-29 and rector of Felpham 1825-29, see CCEd, Horn (*Fasti 1541-1857* II 9) and Foster (*Al Ox* Pt.2 4 1305).

Hartfield, 123E Grave marker for H. H. JACKSON, dated 1841
- North nave aisle, towards East end.
- 31(W) x 31(H) — Sound; cracked (upper left).
- Dark grey marble with M.I. (2 lines, engraved, white).

1. Attributed to Thomas Denman to commemorate Henry Humphrey Jackson d. 1841 cited by Gunnis (*Dict.* 127); 123E cited in Church Guide with date 1811 and hence its inclusion here.
2. NBI records burial of Henry Humphrey Jackson on 29 Oct 1841 at Hartfield.

Hartfield, 123F Mural monument for Christina and John KIDD, d. 1820 and d. 1831
- Chancel, North wall, high.
- 118(W); (H) inaccessible — Very good.
- White marble on grey, on black; a thin black baseplate with stele top; draped mourning female and altar in relief; below, a moulded tablet with cornice, quarter palmettes and flanking panels with decorated sashes; M.I. (10 lines, engraved, black); apron with crossed ferns; signed (lower right): 'J J SANDERS / NEW Rd / FITZROY SQ.r.e LONDON / '.
- Christina Kidd, d. 1 Jan 1820, aet 60; wife of John Kidd, Esq., of New Lodge, Hartfield, d. 27 Apr 1831, aet 79; issue, an unnamed daughter.

1. Patron of 123E was their daughter, probably represented by the mourning figure.
2. Cited by Gunnis (*Dict.* 339) as by J. J. Sanders (fl. 1812-46).

Hartfield, 123G Grave marker for Samuel SLADE, d. 1829
- Nave, centre aisle, opposite 123D.
- 31(W) x 30(H) — Worn.
- A white marble square; M.I. (4 lines, engraved, black).

SAMUEL S...
D.D.
REC...
OF THE PAR...

Hartfield, 123H Mural monument for Bladon SWINEY, d. 1790

- Chancel, South wall.
- 68(W) x c.152(H) — Very good; rust.
- Grey-veined marble tablet setting for M.I. which fills a white oval panel with a light moulded border; all set portrait-wise; cornice over, then fluted urn in relief; below, simple white marble shelf; fluted squared corbels.
- Captain Bladon Swiney, of Colemans Hatch, d. 26 Jul 1790, aet 66.

1. Horsfield (*Sussex* I 392-3) locates 123H in the chancel.
2. M.I. includes a charming reference to Swiney's rural retirement.
3. Gunnis (*Dict.* 350) followed by Church Guide, attributes it to the Holborn shop of Benjamin and Robert Shout, also responsible for Charles Bushby, 1789, at Arundel, Elizabeth Pinnell, 1800, at Fittleworth and 234G (Ellison) at Slaugham.
4. In 1785 Swiney occupied a property of one Isaac Shand (R. Davey 101).

Hartfield, 123I Mural monument for Richard RANDES, d. 1640 [Plate 80]

- South chapel, North wall, at head height.
- 100(W) x c.182(H) — Good; cracks (lower cherub).
- M.I. (Latin) ambitious, on a black slate panel with an arched top, set portrait-wise within a white and brown alabaster frame; flanked by polished black Corinthian columns; decorated relief panels at edges, with scrollwork; above, straight cornice with broken pointed pediment with scrolled decoration; between, a black obelisk on a base; below the base mouldings, 2 cherubs on corbels; another M.I. on a semi-circular panel; at foot a third winged cherub.
- Richard Randes, of York, S.T.B. from Trinity, Oxford, rector of Hartfield, d. c.1640.

1. In situ - Horsfield (*Sussex* I 393).
2. 123I was erected by the subject or at his bequest; note interesting variety of expression and treatment of hair and wings amongst the 3 cherubim; the longer M.I. is a remarkable self-deprecating, moralising and didactic text.
3. Richard Randes is called Rondes in marriage licence with Mary Scrase of Hamsey dated 12 Apr 1630, see Dunkin (*Licences 1586-1643* 181); he established a school under the terms of his will of 1640 (Caffyn 124).
4. NBI records the burial of Richard Ronds [sic] on 5 Aug 1640 at Hartfield.
5. Richard Randes was BA, MA and STB (BD) from Oxford, and incorporated as BD at Cambridge in 1621, see Venn (1 3 419).

Hartfield, 123J Mural monument for Richard DAVIES, d. 1823

- South-East chapel, South wall, high.
- 75(W); (H) inaccessible — Good; colour.
- M.I. (13 lines, engraved, gilded) on unframed, square, black panel; mounted on grey marble frame of strong squared shapes; above, a slim white marble cornice supporting palmettes; escutcheon on a pointed black baseplate; below, chunky corbels; signed (lower left) 'REGN...'; (lower right) 'LONDON / SCULP'.
- Richard Davies, Esq., formerly of West Kent Regiment of Militia, d. 28 Jun 1823, aet 65, son of the late Rev. Chamberlayne Davies, rector of Ashurst and 40 years curate of Hartfield.

1. Dated 1803 by Horsfield (*Sussex* I 392) and located in the chancel; cited as Regnart by Gunnis (*Dict.* 318).
2. For heraldry see Lambarde (*SAC* 67 168-9).

Hartfield, 123K Ledger for John MILLS, d. 1702
- South aisle floor, near South-East chapel.
- 53.5(W) x 150(L) — Worn.
- M.I. (engraved) in upper 25% of a cast iron slab; head to West.
- John Mills, of Cotchford, Hartfield, d. 26 Oct 1702.

1. Engraved lettering in a cast iron slab is unusual.
2. Noted by Willatts (*SAC* 125 102).
3. NBI records burial of John Mills on 27 Oct 1702 at Hartfield.

Hartfield, 123L Mural monument for Elizabeth and Charles ABBOT, d. 1823 and 1866
- South aisle, South wall, towards East end, high.
- Inaccessible — Very good.
- M.I. (10 lines, engraved, black) on an unframed white marble tablet with a shallow pointed pediment; 2 simple block corbels.
- Elizabeth Elliott, d. 16 Sep 1814, aet 34; wife of Charles Abbot, of Bolebrook, Hartfield, d. 22 Jun 1866, aet 83.

1. The consistency of the lettering suggests that 123L is dated after 1866.
2. JH notes that the Sussex Marriage Index records marriage of Charles Abbot and Elizabeth Elliot [sic] Waters on 23 Jun 1807 at St. George in the East, Middlesex.

Hartfield, 123M Ledger for 2 anonymous sons of Rev. Daniel LE PLA, d. 1738/9 and 1741
- Chancel floor, against East wall, partly beneath the altar.
- 60(W) x 80(L) — Very good.
- M.I. (visible are 7 lines, engraved, black) on upper parts of a grey-veined marble slab.
- Anonymous son, d. 19 Jan 1738/9, an infant; another son, d. 5 Oct 1741, an infant; issue of Rev. Daniel Le Pla, rector of Hartfield, and Anne, his wife.

1. Presumably erected after 1741; space was left for additional M.I.s, but never used.
2. JH notes that Daniel Le Pla was rector and vicar of Hartfield 1735-74 and also of St. John sub Castro, Lewes, 1741-74, see 158D.
3. The second son was called Daniel. NBI shows him as buried at Hartfield 11 Oct 1741.

(125) HASTINGS, St. Clements
Post-1377, some walls later, no internal structural divisions - Nairn & Pevsner (519) and *SNQ* (XII 76) with plan; fabric reported as fine in 1686 and in 1724 (Ford), between which dates chancel was decorated under patronage of Archibald Hutcheson and for the altar painting done by Roger Mortimer; ceiling with heavenly virtues, etc., see Horsfield (*Sussex* I 454-5); dramatic social change must have affected the parish as the population grew: 600 communicants in 1603, see Renshaw (*Ecclesiastical Returns*), growing to c.300 families in 1724, to a town population in 1801 of 3,155 and in 1841 of 12,000; Horsfield (*Sussex* I 454-5) mentions none of the many tablets in the North-West corner; the earlier monuments tend to mark town dignitaries, the later ones, fashionable visitors.

Hastings, 125A Mural monument for Edward MILWARD, d. 1811, and his wife Mary, d. 1783
- South aisle wall, above the South door.
- Inaccessible — Very good.
- Fluted outer frame; darker marble inner frame; above, moulded cornice then draped urn in relief; M.I. (14 lines, engraved, centred, black).

- Edward Milward, Esq., of Hastings, d. 25 Jul 1811, aet 87; his wife, Mary, d. 21 Jun 1783, aet 58, daughter of John Collier, Esq.

1. Formerly in chancel - Horsfield (*Sussex* I 454); datable c.1812.
2. In 1785, Edward Milward owned the Ship Inn and many other local properties (R. Davey 234, 236); the 7 surviving children of John and Mary Collier, presumably Mary Collier amongst them, attended Mrs Thorpe's boarding school at Battle (Caffyn 43).
3. For Collier see 125N.

Hastings, 125B Mural monument for Horatio MARTELLI, d. 1817 [Plate 81]
- Nave, West wall, above head height.
- 95(W); (H) unknown — Fine; dirty and fading; colour.
- Prominent coloured arms on a large hood; flaming lamp in relief; below, a white rectangular tablet on a grey sarcophagal form; large base mould; below, large scrolled brackets; between them, another panel with M.I.
- Horatio Martelli, Esq., d. 28 Dec 1817; survived by his wife and 8 children.

1. Formerly on aisle South wall - Horsfield (*Sussex* I 454-5); datable 1817-18.
2. Patron, his widow (see 125C) and children.
3. Heraldry not mentioned by Lambarde (*SAC* 68).

Hastings, 125C Mural monument for Catherine MARTELLI, d. 1818
- Nave, West wall, immediately below 125B.
- 85(W) x 95(H) — Fine; dirty, some losses of detail (lamp); fading.
- A flaming lamp in white marble relief against a rectangular black baseplate; below, an unframed M.I. on a panel with block corbels and cornice; M.I. fills panel (lines engraved, black, centred).
- Catherine Martelli, widow of Horatio Martelli, d. 10 Jun 1818, aet 37; issue unnamed.

1. Patrons were the children.
2. See 125B for her husband.

Hastings, 125D Mural monument for Samuel LICHIGARAY, d. 1812
- Nave, West wall, North-West corner, high up.
- Inaccessible — Very worn, weathered?.
- M.I. (engraved, black), set portrait-wise; oval border.

Sacred
to the Memory of
Samuel Lichigaray Esq.
late of
Phillybrook House, Essex
died June 30th 1812,
in the 62nd Year
of his Age.

1. NBI records burial of Samuel Litchigary on 4 Jul 1812 at Hastings, St. Clement.

Hastings, 125E Mural monument for James SMITH, d. 1812
- Nave, West wall, North-West corner, high up.
- Inaccessible — Fine; dirty.
- A straight moulded cornice; unframed sides; scrolled apron; M.I. (7 lines, engraved, never blacked).
- James Smith, Esq., of Kings Road, Bedford Row, London, d. 18 Jul 1812, aet 39, son of Hugh Smith, M.D.

1. Note the mannered treatment of lower edge, merging corbels and apron contour.

Hastings, 125F Mural monument for William SATTERLEY, d. 1809

- Nave, West wall, North-West corner, high up.
- Inaccessible — Fine; dirty.
- M.I. (10 lines, engraved, black); decorative pediment; meagre cornice, trapezoidal, unframed panel.
- William Satterley, surgeon, of Hastings, d. 29 Jan 1809, aet 30; his son Samuel, d. 7 May 1809, aet 1.

1. Mannered treatment of upper area, merging pointed pediment and palmettes.
2. Below, an additional M.I. perhaps indicating previous or original location only partly visible.

Hastings, 125G Mural Monument for Harriot PARKER, d. 1826

- North aisle wall, North-West corner, high up.
- Inaccessible — Sound; very faded.
- M.I. (10 lines, engraved, black) on an unframed grey marble tablet set portrait-wise; cornice; base moulding; above, a plinth rises to a fluted palmette; small curved apron.
- Harriot Parker, d. 13 Jan 1826, aet 52; wife of Vice Admiral George Parker.

1. Pendant with others nearby, including 125H - to George Parker's second wife and a mural monument to her husband set alongside.
2. On 4 June 1814 Parker became Rear-Admiral; Vice-Admiral on 27 May 1825; nominated KCB on 12 June 1833; became (full) Admiral on 10 January 1837; he died on 24 Dec 1847; George Parker was still Vice Admiral at date of erection of 125G.
3. Harriot Parker was probably a daughter of Peter Butt.
4. There was no issue (see biography of George Parker by J.K. Laughton, rev. Andrew Lambert in *ODNB*).
5. NBI records burial of Harriot Parker on 20 Jan 1826, aet 52, at Hastings, St. Clement.

Hastings, 125H Mural Monument for Dame Arabella PARKER, d. 1850

- North aisle wall, just East of 125G.
- Inaccessible — Sound; very faded.
- Description as for 125 G.
- Dame Arabella Parker, relict of Admiral Sir George Parker, rest illegible.

1. Comments as for 125G.
2. JH notes that Dame Arabella Parker, relict of Admiral Sir G. Parker K.C.B. d. 11 May 1850, in her 65th year - Bax (*SAC* 49 119); NBI records burial on 18 May 1850 at Hastings.

Hastings, 125I Mural monument for Samuel Baldwin HARRISON, d. 1830

- North aisle wall, towards West end, high up.
- Inaccessible — Sound; blackened.
- M.I. (8 lines, engraved, black) in upper 50% of rectangular unframed tablet set portrait-wise; pointed pediment over; cornice; base moulding.
- Samuel Baldwin Harrison … aet 30[?] (mostly illegible).

1. NBI records burial of Samuel Baldwin Harrison on 16 Feb 1830 at Hastings, St. Clement.

Hastings, 125J Mural Monument for Mary Ann WILLIAMS, d. 1819

- North aisle wall, towards East end of group of monuments, high.
- Inaccessible — Sound, legible.
- M.I. (9 lines, engraved, black) on a white marble tablet set portrait-wise; black border; simple grey frame; above, cornice.
- Mary Ann Williams, spinster, of Mitcham and Hastings, d. 11 Sep 1819, aet 39; patron - Thomas Bryan, Esq., his vault.

Hastings, 125K Mural Monument for Dorothea HAWORTH, d. 1821

- North aisle wall, towards East end of group, low.
- Inaccessible — Fine.
- M.I. (11 lines, engraved, black) on a white unframed rectangular marble tablet set portrait-wise.
- Dorothea Haworth, died at Hastings, 9 Nov 1821, aet 54; wife of John Haworth, Esq., of Islington.

Hastings, 125L Mural Monument for Frances Margaret MONTRESOR, d. 1822

- North aisle wall, above and East of 125 K.
- Inaccessible — Good.
- Pendant to 125P; M.I. (engraved, black) fills unframed white marble tablet with pointed base; grey marble tassels and curtains left and right; above, a grey scrolled pediment.
- Frances Margaret Montresor, spinster, of Rose Hill, Kent, d. 11 Feb 1822, aet 49.

1. See also 125P.

Hastings, 125M Mural Monument for Frederick Thomas JEFFERYS, d. 1824

- North aisle wall.
- Inaccessible (vestry ceiling) — Unknown.

1. NBI records burial of Frederick Thomas Jefferys on 4 Mar 1824, aet 20, at Hastings, St. Clement.

Hastings, 125N Mural Monument for John COLLIER, d. 1760 [Plate 82]

- Chancel, South wall.
- 157(W); (H) inaccessible — Very good, some local losses.
- M.I. (engraved, black) fills white dome-topped tablet; immediate frame in column marbles with scroll-work and decorated work (foliage); above, no entablature but 2 scrolled brackets hold up a cornice with broken pointed pediment with achievement in the centre; on summit, an urn flanked by 2 flaming lamps; below, base mould, then a curved apron supporting a group of 3 cherubim in low relief, with central acanthus motif below and flanked by corbels with more acanthus decoration.
- John Collier, Esq., lawyer, mayor of Hastings, canopy bearer at the coronation of George II, d. 9 Dec 1760, aet 75; widow and 6 daughters unnamed; his many virtues.

1. In situ; 'handsome' 'well carved' in *Gent's Mag* 1786 see Gomme (261); Horsfield (*Sussex* I 454-5); Nairn & Pevsner (519); Lambarde (*SAC* 68 234) noting arms.
2. See W.V. Crake, 'The Correspondence of John Collier' (*SAC* 45 62-109), for his canopy-bearing at the coronation of George II see especially pp.68-74. A George II Coronation Staff, made by Pitts and Preedy, of London, in 1820, carried the words – 'This is a Part of one of the Eight Staves / (each being nearly eight feet long) / by which / the Canopy was borne by the Barons of the / Cinque Ports over … [the king]…', see CINOA International Art Treasures Exhibition (V&A London 1962), catalogue no. 295 and plate 181.
3. JH notes C.L. Sayer *Correspondence of Mr John Collier and his family 1716-1780* (1907), and forthcoming SRS edition of his correspondence edited by R.V. Saville.

Hastings, 125O Mural Monument for Thomas and Ann DELVES, d. 1669 and 1686/7

- South aisle wall, towards East end.
- 91(W) x 137(H) — Good, some repairs.
- M.I. (16 + 14 lines, engraved) fills black slate tablet set portrait-wise; framed in alabaster and black panels: above, a motif of crossed ferns; a cornice and broken scrolled pediment with achievement; moulded frame around the tablet with ribbons of foliage above and shouldered profile: below, base moulding on double scrolled brackets; on the apron, cherubs head.
- Thomas Delves, a Baron of Hastings at the coronation of Charles II, mayor, Captain

of Trained Bands etc., d. 4 Sep 1669, aet 57; his brother, Nicholas Delves, Alderman of London; Ann, wife of Thomas, d. 23 Feb 1686/7, aet 63; his nephew, also Nicholas Delves, son of Nicholas, d. 4 Mar 1682, aet 34.

1. In situ, *Gent's Mag* (1786) in Gomme (261); Horsfield (*Sussex* I 454-5) – at that date near 125B; Lambarde in (*SAC* 68 234) noting arms.
2. Patron of 125O was probably Alderman Nicholas Delves.
3. Likely to post-date 1682.
4. Thomas Delves carried canopy at Coronation of Charles II: the Barons of the Cinque Ports, amongst which Hastings claimed precedence, fiercely protected the privilege of carrying the coronation banner, see C. Dawson 'The Services of the Barons of the Cinque ports at the Coronation ... and the Precedency of Hastings Port' (*SAC* 44 45-54) with an engraved view of the ceremony for James II in 1685.

Hastings, 125P Mural Monument for Sarah BREEDS, d. 1822, and her daughter, d. 1825
- South aisle arcade, North wall, facing South, very high.
- Inaccessible — Very good.
- Pendant to 125L.
- Sarah Breeds, d. 31 Aug 1822, aet 79, widow of Boykett Breeds; her daughter, Elizabeth-Blundell Breeds, d. 1 Sep 1825, aet 44, unmarried.

1. See too 125L for same composition.

Hastings St. Clements Additions
Noted by Horsfield (*Sussex* I 454-5) and followed by Turner (*SAC* 23 162-3), Davidson-Houston (*SAC* 78 79-82), etc.
(1) Brass for John Barley, of Hastings, mercer, d. [31] Mar 1601, aet 49; his wife, Mary, daughter of Robert Harley; issue - son, Thomas d. 1 Apr 1600, aet 19; daughter Alice d. 15 Jun 1592, aet 7 (nave floor).
(2) Brass for Thomas Pierse, of Hastings, jurat, d. 10 Nov 1653; his wife, Margery; issue a daughter Elizabeth (nave floor); M.I. only, brass effigy lost; lived 74 years in Hastings, date given as 14 Jun 1606.
(3) Brass for Thomas Wekes, jurat of Hastings, d. 10 Nov 1563, indents for wife Margery and daughter Elizabeth, nave.
Horsfield (*Sussex* I 511):
(4) M.I. for Thomas Bromfeild, late of Udimore, 2 Jul 1610 – 12 Sep 1690.

(126) HASTINGS, All Saints
On North-East fringe of the old town; walls mostly mediaeval, probably early 15th, century with renewals by Butterfield, 1870, see Nairn & Pevsner (519-20) and plan in *SNQ* (XII 102); fabric of church and chancel reported as (now) fine in 1686 and 1724, see Ford (46, 96); parish had 247 communicants in 1603, see Renshaw (*Ecclesiastical Returns*), and in 1724, c. 200 families (Ford); in 1786, there were few monuments, *Gent's Mag* in Gomme (261), though by 1801 the town population was 3,155 and by 1841 it was 12,000, so the All Saints set of early 19th century mural tablets reflects the growing fashion for Hastings c.1800 reflected in the high number of monuments of the 1820s. Three hatchments to the Scott family in the church, see Summers (143).

Hastings, 126A Mural monument for Magnus JACKSON, d. 1830 [Plate 83]
- North wall of North aisle, at West end, above head height.
- 42(W) x 70(H) — Very good, fading.
- M.I. (engraved) on a white marble urn-shaped tablet; grey base.
- Magnus Jackson, of Piccadilly, London, d. 13 Jan 1830, aet 40.

Hastings, 126B Mural monument for Thomas Robert ROBSON, d. 1829

- North wall of North aisle, East of 126A , above head height.
- 95(W) x 67(H) — Very good.
- M.I. (engraved) on rectangular panel set landscape-wise, in white on dark grey; unsigned.
- Thomas Robert Robson, scholar at Trinity College, Cambridge, d. 17 Feb 1829, aet 24; eldest son of Robert Robson, of Exning, Suffolk.

Hastings, 126C Mural monument for Anthony BROWN, d. 1828

- North wall of North aisle, East of 126B, above head height.
- 63(W) x 46(H) — Very good.
- Rectangular panel with moulded frame in white marble on a black baseplate; signed (lower left): 'M.Vidler Sc.'.
- Anthony Brown, Esq., of Highbury Place, d. 24 Nov 1828, aet 41.

Hastings, 126D Mural monument for Elizabeth BARNOUIN, d. 1826

- North wall of North aisle, East of 126C, above head height.
- 70(W) x 62(H) — Very good.
- M.I. (7 lines, engraved, black) on white marble tablet on black baseplate with pointed top, panel with blank pointed pediment, cornice and curving apron; signed (lower right): 'VIDLER & CO'.
- Elizabeth Barnouin, d. 26 Sep 1826, aet 69; wife of James H. Barnouin, Esq., of the Tower of London.

1. Cited by Gunnis (*Dict.* 409) as by Vidler.

Hastings, 126E Mural monument for Sarah THOMSON, d. 1826

- North wall of North aisle, East of 126D, above head height.
- 95(W) x 60(H) — Very good.
- Trapezoidal panel in white marble on a black baseplate; set landscape-wise; moulded frame; signed (lower left): 'W.VENNALL. HASTINGS'.
- Sarah Thomson, d. 22 Aug 1826, aet 27, daughter of William Thomson, Esq., late of Quebec.

1. Pendant to 126 G.

Hastings, 126F Mural monument for daughter of George-Turtliff ROGER, d. 1827

- Centre of North aisle wall, at head height.
- 63(W) x 48(H) — Very good.
- Framed oval tablet in white marble, set landscape-wise.
- Unnamed, buried 24 Feb 1827, aet 1; daughter of George-Turtliff Roger, Esq. and Georgiana Martha.

1. The M.I. suggests that Roger was a Royal Academician but his name does not appear in the list, under Boger, Roger or Turtliff.

Hastings, 126G Mural monument for Eliza BROWN, d. 1823

- Centre of North aisle wall, above head height.
- 60(W) x 97(H) — Good.
- Pendant to 126E, unsigned.
- Eliza Brown, d. 23 Jun 1823, aet 47; wife of Murdoch Brown, Esq.

1. Noted but not located by Horsfield (*Sussex* I 452-3).
2. Pendant to 126E.
3. Also by Vennall.

Hastings, 126H Mural monument for Eliza BEAZELEY, d. 1823
- North aisle wall, towards East end, at head height.
- 110(W) x 95(H) — Good.
- M.I. (20 lines, engraved) fills a white marble panel on a black baseplate, unframed; signed (lower right) 'WINTER & Co HASTINGS'.
- Eliza Beazeley, died at Hastings, 30 Oct 1823, aet 24; wife of Lieut. George Beazeley, R.N.

1. Noted, not located Horsfield (*Sussex* I 452-3).
2. Patron was husband; Swedenborgian; immediately above a M.I. to George Beazeley.

Hastings, 126I Mural monument for John HAMILTON, d. 1792
- South aisle wall, South-East corner, high above an alcove.
- 80(W) x 60(H) — Very good.
- M.I. (4 lines, engraved) in upper 25% of an unframed white marble tablet with double scrolled top, scrolled shoulders and 2 brackets.
- John Hamilton, merchant, of Goldsmith Street, London, d. 22 Aug 1792, aet 52.

1. Noted but not located in Horsfield (*Sussex* I 452-3).
2. The earliest monument in the church.
3. Eccentric design.

Hastings, 126J Mural monument for James ALDERSON, d. 1823
- South aisle wall, towards East end, very high.
- Inaccessible — Very good.
- On a rectangular black baseplate, a trapezoidal panel with pointed pediment and cornice; signed (lower right): 'WINTER'.
- James Alderson, d. 2 Apr 1823, aet 17; son of Robert Alderson, Esq., recorder of Norwich, and Henrietta Maria.

Hastings, 126K Mural monument for Bridget CARTWRIGHT, d. 1794
- South aisle wall, West of 126J.
- Inaccessible — Very good; faded.
- Rectangular white marble panel, unframed, on a black baseplate; unsigned.
- Bridget Cartwright, d. 4 Aug 1794, aet 41; daughter of William Cartwright, Esq., of Aynho, Northamptonshire.

1. Noted but not located in Horsfield (*Sussex* I 452-3).

Hastings, 126L Mural monument for Sir William Lawrence YOUNG, Bart., d. 1824
- South aisle wall, beneath 126K.
- 90(W) x 58(H) — Very good; fading.
- M.I. (8 lines, engraved, black) on white trapezoidal marble panel; black baseplate with chamfered corners; unsigned.
- Sir William Lawrence Young, Bart., of Bradenham House, Buckinghamshire, died at Hastings, 3 Nov 1824, aet 46.

Hastings, 126M Mural monument for Frances MURIEL, d. 1819
- South wall, East of South door, at head height.
- 80(W) x 92(H) — Very good.
- Rectangular white marble panel, set portrait-wise with a black marble cornice and heavy framing; M.I. (engraved, black).
- Frances Muriel, died at school in Hastings, 9 Nov 1819, aet 16; daughter of Robert Muriel, of Ely, Cambridgeshire.

1. Noted but not located Horsfield (*Sussex* I 452-3).

Hastings, 126N Mural monument for William DERING, d. 1823
- South aisle, over South door in South aisle.
- c. 55(H) — Very good.
- M.I. (9 lines) on white oval marble panel set landscape-wise, with a light, moulded frame.
- William Dering, died at Hastings, 24 Aug 1823, aet 12; eldest son of Cholmeley Dering, Esq., of Ayot St. Laurence, Hertfordshire.

1. Noted but not located Horsfield (*Sussex* I 452-3).

Hastings, 126O Mural monument for Thomas OOM, d. 1830
- South aisle, South wall, West end, at head height.
- 91(W) x 70(H) — Very good; fading.
- Rectangular black baseplate; white marble panel with pointed pediment and quartered decorations on cornice; below, a simple moulded base and corbels.
- Thomas Oom, Esq., of Fairlight Place, d. 6 Oct 1830, aet 70.

Hastings, 126P Mural monument for Victoire RUFFO, d. 1816
- West entrance (tower chapel), North wall, at head height.
- 73(W) x 140(H) — Very good.
- M.I. (engraved, black) fills unframed white marble panel, slightly curved top, set portrait-wise.
- Mademoiselle Victoire Ruffo, d. 16 Jul 1816, aet 36; eldest daughter of the Prince de Castelcicala.

1. Noted but not located Horsfield (*Sussex* I 452-3).

Hastings, All Saints Addition
Horsfield (*Sussex* I, 452-3).
(1) Mary Anne, first daughter of Rev. Richard Williams, rector of Great Houghton, Northants, d. 1822, aet 38.

(128) HEATHFIELD, All Saints
Church isolated from the modern town, which lies to the North, beyond the Park; the mediaeval church had Decorated arches - Nairn & Pevsner (530-1); interior reportedly foul in 1724, but for the chancel belonging to John Fuller Esq., see Ford (108-9); church restored - 2 side galleries, 1823, see Horsfield (*Sussex* I 576) - and the ledger stones moved in 19th century; parish had 600 communicants in 1693, see Renshaw (*Ecclesiastical Returns*), c.199 families in 1724 and a population of 1226 in 1801; the first Baron Heathfield (George Augustus Eliott, 1717-90), owner of nearby Heathfield Park (from 1762), was buried here but commemorated later at Buckland Monachorum, Devon (see Additions); estate later sold to Newbery (see 128C; Farrant 248); the terracotta worker Jonathan Harmer was a resident of the parish; there are no Harmer monuments inside the church but one is attached to an external West wall, and there are others on headstones in the churchyard and at the nearby nonconformist chapel (Cade Street); Horsfield notes no monuments at Heathfield (*Sussex* I 576).

Heathfield, 128A Mural monument for Thomas and Mary COURTHOPE, erected 1745
- Choir, North wall, high.
- Width unknown; c.80 (H) — Very good; pigments lost.
- M.I. (15 lines, engraved) on unframed freestone tablet set portrait-wise, scrolled baseplate; above, a straight cornice supporting a double-curved pediment with an escutcheon.

- Thomas Courthope, of Wadhurst; his wife Mary; their son George; also the patron, one James Courthope; all dates unknown.

1. The family were commemorated mainly at Ticehurst and Wadhurst, the latter their place of origin (Church Guide).
2. For heraldry see Lambarde (*SAC* 67 155).

Heathfield, 128B Mural monument for Rev. John DRING, d. 1804

- Sanctuary, North wall, above head height.
- 55(W) x 94(H) — Very good.
- M.I. (11 lines, engraved, in Latin) on an unframed, grey, oval plaque resting on a marble corbel, black finial.
- John Dring, A.M., vicar of Heathfield and chaplain to the bishop of Chichester, died at Orléans, France, 3 Sep 1804, aet 31; [The monument was placed by his mournful widow], F. Dring, daughter of Henry Goring, Baronet.

1. His widow was a daughter of Sir Henry Goring, patron of the living. Dring was vicar of Poling 1800-01, Heathfield 1801-04 and bishop's chaplain 1801-4.
2. JH notes that John Dring married Frances Goring on 13 Jul 1799 (Sussex Marriage Index).

Heathfield, 128C Mural monument for Francis NEWBERY, d. 1818, and others

- Sanctuary, South wall, high.
- c.67(W) x 100(H) — Very good.
- M.I. (22 + 4 lines, engraved, black) on an unframed white rectangular marble tablet, set portrait-wise; black baseplate.
- Francis Newbery, Esq., of Heathfield Park, d. 7 Aug 1818, aet 75; his wife, Mary, d. 31 Jan 1829, aet 81; issue - eldest daughter, Mary, d. 8 Jan 1804, aet 32, wife of Francis Freeling, Esq., Secretary to the General Post Office; second son, Robert d. 13 Aug 1805, aet 29; and youngest daughter, Charlotte d. 24 Aug 1805, aet 24; also, Anne Mary Newbery, d. 14 Dec 1830, aet 21, daughter of Major Gen. Newbery, and adopted daughter of Charles Newbery, Esq.

1. Francis Newbery bought Heathfield Park from second Baron Heathfield (Church Guide); his father left him lucrative interests in publishing and patent medicines in St. Paul's Churchyard, City of London; Newbery admired the first Baron Heathfield (victor at Gibraltar) and erected Gibraltar Tower in the park.

Heathfield, 128D Ledger for Elizabeth WILKIN, d. 1704

- Nave floor, central aisle, at East end.
- 93(W) x 195(L) — Sound; worn.
- M.I. (8 lines) in upper (W) 30% of a freestone slab; head to West.
- Elizabeth Wilkin, d. 25 Jun 1704, aet 66; her husband, Rev. William Wilkin; her virtues.

1. For William Wilkin see 128E.

Heathfield, 128E Ledger for Rev. William WILKIN, d. 1699

- Nave floor, centre aisle, just West of 128D.
- 93(W) x 196(L) — Worn edges; worn; cracks (West end).
- M.I. (17 lines, engraved) in upper (W) 80% of a freestone slab; head to West.
- Rev. William Wilkin, vicar of Heathfield for 44 years, d. 30 Aug 1699, aet 71; his wife, Elizabeth, daughter of William Plomer, Gent., of Cranbrook; their issue - Jane, Richard, Sarah, William and Elizabeth of whom William and Elizabeth are still living in 1742.

1. His virtues (see Church Guide).
2. His first son was an eminent bookseller who gave a library of 229 books to the Heathfield vicarage.
3. For William Wilkin's widow see 128D.
4. Ledgers 128 E-G form a group.

Heathfield, 128F Ledger for Markwick HAFFENDEN, d. 1722/3

- Nave floor, centre aisle, just West of 128E.
- 93(W) x 166(L) — Pitted; very worn.
- M.I. (7 lines, engraved) in capitals, in upper (W) 40% of a freestone slab; head to West.

HERE LYETH YE BODY OF
MARKWICK [?] TE SON OF
MARKWICK HAFFENDEN

...

WHO

DIED ...

AGED ...

1. Markwicke Haffenden of Heathfield, Gent., was presented by the churchwarden of Waldron in 1675 for neglecting a burial plot, see Johnstone (25) and ledgers 128F-L; had the family already transferred its burial interests to Heathfield by this date?
2. NBI records burial of Markwick Haffenden on 22 Feb 1722/3 at Heathfield.

Heathfield, 128G Ledger for George HAFFENDEN, d. 1732

- Nave floor, centre aisle, towards West end.
- 90(W) x 170(L) — Cracked (centre), cut (sides), worn.
- M.I. (8 lines) in upper (W) 50% of freestone slab; head to West.

G.H. - R.H.

HERE LYETH THE
BODY OF GEORGE
THE SON OF MARQVIC..
AND ELIZ HAFFENDE..
Gent WHO DIED MAY
THE 12TH 1732 AGED
69 YEARS

1. For marriage [?] of George Haffenden, 1717-18 and 1721, see Dunkin (*Licences 1670-1729* 253).

Heathfield, 128H Ledger for Mary and Marquick HAFFENDEN, d. 1690 and d. 1744.

- Nave floor, centre aisle, West end.
- 80(W) x 165(L) — Sound; rough edges.
- M.I. (17 lines, engraved) fills surface of a black slab; head to West.
- Mary Haffenden, d. ?? Nov. 1690, aet 22; daughter of Edward Goddin, of Wiston, Sussex; and wife of Marquick Haffenden, buried 7 Dec 1744, aet 92.

1. See comment on 128F.

Heathfield, 128I Ledger for George HAFFENDEN, d. 1769

- Nave floor, centre aisle, West of South/North doors, partly carpeted over.
- 78(W) x 170(L) — Damaged.
- Remains of M.I. in upper (W) 50% of a freestone slab; head to West.
- George Haffenden, 3 Aug 1769, aet 71; third son of John and Elizabeth Haffenden.

1. Other remains of ledgers nearby, one perhaps to memory of another George Haffenden, taxed on lands at Heathfield in 1785 (R. Davey 105). .
2. NBI records burial of George Haffenden 10 Aug 1769 at Heathfield.

Heathfield, 128J Ledger for John HAFFENDEN, d. 1722

- Nave floor, alongside and North of 128I, partly carpeted over.
- 90(W) x 169(L) — Very worn.
- M.I. in upper (W) 80% of a freestone slab; head to West.
- John Haffenden; senior, d. ?? Dec 1722, aet 69; his wife, Elizabeth, d. ?? ??? 1742; age unknown.

1. Other remains of ledgers nearby.
2. For a licence to marry dated 7 May 1687 for one John Haffenden, of Heathfield, and Elizabeth Holbeam, of Heathfield, see Dunkin (*Licences 1670-1729* 101), but may not refer to the subjects of 128J.
3. NBI records burial of John Haffenden on 5 Dec 1722 at Heathfield.

Heathfield, 128K Ledger for James HAFFENDEN, d. 1753
- Nave floor, far West end, neat tower arch, partly covered by modern font.
- 78(W) x 185(L) — Very worn, cracked.
- M.I. (6 lines) in upper (W) 25% of a freestone slab, set head to West.
- James Haffenden, d. ?? Apr 1753; son of John and Elizabeth Haffenden.

1. For a brother see 128L.
2. NBI records burial of James Haffenden on 15 May 1753 at Heathfield.

Heathfield, 128L Ledger for Richard HAFFENDEN, d. 1752
- Nave floor, alongside and North of 128K.
- 78(W) x 185(L) — Very worn, cracked.
- M.I. (6 lines) in upper (W) 25% of a freestone slab; head to the West.
- Richard Haffenden, d. 16 Dec 1752, aet 57; son of John and Elizabeth Haffenden.

1. For a brother see 128K.
2. NBI records burial of Richard Haffenden on 21 Dec 1752 at Heathfield.

Heathfield Addition
Turner (*SAC* 23 163).
(1) Brass for Rt. Hon. George Augustus Elliott, Lord Heathfield, Lieutenant General, d. 6 Jul 1790, at Aix-la-Chappelle, aet 72, made from destroyed Spanish battery at Gibralta (in the church). See biography by James Falkner in *ODNB*.
(2) Two hatchments in the church, for Lord Heathfield and his wife, see Summers (144-5).

(129) HELLINGLY - no monuments found

(131) HERSTMONCEUX, All Saints
Now isolated from its village (c.f. Hooe); North arcade of c.1180-1200; South aisle is Early English; North chapel, in brick, c.1440; Victorian restorations - Nairn & Pevsner (533-4); broken paving reported in 1686; condition fine in 1724 (Ford 110); parish had c.240 communicants in 1603, Renshaw (*Ecclesiastical Returns*); monuments mostly manorial, associated with nearby Castle; terracottas by Harmer in churchyard but (unlike Wadhurst, etc.) not in the church; Horsfield notes only 131D.

Herstmonceux, 131A Mural monument for Margaret BECKETT, d. 1750
- North aisle, North wall, at head height.
- 117(W) x 186(H) — Excellent.
- In mixed grey, cream and white marbles; M.I. (18 lines, engraved, black) on a panel framed by Doric half-columns, cornice and base mouldings; above, an entablature, frieze and broken, pointed pediment; half-urn in the centre; below, scrolled corbels to left and right and at 90 degrees to the wall.
- Margaret Beckett, d. 27 Dec 1750, aet 78; servant of George Naylor, Esq., of Herstmonceux, Esq., and a dependant of his daughter, Grace Naylor, who died 1727.

1. A rare example of a monument recording the death of a servant; 131A is, in fact, mainly about her mistress, the daughter of the then lords of Herstmonceux (Naylor).
2. Unusual setting of corbels.

Herstmonceux, 131B Mural monument for John LANCASTER, d. 1715, and his wives Mary, d. 1696, and Lucretia, d. 1732/3 [Plate 84]

- North aisle, North wall, East of 131A, at head height.
- 45(W) x 95(H) — Excellent.
- A grey marble panel, set portrait-wise; M.I. (13 lines - 6+3+4), engraved, black); simple cornice and base moulding in matching darker grey; below, as corbel, a flattened Ionic capital with space below for a square panel, intended for an escutcheon.
- John Lancaster, of Herstmonceux, d. 4 Aug 1715, aet 75; his first wife, Mary, d. 12 Apr 1696, aet 37; his last wife, Lucretia, d. 18 Feb 1732/3, aet 77.

1. Unusual juxtaposition of panel and capital as corbel.
2. For licences to marry of 19 Jan 1675 for John Lancaster, of Herstmonceux and Mary Mott, of Wartling and 15 Oct 1696 for John Lancaster and Lucretia Dawson, of Selmeston, see Dunkin (*Licences 1670-1729* 24 and 162).

Herstmonceux, 131C A collection of fragments relating to an anonymous [churchyard?] monument

- North aisle, now located near the entrance to the North-East (Dacre) chapel.
- Max (H) of present ensemble 155 — Weathering, some fine, some losses.
- Freestone ensemble includes a hexagonal base with fluted, attached colonettes at the corners and a mourning putto over a draped urn; on the floor 8 smaller fragments.

1. Perhaps from a churchyard memorial to a Naylor.
2. The putto is of high sculptural quality.

Herstmonceux, 131D Wall tomb for the Lords DACRE, dated late 15th century and early 16th century [Plate 86]

- Between the North-East (Dacre) chapel and the sanctuary.
- 330(W) x 340(H) (?taller on the South side) — Fabric worn but well consolidated; many details lost; colour recently restored.
- A substantial wall-tomb filling an arch between chapel and sanctuary; from each side, cusped arches over recumbent effigies of 2 armoured knights, lying with their feet to the East; base with quatrefoils; a decorated frieze over; in the North-East and South-East corners, niches with covers once contained statues (near here, on the North side graffiti: 'IC / WG TC/1722'); on the top frieze on South side, highly decorated achievements-of-arms; no M.I.s.

1. In situ.
2. The Fiennes family were lords of Herstmonceux from the 1330s and were buried in the church from the mid 1480s; the marriage of Sir Richard Fiennes (d.1484) to Joan Dacre brought the barony into the family; in the late 1530s, Sir Thomas Fiennes (1517-41), 9th Baron, initiated the monument, in an ornate latest Gothic, to his father and grandfather (both also Sir Thomas). Antiquaries have long noted contradictions in design and heraldry, explained by Dacre's purchase of two late 15th-century effigies from Battle Abbey, at its dissolution in 1539; these represented Sir Thomas Hoo, Lord Hoo and Hastings (d.1455) and his half brother, (also) Thomas Hoo (d.1486), see *Archaeological Journal* XL 452; CW Scott-Giles, 'The Dacre tomb at Herstmonceux: an exercise in heraldic detection' (*Coat of Arms* XI 1917 46-50); Nairn & Pevsner (534).
3. For the condition of 131D in the mid 19th century, see E. Venables 'The Castle of Herstmonceux and its Lords' (*SAC* 4 191-4).

Herstmonceux, 131E Mural monument for Georgiana NAYLOR, d. 1806 [Plate 85]

- Chancel, North wall, towards the North-West corner, above head height.
- 89(W) x 196(H) — Excellent; black fading but visible.
- Above, in an arched frame, a death-bed scene in bas-relief with an angel, mourners and the deceased; below, a cornice over an unframed panel with M.I. (engraved, black);

below, a blank base panel and another, still lower, with a further M.I. (added after 1855).

- Georgiana Naylor, died at Lausanne, Switzerland on Easter Sunday, 1806; fourth daughter of Jonathan Shipley, bishop of St. Asaph; and wife of Francis Hare Naylor, of Herstmonceux; issue - eldest son, Francis George, d. Palermo, 1842; second son, Rev. August William, rector of Alton Barnes, Wiltshire; third son, Julius Charles, rector of Herstmonceux for 22 years and archdeacon of Lewes 14 years, d. 23 Jan 1855; fourth son, Marcus Theodore; youngest child, Anna Maria Clementina, died in infancy; Geogiana Naylor's eldest sister, Anna Maria, widow of Sir William Jones.

1. By 1745, Francis Hare Naylor (see 131F) was owner of the Castle and the Place, the latter used as a rector's residence; both were sold to his half-brother Robert Hare in 1772, who gutted the Castle in 1777; his son, also Robert Hare, rebuilt the Place in 1792 (Farrant 251).
2. 131E was erected by four brothers to the memory of their mother, aunt and sister.
3. The relief may not be by the same hand as the remainder; Gunnis (*Dict.* 227) attributes 131E to Kesels (sometimes Kessels), Danish (not Belgian), 1784-1836 and dates it 1829, noting that the first version was lost at sea in transit and replaced, a story retold by Nairn & Pevsner (534).
4. See biography of 'Francis Hare Naylor' in *ODNB* (by A Du Toit). See also *BLG* (1972 433).
5. Georgiana Naylor, née Shipley, born c.1755, was a cousin of duchess of Devonshire and fourth daughter of Jonathan Shipley (1713–1788), Bishop of St. Asaph, and his wife, Anna Maria Mordaunt (1717–1803), niece of the earl of Peterborough; Georgiana was described as 'tall, handsome, and self-sufficient, a scholar, and a painter' (C.R. Leslie and T. Taylor, *Life and times of Sir Joshua Reynolds*, 1865); she was a friend and pupil of Sir Joshua Reynolds who 'exhibited with applause' at the Royal Academy in 1781, where she showed a portrait of a lady and two children; she commissioned Flaxman's 39 illustrations to the Iliad and the Odyssey (*SAC* 97 82), which were engraved by Piroli in 1793 and published in a number of editions across Europe (Whinney 1988 344); she died on 6 April 1806 (Easter Sunday), at Lausanne, having been blind from the age of forty-eight; while in Bologna she had befriended the eminent Greek scholar Clotilda Tambroni, in whose hands she left her children.
6. JH notes that the four sons of Georgiana and Francis Hare Naylor used the surname of Hare only, see Hennessy, and GRO records.
7. Hatchment in the church – see Summers (146).

Herstmonceux, 131F Mural monument for Francis Hare NAYLOR, d. 1815

- Chancel, North wall, over door to North aisle, above head height.
- 90(W) x 70(H) — Very good, fading.
- Composite black baseplate supporting a rectangular white marble panel; set landscape-wise; M.I. (12 lines, engraved, black); signed (below): 'PARSONS.LEWES'.
- Francis Hare Naylor, Esq., of Herstmonceux, died Tours, France, 17 Apr 1815, aet 61; his second wife, Anne Maria, died at Bradley House, Devon, 30 Aug 1849, aet 76; issue - 3 unnamed.

1. The later lines of the M.I. were perhaps added after the death of Francis Hare Naylor's second wife in 1849.
2. For Francis Hare Naylor, born 1753, see A Du Toit in *ODNB*; he was grandson of the bishop of Chichester; his father, Robert Hare, assumed the name Naylor, surname of the bishop's first wife Bethia Naylor, daughter of Francis Naylor of Herstmonceux Castle. (see *BLG*, 7th ed.); for the first wife of Francis Naylor, see 131E; early married life was spent in Italy and returning from Rome in 1794, Flaxman settled an account with Francis Hare Naylor perhaps for work on illustrations for the latter's book, *Theodosius, the Enthusiast* (see Flaxman Account Book [BL Add. MS 39, 784 bb] in Walpole Society 1940); Francis Hare Naylor gained the Herstmonceux estate in 1797 but returned to writing for financial reasons; he left Herstmonceux for ever in 1804 and travelled to Weimar; his wife died in 1806; he remarried and sold the Herstmonceux estate; travelling again on the continent, he died at Tours after a lingering illness, his body was returned to Herstmonceux for burial beneath the altar.
3. JH notes that Anne Maria was widow of Lt. Col. Ridgeway Mealy and that the issue of Francis Hare Naylor and Anne Maria were: Gustavus Edward Cockburn, Reginald John and Georgina Frances (all unnamed on monument). See *BLG* (1972 433).

Herstmonceux, 131G Mural monument for Rev. Luke TREVIGAR, d. 1772, and his wife Elizabeth, d. 1780
- Chancel, North wall, to West of 131D, high up.
- 115(W); (H) inaccessible — Excellent; local damage (right cornice).
- M.I. (18 lines, engraved, black) on unframed grey marble panel; cornice and base moulding, the latter supported by corbels left and right; curved baseplate and M.I. (2 lines), dropping to a central ball finial; above, a thin obelisk-shaped, black baseplate supporting an achievement-of-arms and above, a half-urn on a pedestal, these last in white marble.
- Rev. Luke Trevigar, M.A., rector of Herstmonceux and canon residentiary of Chichester; d. 18 Apr 1772, aet 67; his wife Elizabeth, d. 28 Apr 1780, aet 74; their virtues, no issue mentioned.

1. Noted for its arms by Lambarde (*SAC* 68 224), in situ.

Herstmonceux, 131H Ledger stone for Jane PARKER, d. 1598
- Chancel floor, centre, against the sanctuary step.
- 85(W) x 140(L) — Worn, local damage (corners, sides).
- M.I. (9 lines) in capitals of equal size, at East end of a dark freestone slab; double-framed border and arrowhead decoration in corners; head to West.
- Jane Parker, d. 7 May 1598; daughter of William Dautrey, Esq.; and wife of William Parker, Gent.

1. Perhaps only a fragment.
2. One William Parker, perhaps her husband, stood surety for a marriage licence 8 Oct 1616, see Dunkin (*Licences 1586-1643* 101).
3. Arrowhead motif recurs at Alfriston, Lindfield, etc.

Herstmonceux, 131I Mural monument for William MICHELL, d. 1825
- South aisle, South wall, in South-West corner.
- 62(W) x 40(H) — Very good, rust patches, fading.
- M.I. (8 lines, engraved, black) on a white, unframed, trapezoidal panel below a simple straight cornice; signed (lower right): 'C.KING / TOTᵐ CT ROAD'.
- William Michell, ensign in the East India Company, d. Bengal 27 Jul 1825, aet 16.

1. Gunnis (*Dict.* 228) notes that Charles King (fl. 1809-40), whose work he describes as dull, had a yard at Chenies Street, which is off Tottenham Court Rd.

(134) HOLLINGTON - no monuments found

(135) HOOE, St. Oswald
Mostly Perpendicular, with Early English North chapel - Nairn & Pevsner (539); chancel (belonging to Mr Thomas Pelham) reported as bad in 1686, by which date, one Mr Elverey has laid in the chancel, lime and bricks for a communion table; in 1724 it was reported that the chancel has been repaired (Ford 47; 109).

Hooe, 135A Mural monument for family of Rev. Thomas FULLER, d. 1832
- Chancel, North wall, at head height.
- 38(W) x 68(H) — Excellent; fading.
- M.I. (4 lines + 3 + 5 + 3 (added) engraved, black) on unframed white marble panel; pointed pediment over a cornice; base moulding on 2 corbels.
- Rev. Thomas Fuller, M.A., of Heathfield, vicar of Hooe, d. 10 Dec 1832, aet 77; his wife Mary, d. 28 Mar 1822, aet 64; issue - Mary Ann, d. 2 Jun 1817, aet 32; and Frances, d. 23 Jul 1872, aet 89.

1. In situ - Horsfield (*Sussex* I 545); erected after 1822.

2. A later Fuller monument to the East of 135A is designed to create a pendant effect. .
3. JH notes that Thomas Fuller was rector of Hastings All Saints and St. Clements 1779 - c.1796; vicar of Hooe 1796-1832; rector of Chalvington 1782-1832 see Hennessy and Venn (1 2 589).

Hooe, 135B Mural monument for John FULLER, d. 1777, and his wife Mary, d. 1780, and children

- Sanctuary North wall, East of 135A, at head height.
- 72(W) x 96.5(H) — Excellent; fading.
- M.I. (3+2+2+2+2+3 lines, engraved, black) on white marble oval panel; border of pink inlay; above, painted arms on a small base; below, a corbel painted black.
- John Fuller, Esq., of Heathfield, d. 13 Feb 1777, aet 63; his wife, Mary, d. 24 Jan 1780, aet 53; issue - eldest son, Thomas, died in infancy; second son, John, d. 13 Feb 1784 aet 32; fifth son, Edward, died in infancy; youngest son, also Edward, d. 12 Jul 1787, aet 29.

1. In situ in 1835 - Horsfield (*Sussex* I 545) and in chancel in 1927 in Lambarde (*SAC* 68 223) citing arms.
2. John Fuller's descendants were still being taxed at Hooe in 1785 (R. Davey 116).

Hooe Additions
Davidson-Houston (*SAC* 78 89) from Burrell (BL Add. MS 5697 f.77).
(1) Thomas Acrouch, yeoman, d. 28 Dec 1576, his wife, Elizabeth, d. 10 Jul 1569 (nave) (Horsfield adds that the M.I. ends: 'Sancta Margarita ora pro nobis').
Horsfield (*Sussex* I 545):
(2) Richard Hollyer, d. 26 Jan 1539; his wives, Margaret and Alas [sic] (brass in the nave); in the church porch entrance, on [?] a freestone ledger noted by Davidson-Houston (*SAC* 78 89), quoting the M.I. as: 'OF YO CHARITIE PY / FOR THE SOULES OF / RICHARD HOLLYER / & MARGARET PERNELL & ALES, hys wyffe, / whiche RICHARD decessed / ye XXVI of January AD 1539'.

(137) HORSTED KEYNES, St. Giles
Norman with 13th-century additions, North transept now gone, North arcade restored in 1888 - Nairn & Pevsner (540); in 1724 it was reported that the patron is William Pigot, a minor, and that one James Pigott owns a chancel in good repair (Ford); for the journal of the rector of Horsted Keynes (1655-79), Giles Moore, see Bird (*Journal of Giles Moore*); all arms recently restored.

Horsted Keynes, 137A Mural monument for Anthony ELLIS, d. 1712
- North transept, West wall, above head height.
- c.85(W) x 81(H) — Good.
- White on black; pointed pediment over a cornice; M.I. (11 lines, engraved); signed (baseplate lower right): 'R. BROWN / 58, GT RUSSELL ST/ LONDON'.
- Anthony Ellis, b. 1630 - bur. 17 Jul 1712; his son, Thomas, b. 18 Jan 1684 - bur. 8 Mar 1754; their descendant, George Ellis, of East Grinstead.

1. It is unclear what motivated George Ellis, a descendant, to erect 137A as late as 1854.
2. Gunnis (*Dict.* 65) dates Brown as fl. in London 1817-30.

Horsted Keynes, 137B Ledger for Francis WYATT, d. 1713
- North tower arch floor, partly obscured.
- Inaccessible — Damage to East end; repairs and local losses.
- M.I. (engraved) fills upper 50% of a freestone slab; head to East.

> [Here] Interred is the Body of FRANCIS
> [WYA]T late of the Midle Temple
> [Barr]ester at Law and Batchelor
> [of Ar]ts, He was Mo[s]t Compleat in
> [all Ac]complishments; B[elov]ed by
> [all that] see [Him Ad]orned with

[Every] Grace and Virtue: this Bright
[Good and] Extraordinary Man
[Depart]ed this Life Decem br the 14 th
[1713 in the 27 th yea]r of his Age. He
[was E]ldest Son of FRANCIS WYAT
Esq r and ELIZABETH, his wife
[who] were Deprived of Him to their
[Inexpr]essible Greife his Early
[Death] being Lamented by all that
Knew Him

1. Formerly in South transept (now vestry); seen and transcribed by Gower (*SAC* 34 112-13) in North transept floor, alongside 137M; wrongly identified as 'white marble' by Gower.
2. M.I. completed here from Eardley (44).

Horsted Keynes, 137C Mural monument for Richard WYATT, d. 1816 [Plate 87]

- Chancel North wall, at head height.
- 100(W) x 116(H) — Good.
- A thin black lunette on a narrow moulded cornice supported by fluted pilasters; a white oval plaque within a rectangular black panel; base moulding; below, 2 corbels with roundel decoration and a curved apron supporting an escutcheon; signed (lower right): 'Hargraves, Mason, Lewes'.
- Richard Wyatt, Esq., of Treemans, Horsted Keynes, Sheriff of Sussex, d. 11 Jan 1816, aet 67.

1. Formerly on nave North wall, West of chancel arch (photograph of 1880); noted by Gower (*SAC* 34 114) as against nave West wall, near North transept arch, adjoining 137D; associated with gravemarker 137N.
2. In 1785, Richard Wyatt was owner (but evidently not the occupier) of lands at Horsted Keynes (see R. Davey 120), none named Treemans.
3. Isaac Hargraves, according to Gunnis (*Dict.* 188) fl. 1792-6, also signs a tablet (244D) at Stanmer; 137C not noted by Gunnis and perhaps extends Hargraves' known creative period by some 20 years.
4. JH notes that Wyatt had been Sheriff of Sussex. Two of this name are listed in Berry (*Sussex* p. xi), in 1787 and 1810. For heraldry see Lambarde (*SAC* 67 183).

Horsted Keynes, 137D Mural monument for Richard WYATT, d. 1753

- Chancel North wall, at head height.
- 128(W) x 210(H) — Good; faded.
- In grey marble; yellow marble frame around a white panel with M.I. (10 lines, engraved, black); above, an urn within a broken scrolled pediment on a moulded entablature supported on pilasters; below, base mouldings, then, a curved apron with coloured escutcheon; scrolled corbels; signed (left base moulding): 'R. Chambers' (with Hebrew M.I. to right).
- Richard Wyatt, Esq., of Treemans, Horsted Keynes, d. Jan 1753, aet 63; his wife Susanna, d. 29 Jun 1774, aet 72, daughter of late Sir Thomas Molyneux, Knt., of Loseley, Surrey.

1. Formerly on nave North wall, West of chancel arch (photograph of 1880); noted by Gower (*SAC* 34 114) as against nave West wall, near North transept arch, adjoining 137C; noted by Nairn & Pevsner (540).
2. Gunnis (*Dict.* 90-91) notes the interest of Robert Chambers (1710-84) in Hebrew scholarship and his use of Hebrew as an identifier on his monument for Col. Molyneux 1782 at Guildford documented in the Loseley archive (Guildford RO); his work for the family perhaps commenced in the mid 1770s with 137D.
3. For heraldry see Lambarde (*SAC* 67 183).

Horsted Keynes, 137E Mural monument for Elisabeth DALMAHOY, d. 1788

- Sanctuary, North wall, high.
- 80(W) x 110(H) — Very good.
- In white marble, unframed tablet; M.I. (12 lines, engraved, black), set landscape-wise; above, an urn on a straight cornice; below, black base moulding on 2 fluted corbels.
- Elizabeth Dalmahoy, d. 13 Jul 1788, aet 61; daughter of John Board, Esq. of Paxhill; and widow of Alexander Dalmahoy, Esq.; her daughter Frances Ayliffe Dalmahoy.

1. Formerly against East chancel wall, South of East window - Gower (*SAC* 34 108).
2. Elisabeth Dalmahoy seems to have been resident in 1785 in William Saxby's house in Lindfield (R. Davey 146); may be related to John Board (164E).
3. Patron of 137E was Elisabeth's daughter, Frances Ayliffe Dalmahoy.

Horsted Keynes, 137F Mural monument for George HAY, d. 1737, his wife Margaret, d. 1740, and family

- Sanctuary, North wall, at head height.
- 88(W) x 191(H) — Very good; fading.
- Mostly white marble; an escutcheon on a straight moulded cornice over an unframed tablet, set portrait-wise; M.I. (engraved, black) fills surface; ornamental scrolled lines; below, base moulding; black curved apron between fluted corbels.
- Rev. George Hay, A.M., rector at Horsted Keynes, 32 years, d. 1728 [sic], aet 84; his wife of 52 years, Margaret, d. 1732 [sic], aet 84; their issue 11 - youngest daughter, Margaret, d. 16 Aug 1767, aet 70, the wife of William Dalmahoy, Esq., son of Alexander Dalmahoy, Bart.; also, Alexander Dalmahoy, died an infant, first son of Alexander Dalmahoy, Esq., of London; also Alexander Dalmahoy, Esq., of London, d. 10 Oct 1781, aet 57, and his wife, Elizabeth, second daughter of John Board, Esq., of Paxhill, Sussex; their issue - 2 sons and 8 daughters.

1. JH notes that the wording on this monument implies that it is for George Hay Clerk, AM, whereas it is for George Hay, clerk, AM. The misunderstanding is repeated by Horsfield (*Sussex* I 336), Gower (*SAC* 34 107), and Eardley (40-1). Incorrect years of death for George Hay and his wife Margaret are also given. *Miscellanea Genealogica et Heraldica* by J.J. Howard, 1886 (2nd series, vol. 1, pp 195-6) quotes from the parish register of Horsted Keynes, and notes that Rev. George Hay, late rector, was buried 8 Nov 1737, and that Mrs Margaret Hay, widow of Rev. George Hay, was buried 17 Apr 1740. Rev. George Hay was rector of Horsted Keynes 1705-37, see Hennessy (87).
2. Noted by Horsfield (*Sussex* I 336); formerly against chancel East wall, North of East window - Gower (*SAC* 34 107); erected according to will of Alexander Dalmahoy, d. 1781.
3. For the Board family of Paxhill see 164 C-E, G, etc.
4. The arms above this monument are for Dalmahoy and Board. See Lambarde (*SAC* 67 183).
5. See Eardley (40-1) for transcription.

Horsted Keynes, 137G Mural monument for Saphira LIGHTMAKER, d. 1704

- Chancel, South wall, at head height.
- 114(W) x 222(H) — Very good; rust spots; faded.
- Grey marble frame; straight entablature; Ionic pilasters; M.I. (engraved) fills white marble tablet, set portrait-wise; M.I. includes a line of Greek; above, a decorated escutcheon; below, a thick curved base moulding; curved apron with foliate relief; cherub's head as corbel.
- Saphira Lightmaker, d. 20 Dec 1704, aet 81, wife of Edward Lightmaker, Gent., of Broadhurst, Sussex, a widow for 44 years; daughter of Dr. Alexander Leighton, D.D.; sister to Robert Leighton, late archbishop of Glasgow, buried at Horsted Keynes; sister to Sir Ellis Leighton, Knt, also buried at Horsted Keynes. Her grandchildren - Thomas Pigott, son of William Pigott, Gent., of Limesfield, Surrey, d. 8 Mar 1702, aet 11; Mary Pigott, daughter of William Pigott, d. 10 Apr 1702, aet 21. Her great grandchildren - Thomas Osborne junior, d. 4 Apr 1706, aet 4; son of Thomas Osborne, of Newtimber, armiger; - Elizabeth Osborne, daughter of the same Thomas Osborne, 12 Apr 1706, aet 3.

1. Originally in Marie de Bradehurst (Broadhurst) Chantry (South of sanctuary) prior to its demolition in 1850; located by Gower (*SAC* 34 108) against South wall of chancel.
2. Edward, husband of Saphira (preferred nomenclature 'Susan'), was a brewer; she was widowed at 37.
3. In 1664, Giles Moore noted that the costs of repairing a chancel at Horsted Keynes had fallen to him 'through the default and neglect of Mistresse Sapphira Lightmaker in not keeping up her Chauncell'; only in 1678 did she send him some gloves, as compensation, see Bird (50-51); the house, Broadhurst, was sold to Edward Lightmaker by the Michelbournes, then in the 1780s to the Pigotts, then to Viscount Hampden (Farrant 261).
4. 137G-H are pendant, attributed to William Palmer and dateable c.1734.
5. Memorials for Saphira Lightmaker's brothers, Robert and Sir Ellis Leighton, are in the external chancel wall. Interesting biographies by Hugh Ouston, D.W. Hayton and Frances Condick for both of them, and for their father Alexander (who was an MD) are in *ODNB*.
6. The birth of an Edward Lightmaker is recorded in the IGI for 1650, in Sussex. No other details are given. He may have been a son of Edward and Saphira, and the subject of the following two items. Edward Lightmaker presented plate to the church in 1705, see Couchman (*SAC* 55 172). Edward Lightmaker's will (1708) left a legacy for a charity school at Horsted Keynes (Caffyn 147).
7. For heraldry see Lambarde (*SAC* 67 183).
8. See Eardley (42) for transcription.

Horsted Keynes, 137H Mural monument for William PIGOTT, d. 1722
- Chancel, South wall, just West of 137G, at head height.
- 115(W) x 236(H) — Very good; rust.
- Pendant to 137G; signed (lower left): 'Wm PALMER'.
- William Pigott, Esq., of Broadhurst, Horsted Keynes, d. 22 May 1722, aet 39; his wife, Jane, daughter of Rev. William Needham, BD, of Allresford, Northamptonshire; their issue - William, 20 Oct 1711 - (bur) 25 Mar 1729/30; Gervas, 30 Dec 1714 - (bur) 2 Apr 1728; Henry, 30 Dec 1715 - (bur) 7 Mar 1715/6; Robert, 13 Apr 1719 - (bur) 14 Jul 1719; Catherine, surviving in 1734.

1. Formerly in Marie De Bradehurst (Broadhurst) chantry (South of sanctuary) prior to its demolition in 1850; located by Gower (*SAC* 34 109) alongside 137G; arms radically restored.
2. The Pigotts ran a foundry in the parish until 1664.
3. Patron of 137H was Jane Pigott (in 1734).
4. William Palmer lived 1673 - 1739.
5. Neither 137G nor 137H are listed in Gunnis (*Dict.*).
6. See Eardley (43) for transcription.
7. JH notes that despite the information on the monument, Rev. William Needham was rector of Alresford in Hampshire, see Venn (1 3 239) and CCEd.

Horsted Keynes, 137I Mural monument for Thomas PIGOTT, d. 1793
- Chancel, South wall, at head height.
- 77(W) x 61(H) — Good; local losses (left corbel); faded.
- M.I. (7 lines, engraved, black) on grey marble tablet, set landscape-wise; cornice and flanking attached half-columns; below, base moulding and corbels with roundel decoration.
- Thomas Pigott, Esq., 21 Dec 1738 - 5 Feb 1793, aet 55; son of Thomas and Catherine Pigott.

1. Located by Gower (*SAC* 34 109) in chancel, between arch and South wall.
2. In situ photograph of pre-1885[?] reported as formerly visible in vestry.
3. See Eardley (43) for transcription.

Horsted Keynes, 137J Ledger for Audrey WYATT, d. 1693
- Reportedly on vestry floor, beneath carpet and obscured by furnishings.
- 97(W) x 118(L) — Sound.
- M.I. (engraved) on a black slab.

Here lyeth the Body of M[rs]
AUDRY WYATT Wife of
FRANCIS WYATT ESQ. late
of Treemans and daughter of
Robert Spence Esq late of Balcomb in Sussex who by
her puer Modesty true Charity
and Exemplary life Proued
herselfe A widow indeed she
Departed this Life the 13th of Decem[br]
Ano Dom 1693 in the Sixty
Sixt yeare of her age

1. Located by Gower (*SAC* 34 113) in North transept floor, laid South to North, alongside 137K-L.
2. The Parish Register suggests that Audrey Wyatt, widow, was buried 13 Dec 1693 but NBI gives Adarell Wyatt as buried 18 Dec 1693.
3. See Eardley (45) for transcription.

Horsted Keynes, 137K Ledger for Mary LUXFORD, d. 1699

- Reportedly on vestry floor, beneath carpet and obscured by furnishings.
- 85(W) x 168(H) — Sound; cut?
- M.I. (engraved) on a black slab.

...the body
[Mary]...wife of
[George Lux]ford of /[Lyndfeild g]ent and
[second daug]hter of
Francis Wyatt esq.
and awdry his wife
of this p... s...
was buried [Januarie] 19th 1699 aged [36]...
issue one daughter

1. For former location see 137J.
2. Entry in parish register reads 18 Jan 1699, Mary Luxford, wife of George Luxford, died in the Parish of Lindfield 15 Jan, buried at Horsted Keynes.

Horsted Keynes, 137L Ledger for Richard WYAT, d. 1660

- Reportedly on vestry floor, beneath carpet.
- 86(W) x 170(L) — Poor; cut.
- M.I. (engraved) on a black slab.

Nea[r this place] Lyeth the
Body [of] Mr Richard Wyat
Third [son] of Francis Wyat
esq[r] [wh]o Departed this
Life [the] 28th day of June 1660
[M]EMORIÆ
FRANCI[SCI] WYAT ARM QUI VITAM
OFFICIU[MQ] VICECOMITES SIMUL
TERMINABAT QUARTO DIE
MARTII ANNO DNI
1673

1. For former location see 137J.
2. M.I. completed from Eardley (44-5).
3. Giles Moore officiated at the burial of Francis Wyatt but not apparently at Richard Wyatt's, see Bird (338, 340).

Horsted Keynes, 137M Ledger for Francis WYAT, d. 1723

- Reportedly on vestry floor, partly obscured by furnishings.
- 110(W) x 155(L) — Fine.
- M.I. (engraved) in 2 stages on a black slab.

Here Interred is the Body of
FRANCIS WYAT late of Treemans
in this Parish Esqr: A Man Just and
Honest in all his Actions a Tender
Husband and a most Indearing
Parent he Departed this life the
15th July 1723. In the 65th year of
his Age

HERE INTERRED IS ALSO Y^E BODY OF M^{RS} ELIZ. WYAT
WIFE OF Y^E ABOVE NAMED FRANCIS WYAT ESQ DAUGHTE^R
OF ROGER BYSSHE OF FEN PLACE IN THIS COUNTY
OF SUSSEX ESQ^R A WOMAN ENDOWED WITH ALL Y^E
EXCELLENT QUALITYES OF VIRTUE & GOODNESS
SHE DEPARTED THIS LIFE Y^E 17TH OF AUGST 1726 AGED 63

1. For former location see 137B.
2. See Eardley (40) for transcription.

Horsted Keynes, 137N Grave marker for 'RW', no date [Plate 88]

- Nave floor, towards West end.
- Size unknown (standard) — Good.
- 2 initials engraved on a square black panel.

1. Probably refers to 137C or D.

Horsted Keynes Additions

Noted by Gower (*SAC* 34 106-114):
(1) John Wood, clergyman (Horsted Keynes, 25 years), d. 9 Sep 1705, aet 58, in Latin; Chancel floor, near South wall, perhaps lost or hidden by flooring in the vestry, see Eardley (44).
(2) Henry Pigot, third son of William and Jane, d. 1 Mar 1715, aet 9 (adjoining).
(3) William Wyatt, d. 21 Apr 1673, fourth son of Francis (North transept floor, Sussex marble).
Noted in Horsfield (*Sussex* I 336).
(4) Robert Leighton, Archbishop of Glasgow d. 30 Jun 1684, aet 74, buried under a slab in South chancel.
(5) Sir Ellis Leighton, d. 9 Jan 1684.

(139/1) HURSTPIERPOINT, Holy Trinity

Considering that the church (original dedication St. Lawrence) was rebuilt in 1843-5, by Sir Charles Barry, and that all monuments have been relocated, many ('hardly anything in it worth preserving, except the two old sound pillars' - Letter from Archdeacon to Churchwardens 18 Sep 1841 quoted in Church Guide) are in surprisingly good condition; for the original church see *Gent's Mag* 1806; William Hamper's drawings of the interior in 1799, copied by Lydia Hamper in 1845, see (*SCM* II 55); for views see BL Add. MS 5677 f.48; 5672 ff.28-30; for architectural history, see Nairn & Pevsner (541); for an external view from the South-East see Godfrey & Salzman (Pl. 83); the South chancel was originally used by the owners of nearby Danny for family burials and that space in the new church was allocated to William John Campion in lieu of the old space, with the new North chancel and vault allocated to Nathaniel Borrer; Horsfield (*Sussex* I 246-7) noted the medieval effigies from the Danny (South) chancel moved into Mr Campion's coachhouse; however, the new South chancel turned out to be too small a space for the Campions, so the families swapped leaving the Borrers with the South and the Campions with the new North chancel.

Hurstpierpoint, 139/1A Mural monument for George GREENAWAY, d. 1770

- North aisle, against wall, near West end.
- 84(W) x 168(H) x 6(D) — Sound; very faded.
- Pale brown freestone; scrolled pedimental top and other ornament; a relief of the original church; on an arch-top tablet, a short M.I. (engraved).
- George Greenaway, d. 9 Mar 1770, aet 27; also, William Greenaway.

1. Erected by William Greenaway.
2. A headstone brought into the present church for its picture of the original building.

Hurstpierpoint, 139/1B Mural monument for John Pelham ROBERTS, d. 1828, and his family

- North aisle wall, East end, above head height.
- 125(W) x 132(H) — Good; faded.
- A black backplate with a pointed top; a tablet in white marble with a pointed pediment flanked by palmettes and decorated with foliage; M.I. in 2 columns (engraved & black), flanked by asymmetrical scrolls; below, a base moulding and 2 scrolled corbels; signed (lower right): 'LUPTON, / NEW ROAD, LONDON'.
- John Pelham Roberts, d. 5 Feb 1828, aet 62; his first wife, Lydia, d. 22 Feb 1801, aet 33; youngest daughter of Nathan and Elizabeth Avery; their issue - third son, Henry d. 1 Jan 1816, aet 21; his second wife, Mary Ann, d. 24 Mar 1840 aet 57, eldest daughter of William and Mary Borrer; their issue - eldest daughter, Mary Ann, d. 23 Aug 1806, an infant; eldest son, Lindfield, d. 10 Sep 1807, an infant; fourth son, Nicholas Henry, d. 7 Jun 1818, an infant; second daughter, Mary, d. 13 Nov 1822, aet 14; fifth daughter, Fanny d. 13 Nov 1823, an infant; and sixth daughter, Ellen, d. 27 Apr 1825, an infant.

1. For licence to marry dated 15 Feb 1805 for John Pelham Roberts, of Hurstpierpoint, Gent., widower and Mary Ann Borrer, of Hurstpierpoint, spinster, age 21 plus, see Dunkin & Penfold (*Licences* 360).

Hurstpierpoint, 139/1C Mural monument for Henry CAMPION, d. 1761

- North transept, West wall, above head height.
- 125(W); (H) unknown — Very good; rust; colour.
- In grey marble; M.I. (engraved) on tablet set portrait-wise and breaking forward from backplate; cornice; pointed pediment with finial; below, base moulding, large brackets and an escutcheon.
- Henry Campion, d. 14 Apr 1761, aet 81; his wife, Barbery, daughter and heiress of Peter Courthope, Esq., of Danny; issue - William Campion, Esq., of Danny; Catherine, wife of George Courthop [sic], Esq., of Whyligh, Sussex.

1. Moved from the old South aisle (Danny chancel), see *Gent's Mag* 1805 in Gomme (274).
2. For Henry Campion's son see 139/1D; for pedigree see Blencowe (*SAC* 10 34-5) who spells the wife's name as Barbara; cited by Lambarde (*SAC* 71 151) noting arms.

Hurstpierpoint, 139/1D Mural monument for William CAMPION, d. 1778

- North transept, North of 139/1C.
- 105(W) x 198(H) — Very good; colour.
- In grey marble with a scrolled pediment over a cornice and M.I. (engraved) in upper 50% of tablet set portrait-wise; strong base moulding; fluted corbels flanking a black baseplate supporting an escutcheon.
- William Campion, Esq., of Danny, d. 1 Aug 1778, aet 70; son of Henry and Barbara Campion; his wife, Elizabeth, d. 6 Oct 1768, aet 60, daughter of Edward Partheriche, Esq., of Ely, Cambridgeshire; issue - unnamed.

1. Moved from the old South aisle (Danny chancel), see *Gent's Mag* 1805 in Gomme (274).
2. For Campion's parents see 139/1C.
3. Unused space on M.I. perhaps intended for issue.
4. For Henry Campion, owner and occupier of Danny, etc. see R. Davey (120); pedigree, see Blencowe (*SAC* 10 34-5); Lambarde (*SAC* 71 151) noting arms.
5. JH notes that Blencowe shows Elizabeth's father as Richard Partherick, of Aldermiston, Worcestershire.

Hurstpierpoint, 139/1E Mural monument for Henry Courthope CAMPION, d. 1811

- North transept, below 139/1D.
- 104(W) x 85(H) — Very good.
- Against a black baseplate, a white marble tablet with plain pointed pediment over a cornice; a M.I. tablet, unframed, with dropped lower corners; unsigned.
- Henry Courthope Campion, Esq., of Danny, d. 27 Jun 1811, aet 77.

1. Moved from old South transept.
2. For Campion pedigree see Blencowe (*SAC* 10 34-5).

Hurstpierpoint, 139/1F Mural monument for Henrietta CAMPION, d. 1771

- North transept, North wall, North-West corner, high.
- Inaccessible — Very good.
- M.I. (many lines) on a grey marble tablet, set portrait-wise and forward from a darker grey backplate; fluted frieze, then segmental pediment with fan decoration flanked by palmettes; below, base mouldings and 2 scrolled corbels.
- Henrietta Campion, d. 6 Feb 1771, aet 33; daughter of Sir John Heathcote, Bart., of Normanton, Rutland; and wife of Henry Courthope Campion, Esq., of Danny; issue - Bridget, d. 13 Feb 1797, aet 27, buried at Hurstpierpoint.

1. Moved from the old South aisle Danny chancel, see *Gent's Mag* 1805 in Gomme (274).
2. Very like 139/1H - the pediment on 139/1F replacing lamp on 139/1H.
3. For Campion pedigree, see Blencowe (*SAC* 10 34-5).

Hurstpierpoint, 139/1G Mural monument for children of William John and Jane CAMPION, d. 1801, etc.

- North transept, North wall, North-West corner, at head height.
- 70(W) x 92(H) — Very good.
- M.I. (many lines) fill an unframed white tablet; pointed top; black baseplate; below, base mouldings.
- The issue of William John and Jane Campion - Henry Francis, 20 Jul [1801] - 4 Aug 1801; Henry Francis, 18 Oct 1802 - 30 Nov 1809; Mary Anne, 3 Nov 1797 - 28 Oct 1825; Jane Bridget, 16 Apr 1799 - 24 Nov 1840; and Margaretta, 22 Sep 1806 - 8 Nov 1846.

1. Pendant to monument to George Edward Campion d. 1841, alongside it.

Hurstpierpoint, 139/1H Mural monument for Priscilla CAMPION, d. 1795

- North transept wall, North-East corner, very high.
- c.63(W): (H) inaccessible — Very good.
- Description as for 139/1F but with a lamp in relief on the cornice, not a pediment.
- Priscilla Campion, 10 Apr 1781 - 6 Feb 1795; daughter of William and Priscilla Campion, of Lewes.

1. Moved from the old South aisle (Danny chancel), see *Gent's Mag* 1805 in Gomme (274).
2. For design see note on 139/1F.
3. Patrons were Priscilla Campion's parents.

Hurstpierpoint, 139/1I Mural monument for Frances Elizabeth CAMPION, d. 1804

- North transept, below 139/1H.
- 75(W) x c.140(H) — Very good.
- M.I. (engraved, filled), unframed, set portrait-wise, in light grey marble; a black baseplate with a curved top; strong cornice moulding; above, a lamp in relief; below, a modest base moulding and two fluted, scrolled brackets.
- Frances Elizabeth Campion, d. 29 Sep 1804, aet 26; only daughter of Edward and Eleanor Campion of Chichester.

1. The M.I. expresses unusually powerfully, the sentiments of the bereaved parents.

Hurstpierpoint, 139/1J Mural monument for John CLARK, d. 1781

- North-East chapel, West wall, facing East, high up.
- Inaccessible — Very good; rust, fading, some colour.
- M.I. (engraved, black) on white tablet, set portrait-wise; flanked by plain dark grey marble pilasters; above, a blank frieze with panels of triglyphs, as capitals; cornice mouldings supporting a pedestal, an escutcheon and a flaming lamp; below; base mouldings and ornamental apron, all blank.
- Rev. John Clark, S.T.P., Oriel College, Oxford, d. 21 Nov 1781, aet 48; his widow, Anne, d. 1 Aug 1817, aet 80, daughter of the Ven. Christopher Dodson, rector of Hurstpierpoint; their only daughter [Ann], was wife of George Cook, S.T.P.; Anne's sister, Elizabeth, married Thomas Marchant.

1. Patron was widow.
2. Noted by *Gent's Mag* 1805 in Gomme (273).
3. JH notes that John Clark, D.D., was Provost of Oriel 1768-81, see Foster (*Al. Ox.* 2 1 256), and that arms were not noted by Lambarde.

Hurstpierpoint, 139/1K Mural monument for Peter COURTHOPE, d. 1657

- North-East chapel, North wall, near West end, very high.
- c.140(W) x c.300(H) — Very good; heraldic colour.
- M.I. (engraved and gilded) on slate; alabaster surround of flanking pilasters of baluster form; another set at right-angles beyond; adorned with swags and ending in escutcheons; above, entablature with frieze and broken scrolled pediment and achievement; below, a base moulding; on apron, 2 swags flank an escutcheon and 2 decorated brackets.
- Peter Courthope, Esq., late of Danny, also of Cranbrook, Kent, d. 15 Aug 1657, aet 80; his first wife, Elizabeth, daughter of John Sharpey, of Staplehurst, Kent; issue - Henry, Alexander, Frances; his second wife, Jane, daughter of Henry Smith, of Pepperharrow, Surrey, and widow of Ninion Burrell, of Cuckfield, Sussex; issue - Elizabeth.

1. Also commemorated by a ledger (139/1M).
2. Noted by *Gent's Mag* 1805 in Gomme (273) as in Danny Chapel (South aisle).
3. Cited for its heraldry in Lambarde (*SAC* 71 150), in situ.
4. Jane Courthope's first husband was Ninian Burrell (d.1614) see 72M.

Hurstpierpoint, 139/1L Mural monument for Peter COURTHOPE, d. 1724/5
[Plate 89]

- North-East chapel, centre of North wall, above head height.
- 190(W) x c.300(H) — Fine; very faded; heraldic colour.
- 2 M.I. panels (engraved, filled) in grey marble, set portrait-wise and separated and framed in brown-veined alabaster; 3 fluted Doric pilasters; below, gadrooned border; flanking corbels in diamond form, with applied acanthus decoration; central corbel, a death's head; entablature with frieze of triglyphs and blank metopes; straight cornice; gilded, flaming lamps flank an achievement.

- Peter Courthope, Esq., late of Danny, d. 13 Feb 1724, aet 86; his wife, Philadelphia, daughter of Sir John Stapley, Bart., of Patcham; their daughter - Barbara; who married Henry Campion, Esq., of Combwell, Goudhurst, Kent; their issue - Philadelphia, Frances, William, Barbara (all died as infants, all buried at Hurstpierpoint), Peter (son 2), buried Goudhurst, d. ?? Aug 1723, aet 16.

1. M.I. alludes to Peter Courthope's experience in infancy of 'anarchy and confusion', presumably the civil wars of the 1640s.
2. The reference to burial place is, of course, to the original Danny chancel in the old South aisle, see *Gent's Mag* 1805 in Gomme (273), however, see 139/1/M for floor marker for Peter Courthope (but note conflicts of death date).
3. 139/1L was erected after Peter Courthope's death, probably by his son-in-law, Henry Campion.
4. Dates of death given above are from *Gent's Mag*.
5. Peter Courthope's mother-in-law was Mary Springett, later Stapley (see 212BB).
6. NBI records burial of Peter Courthope on 19 Feb 1725 at Hurstpierpoint.
7. JH notes that Lambarde does not mention the heraldry on this monument and see 139/1V for John, their eldest son.

Hurstpierpoint, 139/1M Floor monument for Peter COURTHOPE, d. 1657
- North-East chapel floor, centre, towards West end, partly obscured by furnishings.
- 92(W) x 160(L) — Sound; cut (lower left).
- M.I. (3 lines, engraved) in upper part of a brown freestone slab; head to West.

HERE LYETH THE BODY OF

PETER COURTHOPE ESQ WHO

DYED AVGVST 15 1657

1. Lettering perhaps recut.
2. Peter Courthope was the first of that name to possess Danny, see Blencowe (*SAC* 10 13ff).

Hurstpierpoint, 139/1N Floor monument for a son of Peter COURTHOPE, d. 1672
- North-East chapel floor, abutting South-East side of 139/1 M.
- 50(W) x 89(L) — Sound.
- M.I. (engraved) in upper (W) end of a brown freestone slab; head to West.

FILIVS PET COVRT

HOPE DE DANNY

ARME & PHIL VXORI

NATV MAXIMVS

HÆREDITEM MELIOR

(MINIME DESPERAMVS)

CHRISTO REDEMPTAM

NACTVRVS

IN IRSO[SIC] ÆTAT LIMINE

CORREPTVS OBIIT

DIE SC. IX° DEC V°

1672

RELIQ INTVS POS:

P. M. L.

1. Terms of the M.I. are unclear, 139/1N appears to commemorate the first-born son of Peter Courthope.
2. The M.I. was already mostly illegible in 1805, Gomme (274).
3. JH notes that Peter and Philadelphia Courthope's first son did indeed die on 9 Dec 1672.

Hurstpierpoint, 139/1O Floor monument for William COURTHOPE, d. 1701
- North-East chapel floor, abutting 139/1M, West of 139/1N, partly obscured by furnishings.
- 65(W) x 60(L) — Very worn, cracked.
- M.I. (engraved) on a sandy freestone slab; head to West.

Depositum
Gulielmi Court[hope]
primogeniti ...
Campion ...
Uxoris qui n ...
Martii ... 1701

1. Commemorates William, son of Henry Campion and Philadelphia Courthope, died young, cited on 139/1L.
2. Did these children take the family name Courthope, as heirs to their maternal grandfather?

Hurstpierpoint, 139/1P Mural monument for Christopher SWALE, d. 1645
- Sanctuary, North wall, high.
- c.124(W); (H) inaccessible — Very good.
- M.I. (engraved, gilded, filled, Latin) on black oval panel (slate?); freestone. frame (above); alabaster base moulding; scroll decoration; lamp on top; below, an apron, 3 escutcheons, other ornament.
- Christopher Swale, for about 40 years at Hurstpierpoint, ejected 1644, d. 7 Sep 1645; his cousin was Solomon Swale, Bart., of Swale Hall, Yorks; his first wive, Ursula, daughter of Thomas Waterhouse, Gent., of Braythwell, Yorkshire; second wife, Rose, daughter of John Sackvill, armiger, of Chiddingly, Sussex; third wife, Anne West, daughter of Lord De La Warr; issue - all died by Sep 1645; Christopher Swale adopted a son of Lord Swale (Edward) as his heir, who died 7 Sep 1660.

1. Patron of 139/1P is the adopted son; noted by *Gent's Mag* 1804-5 in Gomme (272).
2. For biographic account see Dunkin (*SAC* 26 19), but some details incorrect; arms noted in Lambarde (*SAC* 71 149), in situ, citing Woolgar MS App. 77.
3. The ledger 139/1S may be associated with 139/1P which is the only monument at Hurstpierpoint noted by Horsfield (*Sussex* I 246-7) with some biography but no location.
4. JH notes that Swale was also rector of Westbourne, 1614 – 45.

Hurstpierpoint, 139/1Q Mural monuments for Rev. Christopher and Mary DODSON, d. 1784 and 1747, and their children
- Sanctuary South wall, high.
- 130(W) x 80(H) — Sound; faded.
- A set of 2 monuments: (A) the lower, in 2 parts: a M.I. (engraved and black) on grey marble panel, unframed, set landscape-wise; a low relief border with flanged sides; above, an achievement on a panel; (B) the upper: a M.I. (engraved & black) filling a marble tablet set portrait-wise; flanked by grey marble colonettes; ogival top with inset trefoil & escutcheon.
- Rev. Christopher Dodson, 51 years rector at Hurstpierpoint, d. 14 Mar 1784, aet 78; his wife, Mary, d. 28 Feb 1747/8, aet 35, daughter of Thomas Marchant, Gent.; issue, (amongst others anon) - eldest son, John Dodson, D.D., scholar of Trinity and fellow of Oriel College, Oxford, vicar of Cubbington, Warwickshire, rector of Yoxall, Staffordshire and of Hurstpierpoint, d. 1 Jul 1807, aet 74; his wife, Frances, d. 15 Apr 1832, aet 82, buried at St. Chad, Lichfield, Staffordshire, daughter of Rev. John and Susanna Dawson, of Stapenhill, Staffordshire; issue - unnamed.

1. Monument to Christopher and Mary Dodson noted by *Gent's Mag* 1805 in Gomme (272-3) in the chancel.
2. Both upper and lower parts of 139/1Q in situ and cited for their arms, see Lambarde (*SAC* 71 150).
3. Patrons of 139/1Q are their children, including Dr John Dodson, whose own monument was erected, in turn, by his (anon) children; Mary Dodson is also commemorated by ledger 139/1R; for her pedigree see E. Turner, 'The Marchant Diary' (*SAC* 25 199); she was daughter of the diarist Thomas Marchant and married Christopher Dodson at Wivelsfield in 1731.
4. Dr John Dodson owned and occupied the church property at Hurstpierpoint in 1785 (R. Davey, 120).
5. Another Dodson, clerk of Hurstpierpoint, was Jeremiah, whose son, also Jeremiah, was apprenticed to an apothecary in Apr 1723, see Rice (56).

6. The lower part of 139/1Q is described by Gunnis (*Dict.* 150) and *SAC* (97 84) described as dull, minor, undistinguished, (a formula used on other occasions) and attributed to Flaxman and dated 1800, followed by Nairn & Pevsner (541).

Hurstpierpoint, 139/1R Ledger for Mary DODSON, d. 1747
- Choir floor, South side.
- 96(W) x 146(L) — Sound; worn.
- M.I. (several lines, engraved) on a slab of oolitic freestone; head to West.
- Mary Dodson, d. 27 Feb 1747, aet 35; wife of Christopher Dodson, rector of Hurstpierpoint.

1. Presumably set up by her husband (d.1784) soon after her death.
2. See too mural monument 139/1Q.

Hurstpierpoint, 139/1S Anonymous ledger, uninscribed and undated
- Choir floor, North side.
- 84(W) x 146(L) — Fine.
- Black slab; no M.I.; escutcheon at West end, sketched in; head to West.

1. An incomplete ledger, arms suggesting relationship with 139/1P, arms of Swale, see Lambarde (*SAC* 71 150).
2. In type, it accords with its neighbours 139/1T-W.

Hurstpierpoint, 139/1T Ledger for Anne COURTHOPE, d. 1690
- Choir floor, North-East of centre.
- 96(W) x 190(L) — Very good.
- M.I. (10 lines, engraved) in upper (W) end of black slab; head to West.
- Anne Courthope, d. 22 Jan 1690, aet 85; daughter of Ninion Burrell, Esq.; and wife of Henry Courthope, Gent.; issue - Jane, Mary, Anne, Elizabeth, Frances, Peter and Dorothy.

1. A characteristic lettering hand.
2. For the Burrell connection see 72M.

Hurstpierpoint, 139/1U Ledger for Philadelphia COURTHOPE, d. 1676 [Plate 90]
- Choir floor, South-East of centre.
- 89(W) x 191(L) — Very good.
- Escutcheon at West end; M.I. (13 lines) fills surface of a black slab; head to West.
- Philadelphia Courthope, d. 18 Oct 1676, aet 25; eldest daughter of Sir John Stapley, Bart.; and wife of Peter Courthope, Esq.; their issue - John, Barbara and Peter.

1. Originally in South (Danny) chancel, see *Gent's Mag* 1805 in Gomme (274); cited Lambarde (*SAC* 71 150) noting arms, by then in situ.
2. Note characteristic handling of figure '1'.

Hurstpierpoint, 139/1V Ledger for John COURTHOPE, d. 1698/9
- Choir floor, North-West of centre.
- 97(W) x 190(L) — Very good.
- M.I. (11 lines, Latin) in upper 50% of a black slab; head to West.
- John Courthope, d. 11 Mar 1698, aet 26; eldest son of Peter and Philadelphia Courthope.

1. See 139/1L for Peter and Philadelphia Courthope.
2. JH notes that John Courthope was elected MP for Bramber on 24 Feb 1698/9, but died a few days later.

Hurstpierpoint, 139/1W Floor monument for Mary BEARD, d. 1688
- Choir floor, South-West of Centre.
- 97(W) x 192(L) — Sound; escutcheon worn.
- M.I. (7 lines, engraved) and escutcheon in upper (W) 55% of a black slab; head to West.

- Mary Beard, d. 12 Jan 1688, aet 57; second daughter of Nicholas Monke, Esq., of Hurston; and wife of Thomas Beard, Esq., of Hurstpierpoint; their issue - Thomas and Barbara.

1. In situ by 1930 - Lambarde (*SAC* 71 150) noting arms.
2. Note characteristic form of figure '1' c.f. an upper case 'J', not unlike the M.I. on 139/1V.

Hurstpierpoint, 139/1X Mural monument for John BORRER, d. 1793 [Plate 91]
- South transept, East wall, high.
- Inaccessible — Very good.
- M.I. (14 lines [7 + 7], engraved, black) fills white marble tablet, set portrait-wise with 4 corners chamfered; narrow dark grey border; rance surround (unframed); above, a cornice and a bare rance frieze with escutcheon; on top, cornice with dome; below, a base moulding and a curving apron; no corbels.
- John Borrer, late of Henfield, d. 11 Sep 1793, aet 32; his widow, Ann, d. 16 Sep 1847, aet 83; daughter of John Hamlin of Sunt, [in Lindfield]; later, widow of John Dennett.

1. In North transept of original church, see *Gent's Mag* 1805 in Gomme (276); in situ in Lambarde (*SAC* 71 151) noting arms.
2. Final lines added after 1847.
3. Composition close to 139/1/Y.

Hurstpierpoint, 139/1Y Mural monument for Barbara and William BORRER, d. 1795 and 1797
- South transept, South wall, South-East corner, very high.
- Inaccessible — Very good.
- M.I. (12 lines, engraved) in upper 80% of unframed white oval tablet, set portrait-wise, within a (slate?) surround; white cornice over and base mouldings; curved apron with 2 rosettes, a cherub and a fluted vase as corbel; above, a frieze with 2 rosettes flanking an escutcheon, topped by a cornice with a domed top.
- Barbara Borrer, d. 12 Apr 1795, aet 73; wife of William Borrer, d. 21 Jan 1797 aet 72.

1. In North transept of original church, see *Gent's Mag*, 1805 in Gomme (275); in situ in Lambarde (*SAC* 71 151) noting arms.
2. Composition very close to 139/1X.
3. William Borrer owned extensive properties in Hurstpierpoint in 1785 (R. Davey 120).
4. Borrer's eldest son, also William (1781-1862), the Henfield-based botanist, see Harrison (17), was perhaps too young to have been the patron of 139/1Y.

Hurstpierpoint, 139/1Z Mural monument for Elizabeth THORP, d. 1624
- South transept, South wall, at head height, below 139/1Y.
- c.100(W) x 160(H) — Fine; local damage (top).
- Alabaster surround decorated with gilded foliage and escutcheons; M.I. (engraved, gilded) in centre, black slate, set portrait-wise; below, a curving apron with death's heads and cherub; straight, plain, thick cornice.
- Elizabeth Thorp, d. 24 Apr 1624, aet 29; daughter of Sir Anthony Colepeper, of Bedgebury, Kent; and wife of John Thorp, Esq., of Cudworth, Surrey; their issue - Anthony, John, Thomas (died an infant) and Anne.

1. Recorded in chancel by *Gent's Mag* 1805 in Gomme (272-3).
2. Cited for its heraldry in Lambarde (*SAC* 71 152) and in situ.

Hurstpierpoint, 139/1AA Mural monument for Mary BORRER, d. 1807, and other Borrers
- South transept, South wall, South-West corner, very high.
- c.100(W) x c.200(H) — Fine; cracks, rust, dirt.
- Light grey marble tablet, set portrait-wise, unframed, with 2 moulded corbels and a narrow dark grey moulded cornice, with separate escutcheon over; now partly buried in

a replastered wall.

- Mary Borrer, 7 Aug 1758 - 30 Aug 1807, daughter of Nathanael and Mary Lindfield; and wife of William Borrer; their issue - Barbara Elizabeth, b. 25 Jul 1792, died an infant; also, Mary Anne Clifford, daughter of Nathanael and Mary Anne Borrer, 5 Jul 1813 - 20 Jun 1822; also William Borrer, 7 Mar 1753 - 18 Jan 1832.

1. Additions to the M.I. over several generations.
2. William Borrer, first son of Mary Borrer, lived 13 Jun 1781 - 10 Jan 1862, an eminent botanist, married in 1810 and a generous benefactor to his church (see biography by P.E. Kell in *ODNB*).
3. JH notes that Lambarde has not recorded the heraldry on this memorial.

Hurstpierpoint, 139/1BB Mural monument for Elizabeth STONE, d. 1723

- South nave aisle wall, East end, high.
- 90(W) x 180(H) — Good; colour.
- An oval tablet with a moulded frame, M.I. fills convex surface; above, an achievement with scrolled and foliate surround; below, escutcheon as corbel.
- Elizabeth Stone, d. 13 Dec 1723, aet 84; daughter of Jeremiah Johnson, Gent., of Charlwood, Surrey; and widow of John Stone, Gent., of Rusper, Sussex; issue - Catherine, d. 8 Apr 1736, aet 64, widow of Thomas Beard, Gent., of Hurstpierpoint; their only issue - Ralph Beard.

1. Roughly in this position in the church in 1805, see Gomme (275).
2. Ralph, son of Katherine Beard, of Hurstpierpoint, was apprenticed to Thomas Honywood, of London, Gent., in Dec 1712, see Rice (16).
3. For heraldry, see Lambarde (*SAC* 71 154).

Hurstpierpoint, 139/1CC Mural monument for Thomas BEARD, d. 1765, and his family

- South nave aisle wall, East end, below 139/1BB.
- 98(W) x 140(H) — Fine; faded.
- Dark baseplate; M.I. on unframed, grey-veined marble tablet in squared sarcophagal form; below, a simple base mould and 2 moulded corbels; above, a moulded cornice and a flattened pointed pediment with shoulder quarterings supporting a draped urn, signed (below centre): 'PARSONS. LEWES'.
- Thomas Beard, Esq., d. Jun 1765, aet 64; his only son, Ralph Beard, Esq., d. 14 Sep 1754, aet 58; Ralph's wife, Mary, d. 10 May 1780, aet 68, daughter of William Constable, Esq., of Burwash; their issue - Catherine, d. Apr 1743, aet 12; Mary, d. 16 Jan 1814, aet 80; Martha, d. 28 Oct 1827, aet 92; Ann, d. 2 Apr 1840, aet 95; Elizabeth, d. 1 Feb 1817, aet 82, buried Portslade; and Sarah, d. 6 Dec 1797, aet 56, buried Wiston, the wife of Charles Goring, Esq.

1. *Gent's Mag* 1805 in Gomme (275) notes M.I.s recording individuals related to 139/1BB-CC: Thomas Beard, d. 22 Sep 1700, aet 42, second son of another Thomas Beard, of Hurstpierpoint, Esq; his wife, Katherine, daughter of John Stone, of the Nunnery, Rusper, gent; their issue, a son Ralph, lawyer, d. 22 Sep 1754, aet 59; his wife, Mary, daughter of William Constable, Esq., of Burwash (see 45M); issue 5 daughters, of whom, Catherine, d. 6 Apr 1743, aet 12; also Mary, d. 12 Jan 1688, aet 57, second daughter of Nicholas Monke, of Hurton, Esq. (see 139/1W); her husband, Thomas Beard, of Hurstpierpoint, Esq.; their issue - Thomas and Barbara.
2. An early date for a tablet by Parsons.

Hurstpierpoint Additions

Noted in Gomme (273):
(1) Rev. Minhardes Shaw, rector of Hurstpierpoint, d. 17 Feb 1701, aet 59; his wife Elizabeth, daughter of George Duke, of Surrey, Esq.; issue 1 son, 2 daughters.
(2) Philadelphia ... pion ... 1705 (possibly related to 139/1L and O).
(3) Courthope ... Henrici ... Barbarae ... 1704 ... 1706.
(4) Campion ... Mar 1703 ... 1705.

(139/2) HURSTPIERPOINT, St. George

Originally built as an Independent chapel by Charles Smith Hannington on his St George's estate. It became Church of England in 1868 when the family joined the established church. It was served from 1875 by Hannington's son, James, later Bishop of East Equatorial Africa, who was massacred in Uganda in 1885.

Hurstpierpoint, 139/2A Mural monument for members of the HANNINGTON family, d. 1797, etc.
- Choir, North wall, at head height.
- 63(W) x 102(H) — Very good.
- M.I. (engraved, black) on a simple white tablet, on a black baseplate.
- Charles Hannington, d. 18 Sep 1797, aet 62; his wife, Mary, d. 16 Apr 1816, aet 69; their third son, Smith Hannington, d. 22 Jul 1855, aet 70, and his wife, Elizabeth, d. 3 Nov 1869, aet 90; later descendants.

1. For licence to marry, dated 9 Apr 1809, for Smith Hannington, of Brighton, linen draper, bachelor, age 24 plus and Elizabeth Baker, of Brighton, spinster, age 28 plus, see Dunkin & Penfold (*Licences* 191).
2. For the origins of the Hannington's store in Brighton see Musgrave (222-3).

(140) ICKLESHAM, All Saints

The 3-bay arcades were built by c.1175, the North and South chapels are of c.1200; Teulon restorations of 1847-52 - Nairn & Pevsner (542-3), T.T. Churton 'Icklesham Church' (*SAC* 32 111ff) and G.M. Livett 'Three East Sussex Churches: Battle, Peasmarsh, Icklesham, Pt. III' (*SAC* 48 38-64); engraved internal view by Moss (1812); pavements of all 3 chancels reported as poor in 1686 (Ford 43); by 1724, North chancel still unpaved, others (owned by the parson, Mr William Burrell and Lady Winchelsea) were paved (Ford 98); monuments now located in the larger East end; for M.I.s and heraldry see Butler (*SAC* 14 259-262) and Lambarde (*SAC* 68 229-230).

Icklesham, 140A Mural monument for Thomas Lewis COOPER, d. 1824
- Choir, North wall, towards the West end, high.
- 110(W) x 160(H) — Good.
- An unframed, white marble M.I. (23 [10 + 13] lines in 2 stages, engraved, black) with chamfered corners, set portrait-wise, within a frame of faded dark grey panels; gilded roundels in corners; pointed pediment and decorated apron; ornamental corbel.
- Thomas Lewis Cooper, d. 4 Feb 1824, aet 7; eldest son of William and Martha Cooper and grandson of Thomas Cooper; also, his uncle, Robert Court [Cooper], d. 24 Nov 1824, aet 31, third son of Thomas Cooper; also, the latter's great grandson, Charles Herbert Cooper, A.R.I.B.A., 3 Oct 1862 - 7 Oct 1894, son of William George Cooper and Anne Elizabeth Cooper of Kensington; quoting, Titus III.1 and Wisdom III.1.

1. Described as 'plain' but not located by Horsfield (*Sussex* 1 476-77).
2. Pendant with 140B, both perhaps relocated, see illustration in Petit's *Remarks on Church Architecture*, 1841 (reprinted in Church Guide).
3. 140A was in situ in 1862, see Butler (*SAC* 14 259) with a partial transcription.

Icklesham, 140B Mural monument for Thomas COOPER, d. 1807, and his wife Mary, d. 1824.
- Choir, North wall, alongside and East of 140A.
- 110(W) x 160(H) — Good.
- Description as for 140A; M.I. (20 [13 + 10] lines in 2 stages, engraved, black).
- Thomas Cooper, Gent., of New Place, d. 9 Apr 1807, aet 54; his wife, Mary, d. 19 Jan

1824, aet 62; her sister, Ann Collins, d. 30 Apr 1835, aet 72; their eldest son, William, d. 31 May 1843.

1. Noted, but not located by Horsfield (*Sussex* 1 476-77).
2. Pendant with 140A.
3. Probably erected after the death of Mary Cooper in 1824.
4. In situ in 1905, see photograph in Livett (*SAC* 48 44).
5. M.I. part-transcribed by Butler (*SAC* 14 259).

Icklesham, 140C Burial marker for T[homas] C[OOPER], d. 1807

- Choir aisle floor, between the stalls, towards the East end.
- 64(W) x 61(L) — Cracked, worn.
- A freestone burial marker, head to East, marked 'T.C / 1807' on the South side.

1. Formerly in chancel - Butler (*SAC* 14 259).

Icklesham, 140D Ledger for Katherine ODIARNE, d. 1740

- Chancel floor, towards North side, between choir stalls and sanctuary, now partly covered by carpet.
- 80(W) x 185(L) — Worn.
- A pale cream freestone slab with M.I.; head to West.

Here lieth the Body of
KATHERINE the Wife of
Mʀ EDWARD ODIARNE
Who died July the 21ˢᵗ 1740
Aged 33 Years.
Likewise A Daughter still
Born 5 days before She Died
And also THOMAS yᵉ Son of
Mʀ EDWARD ODIARNE
and KATHERINE his Wife
Who died the 4ᵗʰ of Februarʸ
following Aged 2 Years
& 5 Months
Here also liethe Body of
EDWARD ODIARNE
Who departed this Life
April 21 1757 Aet 64

1. Note the recurrent bereavements sustained by Edward Odiarne before his own death 16 years later.
2. For licence to marry dated 26 Jul 1728 for Edward Odiarne, Gent., and Catherine Cadman, of Rye, see Dunkin (*Licences 1670-1729* 263).
3. In situ in 1862, see Butler (*SAC* 14 259) with transcription.
4. Noted in the rectorial chancel by Horsfield (*Sussex* 1 476-77).

Icklesham, 140E Floor monument for Rev. Thomas RICHARDS, d. 1843

- Chancel, floor, near sanctuary rail, now obscured by carpet.
- 91(W) x 68(L) — Condition unknown.
- M.I. cut in pale brown, freestone slab.
- M.I. recorded as:

Revᵈ THOMAS RICHARDS
DIED 6ᵗʰ DECEMBER 1843:
AGED 53 YEARS

1. Surveyed as reading 'd.1815', but transcribed as above in Butler (*SAC* 14 259).
2. NBI records burial of Thomas Richards on 14 Dec 1843 at Icklesham.

Icklesham, 140F Mural monument for Arnold NESBITT, d. 1779 [Plate 92]
- South chapel (St. Nicholas), South wall, at head height.
- 120(W) x c.240(H) — Good; recent careful repainting (arms).
- M.I. (9 lines, engraved, black) fills an unframed light grey marble tablet set portrait-wise; moulded entablature set above and breaking forward of grey-veined, flanking panels; below, a decorated black and white ledge, then, an ornamental black baseplate with rosettes, drops, heraldry in relief and a white corbel; above, 2 flaming urns flank a third urn draped with a delicate bead decorated against a tall black backplate in obelisk form; signed (on the urn base): 'J.Marten Sculp[r] / Tenterden'.
- Arnold Nesbitt, Esq., Lord of the Manor of Icklesham, MP for Winchelsea, merchant, etc., d. 7 Apr 1779, aet 57.

1. In situ - Horsfield (*Sussex* 1 476-77).
2. For the Manor chapel (St. Nicholas) see C.F. Trower, 'The Arundel Chancel Case' (*SAC* 30 39-40).
3. See Janet H. Stevenson, 'Arnold Nesbitt and the Borough of Winchelsea' (*SAC* 129 183-193) and her biography in *ODNB* with their accounts of Arnold Nesbitt's business interests and his attempts to preserve his parliamentary interest at Winchelsea against the incursions of the Earls of Egremont and Thomond; Arnold Nesbitt was in the political and social circle of Thrales, Johnson (see *Letters of Dr Johnson* ed Chapmen I, 310-11; II. 748), Goldsmith, Garrick and Reynolds (Henry Thrale was his brother-in-law) an energetic but sometimes incautious general merchant and financier who died insolvent; Arnold's uncle, Albert Nesbitt had started to buy lands in Sussex in the 1740s, probably with support from the Pelhams, to secure a parliamentary seat; the manor at Icklesham was purchased in 1760; Arnold Nesbitt established the first cambric factory in England at nearby Winchelsea in 1763; despite huge debts, there was sufficient in the estate to pay for funeral expenses and perhaps also for the monument; one John Nesbitt was still the major landowner at Icklesham in 1785 (R. Davey 123, with name spelled Nisbett).
4. 140F is cited by Gunnis (Dict. 257) as by Marten.
5. Located in situ in 1862 and 1927 with transcription by GS Butler (*SAC* 14 259) and with heraldry by Lambarde (*SAC* 68 229).

Icklesham Addition
Turner (*SAC* 23 166) notes:
(1) Brass for George Theobald, a lover of bells, d. 10 Mar 1641 (on slab in aisle).

(141) IDEN, All Saints
North aisle and arcade 14th century; North chapel 14th century, raised in 18th century; South aisle has gone - Nairn & Pevsner (544); for plan see *SNQ* (XV 199); condition of rector's chancel in 1724 reportedly fine, the other chancel [of Sir Christopher Pawle?] was poor (Ford); floor monuments must have been lost; 141A-B are modest local productions.

Iden, 141A Mural monument for Sarah BRIDGER, d. 1801
- Choir, North wall, high up.
- Inaccessible — Sound; very faded.
- M.I. in upper 60% of a white marble oval; raised moulded inner frame; painted black outer frame.

To the memory of
SARAH Wife of Mr
Wm BRIDGER of Lympne
in the County of Kent Gent
and Daughter of the Rev[d]
IOHN GOODWIN
by Mary his Wife
She died the 17th Dec
1801
in the 27th Year of her age

1. In situ - Horsfield (*Sussex* I 505).
2. Sarah Bridger was daughter of the rector (Church Guide), see 141B.

Iden, 141B Mural monument for Mary and John GOODWIN, d. 1795? and 1807?

- Choir, North wall, high up over sanctuary rail.
- Inaccessible — Sound; very faded; pigment lost.
- Description: as for 141A.

To the memory of
Mary wife of the Rev^d
JOHN GOODWIN M.A.
Rector of the Parish.
She died March 1795
in the Fifty Second Year of her Age
And alſo
to the memory of
the Revd JOHN GOODWIN
He died Feb. 13th 1807 [?]
in the Seventy Seventh
Year of his Age

1. In situ - Horsfield (*Sussex* I 505).
2. Pendant with 141A.
3. J Goodwin was rector of Playden, East Guildford and Iden in 1795 (Church Guide).
4. NBI records the burial of Mary Goodwin on 24 Mar 1795 at Iden.

Iden Addition

Horsfield (*Sussex* I 505) notes:
(1) M.I. to Richard Martin, rector of Iden, d. 1 Jan 1643, aet 62, within Communion Rail.

(143) IFORD, St. Nicholas

Mostly Norman, relatively unchanged - Nairn & Pevsner (544); plan *SNQ* (V 25); 1686 report of decayed paving and poor state of chancel floor (Ford 39); repaired by 1724 (Ford 135).

Iford, 143A Ledger stone for Samuel CARTER, d. 1708

- North chapel (or vestry) floor, obscured by furnishings.
- 89(W) x 181(L) — Pitted; worn; damaged edge (right).
- M.I. (engraved) in upper 50% of a freestone slab; set East-West.

Here Lyeth the
Body of Samvel
Carter who Departed
this Life the 30 day
of October in the
60 year of his age
1708

1. Cited but not located by Horsfield (*Sussex* I 199).
2. Vestry is modern on site of a 13th-century chapel.

Iford, 143B Mural monument for Richard and Mary HURLY, d. 1818 and d. 1828

- Chancel, South wall, at head height.
- 142(W) x 108(H) — Excellent.
- M.I. (engraved) on white marble panel, set landscape-wise; flanked by fluted Doric pilasters; below, a deep-moulded, pointed pediment containing a floral wreath; at foot,

base mouldings and 2 squared corbels; thin black baseplate; signed (lower centre): 'PARSONS.LEWES'.
- Richard Hurly d. 26 Sep 1818, aet 62; his wife, Mary, d. 23 Mar 1828, aet 68; issue - unnamed.

1. In situ - Horsfield (*Sussex* I 199) 'neat and white'.
2. Other monuments to the family are in the churchyard in the vicinity of the North door.
3. In 1785, one Richard Hurly occupied Mr Ade's farm at Iford (R. Davey 125); see licence to marry dated 22 May 1784 for Richard Hurly, of Iford, Gent., bachelor, age 25 plus and Mary Ridge, of Rottingdean, spinster, age 22 plus; the issue of Richard and Mary Hurly may include Lucy, age 21 in 1823, of Iford and Henry Hurly, of Iford, banker; for all see Dunkin & Penfold (*Licences* 231 & 122).

(145) ISFIELD, St. Margaret

The church is isolated from the village; Norman with 13th-century and Decorated additions (South chapel) - Nairn & Pevsner (545); plan *SNQ* VI 241; in 1724, the chancel needed repair (Ford 134); for views see BL Add. MS 5676 f.93; 5671 ff.96-7; 5673 f.66; Turner (*SAC* 23 167-8) transcribed the M.I.s; the Shurley monuments at Isfield rival West Firle as the most important post-Reformation ensemble in the county.

Isfield, 145A Wall monument for John SHURLEY, d. 1527
- Shurley (South) Chapel, South wall, to West of 145B.
- 153(W) x 119(H) — Fair; local losses.
- In freestone (Purbeck?) with brass panels; flat arch on attached columns with hexagonal shafts over a recess; within, a tomb-chest with flat top; tomb-chest front, decorated with diamond and blank arcade; brasses on back wall (one remaining); above, decoration of quatrefoils and lozenges.

> Here under lyeth the body of Mr John Shurley esquier sum tyme chefe [clerke]
> of the kechen to o[r] sovrayn Lord kyng henry the vii[th], and Cofferer to o[r] sovr
> ayn lord king henry ye viii whych john [de]cessid the iii day of august A[nno] M[vcxxvii]

1. 145A-D are in situ; Horsfield (*Sussex* I 372); the chapel furnishing is also early 16th century; 145A can perhaps be dated prior to 145B and C; 145A and B are positioned to allow direct visual access to the high altar via the squint; 145A is noted by Stephenson (511) and Nairn & Pevsner (545).
2. John Shurley, in a will dated 1 Mar 1527, leaves provision for a chalice to be bought for Rye church, in memory of the soul of his late wife Parnell and also bequests of lands at Winchelsea to be left to his second son William, see Rice & Godfrey (4 66 & 366) and requested his executors to have him buried under a 'Tomb of marbill there sett ... with pyctours prynted in plate and my arms therein shewed and stryken on the said Tombe', see Rice & Godfrey (3 46); John Shurley established the family at Isfield, buying into the estate, see Turner (*SAC* 18 128ff).
3. Davidson-Houston (*SAC* 78 97-98) transcribed the M.I. and notes damage to a corner of the brass giving a date 'mvcxxvi', however, Burrell (BL Add. MS 5697 f.259), gives 'mvcxxvii', which is probably correct.
4. John Shurley's issue - John, William, Edward, Joan, Bridget; his wives, first Margery, and second Parnell Grauntford, sister to John Goring.

Isfield, 145B Wall monument for Edward SHURLEY, d. 1558
- Shurley (South) Chapel, against South wall, to East of 145A.
- 185(W) x 186(H) — Fair; local losses (cresting).
- Larger than 145A and with a different design of column; surviving brasses include a M.I. (engraved; black-letter script) and 2 kneelers Edward Shurley (left), wife to right, child at foot of each; below, tomb-chest with lozenges & trefoil-topped panels; above, a frieze of quatrefoils.

Here lyeth Edwarde Shurley Esquyer ye sone of John Shurley of ye maner of Isfylde Esquyer and
Cofferer
to Kynge Henry ye Eyght & Johane his wyffe doughter to John Fenner
Esquyer wh. Edwarde dep[ar]tyd this
mortall lyfe ye xvi day of marche Anno mccccclviii & Johane his wyfe dep[ar]tyd ye ... day of [blank]
Ao Dni [blank] whose souls god p[ar]don & between them god sente them essue thre sones and one
daughter

1. 145B is in situ; Horsfield (*Sussex* I 372); Turner (*SAC* 18 129), in situ (noting brasses missing); Stephenson (511) noting issue; illustration of part of the brass representing Edward Shurley's wife Joanna, see Andre (*SAC* 42 14) and Davidson-Houston (*SAC* 78 98-99) noting that wife's death date never added; Nairn & Pevsner (545).
2. 145B and 145C are probably close in date, that is, after 1558, and left incomplete by heirs of Joane (who d. pre-1569).
3. Edward Shurley wears armour of an ancient design; he was third son and heir of John Shurley (see 145A); his wife was Joan(e) daughter of John Fenner, Esq.; in his will dated 4 Aug 1557, Edward Shurley seeks burial in the chapel near his father; no mention of a tomb in Rice & Godfrey (3 46); patron of 145B likely to have been heir Thomas, who died at Lewes 1579 (his wife having died at Isfield in 1571); Joan(e) Shurley subsequently married Anthony Morley, of Glynde; she died pre 1569.
4. Until 1779, the base of 145B was formed by the black limestone graveslab, of Norman date, commemorating Gundreda, daughter of William the Conqueror, foundress of St Pancras Priory, Lewes, which was already at Isfield by 1550, was identified there by Rev William Baker, removed to Lewes by Sir William Burrell in 1774 and installed in 1884/5 at St John the Baptist, Southover (*English Romanesque Art 1066-1200*, Arts Council exhibition catalogue 1984 181).

Isfield, 145C Wall monument for Thomas SHURLEY, d. 1579, and his wife, d. 1571 [Plate 93]

- Shurley (South) chapel, against East wall.
- 185(W) x 248(H); brass figures 70(H) — Good; colour.
- In painted freestone; niche; brasses on back wall; flanking, Doric columns with cable-fluted touch shafts; in frieze, adapted gadroon ornament; above, pointed pediment, escutcheon and angled dentils; in brass, 2 large kneelers, 3 escutcheons and a M.I.

HERE LYETH BVRYED THE BODIE OF THOMAS SHVRLEY OF
ISFILD IN THE COVNTIE OF SVSSEX ESQ ELDEST SONE VNTO
EDWARD SHVRLEY OF ISFILD AFORESAYD ESQ AND THE BO
DIE OF ANNE HIS WIFE DAVGHTER VNTO SIR NICHOLAS PELHAM
OF LAVGHTON IN THE COVNTIE AFORESAYD KNIGHT BY ANN
HIS WIFE SISTER VNTO SᴿRICHARD SACKEVILL KNIGHT
THE WᶜʰANNE WIFE VNTO THE SAYD THOMAS SHVRLEY DEPAR
TED THIS MORTALL LIFE AT THE MANOR HOVSE OF ISFILD
THE SIXTHE DAYE OF APRILL IN THE YEERE OF OUR LORDE
1571 AND THE FORESAYD THOMAS SHVRLEY DEPARTED THIS
MORTALL LIFE AT THE TOWNE OF LEWIS IN THE COVNTIE
AFORESAYD VPON THE XVIIIᵀʰ DAYE OF JANVARYE OF THE
YEERE OF Oᴿ LORD 1579 AND IN THE XXIᵀʰ YERE OF YE RAIGNE
OF OVR SOVERAYGNE LADIE QUEENE ELIZABETH.

1. In situ; Horsfield (*Sussex* I 372); noted by Stephenson (511); Turner (*SAC* 18 129); Lambarde (*SAC* 70 159) – noting arms, dating error; Davidson-Houston (*SAC* 78 99-100) – with illustration and transcription; Nairn & Pevsner (545).
2. Thomas Shurley was first son of Edward Shurley (see 145B); IPM for Thomas Shurley notes that his son and heir is John, age 10, see Salzman (*Inquisitions* 132ff).
3. 145C was added to the East wall of the chapel after 145A-B (South wall); it partly blocked the mediaeval window; the heraldic crest (stag's head) is even more prominent here than on 145D; the architectural frame exploits a rustic version of Renaissance forms, e.g. the flat Doric column, the dentils and the frieze.
4. NBI records the burial of Thomas Shurlye on 19 Jan 1579 and Annys Shurlye on 11 Apr 1571, both at Isfield.

Isfield, 145D Wall monument for Sir John SHURLEY, d. 1631, and his two wives [Plate 94]

- Shurley (South) chapel, North wall.
- 240(W) x more than 400(H) — Good.
- High in quality; using black, white and coloured marbles and alabasters; heraldic colour and gilt; all on a raised basement; semi-circular arch over high tomb-chest; 3 recumbent effigies, heads to the right, John Shurley between two wives; on face of tomb-chest, kneeling children face left (names over); arch on black column shafts and Corinthian capitals; high pedestals; behind, on back wall, M.I. (gilt, engraved); arch coffering of cherubim; on top, more cherubs, achievements, escutcheons and allegorical figures (Charity to right).
- Sir John Shurley, Knt, of Isfield, J.P., D.L., Coram [Sheriff] of Sussex; died Lewes, 25 Apr 1631; his first wife, [Jane], daughter of Sir Thomas Shirley, of Wiston, Sussex.; issue - 2 sons; Thomas [with skull] and John [with skull]; 7 daughters; Anne [with skull], Jane, Cicilie, Elizabeth, Charity, Hannah [with skull] and Mary; his second wife, [Dorothy], daughter of George Goring, of Danny; also, her nephew Lord Goring; her first husband, Sir Henry Bowyer, of Cuckfield; John Shurley's fame, magnanimity, justice and stout performance, in good causes; Dorothy Shurley's charity, generosity, sympathy, piety and devotion.

1. In situ; Horsfield (*Sussex* I 372) with engraved view; Turner (*SAC* 18 129-30) – engraved view; Mosse (122-3); Esdaile (*ECM* 103 & 133); Nairn & Pevsner (545) noting the dull faces; Lambarde (*SAC* 70 159) noting arms.
2. Final lines of M.I. must postdate 1631; text of M.I. suggests that the patron of 145D, but not author of the M.I., was John Shurley's second wife Dorothy Goring.
3. The manor was bequeathed to Robert Shurley, first son of John Shurley's younger brother, Sir George Shurley (1569-1647), also buried at Isfield (North chancel).
4. 145D is the most ambitious of the four Shurley monuments at Isfield, the arrangement of which in an increasingly crowded South chapel never blocked the squint, although it is unclear why the issue kneel facing West, not towards the high altar.
5. 145D is attributed to William Wright (living 1607, d. 1654) on grounds of similarity of the kneeling daughters to documented works by Wright (White 147).
6. JH notes that Sir John Shurley was MP for East Grinstead 1593, Steyning 1597, Bramber 1604 and Sussex 1625; and Sheriff of Surrey and Sussex 1616 (Hasler 3 378). Family details from Comber (*Lewes* 253-4) identify that John d. an infant (24 Oct 1611); Anne was wife of Sir Giles Overbury; Jane was wife of Sir Walter Covert, then of John Freake and then of Denzel, Lord Holles; Cicilie was wife of Sir William Somerville; Elizabeth was wife of Sir Thomas Palmer; Charity was wife of James Rivers; Hannah d. an infant; Mary was wife of John D'Oyley; Also Jane (first wife) d. 1605 and Dorothy (second wife) d. 1640.

Isfield, 145E Mural monument for Rev. Edward RAYNES, d. 1755, his wife Ann, d. 1787, and descendants

- Tower, South wall, above head height.
- c.95(W) x c.200(H) — Fine.
- In grey mottled marble; recessed pilasters flank a M.I. (14 lines + 8 lines) fills a panel; above, blank pointed pediment; below, curved apron and scrolled corbels.
- Rev. Edward Raynes, M.A., rector of Isfield and Hangleton, d. 16 Apr 1755, aet 44; his wife Ann, d. 21 Aug 1787, aet 74, third daughter of James Chambers, Esq., of Seaford; issue - eldest son, Edward, d. 10 Apr 1751, aet 5; second son, William, ecclesiastical registrar, d. 16 Nov 1787, aet 39; youngest son, Edward Robert, archdeacon of Lewes, d. 22 Jan 1824, aet 71, his wife, Harriot, daughter of Rev. Thomas Porter, rector of East Hoathly, d. 19 Apr 1806, aet 54; their issue - Mary Ann, d. 5 Nov 1800, aet 14.

1. Formerly on chancel North wall - Horsfield (*Sussex* I 373).
2. Standard type; good quality; final lines added to M.I.; perhaps erected after the deaths of Edward Raynes' widow and second son in 1787; a later Edward Raynes was a clergyman at East Hoathly - licence to marry 1826, see Dunkin & Penfold (*Licences* 350).

Isfield Additions
Horsfield (*Sussex* I 373).
(1) In chancel, under altar, ledger to Sir George Shurley, d. 15 Oct 1647, brother of Sir John (see 145D): 'Here lyeth the body of the honorable Sir George Shurley, Knight, Lord Chiefe Justice of the Chiefe Pleas of Ireland and one of the Privy Councillors there under the late King James and King Charles for 28 years. he was born at Isfield, 1569, and died the fifteenth of October 1647'.

(147) JEVINGTON, St. Andrew
Saxon; Early English North aisle - Nairn & Pevsner (546); church reported to be in fine condition in 1686 and 1724 (Ford 51; 175), when the patron was Sir George Parker (see 297D); Horsfield (*Sussex* I 288) notes many slabs in the chancel; monuments at Jevington are mostly to former residents of Wannock, a house in the parish.

Jevington, 147A A wall-mounted brass fragment commemorating Elizabeth [?MARWICK], d. 1608
- Choir, South wall, 1 of 3 (upper), on wooden blocks.
- 21(W) x 15.5(H) — Fragmentary; damaged (left side).
- M.I. (4 lines, engraved) on a brass plate.
- Elizabeth, d. [9] Apr 1608, wife of John [Marwick], of Wannock.

1. Sometimes reported lost; formerly floor-mounted in sanctuary/chancel see Horsfield (*Sussex* I 288); Turner (*SAC* 23 168); Davidson-Houston (*SAC* 78 101) using Burrell (BL Add. MS 5697 f.253r); Stephenson (511) with uncertain identification.
2. 147A probably commemorates a Marwick of nearby Wannock.
3. Date of death (9 March) was formerly visible.

Jevington, 147B A wall-mounted brass for William MARKWICK, d. 1699
- Choir, South wall, 1 of 3 (centre), on wooden blocks.
- 44.5(W) x 19.5(H) — Very good.
- M.I. (5 lines, engraved) on a brass plate.
- William Markwick, d. 20 Apr 1699, aet 38, youngest son of William Markwick, Esq., of Wannock.

1. Formerly floor-mounted in sanctuary; Horsfield (*Sussex* I 288), Turner (*SAC* 23 168), Davidson-Houston (*SAC* 78 100) with illustration and transcription, and Stephenson (511).

Jevington, 147C A wall-mounted brass for Thomas MARKWICK, d. 1610
- Choir, South wall, 1 of 3 (lower), on a brass plate, then on wood.
- 40(W) x 10(H) — Fragmentary.
- M.I. (3 lines) on an irregular brass plate, other (later) lettering showing through.
- Thomas Marckwycke, of Wannock, buried 9 Mar 1610.

1. Formerly floor-mounted in sanctuary; Horsfield (*Sussex* I 288), Turner (*SAC* 23 168), Stephenson (511), Davidson-Houston (*SAC* 78 100) with illustration and transcription.

Jevington, 147D Mural monument for Charles ROCHESTER, d. 1758 [Plate 95]
- Choir, South wall, at head height.
- 150(W) x 285(H) — Excellent; no colour.
- In grey, white and patterned marbles; male & female portrait reliefs in a framed roundel, with scrolled side and a curved top; above, in half relief, an urn flanked by flaming torches;

below, base mouldings and a sarcophagus on clawed feet, with egg-and-dart and a M.I. on a panel; below, a decorative marble border; then an apron with an escutcheon in a Baroque frame.
- Charles Rochester, Esq., d. 20 Nov 1758, aet 55; his wife, Leonora, d. 3 Mar 1756, aet 48, third daughter of Charles Eversfield, Esq., of Denn, Sussex.

1. Formerly on a pillar in the nave - Horsfield (*Sussex* I 288), perhaps on chancel North wall - Lambarde (*SAC* 70 142) noting arms; also noted by Nairn & Pevsner (546); perhaps erected in c.1760.
2. The composition is very unusual, note the large scale of the torches and the juxtaposition of the portraits, which perhaps derives distantly from Cheere's monument to Sir Edmund Prideaux at Westminster Abbey, see Physick (124-5).

Jevington, 147E Mural monument for Robert ROCHESTER, d. 1725, and members of his family
- Choir, North wall, at head height.
- 101(W) x 184(H) — Excellent; colour mostly lost.
- Fluted Doric pilasters carry a broken, pointed pediment enclosing an achievement; in the centre; M.I. (27 lines, engraved, centred, black) in several stages; below, thick, darker grey base moulding and scrolly corbels; between them a delicate cherub in low relief.
- Robert Rochester, Esq., of Wannock, d. 15 Aug 1725, aet 51; his wife, Jane, d. 21 Mar 1747, aet 69, second daughter of Nicholas Eversfield, Charleton, Steyning; their issue – second son, William, d. 16 Sep 1740, aet 35, and William's only son, also Robert, d. 26 Sep 1739, aet 10; and the youngest son, another Robert, d. 31 Mar 1738, aet 26, buried St. George the Martyr, Queen Square, London.

1. In situ - Horsfield (*Sussex* I 288); Lambarde (*SAC* 70 146) noting arms.
2. Patron was the widow Jane Rochester.
3. Final lines added later.
4. 1747 is TAQ for 147E; for a licence to marry dated 3 May 1701 for Robert Rochester, of Selmeston, bachelor, and Jane Eversfield, of Eastbourne, see Dunkin (*Licences 1670-1729* 184).

Jevington, 147F A cartouche for John MANNINGHAM, d. 1751, and Thomas
[Plate 96]
- Choir, North wall, below 147E.
- 55(W) x 75(H) — Excellent; fading.
- M.I. (8 lines, engraved, centred, black) on convex cartouche; elegant scrolled frame; shell decorations top and bottom.
- John Manningham and Thomas Manningham, no dates.

1. Formerly on South wall - Horsfield (*Sussex* I 288).
2. High quality of the decorative carving.
3. In the churchyard (South-East of the church), there is a monument for these brothers [95(W) x 95(D) x 210(H)]; John Mannington d. 8 Apr 1751, aet 23 and Thomas, died an infant; their parents were Dr Manningham, the rector [Simon] and his wife Elizabeth.

Jevington, 147G Mural monument for Nathaniel COLLIER, d. 1691/2
- Choir, North wall, East side, North-East corner.
- 41(W) x 40(H) — Fine; dirty.
- M.I. (8 lines) scratched on slate; no frame or decoration.
- Nathaniel Collier, M.A., rector of Jevington, d. 1 Mar 1691/2.

1. Perhaps formerly floor-mounted and below 147F - Horsfield (*Sussex* I 288).
2. Collier was perhaps a non-juror [?].
3. JH notes that Nathaniel Collier was rector of Jevington 1690-2.

(148) KEYMER, St. Cosmas & St. Damian

Apse Norman, remainder 1866-90 - Nairn & Pevsner (546-7); tower rebuilt 1864; for a South-East view see Godfrey & Salzman (Pl. 89); condition reported as fine in 1724 (Ford 126); in part, an estate church for nearby Ockley park, held by the Luxfords in the late 17th century, although the lords of Ockley also buried at Clayton; 148 A-B are in the bell-tower, adjacent to the Ockley Vault.

Keymer, 148A Wall monument for members of the WOOD family, d. 1757 etc.

- Bell-tower, South wall, high.
- c.215(W) x c.155(H) — Locally poor (frame).
- A large freestone frame; straight cornice and base mouldings; M.I. on grey rectangular marble tablet (engraved, black) in 2 columns, left filled, right 50%.
- James Wood, called Jnr, buried 25 Jul 1757; James Wood, buried 17 Oct 1759; Mary Wood, buried 6 Aug 1826, aet 19; and further members of the Wood and Packham family.

1. Perhaps a retrospective commemoration of Wood ancestors using the parish records for burials, or a later project summarising information from memorials removed during the restoration.
2. James Wood of Ockley Park was churchwarden for over 20 years (Church Guide); Rev. John Wood owned Ockley in 1785 (R. Davey 127).
3. Not noted by Horsfield (*Sussex* I 242).

Keymer, 148B Wall monument for John WOOD, d. 1818

- Bell-tower, North wall, very high.
- 76(W) x 59(H) — Fine; faded.
- M.I. (10 lines, engraved, black) on unframed rectangular grey marble tablet; on a black rectangular baseplate; unsigned.
- John Wood, Esq., of Ockley Manor, Keymer, d. 29 Sep 1818, aet 46; his widow, Catherine, d. 2 May 1855, aet 82.

1. Unsigned but Parsons-like.
2. For licence to marry dated 30 Nov 1799 for John Wood, of Keymer, Gent., bachelor, age 25 plus and Catherine Hodson, of Westminster, spinster, age 25 plus, see Dunkin & Penfold (*Licences* 476).
3. Not noted by Horsfield (*Sussex* I 242).

Keymer Addition

Cited by Horsfield (*Sussex* I 242):
(1) John Luxford, Gent., son of John and Mary Luxford, Esq., d. 22 Nov 1679.
(2) Ann Plumer, d. 17 May 1704, aet 47, wife of John Plumer, perhaps the slab immediately by the external West door of the present building.

(149) KINGSTON near LEWES - no monuments found

(153) LAUGHTON, All Saints

A 13th-century nave - Nairn & Pevsner (548-9); the state of church repair was reportedly fine in 1686 and in 1724 (Ford 52, 176); however, the Pelhams rebuilt the chancel (in Gothick style) from 1765 to cover their family vault - will extracts in Rice & Godfrey (3 82) and S. Berry (*SAC* 142 107-13) refers to financial accounts, architectural elevations and plans at ESRO; the chancel was rebuilt by John Morris of Lewes in a modest Gothic manner, avoiding orientalist or Rococo mannerisms and the Pelham ledgers (153D-F), with their handsome lettering, were relocated; the nave ledgers are perhaps still in original positions amongst restored flooring; Horsfield (*Sussex* I 352) noted that 40 members of the Pelham family had been buried at Laughton, but not Nicholas Pelham (see 160D); Laughton was the ancient burial place of the Pelhams (see their buckle-stop device on the Perpendicular tower); they developed a property at Halland rather than at Laughton perhaps because the site was unhealthy (Farrant 255); the Pelhams held the benefice from temp Charles I and owned property on Lewes High Street before moving their seat to Stanmer early in the 18th century.

Laughton, 153A Ledger for Dinah BENGE, d. 1721.
- Centre of nave floor, at West end.
- 94(W) x 184(L) — Worn.
- M.I. (5 lines) at West end of a freestone slab; head to West.

> Here Lyes ye Body
> of DINAH wife of W[M] BENGE
> [G]ent: late of Wadhurst.
> who died 7ber 14 1721 Aged
> 63 Years.

1. '7ber' = 'September'.
2. The Benges were iron founders but chose to be commemorated by an engraved stone.
3. NBI records the burial of Dinah Benge on 19 Sep 1721 at Laughton.

Laughton, 153B Ledger for William H[enry] B[ENG]E, d. 1735
- Centre of nave floor, towards West end.
- 96(W) x 200(L) — Very worn.
- M.I. (6 lines) at West end of a Horsham stone slab; head to West.

> To the Memory
> of WILLIAM H[ENRY] B[ENGE]
> Late of the Parish of
> WADHURST in this C[ounty] Gent
> who depar[t]ed this Life
> May y[e] 16[th] 1735 Aged 43[?] Years.

1. For Benge's mother [?], see 153A.
2. For licence to marry dated 3 Nov 1720 for William Henry Benge, of Wadhurst, Gent. and Elizabeth Turk, of Ticehurst, see Dunkin (*Licences 1670-1729* 230).

Laughton, 153C Ledger for Henry BILL, d. 1685/6
- Centre of nave floor.
- 85(W) x 200(L) — Worn but legible.
- M.I. (11 lines) on the upper part of a black slab; head to West.
- Henry Bill, d. 20 Jan 1685/6, aet 89, youngest son of John Bill, Gent., late of Blackfriars, London; his wife, Jane, eldest daughter of Henry Courthorpe, Gent., of Cranbrooke, Kent; issue – John, Henry, Anthony, Nisell and Jane.

1. It is unclear why Bill was commemorated at Laughton.
2. Uncertain cutting of final letters.

Laughton, 153D Ledger for Sir John PELHAM, Bart., d. 1702/3
- Sanctuary floor, towards North side, partly obscured by furnishings.
- 98(W) x 155(L) — Very good.
- M.I. (engraved) in upper parts of a black slab (slate?); head to West.
- Sir John Pelham, Bart., d. 18 Jan 1702, aet c. 77; issue - Thomas, Henry, Lucy, etc.

1. John Pelham had promised to repair the chancel as early as 1675, see Johnstone (23), but see above.
2. 153D is noted for M.I. and heraldry in Lambarde (*SAC* 70 155).
3. Close in date to 153F but note variants in lettering.
4. JH notes that Sir John Pelham was MP for Hastings 1645, and for Sussex in various parliaments between 1654-95 (Henning 3 218-9).

Laughton, 153E Ledger for Elizabeth PELHAM, d. 1681
- Sanctuary floor, centre, mostly obscured by furnishings.
- 110(W); length unknown — Very good.
- M.I. (engraved) in upper parts of a black slab (slate?); head to West.
- Elizabeth, first wife of Thomas Pelham; daughter of Sir William Jones, of Gray's Inn.

1. Heraldry noted in Lambarde (*SAC* 70 155), with date of death as 7 Oct 1681.
2. See also 153D and E.

Laughton, 153F Ledger for Lady Grace PELHAM, d. 1700.
- Sanctuary floor, on South side, partly obscured by furnishings.
- 98(W) x 188(L) — Very good.
- M.I. (engraved) in upper parts of a black slab (slate?); head to West.
- Grace Pelham, d. 13 Sep 1700; daughter of Gilbert, Earl of Clare; and second wife of Thomas Pelham; issue - Thomas, Henry, Grace, Fra[ncis], Mary, Gertrude, Lucy, Margaret.

1. Heraldry noted in Lambarde (*SAC* 70 155).
2. Close in date to 153D but variants in lettering.
3. See also 153E.

(156) LEWES, All Saints

Condition reported as fine in 1724 (Ford 121) when there were c.54 families in the parish, the population of which was 1196 in 1801; the nave and chancel of mediaeval church rebuilt in brick in classical style by Amon Wilds, 1806-7 and reconsecrated on 1 Sep 1807 - Horsfield (*Lewes* I 284) and Nairn & Pevsner (551); East end added in 1883; now redundant, and monuments were preserved and relocated when the building was converted into an arts centre.

Lewes, 156A Vault marker for William DURRANT
- Nave floor, centre, West end, now the staircase lobby.
- 181(W) x 82(L) — Fine, worn.
- M.I. (engraved) in freestone slab; head to East.

ENTRANCE OF
MR DURRRANT'S VAULT

1. For William Durrant's monument see 156J.
2. He was Headborough for Lewes in 1729-30 (Smith 27).

Lewes, 156B Floor slab for William and Mary ROASE, d. 1756 and d. 1765, and others
- Nave floor, West end, now hall lobby.
- 81(W) x 172(H) — Cracked, worn (edges).
- M.I. (13 + 4 + 4 lines, engraved, black) fills 90% of surface of a grey marble slab; head to East.
- William Roase, ironmonger and merchant, d. 4 Sep 1756, aet 47; his wife, Mary, d. 23 May 1765, aet 64, daughter of Isaaca and Jane Guipin; their daughter, Mary, d. 18 Jul 1742, aet 2; his mother, Mary Bywater, d. 9 Oct 1753, aet 72; his nephew, Peter Roase, d. 1 Nov 1738, aet 28.

1. For the lettering style of 156B c.f. 156D-E & J.
2. Probably datable to 1760s.
3. William Roase took Richard Comber, son of Mary Comber, as an apprentice, on 24 Jun 1749, see Rice (45).

Lewes, 156C Mural monument for Thomas and Anne WOOLLGAR, d. 1821 and d. 1815

- Nave, North wall, above head height, alongside other Woolgar monuments.
- 94(W) x 55(H) — Very good; local losses (cornice).
- M.I. (17 lines, Latin, engraved, black), on tablet set landscape-wise with a moulded edge, in grey marble, a straight cornice and dropped lower edges left and right.
- Thomas Woollgar, 1761 - 1821; his wife Anne, 1762 - 1815; married 1794; buried St. John Baptist, Southover; issue – unnamed.

1. Thomas Woollgar held town positions 1797-1813 (Smith 101); note the licence to marry dated 18 Aug 1794 for Thomas Woollgar, of St. Michael, Lewes, mercer, bachelor, age 32 plus and Ann Webb of Southease, spinster, age 30, see Dunkin & Penfold (*Licences* 480).
2. One of the patrons of 156C - 'J.W.W' - appears to have been John Webb Woollgar (d.1851), commemorated by a replica tablet below and described as Gent. of All Saints; aged 21 he was licensed on 19 Jun 1822 to marry Sarah Jenner, of the same, spinster, age 21 plus, see Dunkin & Penfold (*Licences* 480) and was acknowledged by Horsfield (*Lewes* I, 330-31) for allowing access to the valuable MSS of his father, a businessman who retired to pursue literary and scientific pursuits.
3. Thomas Woollgar was buried at Southover but the monument erected at All Saints, his parish of residence.

Lewes, 156D Mural monument for Nathanael and Mary TRAYTON, d. 1714/5 and 1707, and others

- Nave, North wall, alongside and East of 156C, at head height.
- 94(W) x 141(H) — Dirty but fine.
- In grey marbles, a tablet set portrait-wise with a stepped, arched top; M.I. (engraved, black) fills tablet; a large moulded and angled frame on 3 sides; below, a decorated baseplate with a Baroque escutcheon.
- Nathanael Trayton, Esq., d. 18 Mar 1714/5, aet 51; his wife, Mary, d. 21 Oct 1707, aet 37; their eldest son, Edward Trayton, Esq., d. 14 Mar 1761, aet 68; Edward's wife, Frances, d. 20 Apr 1728, aet 30, daughter of Richard Bridger, Esq., of Combe.

1. A replica of 156J.
2. In situ in 1930 when heraldry was noted - Lambarde (*SAC* 71 134).
3. For Bridger of Combe see 120B and J.

Lewes, 156E Mural monument for Sarah TRAYTON, d. 1724

- Nave, North wall, towards East end, at head height.
- 77(W) x 91(H) — Very good.
- M.I. (engraved, black) fills a grey marble, oval tablet; rectangular decorated frame with 2 cherubs and ferns.
- Sarah Trayton, d. 9 May 1724, aet 50, buried at Pinnar, Middlesex, second wife of Nathanael Trayton; son in law, Edward Trayton, Esq.

1. For Nathanael Trayton, see 156D; Sarah Trayton's step-son, Edward Trayton, was the patron (referring to himself as son-in-law).

Lewes, 156F Mural monument for John and Jane STANSFEILD, d. 1626/7 and d. 1650

- Nave, South wall, fragments 1-3 are towards East end, at head height; fragments 4-6, in hall entrance lobby.
- M.I. tablet: 61(W) x 40(H); Kneeling figures: 72(H) — Now dispersed: some parts fine (tablet); others, cracked and heavily restored (figures); colour visible on heraldry and costume.
- Elements remaining are: (1) M.I. (engraved) on a black (slate?) panel with cornice and simple base moulding; (2) a pair of adult kneelers on modern shelves, hands clasped in prayer, in civil dress; (3) an achievement-of-arms, in relief; (4, 5 & 6) one heraldic

supporter and two damaged kneeling figures (children?).
- John Stansfeild, Gent., of Cliffe, Lewes, d. 23 Feb 1626/7; his wife, Jane, d. 10 Dec 1650; charitable bequests.

1. John Stansfeild acted as Headborough 1581-2, see Salzman (*Lewes Town Book* 28); one John Stamfelde of Clive (Cliff) merchant and Ellinor Comber of St. John sub Castro were licensed to marry 20 Mar 1598, see Dunkin (*Licences 1586-1643* 28).
2. In its current state, the M.I. does not mention John Stansfeild's issue [from his first wife ?] evidenced by the dispersed figures of children, which some, e.g. Nairn & Pevsner (551) have confused with elements from the Hassard monument (see Additions).
3. Famously, the diarist John Evelyn was John Stansfeild's grandson and noted the piety of his funeral and the fact that his second wife erected a monument for him (*SNQ* 3 58).
4. The charitable bequest (noted also in Mosse 126-7) refers to South Malling church (239) which John Stansfeild bought from Sir Thomas Sackville in 1623, see Hills, 'The correspondence of John Collier ...' (*SAC* 64 78-9), founding a new church there in 1626, consecrated in 1632; Jane Stansfeild gave plate to South Malling church in 1628, see Couchman (*SAC* 54 232) and later married William Newton and lived at Southover Grange with young John Evelyn.
5. 156F was drawn by Grimm for Burrell (BL Add. MS 5672 f.11R and *SNQ* VII 1-2 with transcription of M.I.).
6. Dismembered during 1806 rebuilding, the tablet with M.I. and arms, also noted in Lambarde (*SAC* 71 134) remained in situ and kneelers removed to the tower, replaced by 1938, but subsequently removed again.

Lewes, 156G Mural monument for Charles and Mary BLUNT, d. 1747 and d. 1765
- Nave, South wall, centre, at head height.
- 61(W) x 162(H) — Fine.
- M.I. (engraved, black) in upper 60% of an unframed white oval marble panel; on a thin black backplate in obelisk form; above, an escutcheon. on ribbons; below, a base moulding and a grey ornamental baseplate.
- Charles Blunt, Esq., d. 18 Jun 1747, aet 47, second son of Sir John Blunt, Bart., of Essex; his wife, Mary, d. 12 Dec 1765, aet 68, youngest daughter of Peter Short, Esq., of Tenterden, Kent; his son, Peter, died an infant; [his sister-in-law ?], Jane Short, d. Jan 1711, aet 22.

1. Charles Blunt was a trustee in Nov 1742 for a project to establish an isolation clinic at All Saints (Smith 34).
2. For heraldry, see Lambarde (*SAC* 71 135).

Lewes, 156H Mural monument for Samuel ISTED, d. 1745 [Plate 97]
- Nave, South wall, West of 1561G, at head height.
- 94(W) x 160(H) — Remains are very good; losses (foot).
- Damaged in a relocation (?); very large M.I. (10 lines, engraved, black) on a grey-veined marble panel, now set portrait-wise, angled on 3 sides, with a moulded frame; achievement-of-arms; lower edge with curved ornament.
- Samuel Isted, Gent., lawyer, d. 21 Oct 1745, aet 73.

1. The large size of the lettering is unusual.
2. The condition too good to suggest that 156H was ever on the floor.
3. In situ in 1930 when heraldry noted - Lambarde (*SAC* 71 135).

Lewes, 156I Floor slab for Rev. John and Elizabeth STUDLEY, d. 1726 and d. 1738
- Nave floor, South side, West end.
- 100(W) x 178(L) — Very worn; cracks (West end).
- M.I. (engraved, his Latin, hers English) on a black slab; escutcheon in low relief; head to

East.
- Rev. John Studley, Gent., d. 25 Sep 1726; his wife, Elizabeth, d. 9 Aug 1738, aet 56.

1. Patron of 156I was widow, Elizabeth Studley.
2. One John Studley, of Lewes, Gent. [father?], stood surety in May 1678, see Dunkin (*Licences 1670-1729* 49).
3. In situ and heraldry noted - Lambarde (*SAC* 71 134).
4. JH notes that there is no trace of this John Studley as a clergyman in Hennessy or CCEd. Not in Foster Al. Ox., or Venn.
5. NL adds that John Studley's gentle status perhaps meant that he never took an incumbency.

Lewes, 156J Mural monument for William and Barbara DURRANT, d. 1751 and d. 1750, and family

- Nave, South wall, near West end (now a lobby), at head height.
- 94(W) x 140(H) — Fine, local losses, fading.
- Description as for 156D; M.I. (8 + 7 lines).
- William Durrant, Gent., d. 7 Dec 1751, aet 59; his wife, Barbara, d. 8 Sep 1750, aet 64; their son, Samuel Durrant, Esq., d. 21 Dec 1782, aet 65; their daughter-in-law, Sarah, d. 18 Aug 1787, aet 73, daughter of William and Mary Constable, Esq., of Burwash.

1. Replica of 156D.
2. Perhaps erected in the 1780s by the later Durrants, by then claiming the rank of Esquire.
3. The Constables of Burwash are commemorated (45M) by a monument by Parsons.
4. 156J was in situ in 1930, see Lambarde (*SAC* 71 135) noting arms.

Lewes, All Saints Additions

From Burrell MS in Phillips (*SAC* 38 125):
(1) Thomas Pellatt, Esq., d. 11 Jun 1680; also Grace, d. 13 Jan 1710, daughter of Apsley Newton, of Southover, wife of William Pellatt, d. 18 May 1725, aet 60, son of Thomas (slab at end of North aisle).
Lambarde (*SAC* 71 135) and *SNQ* (3 58), after coloured illustration in Burrell MS:
(2) Robert Hazzard, of Carshalton, d. 1 Sep 1624, aet 45, squire of the body and jewel house officer to James I; second son of another Robert Hazzard, of Lyme Regis, Dorset; husband of Anne, second daughter of Philip Moys, of Cannons, Banstead, Surrey; issue - Robert, Edm, John, Elizabeth, Albertus, Charles and Margaret; patron Anne Hazzard, then aet 41; monument dated 30 May 1625, drawn by Grimm in 1788 (BL Add. MS 5672 at the foot of f.11R; seen as fragments, at West end of South aisle); noted also by Nairn & Pevsner (551) and Mosse (125-6); why was Robert Hazzard buried at Lewes? Also two hatchments in church. Both unidentified. See Summers (147).
(3) Arms of Spencer/Johnson/Woodroffe.
(4) Arms of Warner/Freville/Hartford.

(157) LEWES, St. Anne

A long, narrow, Norman nave; chancel is Early English, restored in 1889 - Godfrey (*SAC* 69 159-69); South arcade late 12th century; a 18th-century West gallery - Nairn & Pevsner (551-2); fabric was 'fine' in 1724, the chancel having been repaired by the rector (Ford); for a view from North-East see Godfrey & Salzman (Pl. 96); the original dedication of this church - at Lewes 'Westout' - was to St. Mary; it was renamed in the 16th century (*SAC* 131 201); there were c.50 families in the parish in 1724; the population was 590 in 1801; 157N-O have been brought within the building by means of a 19th-century extension, see Godfrey in (*SAC* 68 284); there is an important series of mural monuments between the windows of the North aisle.

Lewes, 157A Mural monument for the LEWIS family, erected after 1825 [Plate 98]

- Nave, North wall, above North door, high.
- c.120(W); (H) unknown — Good.
- A white marble tablet on black marble composite baseplate with M.I.; mouldings top and bottom on 2 corbels with acanthus decoration; above, a female figure kneels at an altar with a rose dropping from a bowl; at top, a cornice, pointed pediment with palmettes flanking and an exhortation.
- Thomas Lewis, Esq., d. Paris 10 Mar 1822, aet 63; his wife, Anna Maria, died at Brighton 24 Jul 1849, aet 79; their issue - eldest daughter, Anna, d. 7 Mar 1826, aet 33; second daughter, Lucy Frances, died at Paris, 5 Jun 1825, aet 30, wife of Thomas Finimore Hill, Esq.; son, Charles Goring Lewis, Esq. and his wife, Elizabeth Jane; their issue, eldest son, Charles Wells, d. 3 Apr 1842, aet 12; and Emma, died at Brighton, 5 Feb 1857, aet 54.

1. The deaths of family members at Brighton and at Paris and the presence of 157A here is perhaps a sign of the fashionable status of Lewes and this church especially in the 1820s.

Lewes, 157B Mural monument for Henry SHELLEY, d. 1805, and family

- Nave, North wall, to East of North door, high up.
- c.105(W); (H) unknown — Very good.
- Pendant to 157C; M.I. (26 lines, engraved, black) on grey marble tablet, set portrait-wise with cornice and base moulding; below, a decorated apron in a dark shelly stone with an escutcheon.
- Henry Shelley, d. 3 Jan 1805, aet 77, eldest son of another Henry Shelley, Esq. and Eleanor; his widow, Philadelphia d. 7 May 1819, aet 81; their eldest son, Henry, d. 31 Dec 1811, aet 44; their second son, Thomas, d. 14 Feb 1780, aet 9; their eldest daughter, Philadelphia, 18 Feb 1818, aet 53; their second daughter, Elizabeth, d. 29 May 1840, aet 75; their third daughter, Cordelia, d. 21 Sep 1768, aet 6 months; and their fourth (and third surviving) daughter, Cordelia, d. 3 Oct 1854.

1. In situ - Lambarde (*SAC* 71 138) noting arms.
2. The various lettering on 157B contrasts with the uniformity of its pendant, 157C.
3. Cordelia was the last of the Shelleys to dwell at the family town-house, now a hotel, opposite the church, see L. Davey (22).
4. JH notes that Henry (d. 1811) was MP for Lewes, 1802-11, see Thorne (5 138).

Lewes, 157C Mural monument for Henry SHELLEY, d. 1735/6, and family

- Nave, North wall, to West of chancel arch, high up.
- c.105(W); (H) unknown — Fine, fading.
- Pendant to 157B; M.I. (30 lines).
- Henry Shelley, Esq., d. 20 Feb 1735/6, aet 42, eldest son of Richard Shelley, Esq.; his wife, Eleanor, d. 22 Apr 1792, aet 90; their issue - Eleanor, died an infant; George, died an infant; second son, Thomas, d. 2 Aug 1758, aet 28; eldest daughter, Elizabeth, d. 26 Mar 1789, aet 65; surviving son, Henry and his wife, Eleanor; their daughter, Eleanor, d. 3 Jan 1813, aet 84.

1. In situ - Lambarde (*SAC* 71 138) - noting arms.
2. Pendant to 157B.
3. 157C records several generations of Shelleys.
4. Final 7 lines of M.I. added.
5. Patrons were their surviving son and daughter, (she is noticed in added lines).

Lewes, 157D Mural monument for John PLUMER, d. 1785

- Chancel, North wall, high up.
- Inaccessible — Fine.

- In white and column marbles; M.I. set landscape-wise (6 lines, engraved) with decorated border and moulded frame; above, a scrolled pediment and an urn in relief; below, 2 scrolled corbels and a curved apron with traces of painted fern decoration.
- John Plumer, Esq., of Lewes, d. 12 Oct 1785, aet 39.

1. Erected in the later 1780s? John Plumer was a house-owner in the parish in year of his death (R. Davey 142) and elected Headborough in 1775 (Smith 64).

Lewes, 157E Mural monument for Rev. William GWYNNE, d. 1818, his wife Elizabeth, d.1810, and three of their sons, d. 1823, d. 1832 and d. 1833

- Chancel, North wall, high up between the windows.
- c.225(W) x (H) unknown — Good.
- M.I. (28 + 7 lines) on white marble obelisk; unframed; below, a sarcophagus with prominent gadroon and acanthus decorated on a rectangular base, supported by a thin base on scrolled corbels; between corbels, escutcheon on apron.
- Rev. William Gwynne, rector of Hamsey and St. Anne Lewes, d. 16 Apr 1818, aet 73; his wife, Elizabeth, d. 19 Apr 1810, aet 57; their issue - Rowland Gwynne, Major (10th Regiment of Native Infantry), died at Madras, 20 Jul 1823, aet 38; John Gwynne, Captain (26th Regiment of Native Infantry) and paymaster of the Dooab district, died at Brighton, 15 Dec 1832, aet 46 and buried in this church; and Iltid Gwynne, Lt. Col. (43rd Regiment of Native Infantry) died at Ellore, 31 May 1833, aet 44.

1. In situ - Lambarde (*SAC* 71 138) noting arms.
2. Rev. William Gwynne was a house-owner in the parish in 1785 (R. Davey 142) and signed a petition in 1780 (Smith 67); Caffyn notes that the Rev. William Gwynne ran a fee-paying educational establishment in Lewes (Caffyn 158, 303).
3. JH notes that Rev. William Gwynne, MA, was rector of St. Anne, Lewes, 1783-1818, and Hamsey 1784-1818. Another son, also Rev. William Gwynne, MA, was rector of St. Michael's Lewes 1815-25.

Lewes, 157F Ledger stone for Anne PEIRCE, d. 1720/1

- Chancel floor, perpendicular to North wall, partly obscured by furnishings.
- 113(W) x 178(L) — Very worn.
- M.I. (6 lines) in black slate; head to South.
- Anne Peirce, d. 15 Mar 1720/1, aet 37.

1. She was the wife of Thomas Peirce who was master of Lewes Grammar School and rector of St. Anne's (instituted 21 May 1720) for a few months (Caffyn 326). .
2. NBI records the burial of Anne Peirce on 15 Mar 1721 at Lewes, St Anne.
3. See also Venn (1 3 329) and Hennessy (100).

Lewes, 157G Ledger stone for Cordelia BINCKES, d. 1724

- Sanctuary floor, against North wall, partly obscured by a step.
- 74(W) x 99(L) — Fine; cut.
- M.I. (8 lines, engraved) on black slab.
- Cordelia Binckes, d. 14 Oct 1724, aet (lost); eldest daughter of Richard Shelley, Esq., of Lewes; and wife of George Binckes of London.

1. For the Shelleys see 157B-C.

Lewes, 157H Ledger stone for Hannah APSLEY, d. 1723

- Sanctuary, North side, adjacent to 157G, partly obscured by a step.
- 52(W) x 83(L) — Fine.
- M.I. (5 lines, engraved) on fragmentary black slab; head to West.
- Hannah Apsley, d. 10 Apr 1723, aet 34; her husband (name lost).

1. One John Apsley, Esq., was a town trustee in 1742 (Smith 34).

Lewes, 157I Wall-mounted brass for Thomas TWYNE, d. 1613
- Sanctuary, East wall, South of window.
- 30(W) x 43(H) — Very good.
- M.I. (20 lines, engraved, black) in Latin on brass plate; above, an achievement.
- Thomas Twyne, M.D., died at Lewes, 1 Aug 1613, aet 70 ('climacterico 70'); Corpus Christi College, Oxford.

1. Roughly in situ; Horsfield (*Sussex* I 214), Stephenson (511), W.H. Godfrey in 'Thomas and Brian Twine' *SNQ* II 197 ff, 229ff, III 40ff, 82, with illustration, and translation of M.I., Lambarde (*SAC* 71 138) - noting arms, Davidson-Houston (*SAC* 78 105-7) - with illustration and transcription.
2. The M.I. uses allegorical and other learned devices to refer to Thomas Twyne's training and impact on local medical practise: 'Bereft of her physician Sussex languishes ...'.
3. Thomas Twyne was a friend of John Dee - see Horsfield (*Lewes* I 319-20) and N. Moore, revised R.E. Davies, in *ODNB* - with an extensive but dull literary output in both prose and verse; Thomas Twyne's son Brian, who had advanced antiquarian interests (first keeper of the Oxford archives) might be credited with the M.I.; father and son corresponded, mostly about money (Godfrey *ibid*).
4. JH notes that Twyne was awarded MD by Cambridge in 1580 (Venn 1 4 281).

Lewes, 157J Anonymous ledger
- Sanctuary floor, South side.
- 92(W) x 75(L) — Wrecked.
- Nothing legible on a fragment of a freestone slab.

Lewes, 157K Wall mounted brass for Robert HEATH, d. 1681
- Chancel, South wall, West of organ.
- Upper: 24.2(W) x 32.5(H); Lower: 60.3(W) x 46.3(H) — Very good.
- The upper panel with an achievement within an oval border; Below, is a panel with a M.I. (10 lines, engraved).
- Robert Heath, Esq., d. 10 Jan 1681, aet 24; son of also Robert Heath, Esq.; his grandfather, William Heath, Esq.

1. In situ; Stephenson (511); Lambarde (*SAC* 71 138) noting arms; Davidson-Houston (*SAC* 78 107-8) with transcription.

Lewes, 157L Stone panel for Thomas ROWE, d. 1625
- Vestry, South wall, West of door.
- (Irregular) 58(W) x 101(H) — Fine, worn.
- M.I. (5 lines, engraved) in a repositioned freestone slab; below, arms.

THOMAS RO[WE]
Natus natalis

Baptizatus in festo circumcisionis domini

Sepultus Epiphaniae
1625

1. The M.I. sets the rites of passage in Rowe's short life against the Christian calendar.
2. JH notes that the shield carved on this stone is mentioned by Lambarde (*SAC* 71 139), and the discovery of the stone in *SAC* 68 (284).

Lewes, 157M Stone panel for [Edward] RAYNES, dated 1636
- Vestry, South wall, to West of window.
- (Irregular) 34(W) x 78(H) — Very worn, cracked.
- M.I. (3 lines, engraved) on a freestone slab; above, traces of cursive ornament.

E[D-US?] RAYNES
IN[F]ANS OBIIT
1636

1. JH notes that the questionable forename could be Edward. Probably the death of an infant. NBI gives burial of Edward Raynes at Lewes St. Anne on 21 Mar 1636/7.

Lewes, 157N Ledger stone for Susanna ROWE, date unknown but well after 1639

- Vestry floor, associated with and South of 157O.
- 91(W) x 187(L) — Sound, very worn.
- M.I. (6 (?) lines, engraved) on a Horsham stone slab, formerly outside.

> HIC IACET SVSANNA IOHANNIS
> ROWE SEN GEN ET SVSANNAE
> VXORIS EVIS [sic] FILIA QVAE DVM
> IN VIVIS ESSET EXIMIAE SVAS
> HIC IVXTA PARENTES REPONI…
> EX … TAVIT OBIIT XXV
>
> ....

1. Horsfield (*Sussex* I 212-3) notes the discovery and transcription of 157N.
2. Date of death was 25 Apr 1678, aet 66.
3. John Rowe is famous in the annals of Lewes, acting as Constable in 1597, contributing to the Lewes Town Book in 1629 and acting as Lord Abergavenny's steward for the Barony of Lewes, see Horsfield (*Lewes* I 321-22); Godfrey (*Book of John Rowe*); Salzman (*Lewes Town Book* 44 ff, 122) and Turner (*SAC* 24 85-98); in 1624, his daughter [Anne?] married Edward Raynes (see 157M); this daughter, Susanna, married Thomas Medley of Buxted Park in 1671.
4. Horsfield (*Lewes* I Pl. XXV) prints a portrait engraving of John Rowe after a lost miniature.

Lewes, 157O Ledger stone for John ROWE, d. 1639, and Susanna

- Vestry floor, North side, associated with and North of 157N, now partly obscured by furnishings, formerly outside.
- 88(W) x 166(L) — Sound, worn.
- M.I. (16 lines, engraved) fill a black slab; above, an escutcheon.

> IOHES ROWE, GENOSVS, & SVSANNA …
> CONDORMIVNT SVB HOC MARMORE …
> 2 DIE NO ANNO DNI 1639, ÆTATIS …
> …9 ILLA OBIIT DIE .. 16 .. ÆTATIS
>
> IN PATREM
> PRO CHRISTI MERITIS MISERIS QVAECVNQ^{VE} DEDIST[I]
> IN CÆLIS NVMERAT MVNERAT IL A D..S
> FIDES
> FRVCTIFERA SALVTIFERA
>
> IN MATREM
> CASTA DOMI VIXIT VIGILANS PROLIQ^{VE} LARIQ^{VE}
> SARA VIRO MVNDO MARTHA MARIA DEO
>
> IOHES ROWE FILIVS EORVM MÆSTISSIMVS
> [P]ARENTIBVS OPTIMIS CHARISSIMIS OFFICIO
> PIETATIS & MEMORIÆ ERGO HOC
> MONVMENTVM POSVIT

1. In situ, originally marking John Rowe's burial place in the churchyard but now within the building.
2. For its discovery see Horsfield (*Sussex* I 212-3) with transcribed M.I.; Lambarde (*SAC* 71 139) noting arms.
3. Repaired and restored by the *SAC* in the mid 19th century, see Turner (*SAC* 24 94) and the area was built over in 1927 to form a vestry.
4. John Rowe, d. 27 Nov 1639, aet 79; Susanna Rowe died date unknown; set up by their son John, perhaps before Susanna's death.
5. John Rowe is famous in the annals of Lewes, acting as Constable in 1597, contributing to the Lewes Town Book in 1629 and acting as Lord Abergavenny's steward for the Barony of Lewes, see Horsfield

(*Lewes* I 321-22), Godfrey (*Book of John Rowe*), Salzman (*Lewes Town Book* 44 ff, 122) and Turner (*SAC* 24 85-98).

6. In 1624, his daughter [Anne?] married Edward Raynes.

7. JH notes that Horsfield (*Lewes* I Pl. XXV) prints a portrait engraving of John Rowe after a lost miniature.

Lewes, 157P Wall-mounted brass for James CRANSTON, d. 1790, and his family [Plate 99]

- East pier between nave and South aisle, South side.
- Upper brass: 61(W) x 46(H); Lower brass: 61(W) x 49.5(H) — Very good.
- M.I. (7 lines, engraved, black) fills a brass plate above another M.I. (5 lines, engraved, black) in upper 50% of a brass plate; Both brasses are set on a grey-green slab; signed (lower right): 'HOLMAN.LEWES'.
- James Cranston, Esq., Captain, RN, d. 1 Aug 1790, aet 58; his wife, Catherine, d. 23 Dec 1808, aet 76; his daughter, Catharine Frances Cranston, d. 8 May 1785, aet 14.

1. A rare, perhaps unique, case of a signed, local early 19th-century brass; John Holman (1765-1855) was a clockmaker, born in Hamsey, apprenticed to and partner with William Kemp (1787-97), served as Constable in 1803 (see Tyler 18 and compare the signature on 157P with the signed clock-faces illustrated in Sautter plates 64, 68 and 72).

2. In 1785, James Cranston lived in a house owned by Rev. John Rideout (see 157Q) (R. Davey 142).

Lewes, 157Q Mural monument for Elizabeth RIDEOUT, d. 1774, and her husbands Richard PAYNE, d. 1732/3, and Richard RIDEOUT, d. 1767 [Plate 100]

- South aisle, South wall, opposite North door.
- c.86(W) x c.150(H) — Very good.
- M.I. (15 lines, engraved, black) on white, marble tablet set portrait-wise; frame, cornice; broken pointed pediment; base moulding, etc. in grey and beige marbles; below, scrolled corbels and apron with escutcheon.
- Richard Payne, Esq., of the parish, d. 17 Jan 1732/3, aet 39; Richard Rideout, Esq., of the parish, d. 28 Apr 1767, aet 52; their wife, Elizabeth, d. 26 Jul 1774, aet 79.

1. In situ - Lambarde (*SAC* 71 139) noting arms.

2. Erected by the twice-widowed Elizabeth Rideout after c 1767, further lines added after July 1774 (see lettering of M.I.).

3. One Richard Rideout was a trustee of the Town in 1742 (Smith 34) and gave plate to the church in 1765, see Couchman (*SAC* 54 229-30).

4. Many tablets of this type in Lewes.

Lewes, 157R Ledger for Mary ..., [18th century?]

- Nave floor, West end, partly under gallery stairs.
- 87(W) x 17(D) — Fragmentary; almost illegible.
- M.I. (engraved) on a sandy freestone slab.

              MARY HIS WIFE WHO WAS ....
              THE 26 ..... NOVEMBER AN .....
              DEPARTED THIS LIFE THE ....

1. Legible data does not match items in Additions.

Lewes, 157S Ledger for Elizabeth TUCKER, d. 1689

- Nave floor, West end, beneath gallery, partly obscured by furnishings.
- 83(W) x 84(L) — Fragmentary; fine, scratched.
- M.I. (visible are 10 lines, engraved) in a black slab.
- Elizabeth Tucker, buried 9 Jul 1689, aet 29; daughter of Richard Payne, Esq., of Lewes and Elizabeth; and wife of Kemvel Tucker, Gent., of Tenterden.

1. The relationship between this Elizabeth and other members of the Payne family is unclear.
2. The Richard Payne of monument 157Q was perhaps her nephew, Anne Payne (see 157T) was perhaps her sister-in-law; for licence to marry for Kemval Tucker and Elizabeth May, see Dunkin (*Licences 1670-1729* 108).

Lewes, 157T Ledger for Anne PAYNE, d. 1689
- Nave floor, West end, beneath gallery, partly obscured by furnishings.
- 83(W) x 104(L) — (Fragmentary), damaged edges.
- M.I. (visible are 11 lines, engraved) on a black slab.
- Anne Payne, buried 30 Nov 1689, aet 17; sixth daughter of Peter Gard, Gent., and Katherine; her husband, Richard Payne, Jnr, Gent.; sole issue, daughter Elizabeth.

1. Characteristic reversed lettering stroke of 'N'.
2. Payne's house was prominent in the parish: it marked the starting point for the route taken by the Town Scavenger towards Westgate, see Salzman (*Lewes Town Book* 104).
3. For licence to marry for Richard Payne and Anne Gard, dated 27 Apr 1687, see Dunkin (*Licences 1670-1729* 101).

Lewes, 157U Ledger for Sarah GEAR, d. 1841
- Nave floor, West end, to West of North door.
- 84(W) x 182(L) — Poor; restored, diagonal crack, faded.
- M.I. (9 lines, engraved) on upper 25% of a freestone slab.
- Sarah Gear, d. 13 Apr 1841, aet 21, first daughter of Robert Gear, Esq., of Lewes and his second wife, Sarah.

1. NBI records the burial of Sarah Gear, aged 22 on 20 Apr 1841 at Lewes, St Anne.

Lewes, St. Anne Additions
Lower (*SAC* 20 45) notes:
(1) Thomas Springett, of Plumpton, d. 4 Oct 1652, second son of Sir Thomas Springett of the Broyle (chancel).
(2) Mary Springett, d. 22 May 1652, her husband, Thomas Springett, of Plumpton, Esq.; her father, John Porter, of Lamberhurst, Kent (chancel).

(158) LEWES, St. John-sub-Castro
The mediaeval church was demolished on an adjacent site in 1839-40 - Godfrey & Salzman (Pl. 95) – a view, and Nairn & Pevsner (552); the patron of the re-built church was the rector, Peter Guerin Crofts (see 158C) and the architect George Cheeseman; also salvaged from the old church were an Anglo-Saxon doorway, the chancel arch and some monuments, the relocation of which in the chancel gives pride of place to Crofts' ancestors (158A, B, C and E); although the structure of the old church was satisfactory in 1724, see Ford (146), it was too small and there had been no chancel 'in memory of man' so was perhaps unsatisfactory for commemorative purposes.

Lewes, 158A Mural monument for Peter Guerin CROFTS (jnr), d. 1859, and his family
- Chancel, South wall, lower left.
- 103(W) x 188(H) — Excellent.
- Curve-topped black slate baseplate with white marble urn in half relief; M.I. (engraved, black) on white marble tablet with black frame, set portrait-wise, with cornice and base mouldings; Doric half-columns flanking; rosettes above; below, decorated brackets.
- Harriet Crofts, d. 13 Mar 1813, aet 34; daughter of William Campion, Esq., of Lewes; first wife of Rev. Peter Guerin Crofts, M.A., rector of this parish for 48 years, d. 16 Jul 1859,

aet 84; his second wife, Elizabeth Frederica, d. 24 Aug 1878, aet 83; their daughter, Mary Henrietta, d. 30 Jan 1829, aet 4.

1. Pendant with 158E, but a little smaller (no frieze has been added for additional M.I.s added through to the 1870s).
2. Peter Guerin Crofts, Jnr. was rector 1799-1844; for licence to marry of Peter Guerin Crofts (of All Saints, Lewes) and Harriet Campion (of St. Michael's, Lewes) dated 18 Jan 1812, see Dunkin & Penfold (*Licences* 105); Harriet Campion's father owned Danny, Hurstpierpoint.

Lewes, 158B Mural monument for James CROFTS, d. 1778
- Chancel, South wall, top left.
- 110(W); height inaccessible — Excellent.
- Black slate baseplate in obelisk form; white marble half urn on a bracket; below, M.I. (6 lines, engraved black) fills a white marble tablet; grey cornice and base mouldings; decorated border on two corbels; between, slate apron with escutcheon; finial at foot.
- James Crofts, of Lincoln's Inn, Barrister, d. 11 Nov 1778, aet 34.

1. In situ in 1930 - Lambarde (*SAC* 71 136) arms noted.
2. For reasons which are unclear, pendant to 158D.
3. Having bought the living, James Crofts installed Peter Guerin Crofts as rector in 1774.

Lewes, 158C Mural monument for Rev. Peter Guerin CROFTS [Snr], d. 1784, and his widow Sarah, d. 1809
- Chancel, South wall, centre, high.
- 103(W) x 188(H) — Excellent; local loss (arms).
- Grey-green baseplate in obelisk form; white marble urn in low relief; above, escutcheon; below, cornice over M.I. (engraved, black) on white marble tablet; rectangular top; curved apron.
- Rev. Peter Guerin Crofts, A.M., late rector of St. John-sub-Castro, Lewes, d. 21 May 1784, aet 39; his widow, Sarah, also widow of Rev. James Smyth, d. 30 Aug 1809, aet 62.

1. In situ in 1930 - Lambarde (*SAC* 71 136) arms noted.
2. Peter Guerin Crofts (Jnr) is commemorated by 158A.
3. JH notes that Rev. Peter Guerin Crofts, MA, was rector of St. John sub Castro, Lewes, 1774-84 - see Hennessy (98).

Lewes, 158D Mural monument for Ann and Daniel LA PLA, d. 1771 and 1774
[Plate 101]
- Chancel, South wall, top right.
- Inaccessible — Excellent.
- Pendant to 158B; M.I. (13 lines).
- Rev. Daniel Le Pla, L.L.B., late rector of St. John-sub-Castro, Lewes, d. 8 Mar 1774, aet 65; his wife, Ann, d. 8 May 1771, aet 60, daughter of Thomas Swallow, M.D., of Thaxted, Essex.

1. For reasons which are unclear, pendant to 158B.
2. Perhaps erected soon after 1771.

Lewes, 158E Mural monument for William and Priscilla CAMPION, d. 1818 and 1833
- Chancel, South wall, lower right.
- 98(W) x 175(H) — Excellent.
- Pendant with 158A but larger; has frieze and black frame for M.I.
- William Campion, Esq., d. 28 Feb 1818, aet 79; second son of William Campion, Esq., of Danny; his wife, Priscilla, d. 10 Oct 1833, aet 86.

1. Pendant with 158A.

2. William Campion owned Danny House; his daughter married the rector, Peter Guerin Crofts Snr (see 158C); he was active in the parish in 1790 (petition to establish a market, see Smith 83).

Lewes, 158F Mural monument for Bridgit SHORE, d. 1681

- South aisle, East end, at head height.
- 58(W) x 72(H) — Fine.
- Rectangular slate panel (once floor-mounted ?); M.I. (10 lines, engraved) in Latin in 2 blocks in upper and central sections.
- Bridgit Shore, d. 9 Aug 1681; wife of John Shore.

1. John Shore was rector of St. John sub Castro 1673/4 - 1722 and also of Hamsey 1674 - 1722; their son, Philip (1677-1725), was master of Cuckfield Grammar School (Caffyn 335).

(159) LEWES, St. John the Baptist (Southover)

Southover was outside the ancient borough of Lewes; church created out of remains of the hospitium at the ancient Priory gates; arcade old; tower rebuilt 1714-38 - Nairn & Pevsner (552-3); chancel collapsed well before 1724, Ford (148), rebuilt 1885; there were 64 families in the parish in 1724 and a population of 487 in 1801; the black limestone slab marking the burial place of Gundreda, foundress of St. Pancras Priory, Lewes, was used as or was in use as a monument at Isfield in 1550 and in 1774 was brought here and later rehoused in 1884/5 in Latter Parsons' neo-Norman South chapel of 1847 (*English Romanesque Art 1066-1200*, Arts Council exhibition catalogue 1984 181); in 1724-5 there was a re-ordering of church seating, which might have impacted on siting access and the display of monuments, see W. Hudson 'Extracts from the first book of the Parish of Southover' (*SAC* 48 32); in the new arrangement Madam Newton for her Mansion House had possession of pews 13 and 32, the Newtons having been prominent in the parish from at least the early 17th century, see T.H. Noyes, 'Some notices of the family of Newton ...' (*SAC* 9 312-342) and M.A. Lower, 'Newton Tombstones at Southover' (*SAC* 17 258-60); Horsfield notes many but unspecified 'neat' monuments on the walls, between the hospitium windows.

Lewes, 159A Mural monument for Joseph Arnold WALLINGER, d. 1827

- Nave, North wall, towards West end, high.
- 102(W) x c.130(H) — Fine.
- Composite black baseplate with a pointed top; white urn on a moulded cornice; M.I. (6 + 4 lines, engraved) on trapezoidal panel; base moulding and corbels; signed (centre below): 'PARSONS'.
- Joseph Arnold Wallinger, Esq., 28 Jun 1771 - 8 Dec 1827; his widow, Anna Maria, 8 Oct 1775 - 5 Mar 1861.

1. The firm of Parsons undertook important building at the church in the 1840s (see above).

Lewes, 159B Mural monument for Rev. George NEWTON, d. 1791

- Nave, North wall, East of 159A, high.
- 66(W) x 55(H) — Good.
- M.I. (11 + 4 lines, engraved, black) fill an unframed panel; cornice, base moulding and scrolled corbels.
- Rev. George Newton, rector of Isfield for 36 years, d. 18 Dec 1791, aet 62; his wife, Elizabeth, d. 7 Feb 1811, aet 82; their issue (unnamed).

1. For the Newton pedigree see Noyes (*SAC* 9 338).
2. Final lines added to the M.I..
3. JH notes that George Newton was rector of Isfield from 1755 to 1791 and that the Newtons had only one child, Elizabeth, who married William Courthope Mabbott.

Lewes, 159C Mural monument for Adria BARTON, d. 1804

- Nave North wall, East of 159B, high.
- 68(W) x 163(H) — Cracked (left and right).
- Oval tablet of white-veined marble; moulded frame; M.I. in centre (10 lines, engraved); pendant to 159E.
- Adria Barton, d. 2 Jan 1804, buried in her family vault; daughter of Apsley Newton, Esq.; and widow of James Barton, M.D.

1. Patron of 159C was Elizabeth Newton.

Lewes, 159D Ledger for Charles NASH, d. 1777

- Nave floor, near pulpit, part-obscured by furnishings.
- 100(W) x 200(L) — Unknown.
- M.I. (engraved, white) on a black slab (slate?); narrow border; scallop shells in four corners.

This Marble is Placed here
... Order of Mrs. Isabella Nash,
... memory of her deceased Husband
Rev[d] M[r] Charles Nash, A.M.
... or of Albourne & Twineham
In this County
Minister of this Parish,
departed this life Nov[r] 15th 1777
the 50th Year of his Age
... whose remains are here
Deposited

1. JH notes that Rev. Charles Nash was rector of Albourne and of Twineham, 1758-77, see Venn (1 3 233).

Lewes, 159E Mural monument for Tabitha NEWTON, d. 1803

- Chancel, North wall, East end.
- 68(W) x 158(H) — Very good.
- M.I. (6 + 3 lines, engraved, black) on oval tablet in white and grey marbles; moulded frame; below, decorated corbel; above, a complex scrolled console and urn.
- Tabitha Newton; widow of Apsley Newton, Esq., buried near; her son, William Newton; no dates on M.I.

1. Patron is son William.
2. Decorated as in 159F.
3. Tabitha Newton's family were from Uckfield; she d. 10 Jan 1803, see Noyes (*SAC* 9 338) and Comber (*Lewes* 201).

Lewes, 159F Mural monument for Col. William NEWTON, d. 1808, and his wife Ann, d. 1837

- Chancel, North wall.
- 89(W) x 220(H) — Good; faded.
- Black marble obelisk; M.I. (7 + 5 lines, engraved, black) on a rectangular white marble tablet; moulded cornice, curved apron; corbel.
- Colonel William Newton, Prince of Wales own Regiment of Light Dragoons, d. 13 Nov 1808, aet 64; his wife, Ann Elizabeth, d. 22 Dec 1837, aet 81, daughter of Sir Edward Knatchbull, Bart., of Mersham Hatch, Kent.

1. William Newton had fashionable contacts in 1793, conducted military exercises in 1804 and business

dealings in the year of his death, see C. Brent (77-78, 94).
2. Widow was patron of 159F.
3. William Newton, Esq., was named in the Town Book for 1800 (Smith 138) and was Col. of 10th Light Dragoons, see Noyes (*SAC* 9 338).
4. Final lines of M.I. were added later.

Lewes, 159G Anonymous ledger, with the date 1717
- Nave floor, far East end.
- 79(W) x 172(L) — Very worn and pitted; brass lost.
- M.I. (engraved) on a grey freestone slab; set East-West; brass indent.

...

E...M FEB 25

1717 ...

Lewes, 159H Ledger for Mary NEWTON, d. 1753
- South aisle floor, far East end, partly obscured by later step.
- 94(W) x 148(L) — Very worn.
- M.I. towards upper end of a pale freestone slab.

... Mary Wife of Will: Newton

Esq who died March 22d 1753 Aged

77 Years

1. Mary Longley was wife of William Newton (1691-1775), see 159L and Noyes (*SAC* 9 338).

Lewes, 159I Mural monument for Louisa Maria BALDOCK, d. 1819 [Plate 102]
- South aisle wall, towards East end, at head height.
- 109(W) x 180(H) — Fine; fading.
- In white marble on dark grey baseplate; framed M.I. (23 lines, engraved, black, including rhyming epitaph) set portrait-wise with dropped corners within a frame; corbels with acanthus decorative; in pointed pediment, wreaths flanked by palmettes; signed (below centre): 'HENRY WESTMACOTT, LONDON'.
- Louisa Maria Baldock, d. 18 Feb 1819, aet 26; daughter of Samuel Durrant, Esq., and Eleanor; and wife of William Baldock, Esq., of Malling House; their issue, infant son and daughter.

1. For her parents see 159J.
2. For licence to marry dated 18 Aug 1814 for William Baldock, of Chartham, Kent, age 22 plus and Louisa Mary Durrent, of Salehurst, age 21 plus, with surety held by Samuel Durrent, of Salehurst, see 159J and Dunkin & Penfold (*Licences* 23).
3. 159I is cited by Gunnis (*Dict.* 422) as being by Henry Westmacott, 1784-1861, the son of Richard Westmacott and brother of the better-known Sir Richard Westmacott.
4. For heraldry see Lambarde (*SAC* 71 139).

Lewes, 159J Mural monument for Samuel DURRANT, d. 1821
- South aisle wall, West of 159I, at head height.
- 112(W) x 183(H) — Fine.
- Close to 159I in form; pediment curved not pointed.

IN THE FAMILY VAULT IN THIS CHURCH YARD

ARE DEPOSITED THE REMAINS OF

SAMUEL DURRANT ESQ.R LATE OF THIS PARISH

WHO DIED THE 1ST OF SEP.R 1821,

AGED 59 YEARS.

ALSO SAMUEL GEORGE THE INFANT SON OF

SAMUEL & ELEANOR DURRANT

WHO DIED 26TH SEP.R 1795.

ALSO OF ELEANOR, RELICT OF

SAMUEL DURRANT, ESQ.R

WHO DIED AT CAME HOUSE,

NEAR DORCHESTER, DORSET;
ON FEBRUARY THE 2ND 1852,
IN THE 83RD YEAR OF HER AGE
THE REMAINS OF GEORGE PIKE ESQR
ARE INTERRE IN THE SAME VAULT
OBT THE 4TH JUNE 1821,
AGED 57 YEARS.

1. In situ - Lambarde (*SAC* 71 139) noting arms.
2. Probably not the Samuel Woodgate Durrent who acted as constable in 1801, 1811, etc. (Smith 98, 184).
3. 159J is a local version of Westmacott's 159I.

Lewes, 159K Ledger for Rev. George NEWTON, d. 1791
- Nave floor, West end.
- 97(W) x 177(L) — Very worn.
- M.I. (engraved) in a pale freestone slab.

HERE LIES INT[ERRED]
THE BODY OF THE
REV GEORGE NEW[TON]
FORMERLY SEQUESTRA[TOR]
OF THIS PARISH & RECTO[R]
IOS I[SFIELD] ...
DIE [D] ON THE ... OF DECEMBER
AGED [62] YEARS

1. George Newton (1729 - 18 Dec 1791), was rector of Isfield and sequestrator of this parish, see also 159B and Noyes (*SAC* 9 338).

Lewes, 159L Ledger for William NEWTON, d. 1775, and his wife Elizabeth, d. 1780
- Nave floor, West end, alongside 159N.
- 99(W) x 199(L) — Worn.
- M.I. (6 + 5 lines, engraved) in upper 60% of a black slab (marble?); head to South; narrow engraved border; fleur-de-lys at corners.

HERE lieth the Body
of WILLIAM NEWTON ESQR
eldeſt Son of *Willm Newton Eſqr*
of this Pariſh
who *died* 31st Octr 1775
Aged 51 Years

Also
[Elizabeth] Second Wife
of WILLIAM NEWTON Eſqr
who died 23d *March* 1780
AGED 65 YEARS

1. Now supporting the font.
2. William Newton (1691-1775) and his second wife Elizabeth, née Heaviside; for his first wife see 159H; for his brother 159M.
3. The group of ledgers with fleur-de-lys decorations includes 4G, 164Q and 164U.

Lewes, 159M Ledger for George Nevill NEWTON, d. 1746/7
- Nave floor, West end, near West door.
- 76(W) x 140(L) — Worn; cracked.
- M.I. (6 lines, engraved) in upper 25% of a grey freestone slab; head to West.

In memory of
George Nevill Newton
Son of William Newton
and Ann his Wife
who died 17 Feb 1746
Aged [5]0 [Y]ears

1. Now supporting the font.
2. Near George Nevill Newton's brother William (159L); George Nevill Newton lived 1696-17 Feb 1746/7, see Noyes (*SAC* 9 338).

Lewes, 159N Ledger for John HOLMWOOD, d. 1740 and his wife, Sarah, d. 1710, and son, John, d. 1736
- Nave floor, West end, alongside 159M.
- 77(W) x 149(L) — Worn.
- M.I. (engraved) fills surface of pale freestone slab; head to West.

To the Memory
of Mʳ John Holmwood
late of the Pariſh
of Sᵗ Thomas in the Cliff
Surgeon
who departed this Life Feb
11ᵗʰ 1740 Aged [78] Years [?]/ Also the Body of Sᴀʀᴀʜ his
wife who departed this Life
Decemᵇʳ yᵉ 10ᵗʰ 1710. Aged 49 Y[ears]

Likewise the Body of the
Revᵈ Mʳ John Holmwood
only Son of the above
mentioned IOHN
and SARAH his wife
who departed this Life
September yᵉ 8ᵗʰ 1736
Aged 36 Years

1. For licence to marry of 16 Jun 1691 for John Holmwood, of Cliffe, bachelor and Sarah Newton, of Lewes, see Dunkin (*Licences 1670-1729* 132).
2. JH notes that there are no details traced of John Holmwood jnr. as a cleric in CCEd, or in Foster (Al Ox) or Venn.
3. See ESRO (AMS 402) for extract of the will of John Holmwood dated 3 Apr 1740.

Lewes, St. John the Baptist (Southover) Additions
(1) Part of a slab, formerly at Southover Grange (the seat of the Newton family), read: 'here l'eth william newton / esquier, who married jane / ernley daughter of will / iam ... james / ... of may', see M.A. Lower, 'Newton Tombstones at Southover' (*SAC* 17 258-60); another part of the slab perhaps in the West nave floor amongst 159K-M [?].

(160) LEWES, St. Michael
Mediaeval West wall and 14ᵗʰ-century South arcade - Nairn & Pevsner (553); plan in *SNQ* (IX 151); wooden North arcade of 1748; South aisle designed and rebuilt by Joseph Daw in 1748, see S. Berry (*SAC* 142 107-9), who notes that Horsfield (*Sussex* I 210) gives the date as 1755; nave windows on South side were Gothicised in 1885, allowing for mural monuments between them; ledgers presumably lost through restorations of church flooring [late 1820s?]; building reported to be in decent order in 1724, see Ford (147); the parish had a population of 786 in 1801, rising from c.100 families in 1724.

Lewes, 160A Mural monument for Thomas MANTELL, d. 1807

- Nave, West wall, North of door to West chapel.
- 87(W) x 84(H) — Fine.
- In freestone; M.I. (19 lines, engraved, black) on unframed panel, pilasters flanking, half ball-finials as corbels; above, a crude pointed pediment.
- Thomas Mantell, of St. John sub Castro, d. 11 Jul 1807, aet 54.

1. Epitaph perhaps written by Mantell's son (d. 1853) who is himself commemorated on the North wall.
2. Family home was near the church, along the High Street.
3. Thomas Mantell (1750-1807) was Headborough in 1791-2 (Smith 92), shoemaker, radical Whig and Methodist; his son was Gideon Mantell, the surgeon and geologist (for whom see biography by Dennis R. Dean in *ODNB*); Thomas Mantell is commemorated here despite his apparent espousal of Methodism.
4. NBI records the burial of Thomas Mantell at St. John sub Castro on 13 Jul 1807, aged 55.

Lewes, 160B Mural monument for Charles BATEMAN, d. 1703, and his wife Dorothy, d. 1732, their son, their daughter and their son-in-law (PHILPOT)

- North aisle, North wall, North-West corner, at head height.
- 82(W) x 115(H) — Fine, faded.
- In grey freestone on a slate base; M.I. (many lines, engraved, black); above, a pointed pediment, without entablature, supporting flaming torches left and right; below, base mouldings and a baseplate on two corbels.

In Memory of
CHARLES BATEMAN Gent. Interr'd
Near this place who died April 3rd 170..
Aged 34[?] Years

Also of DOROTHY his wife who was Buried
the .... day of Aug. 1732. Aged 70

Likewise of CHARLES their son who died
the 12th of *March* 1705, Aged 3 Years.

ALSO of ELIZ. the wife of MR STEPHEN PHILPOT
daughter of the aboveſaid CHARLES & DOROTHY
who *died* Nov. 11th 1761. Aged 60

*Prepare for Death, the God of Truth Adore
Thou'll happy be. When this vain Worlds no more*

Also of MR STEPHEN PHILPOT
who *departed* this Life 2nd December 1770
Aged 68 Years

1. Note the licence to marry, dated 13 Feb 1699-1700, for Charles Bateman, of Lewes, bachelor and Dorothy Page, see Dunkin (*Licences 1670-1729* 178).
2. Their son-in-law - perhaps the patron of 160B - Stephen Philpott (d.1770), was a dancing and music master at Lewes from 1729.
3. His eldest son, also Stephen, was also a musician (Caffyn 327).
4. JH notes the following entries recorded in NBI for the parish for Lewes, St Michael - Challes Buttman, bur. 2 Apr 1703; Dorothy Bateman, bur. 25 Aug 1732; Challes Bulman, bur. 1 Mar 1705/6; (wife) Philpot, bur. 19 Nov 1761; Stephen Philpot, bur. 7 Dec 1770. Perhaps the writing or spelling in the register was poor.

Lewes, 160C Mural monument for Margaret DICKENS, d. 1793

- North aisle, North wall, centre, above head height.
- 82(W); (H) inaccessible — Fine.
- White on black; M.I. (11 lines, engraved, black) on panel with curved apron; cornice below

an urn in bas relief; high pedestal; volute decoration at top; wreathed initials 'MD' in centre; all against a black marble baseplate in obelisk form.
- Margaret Dickens, d. London, 22 Mar 1793, aet 62; daughter of Richard and Elizabeth Lardner, of Lewes; and widow of Rev. Samuel Dickens, D.D., archdeacon and prebendary of Durham.

1. Commemorated in her home town, perhaps by her siblings.
2. For her parents see 160F.

Lewes, 160D Mural monument for Sir Nicholas PELHAM, d. 1559, and his wife Anne (SACKVILLE) [Plate 103]
- North aisle, North wall, near East end, at head height and above.
- 139(W) x 200(H) x 27(D) — Excellent (restored).
- Alabaster and column marbles; male effigy (to right) in armour and wife (as widow) kneeling on cushions (hers tasselled); at draped prayer desk; 2 bound volumes; flanking, polished black columns (touch?); above, an entablature supporting a ceiling with drops and rosettes; helm on wall above; behind, M.I. (15 lines, engraved, black) on framed panel; decorative relief work with cherubim and trophies; below, kneeling children, four females on left, six males on right, the two eldest armoured; between, an hourglass; below, decorative base mouldings and baseplate with scrollwork and corbels, one in ball-finial form.
- Sir Nicholas Pelham, Knt, d. 15 Dec 1559, aet 44; son of Sir William Pelham, Knt, of Laughton; his wife, Anne, daughter of John Sackville, Esq., and granddaughter of Rt Hon. Thomas Sackville, late Earl of Dorset; their issue, 6 sons and 4 daughters; Nicholas Pelham's martial exploits.

1. In situ, drawn by Grimm in 1787, see BL Add. MS 5672 f.5R, and see *Gent's Mag* 1825 in Gomme (279), wrongly dated 1595; Horsfield (*Lewes* I 279) with engraved plate, Horsfield (*Sussex* I 210), Mosse (128-9) and Nairn & Pevsner (553).
2. Nicholas Pelham was first son of Sir William Pelham of Laughton (d. 1539) and his wife Mary Carew; he married Anne Sackville in 1537; their issue - 8 surviving; Nicholas Pelham fell foul of Northumberland in early 1550s; the terms of his will of 1560 suggest Calvinist inclinations (see biography by Alasdair Hawkyard in *ODNB* with date of death of 15 Sep 1560); Pelham's heroic defence of Seaford is referenced in the M.I. by the punning words '...repel them ...', see Mercer (236).
3. Anne Pelham's death gives us a TPQ for this monument.
4. The later 16th-century Pelhams did not erect monuments at Laughton (although they did in the 17th century, see 153D-F); their attention moved to Stanmer in the 18th century (see 244A).
5. One of Nicholas Pelham's daughters is Anne (d.1571), wife of Thomas Shurley, see 145C and L.F. Salzman 'The Early Heraldry of Pelham' (*SAC* 69 70).
6. See Withyham (302) for the monuments to the Sackvilles, earls of Dorset.

Lewes, 160E Mural monument for Katharine WOODWARD, d. 1786
- South aisle (South chapel), South wall, high up.
- 62(W); (H) inaccessible — Fine.
- M.I. (9 lines, engraved, black) in upper 75% of framed white marble oval panel; below centre, a black ball-finial; above, a decorative keystone.
- Katharine Woodward, d. 19 Aug 1786, aet 48; daughter of Rev. Thomas Woodward, rector of West Grinstead.

Lewes, 160F Mural monument for Elizabeth LARDNER, d. 1772
- South aisle (South chapel), South wall, high up.
- 105(W); (H) inaccessible — Fine.
- In mixed marbles; M.I. (7 lines, engraved, black) in upper 50% of a framed white marble panel; flanking, flat brown hardstone pilasters; below, base mouldings; then a curved apron with corbels and ball-finial; above, a blank frieze, then a heavy cornice breaking forward left and right; above, baseplate in obelisk form; with achievement.

- Elizabeth Lardner, d. 7 Mar 1772, aet 72; widow of Richard Lardner, Esq., of Lewes.

1. In situ - Lambarde (*SAC* 71 137) noting arms - which are now indecipherable.
2. Lines were to be added to the M.I.
3. See too 160C for the Lardners.

Lewes, 160G Mural monument for John William Plumer WINDUS, d. 1827
- South aisle, South wall, East end, at head height.
- 89(W) x 76(H) — Fine, fading.
- M.I. (15 lines, engraved, black) on white marble panel; scalloped corners with gilded rosettes; black baseplate; above, a cornice and a plain pointed pediment.
- John William Plumer Windus, A.B., scholar at Exeter College, Oxford, d. 17 Sep 1827, aet 23; mother, sisters and brothers, none named.

1. A young scholar commemorated by his mother and siblings (one of them evidently an accomplished Latinist); another nearby monument commemorates his parents (d. 1833 and 1867).
2. In 1817, Mrs Windus was a subscriber for the Borough Engine House (Smith 223).
3. Note the licence to marry dated 31 Jan 1822 for one Arthur Edward Burtenshaw Windus, of this parish, wine-merchant, bachelor, age 25 plus and Ann Rogers, of St. John the Baptist, Southover (Lewes), spinster, age 23 plus, see Dunkin & Penfold (*Licences* 472).

Lewes, 160H Mural monument for George GORING, d. 1601/2
- South aisle, South wall, near entrance to South chapel, above head height.
- 53(W) x 100(H) — Fine.
- In two parts: below, a copy of an ancient M.I. on a modern grey freestone slab; above, an original achievement in alabaster.
- George Goring, Esq., d. 7 Feb 1601/2; his wife, Anne, daughter of Edward Denny, Esq., of Waltham Abbey, Essex; issue - 5 sons, 4 daughters, none named.

1. Fragments from a lost monument, perhaps originally quite substantial, to rival and balance 160D; the monument removed when South aisle was rebuilt in 1748 (or 1755); the relocated parts are cited in 1924 Church Guide and Lambarde (*SAC* 71 137) following Burrell note in BL Add. MS 5698.
2. Horsfield (*Lewes* I 279) records 160H as opposite 160C and as having a M.I. on a black marble tablet with gilded lettering, lines 1-2 in Latin engraved deep and the remainder shallow engraved in English; the panel was lost by the 1830s but rediscovered in the possession of C.F. Bridgeman, successor to the Lewes mason and tomb-maker John Morris, who had taken it from Joseph Daw, the contractor for the rebuilding, in lieu of a £12 debt, see Dunkin (*SAC* 65 259-60).
3. The Gorings were a major West Sussex family with important links to the East of the county; one Elizabeth Goring, daughter of Sir Henry Goring of Burton, married Thomas Selwyn (Friston 112B); George Goring was MP and Receiver-General in the Court of Wards 1583-93; acted as Lewes JP in 1570 and 1586, see Salzman (*Lewes Town Book* 19, 31) and Hasler (2 209); Sir Henry Goring, a brother, owned an inn on the site of the present Bull House, immediately opposite 160, see L. Davey (17).

Lewes, 160I Mural monument for Lucy PAYNE, d. 1821, and her father Henry VERRALL, d. 1825
- South aisle, South wall, centre, above head height.
- 99(W) x 160(H) — Fine.
- M.I. on a white panel, set portrait-wise; simple black frame; flanking, Doric half-columns; below, base moulding and 2 block corbels with concentric decorations and palmette finials; above, a frieze with 2 rosettes; a heavy entablature breaking forward left and right, supporting a white urn in low-relief on a pedestal, against a curved apron.
- Lucy Payne, d. 12 Dec 1821, aet 39; only daughter of Henry Verrall, Esq., late of Potton, Bedfordshire, d. 6 Feb 1825, aet 72; her husband, William Payne, Esq.

1. Henry Verrall, surgeon at Potton, Bedfordshire for 40 years, later at Lewes and Brighton where he died, son of George Verrall the sixth son of Richard and Sarah Verrall of the 'White Hart', see P. Lucas 'The Verrall Family of Lewes' (*SAC* 58 117-8).

2. He subscribed to the Town Bell/Clock project in 1786 (Smith 89) and he supported the establishment of Sunday schools (*SAC* 132 156).
3. See licence to marry dated 1 Feb 1823 for William Payne, of All Saints, Lewes, widower and one Mary Verrall, of the same, spinster; after Lucy Payne's death, William Payne married his late wife's cousin, see Dunkin & Penfold (*Licences* 328) and Lucas (*SAC* 58 118).
4. The superstructure of 160I repeats that of 160K.

Lewes, 160J Mural monument for Charles RAND, d. 1812, and his nephew Charles RAND, d. 1808

- South aisle, South wall, centre, above head height.
- 120(W) x 125(H) — Good; local losses (arms, above, see fixing holes).
- M.I. (19 lines, engraved, black) on white marble rectangular panel; very narrow black frame; below, decorative moulding; above, cornice with lower section dropping to a point; this balances the pointed pediment; above, attached arms.
- Captain Charles Rand, served the East India Co. for 17 years, d. 13 Oct 1812, aet 57; also his nephew, also Captain Charles Rand, Junior, served the East India Co. for 14 years, d. 21 Aug 1808 aet 31, son of Cater Rand, of Lewes; both subjects campaigned against Tippoo Sultan.

1. Subjects were colonists in India; the elder Charles Rand appears to have been the son of the schoolmaster Cater Rand - established in Lewes in the mid 1730s - and the brother of Cater Jnr, 1749-1825; Caffyn (163) mentions 2 sons in the East India Company, who predeceased Cater Snr; for the licence to marry dated 20 Apr 1775, for Cater Rand, age 23, to Mary Scrace, of the parish, age 20, see Dunkin & Penfold (*Licences* 348).
2. Gunnis (*Dict.* 116) attributes 160J to Michael Crake, fl. 1800-25.

Lewes, 160K Mural monument for Richard COMBER, d. 1817 and his wife Jane, d. 1802

- South aisle, South wall, West end, above head height.
- 104(W) x 190(H) — Good.
- M.I. (15 lines, engraved, black) on a white marble panel set portrait-wise; narrow black frame; curved lower edge; flanking, flat pilasters with floral capitals, leafy corbels and engraved geometric decoration; above, a flat entablature with an urn on a pedestal in low relief; black baseplate in obelisk form.
- Richard Comber, Esq., of Gatewick, Steyning, formerly of Lewes, d. 24 Jul 1817, aet 84, second son of Benjamin Comber, M.D., and Mary, eldest daughter of John Waterman, Gent., of Ashford, Kent; Richard Comber's wife, Jane, d. 26 Jun 1802, aet 53, daughter of John Woodgate, of Lewes.

1. 160K was probably erected after 1817.
2. Richard Comber was a householder in the parish in 1785 (R. Davey 140) and, although the monument makes no mention of the fact, he was one of Sussex' most distinguished clockmakers; he lived near the Star Inn in 1772, at Castle Gateway in 1790, and from 1803-5 on the High Street, see Tyler (11) and Sautter (4); Benjamin Comber of Lewes was listed in the Town Book for 1804 (Smith 156).
3. Superstructure of 160K repeats the form of 160I.
4. JH notes that Richard Comber married Jane Woodgate 7 Dec 1772 at Lewes, St. Thomas Cliffe (Sussex Marriage Index).

Lewes, St. Michael Additions
Davidson-Houston (*SAC* 78 109), from Burrell (BL Add. MS 5698 f.91r).
(1) Brass for William Claggel, d. 10 Sep 1625 (on ledger in North aisle).

(161) LEWES, St. Thomas a Becket, Cliffe

A 14th-century building - Nairn & Pevsner (553-4); the porch - a rare modern addition - was probably designed by Joseph Daw late in his life c.1752, see S. Berry (*SAC* 142 109); for a plan see *SNQ* (XIII 156); for a view of 1793 see Godfrey & Salzman (Pl. 100, from BL Add. MS 5676 f.88); the parish had c.101 families in 1717 and a population of 1113 in 1801; no monuments at Cliffe noted in Horsfield.

Lewes, 161A Mural monument for Robert BALDY, d. 1774
- West porch, North wall, above head height.
- 80(W) x 210(H) — Very good.
- In grey-veined marble; M.I. (engraved, centred, black) on a rectangular tablet; cornice and base mouldings; above, a broken scrolled pediment; urn in relief; below, floral decorated and another urn between brackets.
- Robert Baldy, Esq., of Northumberland Street, London, d. 11 Jan 1774, aet 54; his niece, Elizabeth Lee, patron.

1. In 1771, one Thomas Baldy (1710-82) kept well-known gardens above Cliffe Corner, now Chapel Hill, see Challen, 'Baldy's Garden, the painters Lambert, and other Sussex Families' (*SAC* 90 103-5).
2. C. Brent (119); Thomas Baldy was son of John Baldy and Sarah Verrall, and for many years churchwarden at Lewes, St. Thomas a Becket; in 1754 he presented the church with carved angels from the organ at Chandos (Horsfield I 288); relationship between Robert Baldy and Thomas unknown.
3. Note the high quality lettering on 161A.

Lewes, 161B Mural monument for Susannah BULL, d. 1794 [Plate 104]
- North aisle, East wall, at head height.
- 68(W) x 95(H) — Very good, faded.
- M.I. (engraved, centred) on unframed pale cream marble panel; above, a straight entablature and a flute-patterned frieze; below, a brown base moulding in alabaster; curved apron with relief decoration of crossed ferns; signed (on scroll): 'W.ROGERSON. FECIT. LONDON'.
- Susannah Bull, d. Lewes, d. 17 Mar 1794, aet 20, only daughter of John Thompson Bull, Esq., of Stockwell Hall, Essex, and Susannah, daughter of John Woodgate, late of Lewes.

1. Erected by Susannah Bull's parents.
2. Her grandfather, John Woodgate (c.1736-83), was a draper and shipper of coal and seed potatoes in Cliffe who started a circulating library in 1758, see C. Brent (52, 54 and 127).
3. Gunnis (*Dict.* 325) cites this as by W. Rogerson, fl. 1794-1800.

Lewes, 161C Ledger for Ann STONE, d. 1727
- Nave floor, centre, towards West end.
- 94(W) x 189(L) — Fine; some wear.
- M.I. (engraved) on upper parts of a pale freestone slab; head to West.
- Ann Stone, d. 5 Sep 1727, aet 66; wife of Nicholas Stone, Gent.

1. Nicholas Stone was town constable in 1731-2 (Smith 28); for licence to marry dated 5 Sep 1711 for Nicholas Stone of Framfield, Gent. and Ann Mathew, of Cliffe, see Dunkin (*Licences 1670-1729* 319).
2. For Stone at Framfield see 110D-G, J and K.

(164) LINDFIELD, All Saints

Decorated, much restored; North and South Chancel chapels are Late Perpendicular - Nairn & Pevsner (561); nearly all areas of the church that house monuments date from 13th-16th centuries; an external view from the North in Godfrey & Salzman (Pl. 102); for groundplan see *SNQ* (V 217); there were c.164 families in the parish in 1717, which had a population of 1077 in 1801; in 1845, the fine building was reported to be sadly dilapidated, Gomme (285) and extensive interior alterations commenced, Miss Slater, 'Ancient Mural Painting lately discovered in Lindfield Church' (*SAC* 2 129); transcribed M.I.s have been checked and sometimes corrected by reference to Bax (*SAC* 37 151-172); for Board of Pax Hill pedigrees see M.A. Lower, 'Memoranda relating to the family of Boord ...' (*SAC* 6 197-214) and J. Cooper (*SAC* 42 245).

Lindfield, 164A Mural monument for Mary BRETT, d. 1750 and Mary BRIDGEN, d. 1764

- North aisle, facing West, high up.
- Inaccessible — Very good.
- A white marble tablet set portrait-wise; M.I. (12 lines, engraved, black) in upper 50%; narrow black border; Doric pilasters flanking, set forward; above, cornice then broken pointed pediment with globular urn in centre; below, a base moulding, 2 black scrolled brackets and a blank curved apron.
- Mary Brett, widow, of Lindfield, d. 1 May 1750, aet 69; also, Mary Bridgen, d. 26 Jul 1764, aet 59, widow of Rev. William Bridgen, A.M., rector of Folkington and West Dean.

1. Were these two women related? One Walter Brett, of Lewes and Mary Smith, of Lewes were married in 1720, see Dunkin (*Licences 1670-1729* 162).

Lindfield, 164B Mural monument for John COVERT, d. 1794

- North-East chapel, North wall, above head height.
- 45(W) x 122(H) — Very good.
- Backplate in pink-orange marble in form of an obelisk with a pointed top; supporting an unframed white marble oval tablet with M.I. (7 lines, engraved, black); below, base moulding, curved apron and white ball finial.
- John Covert, Esq., late of Chichester, died Lindfield, 26 Oct 1794, aet 78.

1. Unsigned; a smaller version of a standard late 18th-century type.
2. John Covert was of the Slaugham branch (Church Guide 43).
3. Noted and transcribed by Bax (*SAC* 37 156).

Lindfield, 164C Ledger for Elizabeth BOARD, 1674/5

- South-East chapel floor, North side.
- 45(W) x 79(L) — Good.
- M.I. (6 lines, engraved) in upper 50% of a black slab; head to West.
- Elizabeth Board, buried 10 Feb 1674/5; daughter of John Board, Gent.

1. Noted in Horsfield (*Sussex* I 385); unhelpfully described as amateurish (Church Guide, 41); noted by Bax (*SAC* 37 152).
2. For her father (d. 1697) see Lower (*SAC* 6 202-3) and 164E.

Lindfield, 164D Mural monument for Sarah and Richard BOARD, d. 1765 and d. 1782 [Plate 105]

- South-East (Masset's) chapel, East wall, above head height.
- 75(W); at least 200(H) — Very good; heraldic colour.
- A square white marble tablet, with a narrow border, filled with M.I. (engraved and black), on a dark grey pedestal; full cornice over; below, base moulding and curved white apron with an escutcheon; above, against a black baseplate with pointed top, an urn, draped and decorated, on a small base.
- Sarah Board, d. 6 Oct 1765, aet 26; daughter of Francis and Ann Dalby; and wife of Richard Board, d. 25 Dec 1782, aet 50, son of John Board, Esq., of Pax Hill, Sussex, and Bridget; issue of Richard and Sarah Board - another John, Lieut. (Horse Guards), d. Bruges, Flanders, 21 Sep 1793, aet 29; another Richard.

1. Unsigned but good in quality; consistent lettering suggests that 164D post-dates 1793.
2. Patron perhaps Richard Board, son and surviving brother; noted and transcribed by Bax (*SAC* 37 156); Sarah Board, b. 1739; Richard Board, b. 1732.
3. Heraldry noted (in situ) by Lambarde (*SAC* 69 191).

Lindfield, 164E Ledger for John BOARD, d. 1697/8

- South-East (Masset's) chapel floor, South-East corner, partly obscured on East side.
- 83(W) x 192(L) — Good.
- An escutcheon and M.I. (11 lines, engraved) fill upper (W) 80% of a black slab; head to West.
- John Board, Esq., of Lindfield, d. 28 Jan 1697/8, aet 69; memento mori.

1. Cited in Horsfield (*Sussex* I 385) and Church Guide (41).
2. Quotes traditional memento mori verses.
3. John Board was father of Elizabeth (164C), see Lower (*SAC* 6 202-3), noted by Bax (*SAC* 37 152) in situ.

Lindfield, 164F Ledger for Thomas NEWTON, d. 1688

- South-East (Masset's) Chapel floor, south of pier.
- 42(W) x 60(L) — Sound; cracks; cut (East end).
- M.I. (7 lines, engraved + 2 lines, scratched) fills a black slab; head to West.
- Thomas Newton, d. 8 Jun 1688, aet 2; son of George Newton; also Mary Newton (left incomplete).

1. Church Guide (41, citing Burrell MS, dated 1788) adds that Mary Newton was buried on 13 Nov 1709, so slab cut after that date.
2. There is a wooden vault cover between 164F and H, misidentified[?] by Bax (*SAC* 37 152) as a fragment of blue marble.

Lindfield, 164G Mural monument for William and Harriot BOARD, d. 1790 and d. 1809, and their children [Plate 106]

- South aisle wall, towards East end, at head height.
- 114(W) x c.200(H) — Good.
- Black baseplate with a curved top and a pointed bottom; M.I. (engraved & black) fills white marble tablet, set portrait-wise; below, a base moulding, a finned downward-pointing apron and 2 acanthus corbels; black pilasters with hanging garlands flanking; above, a white cornice and a segmented pediment with foliage and an escutcheon flanked by decorated palmettes; trace of signature (underside of baseplate, now partly obscured by wall plaster): 'MARSHALL (?) FECIT / DEPTFORD'.
- William Board, Esq, of Pax Hill, magistrate, etc., d. 26 Jul 1790, aet 60, elder son of John Board, Esq., of Pax Hill and Board Hill; his widow, Harriot Godolphin, d. 4 Sep 1809, aet 77, daughter of John Crawford, Esq., of Saint-Hill; their issue - Harriot, Countess Winterton; Louisa, d. 14 Jul 1811, aet 56, wife of Rev. William-Moreton Moreton, M.A., of Moreton Hall, Cheshire; and Fanny, d. 16 Feb 1808, aet 40, wife of Gibbs Crawford, Esq.; their issue William-Board-Edward-Gibbs, Harriot-Fanny and Harriot-Louisa.

1. Patron of 164G was Harriot, Countess Winterton, daughter and sister.
2. Probably erected after 1811? 86K has some similarities? Gunnis (*Dict.* 256) attributes 164G to T & G Marshall, of Deptford (fl. 1790-1823); noted and transcribed by Bax (*SAC* 37 155).
3. Heraldry noted (in situ) by Lambarde (*SAC* 69 191).
4. For the Boards, proprietors of the Board Hill estate, west of Lindfield, see 72S.

Lindfield, 164H Ledger for Dorothy and Edmund NEWTON, d. 1730 and d. 1738

- South aisle floor, East of crossing.
- 81(W) x 200(L) — Good.
- M.I. (11 lines, engraved) in upper 75% of a black slab; head to West.
- Dorothy Newton, d. 5 Oct 1730, aet 39; Edmund Newton, Gent., d. 5 Dec 1738, aet 40.

1. Dorothy Newton and Edmund Newton were not husband/wife but brother and sister, see Noyes (*SAC* 9 340), the issue of George and Mary Newton and siblings of Thomas (164F).
2. There is a wooden vault cover between 164F and H; the hand is consistent (see letter 'S') so the M.I. is either completely post-1738, or the letter-cutter returned to complete the entry on Edmund Newton.
3. 164H is noted by Bax (*SAC* 37 157), in situ.

Lindfield, 164I Mural monument for Thomas Gibbs CRAWFURD, d. 1830

- South aisle wall, just East of crossing, above head height.
- 100(W) x c.80(H) — Fine; rust patches.
- Black baseplate with pointed top; a white marble sarcophagus on 2 block corbels; a cornice; flattened, pointed pediment with palmettes flanking and low relief of dove within a wreath; signed (lower centre): 'MARTIN / LEWES'.
- Thomas Gibbs Crawfurd, Esq., of Pax Hill Park, 11 Oct 1769 - 19 Jul 1830.

1. The signature appears original and unrestored but is eccentrically composed: might it have been intended to read: 'Martin & Parsons of Lewes'?
2. 164I is noted and transcribed by Bax (*SAC* 37 155), who omits the forename Thomas.
3. Ninian Board, from Cuckfield, built a house at Pax Hill in 1606, which passed to Gibbs, son of John Crawfurd of Sainthill, East Grinstead, in 1790 (Farrant 272).

Lindfield, 164J Wall-mounted brasses for Stephen and Parnell BOARD, both d. 1567

- On South-East crossing pier, facing East, at head height and above.
- Slab is 72(W) x 187(H) — Fragmented brasses; signs of repair and infill on slab and brasses.
- An oolitic slab now wall-mounted; supports 4 brasses and also indents from others, now lost; below, a rectangular panel, set landscape-wise (restorations to the right), with M.I. (5 lines, engraved); at the top, a skull, flanked by 2 small M.I. panels (fragment only on right).
- Stephen Board, d. 22 Aug 1567; Parnell Board, d. [28] Jun in the same year.

1. Noted and transcribed by Burrell (BL Add. MS 5698 f.102, [accurately?]); Horsfield (*Sussex* I 385) states that both Stephen Board and his wife d. in 1579; Church Guide (24 & 41) identifies the slab as Sussex marble; 164J was in church floor, Bax (*SAC* 37 152), until 1887 or later, then moved to current position, see Davidson-Houston (*SAC* 78 110-113) with transcription; indents suggest that figure groups of children have been lost.
2. Note pre-Reformation sentiments of the wording commending the souls of the dead to God.
3. Stephenson (511) notes the set of brasses, with Stephen Board and Parnell Board and 4 sons and 3 daughters; Turner (*SAC* 23 169) notes matrices of 2 adults and 7 children, brasses themselves at that date missing.
4. For genealogical descent of Stephen Board see Lower (*SAC* 6 202-3).
5. Ninian Board, from Cuckfield, built a house at Pax Hill in 1606, which passed to the Crawfurds in 1790 (Farrant 272).

Lindfield, 164K Ledger for Judeth SPENCE, d. 1659

- Crossing floor, South side, West of 164L, partly obscured by piano.
- 56(W) x 61(L) — Badly scaled.
- M.I. (6 lines, engraved) on upper 60% of a black slab; head to the West.
- Judeth Spence, d. 26 Sep 1659, daughter of John Spence, Esq.

1. Noted by Horsfield (*Sussex* I 385).

2. For Judeth Spence's brother see 164L.
3. Located in situ by Church Guide, after Bax (*SAC* 37 151).

Lindfield, 164L Ledger for Thomas SPENCE, d. 1662
- Crossing floor, South side, East of 164K.
- 65(W) x 60(L) — Fine.
- M.I. (3 lines, engraved) in upper 50% of a fine black slab; head to West.
- Thomas Spence, buried 2 Sep 1662; son of John Spence, Esq.

1. For sister see 164K.
2. In situ in Church Guide, after Bax (*SAC* 37 151).

Lindfield, 164M Painted Arms of Richard and Sarah BOARD, d. 1782 and 1765, and of Charles and Sarah Jollands, d. 1866 and 1838
- Nave screen, West end, South side, high up.
- Inaccessible — Very good.
- An octagonal wooden panel; on each side, a painted achievement-of-arms with M.I. round each perimeter.

(East face):
Richardvs Board
q obiit i festo
nativitat dni
mdcclxxxii
ætat l et Sarah
vxor ejvs qvæ
obiit vi die Oct
a.d. mdcclxv
(West face):
Carolvs Jollands
q obiit die mens [sic]
a.d. mdccclxvi
ætat lxxxii et
Sarah uxor ei
q obiit die mens
a.d. mdcccxxxviii ætat lxi

1. The painter appears not to have know the exact death dates for those commemorated on the West face.
2. Noted and transcribed by Bax (*SAC* 37 154 & 157), over West arch to North chapel.
3. Church Guide notes that the old hatchments to these families were replaced in the 1883-5 restoration and incorporated in this screen in 1991.
4. Richard Board (164M) and William Board (164N) were brothers, sons of John Board, d. 1745.
5. Arms noted and M.I.s transcribed by Lambarde (*SAC* 69 191) (West wall and North transept).
6. JH notes that (East) Richard Board died 25 Dec 1782, aet 50 and Sarah his wife died 6 Oct 1765 and that (West) Charles Jollands died 1866 aet 82 and Sarah his wife died 1838 aet 61. In the GRO, the death of a Charles Jollands is registered in the June quarter of 1866, in Ware, Herts, aged 64. No death of a Sarah Jollands has been registered between 1837 and 1839. Nothing for either name in NBI for Sussex. What was their connection with Lindfield ?

Lindfield, 164N Painted Arms of William and Harriot BOARD, d. 1790 and d. 1809, and Dorothy Newton, d. 1730 [Plates 107 & 108]
- Nave screen, West end, North side, high up.
- Inaccessible — Very good.
- Description see 164M.

(East face):
Gvlielmi Board
q obiit xxvi die
Jvlii a.d. mdccxc
æt. lx e harriot

Godolphin vxor
ejvs qvæ obiit iv
die Septembris
a.d. mdcccix
(West face):
Mementote
Dorotheam
Newton qvæ
obiit v.to die
mens Octobris
anno domino
mdccxxx
ætat xxxix ann

1. See historical note under 164M.
2. Noted and transcribed by Bax (*SAC* 37 157) as over West end of South chapel; arms noted and M.I.s transcribed by Lambarde (*SAC* 69 191) (West wall and South transept).
3. Richard Board (164M) and William Board (164N) were brothers, sons of John Board, d. 1745; one William Board of Lindfield was apprenticed to Obediah Body of Battle, clockmaker, in 1731, see Rice (14-15).

Lindfield, 164O Ledger for Joanna WYATT, d. 1743

- Nave floor, centre, near West end.
- 82(W) x 200(L) — Worn; local losses (South side); slightly cut (sides).
- M.I. (8 + 4 lines, engraved) in upper 50% of a black slab; head to West.
- Joanna Wyatt, d. 18 Jun 1743, aet 76; 4th and last daughter of Francis Wyatt, Esq., late of Treemans, Sussex, and Awdry, his late wife; Joanna Wyatt's nephew, Richard Wyatt, Esq., of Tremans.

1. Perhaps installed by Joanna Wyatt's nephew, Richard Wyatt, on coming into the estate.
2. Church Guide reports that 164O has been moved.
3. NBI records the burial of Joanna Wyatt on 22 Jun 1743 at Lindfield.

Lindfield, 164P Ledger for members of the COMPTON family, 1762-1805

- Chancel floor, centre, East of crossing.
- 96(W) x 184(L) — Worn.
- M.I. (engraved) fills the surface of a pale freestone slab; head to West.

To the Memory of
LUCY COMPTON
wife of
THOMAS COMPTON GENT.
died January 1767[?].
Also
ELIZABETH daughter of
THOMAS and ELIZABETH
COMPTON Died Octr 21st
1769 Aged 7 Months.
Also
THOMAS COMPTON GENT
Died Octr 26th 1791.
Aged 75 Years.
Also
ELIZABETH COMPTON
Widow of THOMAS
COMPTON Died March
26th 1805 Aged 75 Years.

1. Noted and transcribed by Bax (*SAC* 37 154).
2. NBI records the following Compton burials - Lucy on 1 Feb 1762, Elizabeth on 21 Oct 1769, Thomas on 26 Oct 1791 and Elizabeth on 2 Apr 1805, all at Lindfield.

Lindfield, 164Q Ledger for Timothy and Elizabeth BURRELL, d. 1784 and 1755

- Chancel floor, centre, West end of choir.
- 100(W) x 200(L) — Fine.
- M.I. (13 lines, engraved) in upper 80% of a black slab; within a linear border; fleurs-de-lys in corners; head to West.
- Rev. Timothy Burrell, rector of Lindfield and Liddiard Millicent, Wiltshire, d. 30 Apr 1784, aet 87; his wife, Elizabeth, d. 18 Oct 1755, daughter of Ezekiel Bristed, and widow of Joseph Wildber, M.D.; no issue .

1. Noted in Horsfield (*Sussex* I 385); transcribed by Bax (*SAC* 37 153) and J. Cooper (*SAC* 43 24).
2. This Timothy Burrell was son of another Timothy Burrell, rector of Slaugham, in turn the son of Thomas Burrell (1632-1717), in turn third son of Walter Burrell, for whom see 72L; the widow's brother was John Bristed (1696-1783), son of Ezechiel Bristed, rector of Newhaven, master of Lewes Grammar School and rector of St. Anne's Lewes, 1725-83 and of St. Michael's, Lewes, 1731-83 (Caffyn 285).
3. Subjects of 164Q might reasonably have been commemorated at Cuckfield rather than Lindfield.
4. Fleur-de-lys decoration also occurs on 4G, 159L and 164U in the county in the 1780s.

Lindfield, 164R Floor-mounted brass for Isaac ALLEN, d. 1656

- Chancel floor, South of centre, towards East end.
- 56(W) x 37(L) — Fine.
- M.I. (13 lines, engraved) on a brass plate.
- Isaac Allen, died in prison, in London, 24 Jul 1656, aet 63; only son of Abraham Allen, Esq. and Joane

> HERE LYETH INTERRED Yᴱ BODY OF ISAAC ALLEN
> ONLY SONNE OF ABRAHAM ALLEN ESQ. BY HIS
> WIFE IOAN LOVE HEE DYED AT LONDON
> A PRISONER TO Yᴱ VPPER-BENCH, VPON AN
> ACC[CUSATI]ON FOR WORDES, MOST FALSELY &
> MALICIOVSLY, BY ONE SINGLE WITNESS
> SWORNE AGAINST HIM, AS HE HAD OFTEN-
> TYMES, & ON HIS DEATH-BED PROTESTED
> & DECLARED TO SEVERALL FRIENDS. HEE
> DESIRED HIS BODY MIGHT BE BVRYED
> HERE AT LINFEILD NEARE HIS MOTHER,
> & DECEACED Yᴱ 24ᵀᴴ DAY OF IULY ANᵒ DO[MI]NI
> 1656 AGED 63

1. Noted by Stephenson (511); Bax (*SAC* 37 153); and illustrated and transcribed as in situ by Davidson-Houston (*SAC* 78 113-14).
2. During the Commonwealth, the King's Bench was known as the Upper Bench (Church Guide, 40).
3. For Isaac Allen's son see 164T.

Lindfield, 164S Floor-mounted brass for Joan NEWTON d, 1655

- Chancel floor, towards East end, North of centre.
- 56(W) x 37(L) — Fine.
- M.I. (11 lines, engraved) on a brass plate with a skull (left) and crossed bones below.
- Joan Newton, d. 9 Sep 1655, aet 81; daughter of John Love, Esq., of Bishop's Basing, Hampshire; her first husband, Abraham Allen, Esq., of London, serjeant-surgeon to King James; her second husband, late William Newton, Gent., of Lindfield, 'Impropriator' of Lindfield church.

1. Noted by Stephenson (511); and transcribed by Bax (*SAC* 37 153) and illustrated as in situ by Davidson-Houston (*SAC* 78 113).
2. Joan Newton was mother of Isaac Allen (164R); Abraham Allen, admitted to Company of Barber-Surgeons in 1607 was Warden in 1611 and appointed King's Surgeon on 3 Apr 1610.

Lindfield, 164T Ledger for Isaack ALLEN, d. 1672
- Chancel floor, at sanctuary step.
- 82(W) x 151(L) — Worn.
- Achievement-of-arms, 2 escutcheons and M.I. (8 lines, shallow engraved) fill the surface of a black slab; head to West and perhaps cut at East end.
- Isaack Allen, citizen and mercer of London, d. 25 Jul 1672, aet 52; third son of Isaack Allen, of Lindfield.

1. Dated 1572 [sic] by Horsfield (*Sussex* I 385); noted (in situ) and translated by Bax (*SAC* 37 153); arms noted (in situ) by Lambarde in (*SAC* 69 190).
2. This Isaac Allen is the son of subject of 164R; Giles Moore officiated at Isaac Allen's burial 27 Jul 1672, after he had fallen from his horse on 24th, 'towards night ... and dyd thereof the next morning', see Bird (340).

Lindfield, 164U Ledger for Jane BATCHELOR, d. 1761, and Philadelphia
- South porch floor, at church door.
- 100(W) x 200(L) — Very worn.
- M.I. (5 lines, engraved), in upper 30% of a black slab; head to West, an engraved linear border and with fleurs-de-lys at corners.
- Jane Batchelor, d. 15 Jan 1761[?], aet 81[?]; wife of William Batchelor, Gent.; their daughter Philadelphia, d. 31[?] Aug ????, aet 30.

1. Noted and transcribed (in situ) by Bax (*SAC* 37 157).
2. Fleur-de-lys decoration also occurs on 159L, 164Q and on 4G set up at Alfriston to commemorate William Batchelor (d.1783).
3. NBI records the burial of Jane Batchelor on 19 Jane 1764 and Philadelphia Batchelor on 31 Aug 1773 at Lindfield.

(165) LITLINGTON - no monuments found

(166) LITTLE HORSTED, St. Michael & All Angels
Chancel Norman; some other parts Early English - Nairn & Pevsner (563-4); reported to be in good repair in 1686 and in 1724 (Ford 52; 174); restored in 1863; about 20 families in 1724 and a population of 201 in 1801; Horsfield (*Sussex* I 374) did not note any M.I.s relating to 166A.

Little Horsted, 166A Set of engraved brasses for the NOTT family, early 19th century
- Chair, West wall, South-West corner and on nearby window-sill.
- Wall set, in total: 63(W) x 105(H); Window brass: 88(W) x 34(H) — Generally good; some M.I.s worn.
- The upper wall section comprising a small engraved brass, M.I. for Sergison Nott, d. 1802, in Latin, a border, escutcheon to left; its pair, larger and lower, with a decorated border, M.I. for one Anthony Nott, d. 1823, etc.; another M.I. for Anthony Nott on a trapezoidal brass on the window sill.
- First brass: Sergison Nott, Esq., d. 31 Jan 1802, aet 61.
  Second brass: Rev. Anthony Nott, rector of Little Horsted for 40 years and of Litlington for 24 years, Emmanuel College, Cambridge, d. 15 Feb 1823, aet 70; his wife, Susanna, d. Stanford, London, 25 Dec 1840, aet 67, buried at Horsted Place; issue - second son, George Anthony Nott, paymaster of the Royal African Colonial Corps, d. Sierra Leone, 5 Aug 1826, aet 28; eldest son, Lieut. Charles S. Nott of the 41st Regiment, d. Bellary, East Indies 22 May 1837, aet 41; his widow, unnamed; their issue - 6 unnamed.
  Third brass: Anthony Nott, d. 27 Jun 1791, aet 85; on 13 Apr 1732, he married Prudence Warden, d. 27 Nov 1786, aet 74, great niece of Charles Sergison, Esq.; also Mrs Julia Nott, d. 21 Mar 1793.

1. 166A appears to be a mid nineteenth-century brass (perhaps after 1863) in part, replacing and supplementing existing M.I.s; the original M.I.s were noted by *Gent's Mag* 1809 in Gomme (287) and by Horsfield (*Sussex* I 374) as on chancel arch.
2. Anthony Nott, 21 Jun 1705 - 27 Jun 1791, aet 85, owned the glebe and tithes in 1785 (R. Davey 119; also Mrs Julia Nott, d. 21 Mar 1793.
3. Third brass partially transcribed in J. Cooper (*SAC* 49 102).
4. Heraldry noted in Lambarde (*SAC* 70 158-9). .
5. JH notes that the arms of Sergison impaling those of Nott make it probable that Sergison Nott was the son of Anthony (d. 1791) and Prudence. It is likely that Anthony (d. 1823) was another son.

Little Horsted Additions
Lambarde (*SAC* 70 159) noting the arms:
(1) William Hill, of Steyning, surgeon, d. 15 May 1738, and Mary, his widow, d. 1749, daughter of Richard Hay, of Battle (ledger).
Gent's Mag 1809 in Gomme (287) :
(2) Elizabeth Hay, dates unknown; William Hay, dates unknown.
(3) Mary Hill, buried 20 Mar 1744, aet 37; her husband Richard Hill; their daughter Elizabeth, their son Richard buried 8 Jul 1738, aet 2.
(4) William Hill, of Steyning, surgeon, apothecary, d. 15 May 1738, aet 51; his wife Mary, d. 13 Feb 1730, aet 44, first daughter of Richard Hay, Esq., of Battle.

(168) LULLINGTON - no monuments found

(172) MARESFIELD, St. Bartholomew
Norman and Perpendicular but over-restored; for work in 1862, see Turner (*SAC* 14 138-170); transepts and chancel 1875-9 - Nairn & Pevsner (564-5); patron at Maresfield in 1603 was John Gage, of Firle, a recusant Catholic, see Renshaw (*Ecclesiastical Returns*); condition reported to be fine in 1724 (Ford 177) when there were c.70 families in the parish; population was 133 in 1801; there is no mention of monuments in Horsfield (*Sussex* I 374-7); the mural monuments grouped in the West tower are likely to have been moved during the restorations of the 1870s.

Maresfield, 172A Mural monument for Caroline DAY, d. 1823
- Nave, North wall, high.
- c.96(W) x c.83(H) — Fine, fading.
- M.I. (13 lines, engraved, centred, black) in Latin on a rectangular white tablet set landscape-wise; unframed; black baseplate; 2 black block corbels.

D.M.S.
CAROLINAE
GULIELMI DAY DE HADLOW
UXORIS DELECTÆ
MULTIS ILLI MULTOS ANNOS PRECANTIBUS
LAETHALI [?] I PHTHISEOS VENENO CONTABUIT.
UTRIBUSQUE VITE PAULATIM RESOLUTÆ [?]
E TERRIS MELIORA SPERANS EMIGRAVIT
MULTUM AMATÆ MULTUM DEFLETÆ
RELLIQUIIS QUÆ SUBTUS JACENT. MORTALIBUS
HOC MARMOR CONSECRAVIT MOERENS
HEU I [?] CONJUX QUAM BREVIS CONJUGII.
NATA 1795. DUCTA 1819. OBIIT 1823

1. Unsigned.
2. Absolutely standard type.
3. JH notes that Caroline Day (1795-1823) was the wife of William of Hadlow - married in 1819 at St. Margaret's, Westminster. According to the Sussex Marriage Index, her maiden name was Gindlay.

Maresfield, 172B Mural monument for Family of Henry MICHELL, memorial dated 1792

- Chancel, South wall, at head height.
- 34(W) x 58(H) — Very good.
- M.I. (16 lines, engraved, black) in Latin on an unframed marble tablet; above, a generous pointed pediment; below, base mouldings.
- Dorothy, wife of Francis Reade of Bedford; Henry Michell, rector of Maresfield for more than 50 years; Elizabeth; Thomas; erected by F[aith] Michell in 1792.

DOROTHÆ

(FRANCISCI READE

DE BEDFORD

VXORI)

HENRICO MICHELL

HVJVS ECCLESIÆ

PLVS L ANNOS

RECTORI

ELIZÆ ET THOMÆ

MATRI

CONJVGI ET

LIBERIS

HOC MARMOR

P.C.

F. MICHELL

MDCCXCII

1. Unsigned but very neat.
2. Rev. Henry Michell occupied the parsonage in 1785, see R. Davey (151); for his monument see 40D erected in Brighton in 1790. See also *ODNB* for his biography by A. Pollard, revised by P. Carter.
3. JH notes that this monument was erected by Faith Michell for her mother, husband and children. Rev. Francis Reade and Dorothy Ashcroft were Faith's parents. Her husband Henry Michell was rector of Maresfield 1739-89, and of Brighthelmstone (to which Blatchington was attached) 1744-89. Four of their sixteen children, who died in infancy, were two named Elizabeth, died 1749 and 1753, and two named Thomas, died in 1749 and 1751. Faith Michell died in 1809.

Maresfield, 172C Mural monument for Edward KIDDER, d. 1817 [Plate 109]

- Tower, South wall, towards East end, above head height.
- c.62(W) x c.106(H) — Good; colour traces.
- Low relief roundels of arms, top and bottom, that at the top with armoured man with shield; M.I. (21 lines, engraved, centred, black) on an unframed marble tablet; rounded top and shoulders; a curved base with simple moulding.
- Edward Kidder, citizen of London, d. 21 Jun 1817 aet 47, his wife, Maria Emery, of Potton, Bedfordshire; their issue - 2 sons, 6 daughters; descended from George Kidder, of an ancient family in this parish, whose son Vincent, Army Major in Ireland in 1649, married Ellen Loftus, daughter of Sir Thomas Loftus, of Killian, Meath, the fourth son of Adam Loftus, D.D., archbishop of Dublin, etc.; issue of Vincent and Ellen - 3 sons and 6 daughters, of whom the second son, Vincent, distinguished himself in 1689, and also at the Battle of the Boyne [1690], and was later a Colonel of the Dublin Militia, d. 1736; erected by Edward's brother Thomas.

1. Noted by Nairn & Pevsner (565).
2. Patron was Edward's brother Thomas (172F).
3. The Kidders were anciently of this parish, the M.I. recounts the military and family history in 17th-century Ireland, see E. Turner 'Richard Kidder... and the Kidders of Maresfield' (*SAC* 9 125-138).

Maresfield, 172D Mural monument for William NUTT, d. 1769, and his daughter Anne HOLFORD, d. 1796

- Tower, centre of South wall, above head height, above 172E.
- c.108(W) x c.80(H) — Very good; rosette missing (lower right corbel).
- A pointed pediment with a dark grey inlay; frieze (with exhortation); moulded cornice supported by 2 fluted brackets with guttae below; between them, M.I. (9 lines) on an unframed tablet on 2 dark grey block corbels with rosette decoration.
- William Nutt, Esq., d. 14 Jan 1769, aet 66; son of John and Philadelphia Nutt, of Marshalls, Maresfield; his daughter, Ann, wife of Peter Holford, Esq., 3 Oct 1729 - 23 Nov 1796, aet 67.

1. Eccentric composition; presumably erected c.1770.

Maresfield, 172E Mural monument for Louisa RIVETT, d. 1798 [Plate 110]

- Tower, centre of South wall, at head height, beneath 172D.
- 79(W) x 92(H) — Fine; local damage (upper M.I.), faded.
- In grey marble; M.I. (15 lines, engraved, centred, black) fills a tablet set portrait-wise; simple moulded frame; flat cornice; wave decoration on base moulding; below, 2 scrolled corbels.
- Louisa Rivett, died in childbirth, 14 Apr 1798, aet 27; youngest daughter of Culling Smith, Esq., of Hadley, Middlesex; and wife of Thomas Rivett, rector of Maresfield; issue - 3 unnamed; her virtues.

1. Unsigned.

Maresfield, 172F Mural monument for Thomas KIDDER, d. 1829

- Tower, South wall, towards West end, above head height.
- 81(W) x 131(H) — Very good; local losses (top / bottom).
- A white marble tablet; unframed; on trapezoidal, slender, black baseplate with a pointed top; flat cornice moulding; M.I. (7 lines, engraved, centred, black) in the upper 30%; below, escutcheon.
- Thomas Kidder, of London, d. 23 Nov 1829, aet 66; family of Maresfield.

1. The names of later Kidders were never added; for Kidders see 172C.
2. Unsigned.
3. Turner (*SAC* 9 136) suggests a death date of 1820, (misread).
4. NBI records burial of Thomas Kidder on 2 Dec 1829 at Maresfield.

Maresfield, 172G Wall-mounted cast iron ledger for Robert BROOKS, d. 1667

- Tower, North-West corner, against North wall.
- 56(W) x 172(H) — Pitting; rust; fine.
- M.I. (7 lines, raised) in a band across the centre of iron slab; lines 1-4 justified L; lines 5-7 central.

HERE LYETH THE
BODY OF M ROBE
RT BROOKS WHO
DEPARTED THIS
LIFE THE 12
DAY OF IVNE
AEATIS [sic] SVÆ 1667

1. Note compositional errors in lettering.
2. Willatts (*SAC* 125 100-101 and 112) notes variable thickness as sign of inferior workmanship.

Maresfield Additions
Iron slabs noted by Willatts (*SAC* 125 111):
(1) An unattributed slab first recorded in 1852 (perhaps buried in churchyard).
(2) Another similar (perhaps buried in churchyard).

(173) MAYFIELD, St. Dunstan

Mostly post-dates a fire in 1389 - Nairn & Pevsner (565-66); for plan see *SNQ* (VI 179); nearly all areas with monuments are 13th-15th century; Mayfield had 179 houses in c.1760 and a population of 1849 in 1801; Willatts (*SAC* 125 102) lists 7 iron slabs at Mayfield (only 3 noted here - 173G, H and P); Gunnis (*Dict.* 188) notes Jonathan Harmer terracotta monuments (churchyard). For iron slabs at Mayfield, see *Wealden Iron*, second series 22, 2002.

Mayfield, 173A Mural monument for Rev. Peter BAKER, d. 1729/30, and his family

- Nave, West wall, South of tower arch.
- 127(W) x c.250(H) — Fair; local losses (lower right, arms above).
- Pendant to 173B; a pointed pediment supporting flaming urns left (lost) and right; fluted corbels; broken cornice; below, M.I. on unframed white marble tablet; flat arched top; full base mouldings on brackets; black backplate; white corbel at foot.
- Rev. Peter Baker, A.M., vicar of Mayfield 33 years, d. 20 Jan 1729/30, aet 58, son of John Baker, Esq., of the Place; his wife, Marthanna, eldest daughter of Robert Baker, of Middle House; issue - Michael Baker, Esq., of Lower House, born 13 Dec 1716; Michael Baker's wife, Martha, only daughter and sole heir of Walter Roberts, Esq., of Stone House, Warbleton.

1. Cited Horsfield (*Sussex* I 418-19) – for M.I. and Bell-Irving (78) for transcription.
2. Michael Baker, son and heir was patron of both 173A and B, which are by the same hand; Peter Baker was educated Emmanuel College, Cambridge; instituted at Mayfield 1696; third son of John Baker by his wife Ruth, daughter of Peter Farnden, of Sedlescombe, see Dunkin (*SAC* 26 70); he married his cousin - licence dated 7 Oct 1715, see Dunkin (*Licences 1670-1729* 322).
3. NADFAS reports that their portraits are at ESRO, Lewes.

Mayfield, 173B Wall monument for John BAKER, d. 1723/4, and his family

- Nave, West wall, North of tower arch, high.
- 130(W) x 278(H) — Good; cracked apron.
- Pendant to 173A but no losses.
- John Baker, Esq., of the Place, d. 18 Mar 1723/4, aet 80; his wife, Ruth, daughter of Peter Farnden, Esq., of Selscomb; their issue - John, Michael, Peter, Thomas, George, Nizel, Elizabeth, Dorothy, Lucy, Martha, Charity, and Ruth.

1. Horsfield (*Sussex* I 418-9) for M.I. and Bell-Irving (78) for transcription.
2. Michael Baker, grandson of this John Baker, was patron of both 173A and B, which are by the same hand; John Baker was son of John Baker (d.1668) and Elizabeth Rivers; their son, Peter, was vicar of Mayfield (NADFAS report).
3. Unusual line of dots in penultimate lines of M.I..
4. JH notes that there has been a coat of arms, which is now indecipherable.

Mayfield, 173C Free-standing tomb-chest for Anne RIVERS, d. 1742

- Nave, North-West corner.
- Top: 84(W) x 167(L); Base: 87(W) x 172(L) x 79(H) — Fine, rust stains.
- Freestone chest; moulded white-veined marble ledger with escutcheon then M.I. (9 lines, engraved), head to West; moulded base; Four thick balusters integral with framed blank panels on four sides.
- Anne Rivers, d. 28 May 1742, aet 47; daughter of Sir George Rivers, Bart. and Dorothea, of Chafford, Penshurst, Kent.

1. Cited by Horsfield (*Sussex* I 415-20) and by Bell-Irving (79) for transcription.
2. Such a tomb-chest located inside an East Sussex church is rare if not unique; its base is close to versions found in churchyards.
3. Dorothea was daughter of Sir William Beversham, Holbrooke Hall, Suffolk, lawyer, d. 1734; Anne

Rivers' sister was Philadelphia Baker (d. 1741), who left £20 'for a stone ...' for Anne Rivers if she was not to be buried in the Baker vault with her sister Philadelphia (NADFAS).
4. For heraldry, see Lambarde (*SAC* 67 162).

Mayfield, 173D Wall monument for Philadelphia GODFREY, d. 1807

- Nave, North wall, North-West corner, at head height.
- 91(W) x 129(H) — Good.
- M.I. (engraved, black) fills trapezoidal white marble tablet; grey slate baseplate; below, a thick squared base moulding; above, pointed pediment; blank quartered palmettes flanking; signed (lower right): 'BROWNE / & Co / LONDON'.
- Philadelphia Godfrey, 5 Dec 1750 (St. Austle [sic], Cornwall) - 27 Apr 1807 (Islington, Middlesex); eldest daughter of George Baker, Esq. and Mary; her brother, Michael Baker, Esq., co-heir of the Lower House, Mayfield; Philadelphia was the wife of William Elsley, Esq., of Jamaica; issue - 1 son, unnamed; and then the wife of Henry Godfrey, Esq., of London: issue - 1 son, 3 daughters.

1. Formerly at East end of South aisle, probably moved in 1920s; cited Horsfield (*Sussex* I 419) and noted by Bell-Irving (82).
2. A decree in Chancery of 1807 partitioned Mayfield Place and Lower House estate between heirs of Ann Rivers (see 173C) and Philadelphia (NADFAS report).
3. The signature of the maker is carefully positioned to be visible to beholders.

Mayfield, 173E Mural monument for Major Charles GRANT, d. 1828

- North aisle wall, East end.
- 91(W) x 70(H) — Very good.
- M.I. (8 lines, engraved, black) fills an unframed white tablet set landscape-wise; black baseplate; 2 block corbels.
- Major Charles Grant, of the Island of St. Vincent, d. 18 Apr 1828, aet 42.

1. Cited Horsfield (*Sussex* I 419) and noted by Bell-Irving (79).
2. Charles Grant, born 1786; issue - 2 sons, 1 daughter (NADFAS report).
3. Patron of 173E possibly Lieut. Thomas Kirby, son of rector of Mayfield (see 173Q).

Mayfield, 173F Ledger for John EDWARDS, d. 1678

- Nave floor, near North aisle pier.
- 100(W) x 204.5(L) — Worn.
- Escutcheon, then M.I. (engraved) in upper 50% of black slab; head to West.

> Here lyeth intered the
> body of Iohn Edwards
> Gen. who departed this
> life the 23 of Iune Anno
> Dom 1678 and of his Age
> 71

1. Cited by Bell-Irving (77) with transcription.
2. John Edwards, a widower at his death, was son of Abraham Edwards of Brightling (NADFAS report); Edwards owned land in Waldron, Heathfield and Mayfield; John Edwards and Abraham Edwards were presented by the churchwarden in 1675 for not making up an allotted church mark and for not repairing a church gate, see Johnstone (24).
3. For heraldry see Lambarde (*SAC* 67 163).

Mayfield, 173G Iron Slab for Thomas SANDS, d. 1668

- Nave floor, near South aisle pier.
- 59.5(W) x 170(H) — Worn.
- M.I. (raised in 3 blocks, off centre right) on iron slab; head to the West.

HEAR. LYETH
THE BODY OF
THOMAS SANDS

WHO WAS
BVRYED IVLY
THE 20 1668

AGED 72
YEARS

1. Nairn & Pevsner (566) note the M.I. across, not along, the slab; Willatts (*SAC* 125 101, 107) notes reversed numeral and erratic lettering; cruder than that of 173H; cited by Bell-Irving (77) with transcription.
2. NADFAS notes that 173G was probably cast at Hawksden Furnace (repaired in 1667) of which
   Thomas Sands was the lessee, and worked by the Sands until 1727.

Mayfield, 173H Iron Slab for Thomas SANDS, d. 1708 [Plate 111]

- Nave floor, near South aisle pier, immediately East of 173G.
- 74(W) x 180.5(L) — Worn.
- Escutcheon, then M.I. (incised) then floral decoration on an iron slab; head to West; beaded border.

motto
COME AS BRETHREN
Thomas Sands
Citizen And Wine
Cooper Of London
Who Died Dec^{br} Y^e 11th
Ano Domini 1708
In y^e 33$^{th[sic]}$ year of his
Age

1. Noted by Nairn & Pevsner (566) – arms and Willatts (*SAC* 125 107) and cited by Bell-Irving (77) with transcription.
2. Thomas Sands was a member of family of iron masters, grandson or great-grandson of the Thomas Sands commemorated in 173G; these arms are those of the Wine Coopers - Thomas Sands had none of his own, see Lambarde (*SAC* 67 163); wish in his will was to be buried close to his father (d. 1701) (NADFAS report).
3. Quality of casting has improved markedly over 40 years; compare 173G with 173H.

Mayfield, 173I Mural monument for Thomas BAKER, d. 1782, and his wives, Marthanna, d. 1780 and Ann, d. 1804 [Plate 112]

- Chancel, North wall, East end.
- 142(W) x 282(H) — Very good; drapery lost (lower right).
- In white marble on a black baseplate with pointed top; mourning figure in relief; draped urn on a wreathed pedestal; below, a white M.I. on a tablet set landscape-wise, flanked by yellow half-columns with Ionic capitals on scroll corbels with acanthus decoration; above, a cornice; below, a black curved apron from the baseplate with drapes and escutcheon; foliate corbel at foot.
- Thomas Baker, Esq., of the Lower House and London (Grocer's Co.), High Sheriff of Sussex in 1775, d. 25 Jun 1782, aet 53, no issue; second son of George and Philadelphia Baker of Mayfield Place; his first wife, Marthanna, d. 27 Nov 1780, aet 59, daughter of George and Sarah Baker of Warbleton; his second wife, Ann, d. 11 Dec 1804, aet 81, daughter of John and Hannah Baker of the Middle House, Mayfield; all buried at Mayfield.

1. Horsfield (*Sussex* I 418) with aet of Thomas Baker as 52 and cited by Bell-Irving (79) with transcription.
2. Probably erected after 1804 by Trustees, Rev. John Kirby, etc. (NADFAS report).
3. Thomas Baker was apprenticed to John Trymmer, citizen and grocer on 7 Jan 1745, see Rice (10), and supported the local charity school (Caffyn 197).
4. Highly unusual yellowish half-columns.

Mayfield, 173J Mural monument for Robert and Marthanna BAKER, d. 1714 and d. 1693

- Chancel, North wall, high.
- 110(W) x 250(H) — Excellent.
- In grey-veined and white marbles; broken segmented pediments, 1 breaking forward; between, an urn and garlands in relief; flaming lamps flanking; entablature supported on Corinthian 3/4 columns; between, M.I. fills tablet with arched top and (blank) escutcheon with crossed ferns; below, generous base moulding and panelled apron between scrolled and fluted corbels; moulded corbel in centre.
- Robert Baker, Gent., of Middle House, Mayfield, d. 4 Jul 1714, aet 79; his wife, Marthanna, d. 21 Jan 1693, aet 42, only daughter and heiress of Samuell Cole, Gent., of Braybrook Castle, Northamptonshire; their issue - Samuell (died aet 21), John, Robert, Richard, George, Thomas, Marthanna (still living 1714), Elizabeth, Dorothea (still living 1714), Elizabeth, and Mary (still living 1714).

1. Cited in Horsfield (*Sussex* I 418) and in Bell-Irving (80) with transcription.
2. NADFAS notes portraits of Robert and Marthanna Baker in ESRO, Lewes.

Mayfield, 173K Ledger commemorating several generations of PENKHERST, dated 1646

- Choir floor, North side, partly obscured by furnishings.
- (W) unknown x 204(L) — Good.
- M.I. (engraved) on a black slab; head to West.

STEPHANO PENKHERST
WILL[ELMI] F[ILIO]
IOH[ANNIA] N[EPOTI]
IOHANNI PENKHERST
STEPH[ANI] F[ILIO] WILL[ELMI] N[EPOTI]
P[OSUIT]
STEPHANUS PENKHERST
IOH[ANNIS] F[ILIUS] STEPH[ANI] N[EPOS]
DE BUCKSTED ARMIG[ER]
A.D.
MDCXLVI

1. M.I. from NADFAS report; cited in Horsfield (*Sussex* I 418-9) and noted by Bell-Irving (82).
2. The family had long connections with Rotherfield; for licence to marry for John Cooper Penkherst, of Mayfield, Gent. and Anne Fowle of Rotherfield 23 Oct 1626, see Dunkin (*Licences 1586-1643* 156); Stephen Penkherst, ironmaster, had purchased Buxted Park in 1651; family extinct in 1707 and his heirs sold to Thomas Medley (1645-1728) in 1724; Stephen Penkherst is commemorating his father John (d.1631), grandfather Stephen (d.1646), great-grandfather William and great-great-grandfather John.

Mayfield, 173L Mural monument for Michael and Martha BAKER, d. 1750 and d. 1796

- Sanctuary North wall.
- 120(W) x 243(H) — Very good.
- A grey, slate, pointed backplate; a mourning widow in white marble leaning against an urn on a pedestal; below, cornice; M.I. (engraved, black) fills rectangular white tablet; flanked by yellow, 1/4 columns with Doric capitals; 2 corbels with rosette decoration; between, a curved apron with drapes; escutcheon and crossed ferns in grey slate; signed (lower left): 'CH. REGNART / Sculpt^r Cleaveland Str^t'; (lower right): 'Fitzroy Square, / LONDON.'.
- Michael Baker, Esq., d. 16 Jul 1750, aet 34; only son of Rev. Peter Baker, vicar of Mayfield; his wife, Martha, d. 19 Sep 1796, aet 79, buried Warbleton, daughter and sole heiress of Walter Roberts, Esq., of Stone House, Warbleton, and later wife of Rev. Henry Harcourt, rector of Warbleton and Crowhurst; no issue.

1. Horsfield (*Sussex* I 418) - notes M.I.; Gunnis (*Dict.* 317) - by Regnart, dates it 1796; Nairn & Pevsner (566) - by Regniart (mis-spelled); cited by Bell-Irving (80) with transcription.
2. Composition close to 173I.
3. Perhaps Regnart came to see the proposed location, consult the client and designed something in keeping.
4. Michael Baker supported the local charity school (Caffyn 195). .
5. For heraldry, see Lambarde (*SAC* 67 160).

Mayfield, 173M Mural monument for Thomas HOUGHTON, d. 1669, etc.

- Sanctuary, North wall, East of 173L.
- 111(W) x 185(H) — Very good.
- M.I. (engraved, white) fills slate (?) tablet; black Composite pilasters flanking; entablature with blank black frieze; above, a generous cornice with scrolled, broken pediment; large achievement in grey stone; below, scrolled corbels support base moulding; between, an edged, curved marble apron with elaborate garland.
- Thomas Houghton, Esq., principal of Clifford's Inn, London, d. 30 Jul 1669, aet 75; his wife Walsingham, d. 30 Jan 1669/70, aet 65; their youngest son, John, d. 8 Dec 1666, aet 36.

1. Horsfield (*Sussex* I 419) - noting M.I. and cited by Bell-Irving (81) with transcription.
2. Thomas Houghton's family were Devonian; his first wife was Mary, daughter of Thomas Ayncombe (no issue); his second wife Walsingham, was daughter of Thomas Theobald, of Seale, Kent (NADFAS report); were the patrons of 173M two of Thomas Houghton's married daughters, executrices of Walsingham's will? 173M has unusual lettering, the white marble has pinkish tones, the apron design is highly unusual and the quality of lower marble swag is very good.
3. There are 3 iron slabs associated with 173M, largely hidden by choir-stalls on North side, heads to West, each 59 to 60 (W), length unknown (cited also by Horsfield loc cit).
4. For heraldry see Lambarde (*SAC* 67 160).

Mayfield, 173N Mural monument for Samuel and Anne BAKER, d. 1796 and d. 1809

- Sanctuary, South wall, high.
- 78(W) x 55(H) — Good, faded.
- M.I. (11 lines, engraved, black) on a white marble rectangular tablet set landscape-wise; engraved border; bosses in corners.
- Samuel Baker, Esq., of the Middle House, d. 13 Feb 1796, aet 75; his wife Anne, d. 12 Feb 1809, aet 78.

1. Horsfield (*Sussex* I 419) and Bell-Irving (81) – noting M.I.
2. Samuel Baker's parents were John and Hannah; Anne was his cousin, daughter of George Baker and Philadelphia Rivers; issue – 9; Samuel Baker owned 'The Knole' in 1785 (R. Davey 154).
3. 173N is relatively modest c.f. 173R for Samuel Baker's parents-in-law, and other Baker monuments at Mayfield.

Mayfield, 173O Mural monument for John BAKER, d. 1688

- Upper Chancel, South wall, high.
- 117(W) x 219(H) — Good; water damage; local losses to cornice (roof fall?).
- M.I. (engraved) fills white marble tablet against grey-veined backplate; above, pink moulded cornice and escutcheon; below, base mouldings; then an ornamental baseplate; another escutcheon.
- John Baker, Esq., of Stoneland, Sussex, d. 11 Oct 1688, aet 58; his wife, Dorothea, daughter of John Baker, Esq., of Mayfield Place; their issue - John (d. 11 Nov 1667, aet 4), Charles (d. 8 Sep 1685, aet 20), Elizabeth (d. an infant), John (d. an infant), John (d. an infant), Richard (d. an infant), Mary (d. an infant), Robert, George, John, Dorothea, Elizabeth and Marthanna.

1. Horsfield (*Sussex* I 419) - noting M.I. (giving John Baker as aet 69); cited by Bell-Irving (81) with

transcription; cited Willatts (*SAC* 125 103) - mural monument to a wealthy ironmaster, while his son lies under iron (173P).

2. The Bakers became lords of the manor of Mayfield in 1617.
3. Patron of 173O was John Baker's widow.
4. Restored in August 1999 (NADFAS report).
5. The escutcheon is of a rare Baroque design, see Lambarde (*SAC* 67 161).

Mayfield, 173P Iron ledger for John BAKER, d. 1669

- Choir floor, South side, partly obscured by furnishings.
- 60(W); (L) unknown — Pitted.
- M.I. on cast iron slab; head to West; with motto 'VITA BREVIS'.

1. Cited by Bell-Irving (77) with transcription.
2. Cited by Willatts (*SAC* 125 103) as to infant sons of the iron master, John Baker d. 1688 (173N).

Mayfield, 173Q Mural monument for Jane-Ruth STRODE, d. 1819

- South chancel arch, facing North, high.
- 76.5(W) x 64(H) — Very good; fading.
- M.I. (8 lines, engraved, black) fills a white marble rectangular tablet, set landscape-wise; double border; corbels with rose decorated; above, a scrolled pediment with foliate decoration.
- Jane-Ruth Strode, d. 21 Feb 1819, aet 34; daughter of the late Rev. John Kirby; and wife of Charles Strode, Esq., of Frant; issue Grace-Ruth and William-Thomas.

1. Not noted in Horsfield (*Sussex* I 418-9) so is it after 1835?; noted by Bell-Irving (82).
2. Jane-Ruth Strode was daughter of vicar of Mayfield 1780-1810 (who d. 1811); Jane-Ruth married Charles Stone on 28 Jan 1816; for licence to marry dated 15 Jan 1816 for Charles Henry Stone, of Kensington Palace, age 21 plus and Jane Ruth Kirby, of Mayfield, spinster, age 21 plus, see Dunkin & Penfold (*Licences* 410); and see I. Pike 'The Kirby Family of Mayfield' *Sussex Genealogy and Local History*, 2 (1980 75-79); was Charles Strode a crown servant?

Mayfield, 173R Mural monument for George and Philadelphia BAKER, dated 1765 [Plate 113]

- South-East chapel, South wall, near South-East corner, high.
- 130(W) x 260(H) — Very good; fading.
- M.I. (10 lines, engraved, black) fills white marble tablet, unframed; below, an escutcheon in Baroque frame against brown freestone; moulded triangular corbel; base moulding; above, curved cornice supporting a broken scrolled pediment; plaque with cherub's head; on top, flaming urn; signed (right edge of lower cornice): 'S: Oliver Fecit'.
- George Baker, Gent.; his wife, Philadelphia Baker; dated 1765.

1. Not noted by Horsfield (*Sussex* I 418-9); moved early in 20th century; cited by Gunnis (*Dict.* 283 qv Sanders Oliver, c.1719-????) and by Bell-Irving (82) with transcription.
2. George Baker was fifth son of John and Ruth Baker; he married Philadelphia Rivers in 1721; issue - Thomas, George, Anne and Philadelphia.
3. The splendid and confident M.I. fails to record the death dates (Jul 1756 and Dec 1741).
4. George left his son £50 as his executor to erect a monument.
5. An ambitious late Baroque design.

Mayfield, 173S Mural monument for Richard Owen STONE, d. 1824 and others

- South aisle, South wall, high.
- c.106(W); (H) unknown — Fine.
- In freestone; Gothic frame with flanking colonettes topped by finials; M.I. (engraved, black) on tablet set portrait-wise; arched top with quatrefoils; base moulding and corbels; escutcheon isolated below; arch topped dark grey baseplate.
- Richard Stone, Gent., d. 24 Aug 1824, aet 58; his wife, Anna Maria Stone, d. 9 Jan 1838, aet 77; issue, George, d. 6 Aug 1803, aet 4; George, d. 19 Apr 1823, aet 19; William, d. 28

Sep 1839, aet 47; Maria Ann, d. 27 Jul 1882, aet 92; their great granddaughter, Elizabeth Margareta Bell-Irving, 20 Jul 1847 - 11 Dec 1913; Anna Maria Bell-Irving, 25 Nov 1848 - 9 Sep 1928.

1. Cited by Gunnis (*Dict.* 292) as by Parsons with date 1824; noted by Bell-Irving (82); erected after 1839 (too late for Horsfield); final 7 lines added.
2. Patron William Owen Stone, son of Richard Stone; for licence to marry dated 13 Aug 1789 for Richard Owen Stone, of Mayfield, Gent., bachelor, age 23 plus and Anna Maria Verrall, of St. John Baptist, Lewes, spinster, age 22 plus, see Dunkin & Penfold (*Licences* 407).
3. For heraldry see Lambarde (*SAC* 163).

Mayfield, 173T Mural monument for Thomas AYNSCOMBE, d. 1620, and Katherine his wife, d. 1633 [Plate 114]

- South aisle, West wall.
- 160(W) x 310(H) — Fair; colour.
- In different coloured stones/marbles; surface pigment; 2 kneeling effigies in civil dress, male to left at a prayer desk; skulls in roundels behind both their heads; escutcheon on back wall; round arch supporting a pedestal with achievement; beyond, a broken scrolled pediment with allegorical figures (attributes lost) - Justice and Hope?; arch on plain pilasters with escutcheons; below, in the predella, 5 issue kneeling (2 boys to the left); a base moulding on brackets with mask decorated; below, slate tablet with white M.I. in ornamental frame.
- Thomas Aynscombe, Esq., lawyer (Inner Temple), d. 2 Dec 1620; his wife, Katherine, d. 20 Apr 1633, daughter of Thomas Eversfield, Gent.; issue: 2 sons and 3 daughters living, 2 died as infants.

1. Cited by Horsfield (*Sussex* 1 419); Nairn & Pevsner (566); Bell-Irving (82-3) with transcription; erected in accordance with widow's will (Mosse 130-1); restored in 1962 (NADFAS).
2. For a Clerk of the Peace of this name, possibly the father of this Thomas Aynscombe (*SNQ* XIII 147).
3. The Eversfields were from Hollington, near Hastings.
4. Identifications of the allegories as SS Thomas and Katherine are not sustainable; NADFAS report 10 issue.
5. A piece of average quality: unpersuasive attributions to Garret Johnson, see Esdaile (*EMS* 120) and rejected by White (73), and Nicholas Stone (NADFAS) but almost certainly London-made [Southwark?].
6. For heraldry see Lambarde (*SAC* 67 163) and Mosse (130-1), both of whom mention small shields with impaled arms in front of the eldest son and daughter; no longer there.

Mayfield Additions
NADFAS survey and Bell-Irving.
(1) Edward Tench, d. 1830, carpeted (NADFAS no 029).
(2) John Baker, d. 1671, carpeted (NADFAS no 031).

(177) MOUNTFIELD, All Saints

Norman nave; Early English chancel - Nairn & Pevsner (569); in 1724, the church was reported as in very good condition, chancel recently repaired by the Duke of Dorset (Ford 111); Harmer terracottas in the churchyard; Horsfield (*Sussex* I 564) notes only 177A, which suggests a later date for 177B-D.

Mountfield, 177A Mural monument for Thomas HICKES, d. 1736 [Plate 115]

- Nave, North wall, nearly opposite the South door.
- c.85(W) x 140(H) — Fading.
- An elaborate achievement surmounts a flat cornice, supported on coloured pilasters and moulded capitals with rosette decorations; in the centre, an arched, flat M.I. (13 lines,

engraved, black); brown-red hardstone pilasters flanking; below, a base moulding and an ornamental apron in grey marble.

To the memory of
THOMAS HICKES late of this Parifh Gent
And ELIZABETH his Wife who was descended from
the Antient Family of the DUNMOLLS of *WADHURST*
in this County
both deceafed
He departed this life the eleventh day of November
in the year of our Lord 1736
aged 63 years
She Survived him and dyed the firft day of March 1743
aged 74 years
Pallida mors æquo pulsat pede pauperum taberna
Regumque turres

1. Noted by Horsfield (*Sussex* I 564); unusual late moralising quotation (*Horace Carmina* 1.4.13-14) in M.I.: 'Pale death calls equally at both the taverns of the poor and the towers of kings'; notable for the combination of colours; erected soon after 1743?
2. For licence to marry dated 22 Jul 1707 for Thomas Hickes, of Mountfield, Gent. and Elizabeth Dunmoll, of East Grinstead, see Dunkin (*Licences 1670-1729* 88).
3. In situ when heraldry noted by Lambarde (*SAC* 68 222).

Mountfield, 177B Mural monument for William RIGHTON, d. 1818

- Nave North wall, North-East corner, above head height.
- 75(W) x 80(H) — Fine, staining.
- Unframed; a rectangular white M.I. panel is topped by a simple cornice and a pointed pediment with a decorated disk; below, tiny brackets with dentils.
- William Austen Righton, Esq., of Mountfield Park, died Dieppe, France, buried there, 5 Sep 1818, aet 38; widow unnamed.

1. 177B is unsigned.
2. Patron was widow.
3. A gallery for the owners of Mountfield Park formerly stood near this spot or further West, which was accessed via an external stair; this was demolished with the original pews in 1840.

Mountfield, 177C Ledger for John SMEE, d. 1824

- Chancel floor, South-East corner, against the South wall, partly obscured by furniture.
- 62(W) x 114(L) — Worn.
- M.I. (engraved) in upper parts of a freestone slab; head to the West.

Here lie the remains of
JOHN SMEE Esq[r]
of Court Lodge
in this Parish, who died
27th December 1824
in the 57th Year
of his Age.

1. Alongside, a similar, later ledger for Charlotte Smee.
2. 177D is associated.
3. The previous owner of the manor of Court Lodge was John Nicoll (see R. Davey 158).

Mountfield, 177D Mural monument for John SMEE, d. 1824

- Nave, South wall, East of the South door, above head height.
- c.97(W) x c.126(H) — Good, fading, dentil details lost on brackets.
- M.I. (25 lines, engraved, black) on a simple unframed, white marble tablet, set portrait-wise; brackets (formerly) ornamented with dentils below; above, a moulded cornice and a low, pointed pedestal.

- John Smee, Esq., civil servant (30 years East India Co.), died at Court Lodge, Mountfield, 27 Dec 1824, aet 56; issue - unnamed.

1. Unsigned.
2. Associated ledger is 177C.
3. The lost dentils were perhaps like those on 177B.

Mountfield Addition
Church Guide
A slab for Rev. Wilfred Carter, Curate of Mountfield, 1802-29, near chancel South wall, hidden by a curtain.

(180) NEWHAVEN, St. Michael
Norman (12th-century) tower & apse, remade from 1854 - Nairn & Pevsner (570-1), VCH (VII, 65) and see plan in *SNQ* (III 157); floors reported as in bad condition in 1724 (Ford); a view of 1787, see Godfrey & Salzman (Pl.115), seen from North, shows churchyard largely empty, prior to construction of important monuments to Captain James Hanson (d. 1800) and the brewer Thomas Tipper (d. 1785); Horsfield (*Sussex* I 191-5) found nothing inside Newhaven worth noting, somewhat puzzling considering Newhaven's (or Meeching as it was known) importance as a port.

Newhaven, 180A Wall mounted ledger for Edward BURTENSHAW, d. 1704, and his daughter Mary, d. 1717
- Sanctuary (tower chapel), South wall, at head height.
- 52(W) x 56(H) — Worn.
- M.I. (6 + 5 lines) filling most of an unframed grey-veined marble panel, now plastered into the wall.
- Edward Burtenshaw, Gent., d. 30 Dec 1704, aet 46; his wife, Elizabeth; their eldest daughter Mary, d. 20 Nov 1711, aet 23.

1. Last lines of lettering added.
2. One Edward Burtenshaw, of Meeching, is documented in 1685, see Dunkin (*Licences 1670-1729* 89).

Newhaven, 180B Mural monument for Henry HUMPHERY, d. 1792
- Sanctuary (tower chapel), South wall, at head height.
- 78(W) x 100(H) — Good.
- M.I. (12 lines, engraved, black, centred) on a white rectangular panel; thin black baseplate; signed (below, centred): 'PARSONS. LEWES'.
- Henry Humphery, Esq., of Lewes, barrister, magistrate, d. 17 Feb 1792, aet 80.

1. Cited by C. Brent (217).
2. Henry Humphrey lived at 32 School Hill, Lewes in 1783 (Farrant 271) and owned a farm occupied by George Elphick in 1785 (R. Davey 159); it is unclear why Henry Humphrey's burial and monument are at Newhaven.
3. Note spelling of surname on memorial.

Newhaven, 180C Several Anonymous ledgers, dates unknown
- Entrance porch floor, to South of sanctuary, largely covered by furnishings.
- (1) in black slate, 97(W) x 199(L); (2) 97(W) x 199(L) — Very worn.
- (2) 18th century?, possibly shows a family name: Burtenshaw, see 180A.

(181) NEWICK, St. Mary

West part of nave Norman, lengthened later and the chancel rebuilt 1886-7 - Nairn & Pevsner (571); the North Aisle was built in 1836 (Church Guide) and is the location of this set of monuments, commemorating three generations of an aristocratic family; the original position is unknown.

Newick, 181A Mural monument for George VERNON, d. 1773, aged 1

- North aisle, North wall, above head height, forming a group with 181A-C.
- 70(W) x 85(H) — Good.
- A white oval marble plaque with a raised rim; M.I. (9 lines, engraved, black).
- George Vernon, 23 Feb 1772 - 6 Mar 1773, second son of Hon. George Vernon and Lady Louisa Vernon.

1. Noted by Horsfield (*Sussex* I 224).
2. Pendant to 181C.

Newick, 181B Mural monument for George VERNON, d. 1762, aged 1

- As for 181A.
- c.75(W) x 90(H) — Good.
- A white marble plaque with an irregular moulded edge; curved scrolled top; M.I. (10 lines, engraved, black).
- George Vernon, born 18 Nov 1761, died of measles, Sep[?] 1762; son of Hon. George Vernon and Hon. Louisa Vernon, daughter and heiress of Rt. Hon. Bussy, Lord Mansel.

Newick, 181C Mural monument for Charlotte VERNON, d. 1770, aged 1

- As for 181A.
- 70(W) x 85(H) — Good.
- A white oval marble plaque; raised rim; M.I. (9 lines, engraved, black).
- Charlotte Vernon, 2 May 1768 - 21 Mar 1770; second daughter of Hon. George Vernon and Lady Louisa Vernon.

1. Noted by Horsfield (*Sussex* I 224).
2. Pendant to 181A.

Newick, 181D Mural monument for Lady Barbara MANSEL, d. 1763

- North aisle, North wall, towards East end, above head height.
- 110(W) x 180(H) — Good.
- M.I. (8 lines, engraved, black) in upper 60% of a white rectangular marble panel; simple black marble frame; above, a broken, pointed pediment; below, 3 corbels; and an apron.
- Lady Barbara Mansel, d. 12 Jun 1761, widow of Rt. Hon. Bussy, Lord Mansel.

1. Noted by Horsfield (*Sussex* I 224) with date 1761.
2. The grandmother of the Vernon children commemorated in 181A-C.
3. JH notes that she was Lady Barbara Blackett, widow of Sir William Blackett, Bart., and the only daughter of William Villiers, 2nd Earl of Jersey. She married the Hon. Bussy Mansel, MP (later Lord Mansel) in 1729, see Sedgwick (2 242).
4. All monuments in Newick, and some reference works including the History of Parliament, spell the surname as Mansel but others, including *The Complete Peerage*, spell as Mansell.

Newick, 181E Mural monument for [Louisa Barbara] Lady VERNON, d. 1786

- North aisle, North wall, East end, above head height.
- c.110(W) x 130(H) — Good.
- M.I. (10 lines, engraved, black) on a white rectangular panel, set landscape-wise; dark grey marble frame; above, cornice and pointed pediment; below, apron with decoration of vines and ferns; 2 corbels with ornamental roundels.
- L.B. Lady Vernon, d. 16 Feb 1786, aet 53; her husband, G. V., Lord Vernon; daughter of

Bussy, Lord Mansel and Barbara, daughter to William, Earl of Jersey; her charitable virtue.

1. Noted by Horsfield (*Sussex* I 224).
2. The eccentric abbreviated M.I. (engraving unexpanded, as if transcribed from a set of informal notes) refers to Lady Vernon's charitable acts; she endowed the village school from the 1770s (see view in Farrant 285); for her extensive properties in Newick in 1785 see R. Davey (160); for a full account of her educational charities from 1771 see Caffyn 206).
3. JH notes that she was the first wife of George Venables Vernon, MP (1735-1813) who succeeded his father as Lord Vernon in 1780. They married in 1757. See Namier & Brooke (3 580). For her parents see 181D.

(182) NEWTIMBER, St. John the Evangelist

Very restored nave and chancel (1875); tower (1839) - Nairn & Pevsner (572) and VCH (VII 208); view from North-East, see Godfrey & Salzman (Pl. 117); plan (*SNQ* 5 183); reported to be fine in 1724 but chancel poor (Ford 138); the high quality mural monuments reflect the presence nearby of the substantial estate.

Newtimber, 182A Mural monument for John NEWNHAM, d. 1756
- North chapel, East wall, above head height.
- 112(W) x 240(H) — Very good; restored; local damage (top).
- M.I. (16 lines, engraved, black) in upper 60% of an unframed white marble tablet, set portrait-wise; grey-veined marble surround; below, escutcheon with decorated frame on curved apron, block corbel; above, pointed pediment breaks forward from the entablature.
- John Newnham, d. 16 Sep 1756, aet 12; fifth son of Nath[aniel] Newnham, Esq. and Sarah.

1. Originally in chancel - Horsfield (*Sussex* I 180) and Lambarde (*SAC* 71 167) noting arms.
2. Nathaniel Newnham, MP, purchased the manor of Newtimber from the Osbornes in 1741, prior to which they owned Maresfield Park (from 1660) (Farrant 279); John Newnham's widow still owned the estate in 1785, see R. Davey (161).
3. 182A can be compared with Withyham 302J - loss of favoured son.

Newtimber, 182B Mural monument for Rev. John and Jane OSBORNE, d. 1774 and d. 1761
- Chancel, North wall, at head height over sanctuary rail.
- 65(W) x 148(H) — Excellent; restored.
- M.I. (engraved, black) fills unframed white marble oval plaque; above, escutcheon in scrolled frame; below, an ornamental corbel with volutes; lamp in relief.
- Rev. John Osborne, rector of Newtimber for 30 years, d. 6 May 1774, aet 63, youngest son of Thomas Osborne, Esq.; his wife, Jane, d. 7 Jun 1761, aet 49; John's virtues.

1. Originally in chancel - Horsfield (*Sussex* I 180) and Lambarde (*SAC* 71 167) noting arms.
2. Instructive emphasis in the M.I. on Osborne's loyalty to the Church of England; the Osbornes had sold the manor of Newtimber to the Newnhams in 1741, but seem to have retained the living.
3. JH notes that John Osborne was baptised on 8 Nov 1711 at Newtimber, son of Thomas and Elizabeth Osborne.

Newtimber, 182C Mural monument for Anne OSBORNE, d. 1706, and members of her family
- Tower, South wall, at head height.
- 100(W) x 180(H) — Excellent; rust stains (left); restored.
- M.I. (14 + 4 + 9, engraved, black) on a white marble cartouche; scrolled frame; cherubim upper left and right; above, escutcheon; below, simple corbel.
- Anne Osborne, d. 12 Nov 1706, aet 50; late wife of Thomas Osborne, Esq., d. 10 Jun 1710, aet 63; issue – Thomas, died an infant; Thomas, d. 30 Sep 1727, aet 51; John, buried 12 May 1736, aet 49; Charles d. 31 Mar 1733, aet 41; also, Elizabeth, widow of

Thomas, d. 31 Jul 1735, aet 59.

1. Originally in chancel - Horsfield (*Sussex* I 180); cited for arms in Lambarde (*SAC* 71 167).
2. Probably erected after 1727 (death of Thomas Osborne).
3. Thomas Osborne's father, also Thomas Osborne (d. 1710) purchased the estate.
4. Good quality – c.f. other cartouches of the early 18ᵗʰ century – Folkington (108C), Streat, etc.

(183) NINFIELD, St. Mary

Rebuilt by Blomfield, 1885-87 - Nairn & Pevsner (572-3); in good condition in 1724 (Ford 112); the parish had a substantial congregation - c.40 families in 1724 and a population of 492 in 1801.

Ninfield, 183A Wall-mounted brass for Anne and Elizabeth BOWYER, d. 1672 and 1673

- Chancel, South wall, at waist height.
- 40(W) x 10(H) — Worn; polished.
- M.I. (2 lines, engraved) on a brass plaque.

ANNE - ELIZABETH
DAVGHTER OF IOHN BOWYER
CLERKE DIED NOVEMBER
25ᵀᴴ 28ᵀᴴ
1672/3

1. In situ, see BL Add. MS 5697 f.88, Horsfield (*Sussex* I 543), Stephenson (512), Turner (*SAC* 23 170) and Davidson-Houston (*SAC* 79 7).
2. The ambiguities in the M.I. are clarified by the burial register which notes '1673. Nov. 28th Elizabeth, daughter of John and Alice Bowyer departed this life, and was buried December 1st, her knell being the first that was rung since the bells were hanged upon the sally', see J. Sharpe, 'Notes on Ninfield and its Registers' (*SAC* 17 62).
3. Elizabeth's sister Anne had presumably been buried on 25 Nov 1672.
4. JH notes that John Bowyer was vicar from c.1662/3 to 1680 (Hennessy 111).

Ninfield Additions

Horsfield (*Sussex* I 543):
(1) Mrs Mary Luxford, wife of Thomas Luxford, of Windmill Hill, Esq., d. 18 Jun 1678.
(2) John Luxford, late of Moorehall, first son of Thomas Luxford, late of Wartling, by Mary his wife, daughter of Mr Meete of Hailsham.

(186) NORTHIAM, St. Mary

South aisle is Decorated; arcades are Early English (South arcade is earlier); whole East end added on original chancel axis and mausoleum added to building by Thomas Frewen Turner in 1846 - Nairn & Pevsner (573-4) and *SNQ* (IV 139) with plan); state of repair reportedly fine in 1724 (Ford 113) when the rector, Thankful Frewen, owned the chancel; an important series of Frewen family monuments now located in their mausoleum; the Archbishop of York, Accepted Frewen, 1588-1664 (see biography by William Joseph Sheils in *ODNB*), was of this family and his descendant re-established the Frewens in the district under Charles II, see family account books in W. Cooper *Extracts from Account-books of the Everenden and Frewen Families* (*SAC* 4 22-30); Rev. Thomas Frewen Turner was major 19ᵗʰ-century landowner, see R. Davey (162), and the family supported the school in Beckley at that time (Caffyn 44); Longley's work on 186A suggests that Northiam was within the manufacturing ambit of Canterbury; for the parish, see W.L. Davis *O Rare Norgam*; it had c.70 families in 1724 and a population of 997 in 1801; 186H-P were probably relocated to their present positions in 19ᵗʰ century.

Northiam, 186A Mural monument for William BUNCE, d. 1830

- Nave, North wall, East of North door, above head height.
- 68(W) x 67(H) — Fine; local damage (corbels).
- M.I. (11 lines, engraved) on upper 40% of an unframed rectangular freestone tablet; 2 block corbels; signed (below): 'LONGLEY CANT.Y'.
- William Bunce, Gent., died at Northiam, 10 Feb 1830, aet 77; son of Rev. William Bunce, L.L.B., vicar of St. Clement and rector of St. Peter, both in Sandwich, Kent; grandson of Stephen Odiarn, Gent.

1. The firm of Thomas Longley of Canterbury fl. 1802-45.
2. This memorial is not listed in Gunnis (*Dict.* 242).

Northiam, 186B Mural monument for Mary FREWEN, d. 1811

- Frewen Chapel, West wall, South end, facing East, high.
- 95(W) x 145(H) — Excellent.
- Scrolled pediment; M.I. (many lines, engraved, black) fills marble panel set portrait-wise on grey baseplate; Greek key and guttae decorate base moulding and corbels.
- Mary Frewen, died Brickwall, Northiam, 7 Dec 1811, aet 57; daughter of Rev. Thomas Frewen Turner, of Cold Overton Hall and rector of Sapcote, Leicestershire; her virtues.

1. Until 1837 186B was in the chancel, relocated in 1847.

Northiam, 186C Mural monument for Thomas FREWEN, d. 1738, and relatives

- Alongside and North of 186B.
- 95(W) x 280(H) — Very good; fading.
- M.I. fills marble panel set portrait-wise; flanked by fluted Corinthian pilasters in grey-veined marble; above, broken pointed pediment and large achievement; below, base moulding, apron with acanthus and another M.I. on a huge corbel with acanthus decoration.
- Thomas Frewen, Esq., of Brickwall, d. 3 Apr 1738, aet 50; father of Thomas Frewen; and grandson of another Thomas Frewen of Surrey, d. 8 Sep 1702, whose late wife was Jane Wymondesold, d. 20 Jun 1718, aet 70, relict of Sir Daws Wymondesold and daughter of Sir Robert Cooke, of Gloucestershire.

1. Noted by Horsfield (*Sussex* I 517) and Lambarde (*SAC* 68 215); in chancel until 1837, relocated in 1847.
2. Thomas Frewen presented plate to the church in 1724 and in 1740, see Couchman (*SAC* 55 202-3); the younger Thomas Frewen lived in Lewes and was a pioneer of inoculation, see L. Davey (14).
3. Patron of 186C was the son (also named Thomas) of the Thomas Frewen who died in 1738.
4. 186C is very like 186D to which are added further notes on the family.

Northiam, 186D Mural monument for Sir Edward FREWEN, d. 1723, and his wife Selina, d. 1714 [Plate 116]

- Alongside and North of 186C, over chapel West door.
- c.140(W); (H) inaccessible — Excellent; fading.
- M.I. (engraved, black) on a white marble panel framed by fluted Corinthian pilasters of grey-veined marble; beyond, scrolls; above, segmented pediment over broken cornice with achievement; below, gadroon ornament on base mould; then scrolled apron and acanthus corbel; on the pediment; achievement below an urn.
- Sir Edward Frewen, of Brickwall, Northiam, d. 8 Oct 1723, aet 61; his wife, Dame Selina, died at Hawkhurst, 25 Nov 1714, aet 54, daughter of John Godschall, of East Sheen, Surrey; their issue - eldest daughter, Jane, wife of William Ives, Esq., of Braden, Northamptonshire, died no issue; youngest daughter, Selina, wife of John Turner, Esq., Cold Overton Hall, Leicestershire; sons, John and Edward, died young, and Thomas, married Martha, daughter of Henry Turner, Esq.

1. Noted by Horsfield (*Sussex* I 517); until 1837 in the chancel, relocated in 1847; noted by Lambarde (*SAC* 68 215) on West wall.
2. Patron was Edward Frewen's son Thomas.
3. 186D is a near pendant to 186C.
4. JH notes from Henning (2 368), Cruikshanks (3 1121), *BLG* (various editions inc. 1965) and Shaw (2 260) that Thomas Frewen of Brickwall House, Northiam, was baptised in 1630. He was MP for Rye between 1675 and 1695. He d. 8 Sep 1702, aet 72. He married firstly, c.1656, Judith Wolverstone (d. 1666) by whom he had 2 sons, including Edward, (see below), and a daughter. He married secondly, 1671, Bridget Laton (d. 1679) by whom he had 5 sons and a daughter. He married thirdly, 1681, Jane Cooke (d. 1718) widow of Sir Dawes Wymondsold. There were no children of this marriage.
5. Major Sir Edward Frewen of Brickwall, eldest son of Thomas, was born in 1661. He d. 1723 (see 186D). He married, 1684, Selina Godschall (d. 1714) by whom he had 3 sons, Thomas (see below), 2 dying young, and two daughters. Edward was knighted on 25 Feb 1684/5, and was a major in the 1st Regiment of the Cinque Ports.
6. Thomas Frewen of Brickwall, eldest son of Edward, was born in 1687. He d. 1738, aged 50 (see 186C). He married, 1713, his cousin Martha Turner (she was burned to death in 1752 at Brickwall), by whom he had an only son, Thomas, born 1716, d. 1766.

Northiam, 186E Wall-mounted brass for John SHARP, d. 1583

- North aisle, East wall.
- 35(W) x 13(H) — Fair.
- 5 lines engraved on a brass plate.
- John Sharp, Esq., of Northiam, d. 8 Apr 1583; his wife Alice Odyer[ne]; issue - 6 sons and 7 daughters.

1. Noted by Horsfield (*Sussex* I 517); Stephenson (512); formerly in the South aisle, see Turner (*SAC* 23 170) and Davidson-Houston (*SAC* 79 79 – with transcript), who describes it as a palimpsest brass.

Northiam, 186F Wall-mounted brass for Nicholas TUFTON, d. 1539

- North aisle, East wall.
- 43(w) x 66(H) — Fair.
- Standing robed male figure; below, M.I. (6 lines, engraved, Latin); decorative flourish in end space.
- Nicholas Tufton, d. 31 Dec 1538.

1. 186F has a complicated history; the Tufton family chapel was built near here in the 1420s; Nicholas Tufton's will dated 2 Jan 1539 and proved 1 Feb 1539, see Rice & Godfrey (3 251), however, see date on M.I.; Nicholas Tufton left money to improve the roads between Northiam and Rye, see Rice & Godfrey (4 79) and 26 shillings 8d towards a stone 'cum pictura et scriptura' to be set up over his grave, see Rice & Godfrey (3 253).
2. 186F was drawn by Grose (1777) when in care of the 'clerk' (Farrant); Horsfield (*Sussex* I 517) noted it, as torn from its slab; Turner (*SAC* 23 170) (wrongly dating it 1528) notes its removal; Stephenson (512) notes both Nicholas Tufton's civil dress and his tonsure; in Davidson-Houston's day (*SAC* 79 76-8), 186F was in the nave; he cites Burrell's MS entry (BL Add. MS 5697 f.94r); also noted in Nairn & Pevsner (574).

Northiam, 186G Ledger for Thankful FREWEN, d. 1749, and his wife

- Chancel floor, just North of central aisle, mainly obscured by furnishings.
- 112(W) x 202(L) — (Visible is) Sound.
- Escutcheon, then M.I. (many lines, engraved) in Latin fill a polished black slab (marble?); head to West.
- Thankful Frewen, of Northiam, d. Sep 1749, aet 81; his wife, d. 4 Aug [1734], aet ??

1. Noted by Horsfield (*Sussex* I 517).
2. Thankful Frewen's wife Sarah, daughter of Luke Spenser of Cranbrook in Lambarde (*SAC* 68 210) - noting arms, not now visible.
3. Thankful Frewen (b 1669) was a courtier (Church Guide) and paid for the oak panelling, altar table and rails in the church; Caffyn (209 & 299) notes the school he ran at Northiam teaching classics to the sons of the local gentry; despite these courtly pretensions, Thankful Frewen apprenticed his

sons Edward and Thomas to a barber surgeon in 1725 and to a surgeon in 1719-20 respectively, see Rice (72).

4. NBI records burial of Sarah Frewen on 8 Aug 1734 at Northiam.

Northiam, 186H Floor slab for Henry WARNER, d. 1821
- South aisle floor, East end, centre of vestry floor.
- 60(W) x 103(L) — Very worn.
- Head to West; M.I. on upper section which has pointed top and engraved border; hinge-like corbels; lower section is a framed rectangular panel set landscape-wise.
- Henry Warner, d. 13 [or 15?] Oct 1821 aet 9; only son of Thomas and Elizabeth Warner, of Northiam.

1. NBI records burial of Henry Warner on 19 Oct 1821.

Northiam, 186I Floor slab for William JONES, d. 1734/5
- Alongside 186H.
- 60(W) x 133(L) — Fine.
- M.I. (engraved) fills upper 50% of a freestone slab; at top, 2 cherubim, a skull and crossed bones, an open book and other decorations.
- William Jones, d. 11 Mar 1734/5, aet 18, son of William Jones and Elizabeth his wife.

1. Licence to marry dated 1 Apr 1697 for William Jones and Elizabeth Fissenden, of Cranbrook, see Dunkin (*Licences 1670-1729* 169).

Northiam, 186J Floor slab for John and Elizabeth BLUNDY, she d. 1702
- As for 186H, partly obscured by furnishings.
- 50(W) x 70(L) — Poor.
- A few lines engraved on a wrecked freestone slab.
- John Blundy Snr; his wife Elizabeth, d. 14 Dec 1702.

Northiam, 186K Floor slab for Mary, Afra and Robert COOPER, d. 1731/2, 1735 and 1739
- As for 186H.
- 70(W) x 116(L) — Fine.
- Double headed freestone slab; head to West; each side has curved top and decoration over M.I. (engraved) filling upper 75% of slab.
- The parents, Robert and Judith Cooper; issue - Mary, d. 25 Jan 1731/2, aet 8; Afra, d. 25 Oct 1735, an infant; Robert Jnr, d. 14 Sep 1739, aet 9.

Northiam, 186L Floor slab for John BLUNDELL, d. 1747/8, and his wife Elizabeth, d. 1771
- South aisle, East of 186K.
- 96(W) x 140(L) — Worn.
- A cross engraved in a slab dividing M.I. (engraved); at foot, 2 cherubim with flowers.
- John Blundell, d. 17 Jan 1747, aet 50; his wife, Elizabeth, d. 14 Apr 17[71]; their issue - 2 sons and [?] daughters.

1. Erected after 1747, before the death of Elizabeth.
2. JH notes that John Blundell married Elizabeth Hollands at Northiam on 28 Mar 1722 (see Sussex Marriage Index). Their children included Elizabeth (see 1860), John (see 186M) and others unnamed. John Blundell was buried on 23 Jan 1747/8 and his wife Elizabeth on 19 Apr 1771, both at Northiam.

Northiam, 186M Ledger for John BLUNDELL, d. 1759
- South aisle floor, East end, South side of vestry.
- 96(W) x 145(L) — Poor (East end).
- M.I. (engraved) on upper 60% of a freestone slab; head to West.

- John Blundell, d. 25 Dec 1759, aet 34; his wife, Elizabeth still living; their issue - Ann, Mary and Elizabeth.

1. JH notes that this John Blundell is the son of John and Elizabeth – see 186L. He was baptised at Northiam in 1725. He is probably the John Blundell who married Elizabeth Baker on 27 Jan 1752 at Battle. Three girls with the names, Ann, Mary and Elizabeth, and parents John and Elizabeth were all baptised at Rye between 1752 and 1759 (see IGI).

Northiam, 186N Floor slab for Elizabeth JONES, d. 1729
- South aisle floor, East end, near South-East corner of vestry, partly obscured.
- 48(W) x 90(L) — Fine.
- Above, 2 cherubim and flowers engraved in a freestone slab; below M.I. (engraved) within a circular border; head to West.
- Elizabeth Jones, d. 16 Feb 1729, aet 46; wife of William Jones.

Northiam, 186O Ledger for Elizabeth [BLUNDELL?], d. 1747/8
- South aisle floor, East end, close to South wall of vestry, partly obscured by furnishings.
- 56(W) x 140(L) — Very worn.
- M.I. (engraved) fills upper 80% of a freestone slab; head to West.
- Elizabeth B..., d. 23 Feb 1747/8, aet 20; daughter of John and Elizabeth.

1. See 186L for parents.
2. NBI records burial of Elizabeth Blundel on 29 Feb 1748 at Northiam.

Northiam, 186P Ledger for Thomas [BLUNDELL?], d. 1791
- As for 186O.
- 84(W) x 146(L) — Poor.

Also Thomas their Son died
May the 6th 1791 Aged 20
Years

Northiam, 186Q Ledger for Richard SEAMER, [d. 1699]
- Chancel floor, near pulpit, alongside 186R-S.
- Inaccessible — Very worn.
- M.I. (engraved) in Latin on a black slab.
- Illegible.

1. Formerly in churchyard - Horsfield (*Sussex* I 517).
2. Richard Seamer was the second husband of subject of 186R.
3. Turner (*SAC* 23 170) notes a brass on a gravestone in the churchyard at Northiam to Richard Seamer, d. 1699.
4. JH notes that Richard Seamer was rector of East Guilford 1694-99.

Northiam, 186R Ledger for Mary SEAMER, d. 1721/2
- Chancel floor, alongside 186Q and 186S, partly obscured.
- 93(W) x 116(L) — Cracked.
- (Visible) M.I. (14 lines, engraved, centred, Latin) on a polished slab.
- Mary Seamer, née Ever(e)nden, d. 9 Jan 1721/2, aet 76.

1. JH notes that Mary Evernden married in 1664 at Sedlescombe, Rev. Thomas Frewen, see 186S, (rector of Northiam). They had 5 sons and 3 daughters. He died in 1676/7. In 1684, Mary married Rev. Richard Seamer, see 186Q, (rector of East Guilford). He died in 1699.

Northiam, 186S Ledger for Thomas FREWEN, d. 1676/7
- Chancel floor, alongside 186Q and 186R, partly obscured by choir stalls.
- 93(W) x 170(L) — Fair.
- M.I. (12 lines, engraved, Latin) on a freestone slab.
- Thomas Frewen, d. 25 Jan 1676/7, aet 47; son of John Frewen and grandson of another

John Frewen, of Northiam; husband of Mary Frewen.

1. Formerly in churchyard - Horsfield (*Sussex* I 517) and Turner (*SAC* 23 170) noted as a brass.
2. Patron was Mary, widow.
3. JH notes that Rev. Thomas Frewen (rector of Northiam 1654-76/7), d. 25 Jan 1676/7, aet 47, was son of Rev. John Frewen (rector of Northiam 1628-54), and grandson of Rev. John Frewen (rector of Northiam 1583-1628). In 1664 Thomas Frewen married Mary Evernden (see 186R).

Northiam Additions
Reported by Lambarde (*SAC* 68 214):
(1) Thomas Scott 1617 and wife Elizabeth, daughter of Thomas Piers, of Westfield, mural brass (North wall), cited by later sources as in use as an achievement on North wall of Frewen mausoleum.
Noted by Davidson-Houston (*SAC* 79 78) and D'Elboux (*SAC* 86 119-120):
(2) Richard Sharp, d. 10 Jan 1553/4, palimpsest in window of South aisle, reportedly in worn state and lost in Stephenson's day (512).
Horsfield (*Sussex* I 517):
(3) Stephen Odiarne, 1733 and Jane Odiarne, 1749 – M.I.
(4) Thomas Frewen, 1656.
(5) Rev. John Frewen, 1628.
(6) Acceptus Frewen, 1664 (the Archbishop, see Northiam Introduction).
(7) Stephen Frewen, no date - M.I..

(190) ORE, St. Helen
Reportedly fine but with poor chancels in 1724 (Ford 99); enlarged in 1821 by a new aisle with 200 seats - Horsfield (*Sussex* I 440-1); totally replaced in 1869 - Nairn & Pevsner (577); 190A was moved to the new building from the 'Old Parish Church', in 1882, as perhaps were others in this period; some backplates and corbels are, perhaps, replacements; Ore had c.25 families in 1724 and a population of 243 in 1801; now a suburb of Hastings.

Ore, 190A Mural monument for James MURRAY, d. 1794
- South aisle, South wall, towards East end, at head height.
- 89(W) x 83(H) — Excellent.
- Black baseplate with pointed pediment and ornamental palmettes; M.I. (16 lines engraved and black) on a white rectangular panel with cornice and dropped ends; 2 small corbels; signed: 'VIDLER & Co. HASTINGS'.
- General, the Hon. James Murray, of Beauport, Ore, 18 Jun 1794, aet 75; youngest son of Alexander, 4th Lord Elibank, of Scotland; his second wife, Anne, daughter of Abraham Whitham, Esq., d. 2 Aug 1824, aet 63; issue, Elizabeth-Mary d. 8 Apr 1785, aet 1; George d. in Feb 1794, infant; other issue unnamed.

1. In chancel of old church - Horsfield (*Sussex* I 440-1).
2. Moved here in 1882 by subject's grand-daughter, Lady Trollope.
3. General Murray (1722-94) was owner and resident of Beauport or Ore Place, see R. Davey (165), biography by James Dreaper in *ODNB* and noted in 1777 by Grose as he passed (Farrant); in 1748, while on garrison duty on south coast, he married Cordelia (d. 1779), daughter of John Collier of Hastings, no issue; he then married in 1780, Anne, much younger; James Murray was commander of Quebec, Governor of Canada and Minorca.
4. Design of 190A is close to that of 190C, which is signed by Whitelaw.

Ore, 190B Mural monument for Ann NORTH, d. 1801
- West wall, at West end of South aisle, facing East, at head height.
- 68(W) x 63(H) — Excellent.
- M.I. (7 lines, engraved and black) fills upper 60% of white marble rectangular panel; thin black baseplate; below, 2 tiny corbels.
- Ann North d. 11 Aug 1801, aet 26; daughter of Fountain and Arabella North of Hampstead

Heath, Middlesex.

1. Not noted by Horsfield (*Sussex* I 440-1): similar to 190E; unsigned.

Ore, 190C Mural monument for Francis Frederick NORTH, d. 1821
- Centre of West wall, facing East, to South of East window, high.
- c.88(W) x c.74(H) — Excellent.
- Very close to 190A in form; M.I. 6 lines; signed (lower right): 'W.WHITELAW. LONDON'.
- Francis Frederick North, Esq., of Rougham Hall, Norfolk and of Hastings, d. 8 Oct 1821, aet 43.

1. Horsfield (*Sussex* I 440-1) also notes a M.I. to Edward North, grandson of Francis Frederick North, 1 Jul 1826 – 16 Apr 1827.
2. Whitelaw (fl.1805-43) was based in London and is described by Gunnis (*Dict.* 431) as prolific but dull.

Ore, 190D Mural monument for Rev. Mitford PEACOCK, d. 1828
- West wall, facing East, to South of East window, at head height.
- 124(W) x 90(H) — Very good; cracks (above).
- M.I. (16 lines, engraved, black) on trapezoidal, unframed panel; 2 small black corbels; above, a cornice and a plain pointed pediment.
- Rev. Mitford Peacock, Fellow of Corpus Christi, Cambridge, died Hastings, 20 May 1828, aet 27; eldest son of Rev. D.M. Peacock, rector of Great Stainton, Durham; his Christian virtues.

1. JH notes that Mitford Peacock obtained his BA in 1822, was 2nd Wrangler, winner of 2nd Smith's Prize and MA in 1825. He was ordained 1824 and 1825, but was never beneficed.

Ore, 190E Mural monument for Fountayne NORTH, d. 1810
- West wall, facing East, to North of East window, high.
- 90(W) x c.70(H) — Excellent.
- M.I. (19 lines, engraved, black) on a white marble rectangular panel; substantial black slate base; below, 2 tiny corbels.
- Fountayne North, Esq., of Rougham Hall, Norfolk, also of Hampstead Heath, Middlesex, died at Hastings, 21 Sep 1810, aet 62; his widow, Arabella, died at Weymouth, 8 Jan 1832 aet 78.

1. Not cited in Horsfield (*Sussex* I 440-1); similar to 190B; unsigned.
2. Beautiful lettering.
3. JH notes differences in spelling c.f. 190B. NBI records him as Fountain.

Ore, 190F Mural monument for Rev. William and Elizabeth WHITEAR, d. 1804 and d. 1808
- West wall, facing East, to North of East window, at head height.
- 91(W) x 84(H) — Excellent.
- Thin black baseplate; M.I. (11 lines, engraved, black) on white marble trapezoidal tablet; corbels decorated with guttae; pointed top; flanking, crossed ferns and decorative palmettes.
- Rev. William Whitear, L.L.B., minister of Ore for 44 years, d. 8 Feb 1804, aet 66; his wife Elizabeth, d. Hastings 29 May 1808, aet 60.

1. On nave wall of original church - Horsfield (*Sussex* I 440-1): unsigned.
2. Notably cavalier treatment of pediment and palmettes.
3. JH notes that William Whitear was ordained deacon in 1760, so could claim to have been a minister for 44 years. However, despite the statement on this monument, Whitear was rector here 1772-1804, i.e. 32 years. He was also rector of All Saints, Hastings 1763-79, rector of Slinfold 1779-1804, and prebendary of Chichester 1776-1804. See Hennessy (80 113), Horn (*Fasti 1541-1857* II 45) and Venn (2 6 443).

Ore, 190G Mural monument for Mary WHITHAM, d. 1797, and others
- West wall buttress, facing South, to North of East window, at head height.
- 68.5(W) x 52(H) — Very good; rust.
- M.I. (18 lines, engraved, black) on an unframed white marble panel; 2 tiny black corbels.
- Mary Whitham, died at Hastings, 13 Mar 1797, aet 73; widow of Abraham Whitham, Esq.,
  diplomat (Majorca); issue - youngest son, Hugh-William Whitham, d. 26 Jul 1785, aet 23;
  second daughter, Mary, d. 2 Mar 1825, aet 75; third daughter, Susanna, d. 5 Mar 1830,
  aet 76; other son(s) unnamed.

Ore Additions
Horsfield (*Sussex* I 440-1), notes in old church:
(1) Grave slab in aisle – John Crisp, son of William, d. 27 Sep 1625 (M.I. in Latin).
(2) Grave slab in aisle – William Crisp, son of John, and Mary, daughter of Edward Gage, of Bentley,
d. 16 Nov 1641.
(3) Grave slab in aisle – Hawley family?
(4) 2 other grave slabs in aisle, illegible.

(192) OVINGDEAN, St. Wulfran
Norman - Nairn & Pevsner (577-8); West end reportedly unpaved in 1686 (Ford 37);
condition tolerable in 1724 (Ford 139); re-floored in 1852 and in 1867 and ledgers
relocated (see 192E, H and I); parish had 4 families in 1724 and a population of
85 in 1801.

Ovingdean, 192A Mural monument for Mary PALLISER, d. 1826
- Loose in vestry cupboard.
- 62(W) x 39(H) — Good; local damage to left side.
- M.I. (9 lines, engraved) on a rectangular white marble panel; engraved border.
- Mary Ann Rachel Palliser, died at Brighton, 10 Dec 1826, aet 28; daughter of the late Sir
  Hugh Palliser Palliser, Bart.; patron her brother, unnamed, current Bart.

1. Formerly on South wall of tower.
2. Identified by Horsfield (*Sussex* I 189) as a sister of Sir Hugh Palliser.
3. The name 'Palliser' is, or was, legible on a floor stone near the South door (Church Guide).,.

Ovingdean, 192B Mural monument for Catherine COOPER, d. 1816
- Detached from South Tower wall, now in vestry cupboard.
- 49.5(W) x 75(H) — Good.
- Unframed white oval marble plaque; M.I. (14 lines, engraved).
- Catherine Cooper, d. 13 Feb 1816, aet 62; daughter of Thomas and Elizabeth Jackson,
  formerly of Uckfield; and widow of William Cooper, Gent., late of Lewes.

1. Formerly on South wall of tower - Horsfield (*Sussex* I 189).
2. William Cooper was perhaps the lawyer cited in 1788 as a patron of the Sunday School (*SAC* 132
   156).

Ovingdean, 192C The MARSHALL mural monument, d. 1776 etc.
- Tower North wall, above head height.
- 152(W): H unknown — Very good.
- As a temple facade, in shallow stone, flat on the wall; white with black frame; pointed
  pediment and urn in relief at very top; 2 narrow borders left and right; all supported by 2
  corbels with paterae.
- Erected in 1832 by Ann Marshall;
  William Marshall, d. 7 May 1776, aet 5, buried at Hurstpierpoint; son of William and Ann
  Marshall.
  Christiana, d. 2 Oct 1805, aet 28, buried at Hurstpierpoint; daughter of H. and S. Hughes

of West Grinstead, and wife of Rev. John Marshall.

William Marshall, Gent., patron of Ovingdean, d. 10 Feb 1812, aet 65, buried at Hurstpierpoint.

Christiana, d. 24 May 1826, aet 27, buried at Collingbourne Ducis, Wiltshire; daughter of Rev John and Christiana Marshall, and wife of George I. Hooper.

Sarah, d. 24 Dec 1829, aet 75, buried at Ovingdean; widow of Henry Hughes.

Mary Elizabeth, d. 2 Aug 1831, buried at Ovingdean; infant daughter of Rev. J.W.H. and Jane Marshall.

Ann, d. 14 Feb 1834, aet 82, buried at Ovingdean; daughter of William and Barbara Borrer, of Hurstpierpoint, and widow of William Marshall, Gent.

Rev. John Marshall, rector of Ore for 31 yrs, d. 2 Aug 1835, aet 62, buried at Ovingdean.

Rev. John William Henry Marshall, rector of Ovingdean for 5 years, d. 23 Mar 1841, aet 38, buried at Ovingdean; son of Rev. John Marshall.

John Cragg, Esq., of Croydon, d. 16 Sep 1839, aet 73, buried at Ovingdean.

Sarah Jane, d. 23 Jun 1875, aet 48, buried at Brompton cemetery; eldest daughter of Rev. J.W.H. and Jane Marshall, and wife of C.M.S. West.

Jane, d. 24 Dec 1878, aet 78, buried at Ovingdean; daughter of John Cragg, and widow of Rev. J.W.H. Marshall.

Louisa Maria, d. 14 Jun 1891, aet 61, buried at Ovingdean; second daughter of Rev. J.W.H. and Jane Marshall.

Annie Emma West, d. 10 Jul 1893, aet 38, buried at Ovingdean; granddaughter of Rev. J.W.H. and Jane Marshall, and second daughter of C.M.S. and S.J. West.

Emily Mary Marshall, 15 Feb 1841 - 14 Feb 1917, buried at Ovingdean; youngest daughter of Rev. J.W.H. and Jane Marshall.

Lieut.-Col. John William Henry Marshall-West, (Somerset L.I.), 27 Jun 1857 - 31 Mar 1928, buried at Haslemere; grandson of Rev. J.W.H. Marshall and eldest son of C.M.S. and S.J. West.

Ellen Constance Jane West, 10 Mar 1862 - 13 Apr 1928, buried at Ovingdean; youngest daughter of C.M.S. and S.J. West and granddaughter of Rev. J.W.H. Marshall.

Emily Mary Louisa West, 1 Feb 1853 - 14 Feb 1939, buried at Ovingdean; eldest daughter of C.M.S. and S.J. West and granddaughter of Rev. J.W.H. Marshall.

Algernon Edward West, 24 Feb 1865 - 16 Jun 1944, buried at Ovingdean; youngest son of C.M.S. and S.J. West and grandson of Rev. J.W.H. Marshall.

1. Noted by Horsfield (*Sussex* I 189) as 'plain, large'.
2. 19 members of the Marshall family are commemorated.
3. Perhaps the largest monument of its kind in the county; the type perhaps has its local origins in the Sheffield mausoleum (107C).

Ovingdean, 192D Mural monument for Sir John EAMER, d. 1823

- Nave North wall, over North door arch, high.
- W inaccessible; 103(H) — Very good.
- White marble on dark grey; pointed pediment over an unframed tablet; M.I. (10 lines, engraved, black); below, achievement; 2 fluted brackets.
- Sir John Eamer, Knt., Colonel of the Royal East London Militia, died at Brighton, 29 Mar 1823, aet 73; his widow, Mary, d. 13 Aug 1842, aet 83.

1. In situ - Lambarde (*SAC* 71 142) noting arms.
2. The Eamers were the parents of Nathaniel Kemp's second wife (see 192G).
3. JH notes that Sir John had been Lord Mayor of London in 1801-2.

Ovingdean, 192E Ledger for Elizabeth DEANE, d. 1819

- South-East chapel floor, near South wall.
- 57(W) x 133(H) — Good, faded.
- M.I. (engraved) in upper (W) 50% of a pale freestone slab; head to West.

To the *MEMORY* of
ELIZABETH DEANE
eldest *DAUGHTER* of
RALPH DEANE *Esq*
and ELIZABETH his *wife*
of *Eastcote Middlesex*
who died at *Brighton*
March the 28th 1819
aged three years
and ten months

1. Formerly elsewhere in the church (a parishioner's informal report).

Ovingdean, 192F Mural monument for Thomas Holles PAYNE, d. 1800 [Plate 117]

- Nave South wall, East end, above head height.
- 100(W) x 87(H) — Very good.
- Above, a cornice; M.I. (8 lines, engraved) on a white marble tablet; base mouldings; brackets with foliage and pointed bases; ornamental apron with dark grey skull.
- Thomas Holles Payne Esq., d. 12 Feb 1800, aet 66; also, Sophia Elizabeth Beard, his executrix.

1. Horsfield gives it as 'Layne' (*Sussex* I 189).
2. In 1785, Thomas Holles Payne was Lord of the Manor but not an occupier (R. Davey 166).
3. An eccentric composition, c.f. 192D.

Ovingdean, 192G Mural monument for Martha KEMP, d. 1821

- Nave, high over South door.
- c.130(W); H unknown — Very good, faded.
- Pointed pediment in black; no entablature; box-like pilasters; above, Greek key ornament in frieze; foliate corbels; M.I. (many lines, engraved) in upper 75% of a white tablet with a pointed top; below, ornamental black baseplate with escutcheon; unsigned.
- Martha Kemp, d. 12 Feb 1821, aet 66; wife of Nathaniel Kemp, Esq., of Ovingdean.

1. In situ - Horsfield (*Sussex* I 189) as 'very handsome' and Lambarde (*SAC* 71 143) noting arms.
2. Martha Kemp was first wife of Nathaniel Kemp who was soon remarried (see licence to marry dated 20 May 1823, for Nathaniel Kemp, of Ovingdean, Esq., widower, age 21 plus and Augusta Caroline Eamer, of Brighton, spinster, age 21 plus) and brought his new parents-in-law into the parish, see 192D and Dunkin & Penfold (*Licences* 246).
3. The stained-glass artist Thomas Eamer Kempe (1837-1907) was Nathaniel's son by Augusta Eamer.
4. The nearby, later monument to Nathaniel Kemp himself is signed by 'Denman 82 Regent St, London'.

Ovingdean, 192H Ledger probably for a sister of Thomas YATES, d. 1820

- Nave floor, at South door.
- 105(W) x 195(L) — Very worn.
- Traces of M.I. visible at upper (North) end of a pale sandy freestone slab; head to South.
- Is the name Thomas Yates legible?

1. Horsfield (*Sussex* I 189) notes, in the aisle, a sister, 1820, of Dr Yeates.

Ovingdean, 192I Anonymous ledger, date unknown

- Nave floor, at South door, West of 192H, partly obscured by furnishings.
- (W) inaccessible; 197(L) — Very worn.
- Traces of M.I. visible in upper end of a freestone slab; head to South.
M.A.R.P....
MDCCCx[?]...

(195) PATCHAM, All Saints

Norman and 13th century; 'fine' in 1724, the chancel belonging to Dowager Lady Abergavenny (Ford); restored after 1824, in 1856 and in 1883; North aisle of 1898 - Nairn & Pevsner (458-9); 30 families in the parish in 1724; in 1801 the population was 286; no floor monuments have survived.

Patcham, 195A Mural monument for Benjamin TILLSTONE, d. 1829

- North wall of North aisle, West end, above head height.
- 85(W) x 111(H) — Good; black very faded; some local damage to cornice.
- (Now) in a recess; austere in white marble; raised square tablet with M.I. (10 lines, engraved, black) within a light moulded frame; base mouldings; above, a shallow pointed pediment; below, small foliate corbels; signed (on corbels, left and right): 'W. LAMBERT & SON / BRIGHTON'.
- Benjamin Tillstone, Esq., of Moulse Coomb Place, Patcham, d. 23 Nov 1829, aet 76.

1. Original location uncertain: a new window was set into the North wall in the early 19th century; the Tillstone vault was identified in 1989 in the (South-East corner of nave); Moulsecomb did not become a separate parish until the 1920s.
2. No mention of a spouse, but see licence to marry dated 26 Sep 1811 for Benjamin Tillstone, of Patcham, bachelor, age 40 plus and Susan Hudson, of Brighton, spinster, age 30 plus - Dunkin & Penfold (*Licences* 422); they married at Patcham on 28 Sep 1811, see Sussex Marriage Index.
3. Maker of 195A, W Lambert, unknown to Gunnis; probably a descendant of the A Lambert who signs a tablet at Telscombe (255E, after 1816).

Patcham, 195B Mural monument for Richard JONES, d. 1821

- North wall of North aisle, centre, very high.
- Inaccessible — Very good.
- An unframed rectangular tablet, set landscape-wise with chamfered corners; M.I. (8 lines, engraved, black, elegant Latin).
- Richard Jones, armiger, of Tunbridge Wells, born Montgomeryshire, 8 Jun 1753 and died Brighton, 17 Nov 1821.

1. Son was patron.
2. Perhaps in original location; a new window was set into the North wall in the early 19th century.

Patcham, 195C Mural monument for Richard SHELLEY, d. 1594 [Plate 118]

- Chancel North wall, at head height.
- 173(W) x 139(H) — Fragments only; worn; local damage; traces of lime wash(?).
- In soft freestone; no effigy; M.I. (3 lines engraved, recut?) on convex frieze with cornice and dentils over; below, an entablature; in the centre, a large achievement-of-arms flanked by two nude mourning or allegorical figures (Labour and Rest?), one (right) holding a spade; baluster columns between; below, a moulded ledge, a blank basement and more mouldings on four ruined corbels, close to the baluster capitals in form.

HEER LYETH RYCHARD SHELLEY ESQUIRE: WHO DECEASED THE 4TH
DAY OF OCTOBER: IN THE YEAR OF OUR LORD 1594
AND ABOUT THE 57TH YEARE OF HIS AGE

1. In situ - Horsfield (*Sussex* I 174), Lambarde (*SAC* 71 162) noting arms, Nairn & Pevsner (458) and views in BL Add. MS 5672 f.21; 5677 ff.62-3, f.73; 5675 f.68.
2. Monuments of this date are rare in East Sussex, c.f. 77I at Ditchling.
3. For later Shelley monuments see St. Anne Lewes (157B-C); they owned Patcham Place (vault under chancel) and were precursors to the Stapleys and the Paines (see 195D-F); one Richard Shelley, perhaps this one, was 'cousin' to Philip Sidney.
4. Horsfield calls the figures of the grave diggers 'rude'.

Patcham, 195D Mural monument for John PAINE ('the Second'), d. 1805
- Chancel South wall, South-East corner, above head height.
- 88(W) x 154(H) — Good.
- A dark grey rectangular frame set portrait-wise; within this, a yellow border, then a rectangular grey marble panel with M.I. (many lines); all resting on 2 small corbels with a decorated apron and an escutcheon (now blank); signed (on baseplate, lower right) 'WILLIAMS / BRIGHTON'.
- John Paine, Esq., d. 8 Oct 1805, aet 56; his wife, Grace, d. 6 Feb 1851, aet 93, late the widow of John Hoper, Esq.; her unnamed son.

1. In situ - Horsfield (*Sussex* I 174) and Lambarde (*SAC* 71 162) noting arms.
2. Erected by Grace Paine; M.I. added by her son; a later brass, now mounted nearby, reads: 'The family vault of Lieut. Col. Paine'.
3. For the maker Williams (fl. 1800-29), see Chailey 49C.
4. Attributed by Gunnis (*Dict.* 432) to 'Payne'.
5. The owners of Patcham Place also owned the chancel vault (see 195C and F); one John Paine, Esq. (perhaps the father of this John Paine, perhaps the same) was owner and occupier of extensive lands in Patcham in 1785 (R. Davey 166); for licence to marry dated 12 Apr 1777 for John Paine, of Patcham, Esq., bachelor, age 25 plus and Grace Kemp, of Brighton, spinster, age 19 plus, consent given by Grace Kemp's mother, also Grace, widow and guardian, see 195E and Dunkin & Penfold (*Licences* 322).

Patcham, 195E Mural monument for John PAINE, d. 1768
- Chancel South wall, immediately West of 195D.
- 89(W) x c.160(H) — Very good.
- A grey marble M.I. tablet set portrait-wise; flanked by recessed darker grey plain pilasters with fluted capitals; below, a base moulding and dentils dropping to an ornamental apron; above, 2 small finials flank a flattened triangular pediment and an urn in relief.
- John Paine, Esq., of Falmer, Patcham, d. 6 Jun 1768, aet 56; his widow, Hannah, d. 4 Apr 1779, aet 72; Grace, daughter of John Paine, Esq., and Grace, d. 17 Jun 1786, aet 4; also Sarah, wife of (another) John Paine, d. 4 Oct 1865.

1. Probably erected after the death of Grace Paine in 1786.
2. 6 lines added after 1865.
3. Paine bought the Patcham Place estate in 1764, see too comments on 195D.

Patcham, 195F Brasses commemorating Anne and Ann STAPLEY, d. 1637 and d. 1645
- Chancel South wall, close to the floor.
- Left: 39(W) x 18(H); Right: 39(W) x 14(H) — Good; polished.
- Rectangular brass plates with M.I.s: left (7 lines); right (4 lines).
- Anne Stapley, d. 9 Nov 1637; wife of Anthoney Stapley, Esq., of Patcham; her brother, Rt. Hon. George Lord Goring; Ann, only daughter of Anthony Stapley, Esq., d. 1645.

1. Original location unknown; formerly fixed to the South sanctuary floor; Church Guide following Horsfield (*Sussex* I 174); both noted by Stephenson (512) and by Turner (*SAC* 23 171) with death date for the younger Ann Stapley given as 1643; located in situ by Davidson-Houston (*SAC* 79 83), with illustration and transcription.
2. As owners of Patcham Place, the Stapleys (this branch came from Framfield) had burial rights in the chancel vault (see 195C-E); Anthony Stapley (1590-1655), sometimes called Colonel Stapley, acquired the Patcham Place estate c.1620 from the Shelleys; for his licence to marry 11 May 1614: Anthony Stapley of Lewes, Esq. and Anne Goringe of All Saints, Lewes, see Dunkin (*Licences 1586-1643* 89); later a MP and associated with Oliver Cromwell; he became a Presbyterian in 1643 and signed Charles' I death warrant; Herbert Stapley, aet 11, was commemorated by a gift of a silver-plate footed salver to the church in 1666, made by James Emery I of Lewes, see Couchman (*SAC* 54 242) and Kent (29) with illustration.

Patcham, 195G Mural monument for Susanna Margaret ROE, d. 1821
- Nave, South wall, by South door, high up.
- 113(W) x 152(H) — Very good; pigment visible.
- On a simple base, an unframed M.I.; above, a small escutcheon on a circular plaque; final 6 lines added; below, a base moulding.
- Susanna Margaret Roe, died at Brighton, 6 May 1821, aet 76; daughter of Sir William Thomas, Bart., of Yapton Place and Ratton Lodge, Sussex; and wife (45 years) of William Roe, Esq., lawyer, public servant, of Withdean, Patcham, 10 Apr 1748 - 6 Mar 1826; their issue, 2 surviving sons, 1 daughter.

1. In situ in Lambarde (*SAC* 71 163) noting arms.
2. Lines of M.I. added after 1826; erected by widowed husband and issue after 1821.
3. A brass plate now in the centre of the nave, with the Roe arms, formerly marked the family vault in the South-East nave; William Roe (d.1834) bought the Withdean estate in 1794 and was succeeded by his son, William Thomas Roe, in 1826 (see 195H).

Patcham, 195H Mural monument for William ROE, d. 1826
- Nave, South wall, at head height, immediately below 195G.
- 130(W) x 55(H) — Very good.
- An unframed oval plaque; M.I. (12 lines, engraved and black); set landscape-wise giving biography of William Roe.
- William Roe, Esq., of Withdean, 10 Apr 1748 - 6 Mar 1826, his career.

1. Perhaps erected when 195G was erected.
2. Comment on former burial vault, see 195G.
3. JH notes the full name as William Thomas Roe, see Foster (*Al Ox* 2 3 1218).

Patcham Additions
Horsfield (*Sussex* I 174):
(1) Floor slab in Sussex marble for John Stapley and Mary Stapley 1677 - chancel.
(2) Brass for Mary, daughter of John and Mary Stapley, 1657 - chancel.
(3) Brass for Dame Anne, second wife of John Stapley, 13 Feb 16?? - chancel.

(197) PEASMARSH, St. Peter & St. Paul
Norman core, chancel is Early English, Decorated South aisle - Nairn & Pevsner (578) and Livett (*SAC* 47 35-46); largely unrestored and full of atmosphere, now isolated from the village but within sight of the manor (Peasmarsh Place); paving in bad repair in 1686 (Ford 42); in 1724, the chancel belonged to one Edward Woodward (Ford 113); the parish had c.70 families in 1724 and a population of 611 in 1801.

Peasmarsh, 197A Grave marker for J.F., dated 1785
- South aisle, towards West end.
- 33 x 33 — Local damage.
- M.I. engraved on a square freestone slab.

J.F.
1785

1. JF is not otherwise commemorated.
2. NBI records burial of Joseph Fearon on 28 Nov 1785 at Peasmarsh.

Peasmarsh, 197B Painted wooden panel commemorating the bequest of Rev. Jeremiah SMITH, dated 1815
- West tower, North wall, above head height.
- 137(W) x 106(H) — Faded; dirty.

- Black painted fluted frame with roundels at corners; in centre, M.I. painted in black on grey.
- Rev. Jeremiah Smith, of Woodside, Peasmarsh. Details of bequest.

1. For Jeremiah Smith's monument see 197E.

Peasmarsh, 197C Mural monument for Robert MASCALL, d. 1815, his wife and children

- Sanctuary, North wall, above head height.
- 128(W); (H) inaccessible — Good; faded.
- A freestone support; a black slate baseplate; the monument in mixed marbles; at the top a draped urn; in centre, M.I. (11 lines, engraved) filling most of panel; signed (lower right): 'J. BACON. FT. LONDON'.
- Robert Mascall, Esq., of Peasmarsh Place, magistrate, d. 26 Feb 1815, aet 52; his wife, Martha, d. 11 Sep 1845, aet 76; eldest daughter, Mary Jane, died Torquay, 20 Dec 1810, aet 19; only son, Robert Curteis Mascall, Esq., died Venice, 19 May 1816, aet 21[?].

1. In situ - Horsfield (*Sussex* I 508) who misreads 'Venice' as 'Nice' and in the chancel in Lambarde (*SAC* 68 219) noting arms.
2. Probably erected by Martha after 1816.
3. Robert Mascall was owner but not occupier of lands at Peasmarsh in 1785 (R. Davey 166-7).
4. Not listed by Gunnis, who did know 197F.
5. By 1816, Bacon had little to do with the works being produced over his signature.

Peasmarsh, 197D Ledger for Edward SHEPHARD, d. 1685/6

- Sanctuary floor, South side.
- 78(W) x 147(L) — Worn.
- M.I. (4 lines, in upper 30% of a dark freestone slab; head to West.
- Edward Shephard, Esq., d. 12 Jan 1685/6.

1. Noted by Horsfield (*Sussex* I 508).
2. NBI records burial of Major Shephard on 18 Jan 1685/6 at Peasmarsh.

Peasmarsh, 197E Mural monument for Jeremiah SMITH, d. 1815, and his wife Ann

- Sanctuary South wall, high.
- 70(W) x 107(H) — Very good; fading.
- M.I. in 2 stages; pointed top; base moulding and corbels.
- Rev., Jeremiah Smith of Woodside, Peasmarsh, rector of Berwick, vicar of Wartling, d. 5 Jul 1815, aet 60; his widow, Ann, d. 13 Jun 1822, aet 67, daughter of Edward Leeds, Esq., of North Milford, Yorkshire.

1. In situ - Lambarde (*SAC* 68 219) noting arms: his bequests commemorated on 197B; for his daughter see 197F.
2. JH notes that he resigned livings of Berwick and Wartling 'when called to residence, that he might not be prevented from dwelling in his own mansion and estate' (of Woodside), see Venn (2 5 559).

Peasmarsh, 197F Mural monument for Elizabeth DELVES, d. 1819 [Plate 119]

- Choir, South wall, high.
- 59(W) x 105(H) — Very good.
- M.I. on oval panel with foliage in relief; pointed top; the motto 'Blessed are the weak' below; signed (lower right): 'BACON, FT. LONDON'.
- Elizabeth Delves, d. 9 Apr 1819, aet 25; youngest daughter of Rev. J. Smith of Woodside, Peasmarsh, and wife of Rev. William Delves, rector of Catsfield.

1. In situ - Horsfield (*Sussex* I 508) and see photographs in Livett (*SAC* 47 opposite p.43 & 45).
2. For her parents and sister see 197E and 197G; Rev. Smith owned lands in Peasmarsh in 1785 (R. Davey 166).

3. Cited as by Bacon by Gunnis (*Dict.* 31) and Nairn & Pevsner (578).
4. The carved quality of the decorative foliage is exquisite.
5. By 1819, Bacon had little to do with the works being produced over his name.

Peasmarsh, 197G Mural monument for Sarah SMITH, d. 1807

- Choir, South wall, West end, above head height.
- 60(W); (H) inaccessible — Fine; faded.
- M.I. (8 lines, engraved) on an oval panel; above, an urn; below, a decorated corbel.
- Sarah Smith, d. 3 Jan 1807, aet 16, daughter of Jeremiah and Ann Smith, of Woodside, Peasmarsh.

1. In situ - Horsfield (*Sussex* I 508) and visible in photographs in Livett (*SAC* 47 opposite p.43 and 45).
2. For her parents and sister see 197E-F; Rev. Smith owned lands in Peasmarsh in 1785 (R. Davey 166).

Peasmarsh, 197H Ledger for Thomas PARR, d. 1718, and his brother Steven, d. 1722.

- South aisle floor, near South door.
- 59(W) x 144(L) — Very worn; pitted.
- M.I. (engraved) fills freestone slab; head to West.

Here Lyeth
the Body of M^r
Tho~ Parr who
died Decemb^r the
15th 1718 Aged 50
years

Here also
... the Body of
the Rev Mr Steven
Parr ... Vicar of
.... who died
August the 8th 1722
Aged .....
Both Sons of Mr Iohn
Parr of Northampton
Mercer

1. Horsfield (*Sussex* I 508) notes that Thomas Parr and Stephen Parr were brothers.
2. NBI records the burials of Thomas Parr on 15 Dec 1718 and Steven Parr on 11 Aug 1722, both at Peasmarsh.

Peasmarsh Addition

Horsfield (*Sussex* I 508):
(1) Ann Marten, daughter of John and Elizabeth Holt, d. 1803, aet 85 – on floor.

(198) PENHURST - No Monuments Found

(199) PETT, St. Mary and St. Peter

Built in 1864 by B Ferrey, replacing a mediaeval building - Nairn & Pevsner (579-80); the parish population in 1801 was 185.

Pett, 199A Mural monument for Cordelia SAYER, d. 1820

- Chancel, South wall, high over vestry door.
- 62(W) x 120(H) — Good; faded; rust stains.
- M.I. (16 lines, engraved, black) fills white marble tablet; unframed; set portrait-wise; moulded and scrolled corbels; above, decorated motif of wheat sheaves and a sickle in

relief; unsigned.
- Cordelia Sayer, 18 Apr 1766 - 31 Jan 1820, died Hastings and buried Pett; daughter of Henry and Sarah Sayer, of London; granddaughter of John and Mary Collier, of Hastings.

1. In the same location in the old church, see Horsfield (*Sussex* I 471); for attribution to Westmacott see Nairn & Pevsner (579).
2. Patron of 199A is Cordelia Sayer's mother, Sarah.
3. The final 2 lines of the M.I. echo Shakespeare's *King Lear*.
4. Many of the Collier children, perhaps including Cordelia's mother, attended Mrs Thorpe's boarding school at Battle (Caffyn 43).

Pett Addition
Noted in Horsfield (*Sussex* I 471); Stephenson (512); Davidson-Houston (*SAC* 79 84) - with illustration and transcription:
(1) a brass on a slab commemorating George Theobald, d. 10 [or 16?] Mar 1641, a 'lover of bells' and a donor of a church bell (in 1835, in aisle near door, in 1938, in nave).

(201) PEVENSEY, St. Nicholas
Mostly Early English, much rebuilt by GG Scott Jun (North chapel) - Nairn & Pevsner (581); chancel reported in 1686 (Ford 51) to belong to Dr George Stradling, Dean of Chichester and to be in a very bad state of repair, though fine by 1724 (Ford 51); rebuilding and somewhat remote ownership of chancel explains notable absence of ledgers and mural monuments in this spacious and ancient church; the ancient parish had 26 families in 1724 and a population of 192 in 1801.

Pevensey, 201A Wall monument for John WHEATELY, d. 1616 [Plate 120]
- North aisle, North wall, standing West of the North door.
- 258(W) x 384(H); effigy 180(L) — Restored; colour visible; M.I.s almost lost.
- Largely alabaster; other coloured marbles; effigy semi-recumbent on black slate on a sarcophagus (head to West), all on modern base; 2 M.I.s (engraved, gilded) on inlaid slate panels on face of sarcophagus; to left and right, polished black Corinthian columns set forward; behind, flat pilasters decorated with strap-work and ribbon-work; 2 female allegories, left and right, with gilded hair; a semi-circular arch over effigy, with small blank shields in the spandrels and ribbon-work; M.I. (8 lines, shallow engraved, gilded) on rectangular slate panel; over, a cornice with obelisks left and right on black bases and behind and between, a pointed pediment with a column achievement at the apex; prominent decorated waves and scrolls.

(M.I. 1: upper):

TO THE MEMORY OF HER
WORTHY & DEARE BELOVED
HUSBAND IOHN WHEATELY
GENT: SONNE OF THOMAS
WHEATELY OF THIS PARISHE
GENT: BY IONE DAVGHTER
OF IOHN DVNSTON OF COW
FOLDE IN THIS COVNTY
GENTLEMAN

(M.I. 2: lower left):

HIS SORROWFVLL WIFE ELIZABETH
DAVGHTER OF MICHAELL SMALPAGE
ESQ^R BY KATHERINE DAVGHTER OF
WILLIAM DEVENISH OF HELLINGLY IN
THIS COV^TY ESQ^R IN REGARDE OF HIS
VIRTVES & HER LOVE ERECTED
THIS MONVMENT

(M.I. 3: lower right):
HE DIED THE 23ᵀᴴ DAY OF
MARCHE ANᵒ DOMINI: 1616
LEAVINGE BEHINDE HIM
KATHERINE THEIRE ONLY
DAVGᴴᵀER & HEIRE

1. Probably in its original location - Horsfield (*Sussex* I 303-316), Lambarde (*SAC* 70 134) noting arms and Nairn & Pevsner (581); quality of effigy admired by Horsfield.
2. The 2 lions now positioned on the church floor, against the front of 201A, do not belong with it (Church Guide).

Pevensey Additions
Noted in Stephenson and Davidson-Houston (*SAC* 79 93):
(1) Brass for John Millward, 20 Aug 1599 (South aisle).
(2) Brass for Elinor Millward, wife of John Millward, 19 Apr 1614 (South aisle).
(3) Brass for Edward Millward, 3 Feb 1619 (South aisle).

(202) PIDDINGHOE, St. John
North arcade Norman; South arcade of c.1200; North and South chapels early 13ᵗʰ century; all rebuilt in 1882 - VCH (VII 68), Nairn & Pevsner (582) and *SNQ* (VII 50) with plan; a pre-restoration view in Godfrey & Salzman (Pl. 125); reportedly fine but for North aisle pavement in 1724 (Ford 140); South aisle (1882) built over an ancient burial place (see 202F); the parish had 23 families in 1724 and a population of 194 in 1801; unusually, Horsfield (*Sussex* I 195-6) omits to mention the monuments at Piddinghoe.

Piddinghoe, 202A Mural monument for William DAVIES, d. 1830
- Nave, North wall, West end, facing South, high up.
- c.61(W) x c.132(H) — Good.
- M.I. (11 lines) on upper 80% of white marble oval tablet; moulded frame set portrait-wise; above, urn in relief; below, scrolled triangular corbel.
- William Davies, d. 3 Mar 1830, aet 80; his wife, Sara, d. 28 Jan 1820, aet 70; grandson William Waterman.

1. 202A-C are a matching set.
2. Patron of 202A is the grandson William Waterman.

Piddinghoe, 202B Mural monument for Edward WATERMAN, d. 1789
- Nave, North wall, centre, facing South, high up.
- c.61(W) x c.132(H) — Good.
- Matches 202A; M.I. (9 lines); upper 50%.
- Edward Waterman, d. 19 Sep 1789, aet 46; his wife, Francies [sic], d. 22 Jan 1794, aet 52.

1. 202A-C are a matching set.
2. Edward Waterman had extensive property at Piddinghoe, in 1785 (R. Davey 169) when he acted as land tax assessor.

Piddinghoe, 202C Mural monument for Fanny and Edward WATERMAN, d. 1821 and 1840
- Nave, North wall, East end, facing South, high.
- c.61(W) x c.132(H) — Fair; crack (upper right).
- Matches 202A; M.I. in upper 80%.
- Fanny Waterman, d. 13 Mar 1821, aet 36; wife of Edward Waterman, d. 24 Aug 1840, aet 61.

1. 202A-C are a matching set.
2. JH notes that the Sussex Marriage Index records Edward Waterman marrying Frances Davies on 11 Aug 1802 at Brighton, after licence dated 10 Aug 1802.

Piddinghoe, 202D Mural monument for Elizabeth and John FAULCONER, d. 1812 and 1823

- Nave, North wall, towards chancel arch, facing South, high up.
- (W) unknown x c.130(H) — Good; faded.
- M.I. (10 lines, engraved, black) on a white rectangular marble tablet set landscape-wise; thin red inset border; above, a moulded cornice in grey-veined marble and an urn; below, in grey-veined marble, a curved apron between 2 corbels with roundels.
- Elizabeth Faulconer, d. 11 Mar 1812, aet 18, eldest daughter of Thomas C. Faulconer, Esq., and Sarah; also John Faulconer, d. 28 Dec 1823, aet 17, son of T. C. Faulconer, Esq., and Mary.

1. Immediately to the West is a monument to Thomas Chippen Faulconer, the father of the subjects of 202D (d.1836); there is another Faulconer monument at Plumpton (204B); a Mr Faulconer occupied Rt. Hon. Lord Pelham's land at Piddinghoe in 1785 (R. Davey 169).
2. JH notes that Thomas Chippen Faulconer married Sarah Noakes at Clapham on 26 Sep 1792, see Sussex Marriage Index. She died 1797 and Thomas Chippen Faulconer married Mary Ann Towner on 9 May 1805 (IGI).

Piddinghoe, 202E Mural monument for Mary Ann TOMPSETT, d. 1812

- Between South aisle and chancel, on pillar, facing East, at head height.
- 53(W) x 36(H) — Good.
- M.I. (4 lines, engraved, black) on unframed white marble tablet with pointed top and squared bottom; above, relief of butterfly and foliage.
- Mary Ann Tompsett, 16 Jan 1812 - 3 Nov 1812, daughter of Joseph Tompsett and Mary Ann Tompsett.

1. Almost certainly a replacement of an earlier monument lost in the 1882 restoration of this part of the church (see 202F).
2. For licence to marry dated 21 Sep 1809 for Joseph Tompsett, of Meeching (that is, Newhaven), Gent., bachelor, age 30 plus and Mary Ann Winton, of Piddinghoe, spinster, age 18, see Dunkin & Penfold (*Licences* 424). They married 23 Nov 1809 at Piddinghoe (Sussex Marriage Index).

Piddinghoe, 202F Mural monument for Francis WINTON, d. 1821

- South aisle wall, towards East end, facing North, at head height.
- 75(W) x 46(H) — Good.
- M.I. (7 lines, engraved, black) on unframed grey marble tablet set landscape-wise.
- Francis Winton, d. 1821; his wife, Sarah d. 1806; their issue, unnamed, died in infancy.

1. Final lines of the M.I. suggest that 202F post-dates the 1882 restoration of the church and, perhaps as with 202E, replaces an earlier monument lost then.
2. Francis Winton married Sarah Winton at Beddingham on 9 Mar 1790 (Sussex Marriage Index); she was buried 1 Oct 1806 at Piddinghoe (NBI); for licence to marry dated 24 Dec 1806 for Francis Winton, of Piddinghoe, yeoman, widower and Mary Charlotte Potts, widow, see Dunkin & Penfold (*Licences* 473) and they married 14 Jan 1807 at Piddinghoe (Sussex Marriage Index).

(203) PLAYDEN, St. Michael

Essentially c.1200 - VCH (IX 161) and Nairn & Pevsner (583); for a view from the North-East see Godfrey & Salzman (Pl. 126); paving reported as bad in 1686 but repaired by 1724 (Ford 42); parish had 12 families in 1724 and a population of 179 in 1801.

Playden, 203A Ledger for Stephen WILMSHURST, d. 1742, his wife Ann, d. 1737, and their son Stephen, d. 1781.
- Nave floor, far West end.
- 78(W) x 176(L) — Stained, worn, cracked.
- M.I. fills surface of a cream freestone slab, head to East.
- Stephen Wilmshurst, d. 31[?] May 1742[?], aet 41; his wife, Ann, d. 10 Apr 1737, aet 25; their daughter, Elizabeth d. 24 Sep 1758, aet 27; [their son], Stephen Wilmshurst, d. 24 Apr 1781, aet 43.

1. NBI records burial of Stephen Wilmshurst on 3 Jun 1742, Ann Wilmshurst on 15 Apr 1737 and Stephen Wilmshurst on 28 Apr 1781, all at Playden.
2. Stephen Wilmshurst was baptised at Warbleton on 27 Dec 1742, the son of Stephen and Ann Wilmshurst, see IGI.

Playden, 203B Ledger for John TURK, d. 1793
- Nave floor, near West end.
- 95(W) x 189(L) — Stained.
- M.I. fills upper 80% of a cream freestone slab, head to East.
- John Turk, d. 13 Apr 1793, aet 63; his son, William, d. 1[?] Apr 1803, aet 19; John's sister, Ann, d. 10 Apr 1765, aet 30.

1. In 1785, John Turk occupied a large property at Playden, owned by Sir Charles Goring (R. Davey 170).

Playden, 203C Floor slab for Cornelis ZOETMANS, dated c.1530 [Plate 121]
- North aisle floor, near West end.
- 58(W) x 87(L) — Very worn; cracked.
- M.I. (2 lines, now engraved, Dutch) on a limestone slab; engraved decoration of 2 barrels and crossed fork and mash stick.

Hie is begraven Cornelis
Zoetmans bidt vuer de ziele

1. In situ - Horsfield (*Sussex* I 506-7) mistranscribed and Turner (*SAC* 23 172-3) wrongly dated 15th century.
2. M.I. originally inlaid in brass (*SAC* 23, Church Guide), since removed.
3. 203C is apparently imported from Belgium, datable c.1530, in a carboniferous limestone quarried near Liège, includes emblems of brewer's trade.
4. Nairn & Pevsner (583) mistakes M.I. 'Roetmans'.
5. A unique survival.

Playden, 203D Ledger for Nathanall LEGG, d. 1754
- Sanctuary floor, against South wall.
- 88(W) x 165(L) — Fine; stained (East end).
- M.I. (7 lines, engraved) in upper 50% of a grey freestone slab; head to East.
- Nathanall Legg, rector of Playden for 40 years, d. 14 Dec 1754, aet 65.

1. Noted by Horsfield (*Sussex* I 506-7).
2. JH notes that Nathaniel Legg was rector of Playden 1713/4 - 54.

Playden, 203E Mural monument for William JACKSON, d. 1828
- Sanctuary, on wall above Priest's (South) door.
- 90(W) x 103(H) — Good; badly faded above.
- Unframed panel; above, a cornice; at top, pointed pediment with lion in centre; palmettes flanking; below, corbels left and right and arms in centre.

SACRED
TO THE MEMORY OF
THE Rev° WILLIAM JACKSON, CLERK
CURATE OF THIS PARISH, AND OF EAST GUILDFORD.
AND MASTER OF
THE GRAMMAR SCHOOL IN RYE 36 YEARS.
HE DIED ON THE 19TH OF AUGUST 1828
AGED 72 YEARS
AND HIS REMAINS ARE DEPOSITED
IN A VAULT BENEATH THIS TABLET.

ALSO OF ANN HIS WIFE.
BORN 16TH SEPTEMBER 1762:
DIED 26TH DECEMBER 1843.

1. In situ - Horsfield (*Sussex* I 506-7) and Lambarde (*SAC* 68 219) noting arms.
2. William Jackson was appointed master of the combined Peacock's and Saunders' schools at Rye in 1791; he was curate at both Playden and East Guldeford; his wife Anne, d. 26 Dec 1843 (Caffyn 228 & 311).

(204) PLUMPTON, St. Michael

Vestry & East end wall modern; nave Norman, chancel 13th century - Nairn & Pevsner (583-4) and plan in *SNQ* (XIV 15); condition reported 'fine' in 1724 (Ford 141); Plumpton had 40 families in 1724 and a population of 1710 in 1801.

Plumpton, 204A Anonymous ledger ?1711
- Nave floor, near chancel step.
- 71(W) x 169(L) — Stained; worn.
- A few letters of a M.I. visible, engraved in a light brown freestone slab; head to North.
             ... THE ... OF ... 11

1. Close in type to other ledgers in the church.
2. Unusual orientation suggests disruption.

Plumpton, 204B Mural monument for Arthur FAULCONER, d. 1822, and Anne WOOLGAR, d. 1830
- Nave North wall, near chancel arch, above head height.
- 30(W) x 56(H) — Fine; rust; faded.
- M.I. (14 lines, engraved, black) in upper 60% of a grey-veined marble oval plaque; lightly engraved border; small corbel.
- Arthur Faulconer, d. 23 Dec 1822, aet 26; youngest son of William Faulconer, Esq., of Henfield Place; his sister, Anne Woolgar, d. 9 Mar 1830, aet 49, daughter of William Faulconer, and wife of Philip Woolgar.

1. Pendant with another later Faulconer monument on the opposite wall.
2. For other Woollgar monuments see Lewes, All Saints (156).

Plumpton, 204C Ledger for Henry WOODWARD, d. 1772
- Chancel floor, West end.
- 98(W) x 190(L) — Very worn.
- M.I. (engraved) in upper 60% of a freestone slab; head to West.
             HERE Lieth the Body
           of *HENRY WOODWARD* Gent
                 third Son
         (of the Revd THOS WOODWARD
          late Rector of West Grinstead
               in this *County*
          and *KATHERINE* his Wife)

He Departed this *Life*
May the 4th 1772
AGED 30 YEARS

1. Cited by Horsfield (*Sussex* I 232).
2. JH notes that the NBI records the burial on 27 Mar 1772. The ledger stone definitely has May.

Plumpton, 204D Ledger for Sir Walter WALKER, d. 1706
- Chancel floor, centre.
- 85(W) x 200(L) — Pitted; cracked (West end).
- M.I. (7 lines, engraved) in upper 50% of a black slab; head to West.
- Sir Walter Walker, Bart., d. 14 Apr 1706, aet 23.

1. Cited by Horsfield (*Sussex* I 232); lettering perhaps recut?
2. JH notes that the sources relating to Walker are inconsistent. Sir Walter Walker, 2nd and last Baronet, is recorded as having died a minor, and unmarried, before 1703, see Cockayne (*Baronetage* 4 114). However, the NBI records the burial of William Walker on 14 Apr 1706 at the age of 18, at Plumpton.

Plumpton, 204E Floor slab for Ann GODMAN, d. 1649
- Choir floor, North side, between choir stalls and sanctuary.
- 69(W) x 163(H) — Very worn.
- M.I. (7 lines, engraved) in upper 50% of a grey freestone slab; head to North.
- Ann Godman, d. 8 Jun 1649; wife of Edward Godman, Gent., of Wo.. [?].

1. For licence to marry for Edward Godman, of Wivelsfield, Gent. to Anne Bennet, of Chiltington, Westmeston, widow 15 Oct 1636, see Dunkin (*Licences 1586-1643* 233).
2. The individuals named on 204E do not correspond with individuals in a pedigree, see Attree (*SAC* 35 44) and Attree (*SAC* 36 73).
3. Lettering perhaps recut?

Plumpton, 204F Mural monument for Rev. William HAMPTON, d. 1770, and his wife Mary, d. 1793 [Plate 122]
- Sanctuary North wall, at head height.
- 81(W) x 114(H) — Very good; colour.
- M.I. (10 lines, engraved, black) on an unframed white marble tablet; above, straight cornice in veined marble; above, an escutcheon on a diamond backplate; below, a simple base mould and 2 scrolled corbels.
- Rev. William Hampton, A.B., patron and rector of Plumpton, d. 30 Aug 1770, aet 44; his wife, Mary, d. 16 Sep 1793, aet 73.

1. Cited by Horsfield (*Sussex* I 232); in situ Lambarde (*SAC* 71 147) noting arms.
2. JH notes that Rev. William Hampton was rector of Plumpton 1753-70, see Hennessy (120).

Plumpton, 204G Mural monument for Samuel CLARKE, d. 1828
- Sanctuary South wall, at head height.
- 74(W) x 47(H) — Good.
- M.I. (engraved, black) on a white marble tablet on a black base plate, set landscape-wise; 2 white corbels.
- Samuel Clarke, d. 17 Feb 1828, aet 26.

1. Unsigned.
2. In the manner of Parsons of Lewes.

Plumpton, 204H Floor slab for Elizabeth [T....], d. 1683
- Choir floor, South side, between choir stalls and sanctuary.
- 74(W) x 161(L) — Worn; pitted.
- M.I. (7 lines, engraved) in upper 50% of a grey freestone slab; head to South.

Here Lyeth y[e] Body of
Elizabeth .... Late Wife
of M[r] A..... T.... y Cittize[n]
And Goldsmith of London
Daughter of Thomas ..agra...e
Esq of Shrivenham In Berkshire
Deceased y[e] 10th of Sept[r] 1683 [?]

Plumpton, 204I Mural monument for Dorothy [?] SPRINGAT, d. 1670

- South chancel wall, set in, above floor.
- 39(W) x 79(H) — Good.
- M.I. (15 lines, engraved) in a light brown freestone slab, now wall-mounted.

HEERE LIETH BVRI[ED]
THE BODY OF DOR[T]HI
SPRINGAT DAVGHT
OF ANTHONY SPRI
NGAT ESQ AND
DORITHI HIS W[IFE]
AGED SIX M[ON]THS
AND THREE WIE
KES WHO DIPAR
TED THIS LIFE
THE 9TH DAYE
OF MARCHE IN
THE YEARE OF
OVR LORD GOD
1670

1. Lower (*SAC* 20 46) records that Dorothy is the sister of Anthony and William Springett, see 204J.

Plumpton, 204J Mural monument for Anthony SPRINGETT, d. 1735, and his brother William, d. 1732

- Chancel South wall, at head height.
- 96(W) x 125(H) — Good.
- M.I. (many lines, engraved, black) on a marble panel, set portrait-wise; simple, moulded grey marble frame.
- Rev. Anthony Springett, clerk, of Plumpton Place, for nearly 19 years rector of Westmeston, d. 6 Oct 1735, aet 72; his younger brother, William Springett, Gent., d. 3 Aug 1732, aet 66; his ministry and virtues.

1. See Horsfield (*Sussex* I 232) and Woodward (*SCM* II 547) - with transcription.
2. Anthony Springett (1652-1735), left provision for a charity school at Falmer (Caffyn 114, 216-7); for the family, see Lower (*SAC* 20 34-46), including their sister Dorothy (204I).

Plumpton Additions
Cited by Horsfield (*Sussex* I 232):
(1) Anthony Springett, d. 1689, aet 49;
(2) Dorothy Springett, wife of Anthony (see Addition 1), d. 1695 and daughter Dorothy, d. 1670, infant.

(206) PORTSLADE, St. Nicholas

12th-13th century; North aisle (1874) with mausoleum-like Brackenbury Chapel at its West end - Nairn & Pevsner (459-60) built in matching style; pavement described as decayed in 1686; fabric described as very good in 1724 (Ford 141).

Portslade, 206A Anonymous floor slab, undated
- Nave floor, West end, West of South door, partly obscured by pews.
- 45(W) x 54(visible L) — Worn.
- A pale yellow freestone slab; 2 skulls in low relief in an oval recess.

1. Perhaps the slab to Abraham Edwards, 1654, noted in Horsfield (*Sussex* I 164) (but see 206B).

Portslade, 206B Anonymous floor slab, undated
- Nave floor, West end, near tower arch.
- 90(W) x 61(L) — Very worn.
- Pale yellow freestone slab; an escutcheon; M.I. invisible.

1. Perhaps the slab to Abraham Edwards, 1654, noted in Horsfield (*Sussex* I 164) (but see 206A).

Portslade, 206C Ledger for the children of Robert CARPENTER and his wife Hester, d. 1742
- Nave floor, centre aisle, West end.
- 115(W) x 220(L) — Worn.
- Escutcheon, then M.I. (engraved) fills surface of a black slab; head to West.
- Robert Carpenter, Esq.; his wife, Hester, d. 31 Dec 1742, aet 45; their issue - Sarah, d.
   12 Mar 1726/7, an infant; (another) Sarah, d. 12 Aug 1728, an infant; Robert, d. 19 Jan
   1731/2, an infant; Esther, d. 12 Jan 1738/9, aet 15; Henrietta, d. 9 Apr 1739, an infant.

1. Called Henrietta Carpenter, 1742 by Horsfield (*Sussex* I 164); arms noted in Lambarde (*SAC* 71
   165).

Portslade, 206D Ledger for Thomas COOKE, d. 1742
- Nave floor, centre aisle, East of 206C.
- 102(W) x 200(L) — Worn.
- Escutcheon, then M.I. (5 lines, engraved) in upper 60% of a black slab; head to West.
- Thomas Cooke, Gent., d. 26 Dec 1742, aet 82.

1. Noted in Horsfield (*Sussex* I 164).
2. In situ in Lambarde (*SAC* 71 165) citing arms.

Portslade, 206E Ledger for Mary COOKE, d. 1717
- Nave floor, centre aisle, in line with South door.
- 102(W) x 202(L) — Very worn.
- Escutcheon, then M.I. (3 lines, engraved) in upper 60% of a black slab; head to West.
- Mary Cooke, d. 19 Jul 1717, aet 44; wife of Thomas Cooke, Gent.

1. Noted in Horsfield (*Sussex* I 164); in situ in Lambarde (*SAC* 71 165) citing arms.

Portslade, 206F Ledger for Thomas COOKE, date unknown
- Nave floor, centre aisle, East of 206E.
- 100(W) x 185(L) — Very worn; cracked (East end).
- M.I. (a few letters visible) in upper parts of freestone slab (Horsham stone?); set head to
   West.

Here lieth the body of Thomas
Cooke, Gent., who died on the day 11 Jul

and the bodies of … daughters
who … children of the
Cooke … his wife
who died … year 1711
1712 and 171[?]

1. Perhaps the slab to Thomas Cooke d. 1709, noted in Horsfield (*Sussex* I 164).

Portslade, 206G Anonymous ledger, with a date 1817

- Nave floor, North aisle, towards West end.
- 94(W) x 195(L) — Nearly illegible.
- M.I. (? 9 lines, engraved) in upper 60% of a freestone slab; head to West.
- The date 1817 visible in penultimate line.

1. Horsfield (*Sussex* I 164) notes a slab to Catherine Cooke 1717.

Portslade, 206H Ledger for Charles BRIDGER, d. 1779

- Nave floor, North aisle, East of 206G.
- 98(W) x 181(L) — Damaged; cracked.
- M.I. fills surface of a freestone slab; head to West.
- Charles Bridger, Gent., d. 12 Jan 1779 aet 29; son of (another) Charles Bridger, Gent.; his wife, Elizabeth, d. 18 Feb 1817, daughter of Robert H...., Gent, of Southwick; his 12th son, Charles, died 11 Jan 1779, died an infant, buried on the same day as his father.

1. Elizabeth Bridger was landowner at Portslade in 1785 (R. Davey 171).

Portslade, 206I Ledger for John FRIEND, d. 1736

- Nave floor, North aisle, East of 206H.
- 104(W) x 198(L) — Very worn; scratched.
- M.I. (4 + 5 lines, engraved) on a pale freestone slab; skull motif in centre; head to West.
- John Friend, Gent., d. 12 June 1736, aet 55; his son, Thomas, d. 19 June 1737, aet 24.

1. For licence to marry for John Friend of Portslade, Gent., and Mary Miller of Lewes, spinster 25 Apr 1710, see Dunkin (*Licences 1670-1729* 199).

Portslade, 206J Mural monument for the BORRER family, from 1811 [Plate 123]

- North aisle, North wall, North-East corner, above head height.
- c.105(W); (H) unknown — Excellent.
- White on black; pointed and moulded arched top; base moulding and 2 simple block corbels; M.I. (engraved, in 2 columns); signed (lower right): 'BRINE fecit / NEW ROAD LONDON'.
- John Borrrer, d. 12 Aug 1866, aet 81; his first wife, Kitty, d. 7 Apr 1811, aet 27; his second wife, Mary Anne, d. 13 Jul 1819, aet 27; issue with Mary Ann: Nathaniel, 1 Jun 1818 - 24 Aug 1818; Frederick Leopold, 3 Jul 1819 - 3 Sep 1819; Ellen, 10 Feb 1817 - 12 Apr 1834; his third wife, Sarah Anne, d. 4 Jan 1866, aet 72; issue with Sarah Anne: Lindfield, 3 Sep 1823 - 24 Oct 1823.

1. Brine also signs two other smaller mural monuments dated in the mid - late 1840s, just to the West of 206J.
2. For licence to marry dated 2 Oct 1821 for John Borrer, of Portslade, Gent., widower and Sarah Anne Hall, of Albourne, spinster, age 21 plus, see Dunkin & Penfold (*Licences* 49).

Portslade, 206K Floor marker for Susanna WHITPAINE, d. 1802

- Nave floor, East end, near chancel step, partly obscured by furnishings.
- 71(W) x 61(H) — Very worn; damaged edges.
- M.I. (5 lines, engraved) on a mid-brown freestone slab; head to South.

IN MEMORY OF
SUSANNA *Daughter of*
WILLIAM & MARY WHITPAINE
who died March 30th 1802
.... year

1. JH notes that Susanna Whitpaine, daughter of William and Mary, was baptised at Portslade on 24 May 1799.

Portslade, 206L Floor marker for William GODSMARK

- Nave floor, East end, South of 206K, partly obscured by furnishings.
- 71(W) x 66(L) — Almost illegible.
- Traces of M.I. (engraved) in upper (South) end of a mid-brown freestone slab; head to South.

IN MEMORY OF
WILLIAM GODSMARK
......
.......MARK
....
....
...
...

1. JH notes that NBI records burial of William Godsmark, aged 11 months, at Portslade 26 Jul 1829. Also William Godsmark, aged 29, buried at Portslade 2 Oct 1829.

Portslade, 206M Floor marker for Thomas SMITH, d. 1730

- Nave floor, East end, South of 206L, partly obscured by furnishings.
- 71(W) x 89(L) — Worn.
- M.I. (4 lines, engraved) in centre of a mid brown freestone slab; head to South.

Here lieth Y^e Body ...
Thomas Smith w...
Died ye 25th of July
1730 Aged 83 Ye ...

1. For licence to marry for Thomas Smith and Dorothy Harman, both of New Shoreham, 4 Dec 1679, see Dunkin (*Licences 1670-1729* 56).

Portslade, 206N Mural monument for Theophilus CLARKE, d. 1840 [?]

- South nave aisle, East wall, very high.
- Inaccessible — Fine.
- An unframed white marble tablet; corners chamfered.
- Theophilus Clarke, assistant surgeon, H.E.I.C.S., died Coco, East Indies, 8 Nov 1840 [?], aet 27.

Portslade, 206O Mural monument for Ralph CLUTTON, d. 1761 [Plate 124]

- South aisle wall, East wall, above head height.
- 77(W) x 96(H) — Very good.
- M.I. (engraved, black) fills unframed white rectangular tablet; black rectangular backplate; all set portrait-wise; M.I. within an engraved border.
- Rev. Ralph Clutton, A.M., vicar of Portslade and rector of Horsted Keynes, d. 8 Jan 1761, aet 66; his widow, Elizabeth, d. 14 May 1785, aet 79; their issue - Rev. Ralph Clutton, A.B., rector of Horsted Keynes and Aldrington, d. 13 Apr 1772, aet 44.

1. Noted by Horsfield (*Sussex* I 164).
2. Ralph Clutton instituted as vicar at Portslade in 1722 (as reported in 1724 report, see Ford); rector of Horsted Keynes in 1738; he held both posts until his death in 1761; married Elizabeth Dobson in 1726; his son, also Ralph Clutton (1727-1772), rector of Aldrington 1751 and of Horsted Keynes 1761 (see family tree of Giles Moore in Bird).
3. 206O-Q are a matching set dating from the second decade of the 19th century.

Portslade, 206P Mural monument for Owen CLUTTON, d. 1796

- South aisle wall, West of 206O, above head height.
- 77(W) x 95(H) — Very good.
- Matches 206O.
- Owen Clutton, Esq., d. 3 Dec 1796, aet 63, third son of Rev. Ralph and Elizabeth Clutton;

his wife, Elizabeth, d. 16 Nov 1802, aet 78, daughter of Isaac Townsend, Esq., Admiral of the White and Governor of the Royal Hospital at Greenwich.

1. Noted by Horsfield (*Sussex* I 164).
2. Owen Clutton, son of Rev. Ralph Clutton, d. 1761, was apprenticed in Oct 1748 to Charles Chatfield, of Cuckfield, apothecary, see Rice (42).
3. 206O-Q are a matching set dating from the second decade of the 19th century.

Portslade, 206Q Mural monument for Rev. John CLUTTON, d. 1815
- South aisle wall, West of 206P, above head height.
- 78(W) x 96(H) — Very good.
- Matches 206O.
- Rev. John Clutton, M.A., vicar of Portslade for more that 50 years and rector of Hangleton, d. 5 Jan 1815, aet 83; his sister, Elizabeth, d. 25 Nov 1813, aet 85.

1. John Clutton owned land at Portslade in 1785 (R. Davey 171).
2. 206O-Q are a matching set dating from the second decade of the 19th century.
3. JH notes that Rev John Clutton was vicar of Portslade 1761-1815 and rector of Hangleton 1757-1815. He was the son of Rev. Ralph Clutton, d. 1761 (see 206O).

Portslade Additions
Noted Horsfield (*Sussex* I 164):
(1) Slab for Elizabeth Ann Woodcock, 1780 (perhaps one of 206A, 206B or 206G).
Noted in Stephenson:
(2) A brass for members of the Scrase family, the latest of them being Edward Scrase, of Blatchington, Gent., 1579, probably preserved from the ruins of West Blatchington church (p. 513) His source is Lower (*SAC* 24 17).

(207) POYNINGS, Holy Trinity
Perpendicular (after 1369); North transept was Montague Chapel, the South transept was the Poynings chapel - Nairn & Pevsner (586); plans in *SNQ* (4 111) and Holland (*SAC* 15 33), with external view from North-East (p.46); condition reported in 1724 to be fine (Ford 142).

Poynings, 207A Mural monument for Dame Mary BALL, d. 1832, and Sir Alexander John BALL, d. 1809 [Plate 125]
- Sanctuary, North wall, at head height.
- 114(W) x 190(H) — Very good.
- M.I. (100%) on white tablet on a black baseplate; urn on plinth, cornice on attached hexagonal columns.
- Dame Mary Ball, d. 28 Sep 1832, aet 85; widow of Sir Alexander John Ball, Bart., captain of HMS Alexander, rear admiral of H.M. Red Squadron and Governor of Malta, d. 25 Oct 1809, aet 52, another memorial at Malta.

1. Must post-date 1832; noted by Horsfield (*Sussex* I 177); not mentioned by *Gent's Mag* visit dated Oct 1810 in Gomme (306-7); transcribed in Holland (*SAC* 15 231) in situ.
2. Alexander John Ball was b.1756; friend and comrade of Nelson; rescued Nelson in HMS Alexander in 1798; directed blockade of Malta when the island rose against the French in 1798; involved with Malta thereafter; created Baronet in 1800; d. 25 Oct 1809, Valletta and buried there; memorial in Lower Barracca gardens, see biography by Henry Frendo in *ODNB*.
3. His wife Mary d. 27 Sep 1832.

Poynings, 207B Mural monument for George BEARD, d. 1786
- Sanctuary, East wall, South of East window, at head height.
- 70(W) x 133(H) — Very good; fading.
- M.I. on white tablet; above, dark-veined marble with curved; below, an escutcheon.

- Rev. George Beard, 54 years curate and rector at Poynings, d. 25 Jun 1786, aet 77; unnamed sibling(s); his many virtues (piety, zeal, fraternal affection, patience, frugality, generosity, charity).

1. Probably in situ; in situ in Oct 1810 and noted by *Gent's Mag*, see Gomme (306-7); noted by Horsfield (*Sussex* I 177); transcribed Holland (*SAC* 15 231); cited Lambarde (*SAC* 71 168) noting arms.
2. George Beard had property at Poynings in 1785 (R. Davey 172).
3. Despite the zeal noted in the M.I., it was reported that George Beard preached from just two texts 'Simon the Tanner' and 'Felix trembled' (Horsfield loc cit).
4. JH notes that Rev. George Beard was curate of Poynings 1732-49, rector 1749-86 and rector of Bepton 1736-49. He left £100 for the education of poor children of the parish (Caffyn 217).

Poynings, 207C Mural monument for Charlotte WHITCOMBE, d. 1806
- Sanctuary South wall, above head.
- 72(W) x 55(H) — Very good; faded.
- M.I. (12 lines) fills a light grey, veined marble tablet, unframed, set landscape-wise.
- Charlotte Whitcombe, d. 20 Jul 1806, aet 36; her brother, Francis Whitcombe, rector of Poynings.
1. Probably in situ; seen on visit dated Oct 1810 by *Gent's Mag* in Gomme (306-7); transcribed Holland (*SAC* 15 231).

Poynings, 207D Grave marker for one 'LRR', dated 1817
- Nave floor, crossing, South side.
- 25 x 25 — Very good.
- Set with head to East, a grey hexagonal stone, inscribed 'L.R.R. / 1817'.
1. Probably relates to one Louisa Revell (Church Guide) as NBI records the burial of Louisa Revell on 11 Nov 1817, aet 29, at Poynings.

Poynings, 207E Mural monument for Thomas and Lucy PIPON, d. 1830 and d. 1829
- Nave, South wall, above head.
- 80(W) x 48(H) — Very good.
- M.I. (8 lines) fills a white unframed tablet.
- Thomas Pipon, Esq., died at Brighton, 16 Feb 1830, aet 85; his wife, Lucy, d. 7 Dec 1829, aet 74.
1. Probably in situ; transcribed in Holland (*SAC* 15 232).

Poynings, 207F Mural monument for William OSBORNE, d. 1807
- Nave, South wall, below 207E.
- 38(W) x 24(H) — Very good; rust stains.
- M.I. fills the surface of an unframed grey plaque; upper corners chamfered.
- William Osborne, yeoman, d. 15 Jun 1807, aet 70.

1. Probably in situ; noted by *Gent's Mag* visit dated Oct 1810 in Gomme (306-7) and by Horsfield (*Sussex* I 177); transcribed in Holland (*SAC* 15 232).
2. Designation as 'yeoman' is very unusual on a M.I. in this collection.
3. William Osborne did own his own farm and also farmed the church lands in 1785 (R. Davey 172).

(208) PRESTON, St. Peter
Originally a chapel of ease (for St. John's); now redundant; Early English, in flint - Nairn & Pevsner (460); unpaved in 1686 (Ford 40); condition reportedly fine in 1724 (Ford 143); restored generally in c.1872; chancel restored in 1878; restored again after a fire of 1906; the parish had 20 families in 1724 and a population of 222 in 1801; the set of monuments on the West nave wall evidences the popularity of the church as a fashionable burial place, near Brighton, in the early 19th century.

Preston, 208A Ledger for Rev. John WHELER, d. 1818
- Nave aisle floor, centre.
- 91(W) x 181(L) — Worn.
- M.I. (12 lines, engraved) on a pale cream freestone slab; head to West.

HIC R...

JOHN WHELER

Brother to

Sir Ch. WHELER

Bar[t]

Prebendary of

WESTMINSTER ABBEY

and RECTOR of

Mareham le Fenn

LINCOLNSHIRE

Ob[t] 11th Feby 1818

Ætat 82 Years

1. JH notes that Rev. John Wheler, LL.B., and his brother Charles (later Sir Charles, Bart.) were sons of Sir William Wheler, Bart., and his wife Penelope, daughter of Sir Stephen Glynne, Bart. Rev. John was rector of Mareham le Fen in Lincolnshire, and prebendary of Westminster Abbey 1797-1818.

Preston, 208B Ledger for Agnes PALMER, d. 1804
- Nave aisle floor, centre, near chancel arch.
- 94(W) x 181(L) — Worn.
- M.I. (17 lines, engraved) fills surface of a pale cream freestone slab; head to West.
- Agnes Palmer, of Brighton, d. 28 Jun 1804, aet 66.

1. Unusual juxtaposition of quotations from the Book of Psalms with biographical details.

Preston, 208C Floor stone for Grace CHEYNELL, d. 1696
- Nave floor, before the chancel arch.
- 75(W) x 58(L) — Sound; dirty.
- M.I. (6 lines, engraved) on a small freestone slab; head to West.
- Grace Cheynell, d. 15 Jan 1696; wife of Francis Cheynell, D.D.

1. Francis Cheynell, a contentious Puritan, married Grace, daughter of Robert Seaman, on 19 Sep 1644 at Hove. He was rector of Petworth in 1643, sequestered, restored in 1655, and ejected at the Restoration. For details of his life see biography by Roger Pooley in *ODNB* and Matthews (114-5). He suffered bouts of insanity and was buried in the nave of Preston church. There is some doubt as to whether he died in 1665 or 1671.
2. His grave slab was noted as already worn by Horsfield (*Sussex* I 170). He was survived by his wife and five children. This stone gives Grace's death as 15 Jan 1696, whereas she is recorded as having died on 5 Apr 1697 by Thomas-Stanford (SRS 27. 67-8, 71, 74, 76). *ODNB* and Matthews (114-5) quote 1683, possibly confusing her with her daughter, also Grace. (see 208I).

Preston, 208D Ledger for Elizabeth ..., unknown date
- Nave floor, South of centre, opposite South and North doors.
- 91(W) x 183(L) — Very worn; irregular at East end.
- M.I. (10 lines?, engraved) in upper 50% of an irregular freestone slab.

Here lie the remains of

ELIZABETH ...

the ..... of

... John ...

...

[remainder illegible].

1. The lettering looks early 19th century.
2. Dimensions suggest that 208D-E were recut and replaced.

Preston, 208E Anonymous ledger perhaps c.1800

- Nave floor, South of 208D, in line with South door.
- 91(W) x 184(L) — Very worn; cracked.
- M.I. (traces only) on a pale grey freestone slab; head to South.

Here lie the remains ...

1. Dimensions suggest that 208D-E were recut and replaced.

Preston, 208F Mural monument for James DOUGLAS, d. 1819

- Nave, West wall, South of tower arch, facing East.
- 91(W) x 60(H) — Fine; faded.
- M.I. (8 lines, engraved, Latin) on a white marble tablet set landscape-wise; incised chamfered frame.
- James Douglas, A.M., d. 5 Nov 1819, aet 67.

1. 208F is in a set of six early 19th-century tablets.
2. Both the lettering and language of the M.I. evidence an ambitious neo-Classicism.
3. JH notes that James Douglas was an antiquary, geologist, author, artist and clergyman. For details of his interesting and varied life, see biography by Dennis R. Dean in *ODNB*.
4. Venn (2 2 325) and Horsfield (*Sussex* 1 171-2).

Preston, 208G Mural monument for Elizabeth SHIRLEY, d. 1684

- Tower, North wall, facing South.
- 46(W) x 58(H) — Very worn; cracked (lower right).
- M.I. (9 lines, engraved) on a cretaceous freestone slab.
- Elizabeth Shirley, d. 23 Apr 1684, an infant; daughter of Sir Richard Shirley, Bart.

1. The Church Guide notes that 208G was brought inside at 1870s restoration; however, it may originally have been located near the monument to Anthony Shirley, see 208O and Turner (*SAC* 19 63-4).
2. JH notes that Elizabeth Shirley was daughter of Sir Richard, the 2nd Baronet, and his wife Judith née Bateman (see IGI) and Cockayne (*Baronetage* 4 27).

Preston, 208H Ledger for Charlotte CARBONELL, d. 1819

- Nave floor, centre, far West end.
- 64(W) x 131(L) — Cracked; repaired; stained.
- M.I. (5 lines, engraved) in upper 80% of a freestone slab; head to West.

CHARLOTTE
CARBONELL
... *Brighton*
26 May 1819

...
(remainder illegible).

1. Another Carbonell slab is 208J.
2. NBI records the burial of Charlotte Carbonelle on 2 Jun 1819, aet 9 months, at Preston.

Preston, 208I Ledger for Grace CHEYNELL, d. 1683

- Nave floor, West end, centre, East of 208H.
- 81(W) x 150(L) — Sound; edges worn.
- M.I. (5 lines, engraved) in upper 20% of surface of a freestone (Horsham?) slab; head to West.

HERE LYETH THE BODY OF
GRACE CHEYNELL DAVGH
TER OF FRANCES CHEYNEL
DR INDEVENITY DECEASED
APRIL 23 1683

1. See 208C for a slab for this Grace Cheynell's mother, who married her husband Francis Cheynell in 1644.

2. Horsfield (*Sussex* I 175) notes Francis' worn slab.
3. OED records the word 'indevenity' (indivinity) used by Sir Thomas Browne in 1646.
4. JH notes that the historian Edmund Calamy records this Grace as daughter of Francis, who survived him, see Matthews (114/5).
5. NBI records the burial of Grace Cheynell on 4 May 1683 at Preston.

Preston, 208J Ledger perhaps for J ... CARBONELL, unknown date
- Nave floor, towards West end, centre, East of 208I, North of 208D.
- 80(W) x 166(L) — Very worn; cracked (West end).
- Illegible.

1. Another Carbonell slab is 208H.

Preston, 208K Mural tablet for Theodosia, Countess of CLANWILLIAM, d. 1817
- Nave, West wall, North of tower arch, facing East.
- 70(W) x 41(H) — Very good.
- M.I. (engraved) on a white marble tablet, set landscape-wise; incised chamfered border.
- Theodosia, Countess of Clanwilliam, d. 2 Mar 1817, aet 74.

1. JH notes that Theodosia, daughter of Robert Hawkins-Magill of Gill Hall, Co. Down, was married on 29 Aug 1765 to John Meade, Baronet, MP for Banagher. He was created Baron Gillford and Viscount Clanwilliam in 1766, and Earl Clanwilliam in 1776. He died in 1800 and was buried in Dublin. See Cockayne (*Peerage* 3 239).

Preston, 208L Mural tablet for Charlotte WHELER, d. 1825, and Rev. John WHELER, d. 1818
- Nave, West wall, below 208K.
- 58(W) x 81(H) — Very good.
- M.I. (engraved, black) on an unframed white marble tablet, set portrait-wise.
- Charlotte Wheler, d. 14 Nov 1825, aet 79; wife of Edward Wheler, Esq., late member of the Supreme Council in Calcutta; 2 surviving daughters, unnamed; her brother-in-law, Rev. John Wheler, prebendary of Westminster and rector of Mareham le Fenn, Lincolnshire, d. 14 Feb 1818, aet 82.

1. For John Wheler, see 208A.

Preston, 208M Mural monument for Joseph ARMSTRONG, d. 1804
- Nave, West wall, near 208G.
- 48(W) x 98(H) — Worn; cracked; dirty.
- M.I. (11 lines, engraved) on a white marble tablet.
- Joseph Armstrong, d. 23 May 1804, aet 1; son of unnamed Armstrong, quartermaster of the 6th Dragoons.

Preston, 208N Mural monument for William HAMSHAR, d. 1738, wives and descendants
- Nave, West wall, South of 208M; mostly obscured by an organ.
- (W) unknown x 80(H) — Good (some obscured).
- M.I. (engraved) on an unframed white marble tablet, set portrait-wise.

.... HAMSHAR
.... PATRI ELIZÆ
....ANNI MICHELL
.... ARMIGERO
... O MICHELL
....EWES ARMIGERIS
....ET CAROLO

....DINENSIBVS

....LEWES ARMIGERO

.... BAKER VXORI

....RATRIBVS ET SORORI

.... MICHELL A.M.

.... STES POSVIT

.... LXXXIX

.... IBI

1. JH notes the following details on the Hamshar/Hampshire family of Preston, see Comber (*Lewes*). William Hamshar 1654 - 1738 married firstly, at Preston on 21 May 1689, Elizabeth, daughter of Richard Webb of Moulscomb, and widow of John Farncombe. She was buried at Preston 29 Oct 1694. He married secondly, (lic. 22 Mar 1698/9), Margaret, daughter of John Bradford, and widow of John Webb (brother of Elizabeth Webb, above named). She died 23 Jan 1730/1 aet 73. Issue of William and Elizabeth: Richard (born and died Oct 1694) and Elizabeth, baptised at Preston 1 Jan 1690/1. She married (lic. dated 21 Aug 1707) John Michell, attorney, of Lewes, who died 12 Nov 1735, aet 35. Elizabeth died 18 Oct 1752, aet 62. Their issue: William, baptised 1708; Thomas baptised 1712; Henry, baptised 1715; Elizabeth, baptised 1717; Charles, baptised 1719; and James baptised 1721, (see IGI). Issue of William and Margaret: Sarah, baptised at Preston 1699.
2. The last name on this monument is Henry (baptised 1715) who was MA, Cantab., vicar of Brighton, etc.. He died in 1789. For fuller details, see Brighton 40D. He is presumably patron of the monument.
3. A family member appears to be related by marriage to Baker of Lewes.

Preston Additions

Anthony SHIRLEY / Edward ELRINGTON monuments (not seen).
Horsfield (*Sussex* I 175); a fuller account in Turner (*SAC* 19 63-4) and Church Guide note monument to Anthony Shirley (datable after 1660), on the sanctuary wall at Preston, on the North side, by his day defaced by whitewash; it had quatrefoils and arms and male and female kneelers at a prayer desk and 12 issue (7 males and 5 females); subject was Anthony Shirley d. 7 Dec 1624, second son of William Shirley; also Barbara, d. 2 Jan 1623, wife of Anthony Shirley and daughter of Sir Thomas Walsingham, of Seadbine, Kent; a related ledger was used as an altar stone (Church Guide); Anthony Shirley was of the Wiston branch of the family and inherited the manor of Preston in 1569[?] from his mother Mary, who had married as her second husband the son of one Richard Elrington, see Thomas-Stanford (42); for a later Shirley panel see 208G; Turner (*SAC* 19 63-4) repeats claims that the monument was to Elrington, rather than to Shirley.
Turner (*SAC* 23 174).
A brass for Edward Scrase, of Blatchington, Gent., d. 1579 (or 1578) was once in church.

(210) PYECOMBE, The Transfiguration

Norman nave and chancel with 19th-century alterations - Nairn & Pevsner (587); reportedly in fine condition in 1724 (Ford 143); the church was at a staging-post for the London coach (Brighton, Pyecombe, Cuckfield) but nothing survives from this period; the parish had 14 families in 1724 and a population in 1801 of 134; surviving ledgers have been arranged down the nave.

Pyecombe, 210A Mural monument for Michael BARRETT, d. 1702, and others

- Sanctuary North wall, North-East corner, at head height.
- 55(W) x 110(H) — Good; faded.
- 2 grey marble panels combined; upper panel with shouldered, domed top and M.I. (10 lines); lower panel has M.I. (7 lines) in upper 50% of its surface.
- Rev. Michael Barrett, rector of Pyecombe, d. 29 Sep 1702, aet 71; his widow, Anne, daughter of Edward Kelyng, Esq.; issue - eldest son, Michael, aet 19, buried at Pyecombe; youngest son, Edward, d. 13 Mar 1698/9, aet 20, buried at Oxford; 3 other unnamed sons; daughter, Hester died an infant, buried Pyecombe; and an unnamed daughter.

1. In situ - Horsfield (*Sussex* I 182).
2. The two named sons died as students at Oxford.
3. JH notes that Michael Barrett was rector of Pyecombe from 1670 to 1702.

Pyecombe, 210B Floor slab for Thomas NORTON, d. 1722/3
- Sanctuary floor, South-East corner.
- 46(W) x 72(L) — Cracked.
- M.I. (8 lines, engraved) fills surface of a freestone slab; head to West.
- Thomas Norton, d. 20 Jan 1722/3, aet 4; son of Thomas Norton, Gent., and Ann.

Pyecombe, 210C Ledger for Sir Lewis BEAUMONT, d. 1738
- Chancel floor, North of centre.
- 83(W) x 180(L) — Sound; damaged edges.
- M.I. (English and Latin) fills surface of a black slab; head to West.
- Rev. Sir Lewis Beaumont, Bart., rector of Pyecombe for 36 years, d. 23 Dec 1738, aet 64.

1. Noted in Horsfield (*Sussex* I 182).
2. High standard of lettering.
3. Same engraver as 210E.

Pyecombe, 210D Ledger for Thomas BYSSHE, d. 1681
- Chancel floor, South of centre and South of 210C.
- 71(W) x 131(L) — Sound.
- M.I. (7 lines, engraved) on upper 35% of a freestone (Horsham?) slab; head to West.
- Thomas Bysshe, Gent., of Cowfold, d. 15 Jul 1681, aet 42.

1. Thomas Bysshe, baptised 13 Jul 1637 and buried 19 Jul 1681, the youngest son of John Byshe, rector of Pyecombe (Caffyn 287) and Margaret Killingbeck, see Attree (*SAC* 36 60) and W. Berry (*Sussex* 199). Thomas Bysshe, 1659-1720, master of Cuckfield Grammar School, 1682-1704, was son of Christopher Bysshe, the eldest son of John Bysshe.
2. Choice of material and aspects of orthography (the word 'this' initially omitted from line 4), suggest that 210D was made very locally.

Pyecombe, 210E Floor slab for Elizabeth BEAUMONT, d. 1750
- Chancel floor, South of centre, South of 210C and West of 210D.
- 83(W) x 50(L) — Sound.
- M.I. (4 lines, engraved) fills surface of a small black slab; head to West.
- Elizabeth Beaumont, d. 13 Jul 1750, aet 84, widow of Sir Lewis Beaumont, Bart.

1. Noted in Horsfield (*Sussex* I 182).
2. By the engraver responsible for 210 C (see tail of figure '1').

Pyecombe, 210F Ledger for John SCRACE, d. 1689
- Nave floor, centre, towards East end.
- 79(W) x 173(L) — Sound; very worn.
- M.I. (5 lines, engraved) in upper 25% (W) of a pale cream freestone slab; head to West.

HERE LYETH BURIED THE
BODY OF JOHN SCRACE
WHO DEPARTED THIS LIFE
THE 27 DAY OF SEPTEMBER
1689

1. Horsfield (*Sussex* I 182) identified 210F as to William Scrase, d. 23 Sep 1689.
2. Lettering notably irregular.

Pyecombe, 210G Anonymous ledger probably for William SCRACE, d. 1689

- Nave floor, centre, immediately West of 210F.
- 82(W) x 190(L) — Good.
- Traces of M.I. (engraved) visible in the upper (W) 60% of a pale cream freestone slab.

HERE LYETH BURIED THE
BO.. .. WILLIAM SCRACE
... PE ...IOY
... ON ... IO
...A..ED THIS LIFE THE
... OF MARCH ANO
D.... [16]89 HE LIVED TO
.... OF 78 YEARS
... DEATH BE T...
.... H AND BLOOD
... CH ADVANTAGE
TO .... D TO ALL THEIRE
... THE DATE
AND TO THE LIFE ETERNAL
THE GATE

1. Noted in Horsfield (*Sussex* I 182) as commemorating William Scrase d. Mar 1689, aet 78.

Pyecombe, 210H Ledger for George SCRACE, d. 1652

- Nave floor, centre, West of 210G, opposite North door.
- 80(W) x 170(L) — Worn.
- M.I. (4 lines, engraved) in upper (W) 25% of a dark grey freestone slab.

HERE LYETH BVRIED THE BODY
OF .... SCRACE DEPARTED
THIS LIFE ...
ANNO DOM 1652[?]

1. Noted in Horsfield (*Sussex* I 182) as commemorating George Scrase, son of William Scrase d. 1 Oct 1652.

Pyecombe Additions

Noted in Horsfield (*Sussex* I 182):
(1) Slab for John Bysshe, d. 21 Apr 1680, aet [?] 47.

(212) RINGMER, St. Mary the Virgin

Described by Horsfield (*Sussex* I 350) as 'Truly Sussex – rude, irregular and ancient'; aisle arcades are 13th-14th century; chancel chapels are Perpendicular (perhaps c.1500 and after 1535); for poor state of fabric and missing tower in view from North-East see Godfrey & Salzman (Pl. 132); nave extended West and tower rebuilt in 1884-5, see W.F. Martin, 'Notes on the rebuilding of Ringmer church tower' (*SAC* 39 197-200), Nairn & Pevsner (587-8) and plan in *SNQ* (III 117); parish had c.300 communicants in 1603, see Renshaw (*Ecclesiastical Returns*); c.90 families in 1717; population of 897 in 1801; prominent were the Springetts (sometime Springate), see 212V, etc., of the Broyle who also owned property on Lewes High Street; series at Ringmer especially strong for 17th century and early 18th century.

Ringmer, 212A Mural monument for Richard SHADWELL, d. 1785

- North aisle, West wall.
- 120(W) x 175 (H) — Fair; colour remains on shield below; blacking faded.
- In black and grey marble; M.I. (engraved, black).

- Richard Shadwell, Esq., d. 5 Jun 1785, aet 64; his wife, Mary, d. 11 Feb 1777, aet 58; issue: Thomas Shadwell, Esq., d. 3 Apr 1785, aet 32[?]; their last surviving son, Henry Thurloe Shadwell, Esq., d. 1 Oct 1807, aet 51.

1. In situ - Lambarde (*SAC* 70 163) noting arms.
2. Richard Shadwell owned property in the Middleham division of the parish, see R. Davey (175).

Ringmer, 212B Wall-mounted brass for Henry Thurloe SHADWELL, d. 1807
- North aisle, West wall, below 212A.
- 23(W) x 15 (H) — Very good.
- M.I. (5 lines, engraved) on a brass plate set landscape-wise.
- Henry Thurloe Shadwell, Esq., d. 1 Oct 1807, aet 51.

Ringmer, 212C Ledger for Susanna [?] SHADWELL, d. 1763 [?]
- North aisle floor, against West wall, below 212B, partly obscured.
- 57(W) x 64(L) — Very worn.
- M.I. (at least 6 lines, engraved) on a freestone slab set head to West.

... The remains ...
... Daughter of
W... hadwell
... Mary [?] his Wife ...
who departed this l ...
the 2[5th] day of May 1 ...
Aged ... Years

1. JH notes that this ledger is probably for a daughter of William and Mary Shadwell.
2. Susanna Shadwell was baptised 5 May 1761 (IGI) to parents William and Mary and buried 2 Jun 1763 at Patcham (NBI).

Ringmer, 212D Mural monument for Lt-Col. Abraham DU VERNET, d. 1806
[Plate 126]
- North aisle, North wall.
- 100(W) x 93 (H) — Very good condition; painted arms partly lost (since 1928?).
- In white and pale grey marble; M.I. (6 lines, engraved, black) set landscape-wise in an oval tablet; darker grey, rectangular, slate setting; flanked by fluted pilasters, left and right; segmented pediment over with military emblems of cannon and flags in low relief; rose motif on corbels left and right; arms lost from curved basement below.
- Lt. Col. Abraham Du Vernet, of the Royal Artillery, d. 23 Oct 1806, aet 47.

1. In situ - Lambarde (*SAC* 70 163) noting arms.

Ringmer, 212E Floor-mounted brass for Mary ELLIOT, d. 1809
- North aisle, floor, near North door, slab partly obscured by pews.
- Brass plate 33(W) x 18 (H) on a ledger 85(W) of which visible (H) is 66 — Brass - good.
- Brass plate set irregularly on a black slab, head to West.
- Mary Elliot, d. 11 Jan 1809, aged 35; daughter of Obadiah and Sarah Eliot, of Middleham, Ringmer.

Ringmer, 212F Ledger for Sibylla STAPLEY, d. 1697
- North transept floor, South-East corner.
- 81(W) x 167(L) — Very good.
- M.I. on black marble (?) slab set head to West.
- Sibylla Stapley, d. 24 May 1697, aged 23; youngest daughter of Sir John Stapley, Bart., of Broyle Place, Ringmer and Mary his wife.
truly pious and most ingenious young lady

1. Sibylla Stapley supported the local charity school in 1695 (Caffyn 219).
2. For a summary of her will in Budgen (*Dobell* 700).
3. See 212EE for Sir John Stapley and 212BB for his wife Mary.

Ringmer, 212G Ledger for Margaret PLUMER, d. 1669/70, and Mary Plumer, d. 1728

- North transept floor, South side.
- 93(W) x 184(L) — Fine, legible.
- M.I. on freestone (Horsham?) slab set head to West.
- Margaret Plumer, d. 18 Feb 1669/70, aged 58, youngest daughter of John Bulman, Gent.,
  of Hartfield, Gent., and wife of James Plumer, Gent., of Ringmer.
  Also Mary Plumer, d. 8 Aug 1728, aged [?] years, daughter of John Weekes, Gent., of
  Westfield, Sussex, and wife of Henry Plumer, Gent., of Ringmer.

1. For Plumer see 212I.

Ringmer, 212H Ledger for Anna SALTER, d. 1658

- North transept floor, centre.
- 73(W) x 163(L) — Worn; just legible.
- M.I. (10 lines, engraved, punctuation marks between each word) on pale brown freestone
  slab (Horsham stone?), set head to West.

here lieth enterred
the body of Anna
wife of Tho Salter
iunior and youngest
daughter of Tho
Tyrone late of Ring
mere who departed
life the 16 of august
anno 1658 aged
26 H yeares

1. The letters 'tho' in line 3 are partly overwritten.

Ringmer, 212I Ledger for John PLUMER, d. 1676

- North transept floor, centre.
- 70(W) x 152(L) — Fair.
- M.I. (6 lines, engraved at top, remainder blank) on brown freestone slab (Horsham stone?),
  set head to West.

HERE LYETH BURIED THE
BODY OF IOHN PLUMER
ELDEST SONNE OF HENRY
PLUMER GENR AND IANE
HIS WIFE, WHO DYED DECEMBER
THE 23TH 1676 IN THE SIXTH
YEARS OF HIS AGE

1. For Plumer see 212G.
2. Lambarde (*SAC* 70 163) notes a Jane Plumer, wife of Henry of Ringmer, only daughter of John Warde,
   of Cuckfield, 1677. *SAC* source is *Topographer* (IV 297) and implies that 212I was inaccessible in
   1929.

Ringmer, 212J Ledger for Thomas NORTON, d. 1641 [?]

- North transept floor, North side.
- 83(W) x 170(L) — Very worn; pitted.
- M.I. (5 lines, deeply engraved at top, reminder blank) on freestone (Horsham?) slab.
- Died 26 Jan 1641 [?].

1. One Thomas Norton of Lewes, woollen draper, was licensed to wed on 5 Jun 1634; the same, or another of same name described as yeoman, stood surety for other licences on Feb 1614 and Jan 1633, see Dunkin (*Licences 1586-1643* 213 & 202).

Ringmer, 212K Brasses for Richard MASCALL, d. 1631, and Jane his daughter, d. 1631.

- North transept, North wall.
- (a) 66(W) x 47 (H), (b) 15.5(W) x 17 (H), (c) 21(W) x 26 (H), (d) 18(W) x 22 (H) — All fine.
- A set of brass plates: (a) a large inscribed plate, (b) left-hand heraldic shield, (c) centre heraldic panel, (d) right-hand heraldic shield.
- Richard Mascall, Esq., of Malling, d. 17 Aug 1631; husband of Francis [sic], daughter of Sir George Paulett, Knight, of Crandol, Hampshire; issue - Henry, Jane, Charitie and Ciseley; also Jane Mascall, d. 11 Mar 1631, aged 10.

1. In situ - Lambarde (*SAC* 70 162) noting arms, Davidson-Houston (*SAC* 79 104-5) with illustration and transcription and Stephenson (513-14).
2. Found when pews with high backs were removed in 1872, see Church Guide following W. Cooper *Notes and Queries - Sussex Brass - Ringmer* (*SAC* 25 225).
3. Richard Mascall was commemorated at Ringmer, then owned by Malling College, because the church at Malling was in disrepair (*SAC*).

Ringmer, 212L Mural for Elizabeth JEFFERAY, [c.1620]

- North transept, North wall.
- 130(W) x 150(H) — Fine; loss of details (from top?), gilding and other colour.
- In alabaster; kneeling figures flank an obelisk; M.I. (shallow engraved, gilded) on slate panel.
- Elizabeth Jefferay, d. 23 Sep year not given, aet 40; daughter of Walter Mayney, Esq., of Kent, and wife of Frances Jefferay, Esq., of South Malling.

1. In situ - Lower (*SAC* 14 222) with transcription and Nairn & Pevsner (588).
2. Repainted in 1960s (Church Guide).
3. Datable c.1620.
4. Elizabeth Jefferey was first wife of Francis Jefferay of South Malling, Esq., the son of Richard Jefferay (see 56c) and patron of that monument which is dated 1612 [?].

Ringmer, 212M Ledger for John SNOOK, d. 1701

- North transept floor, North-East corner, partly obscured by later step.
- 75(W) x 91(L) (still visible) — Very worn.
- M.I. on dark freestone slab (Horsham stone?), set head to West.
- John Snook, d. 19 Oct 1701.

1. The Snooks lived at Delves House (Farrant 296).
2. See 212O, 212P and 212Q.

Ringmer, 212N Wall-mounted brass for Rev. John SADLER, d. 1640

- North-East chapel, South wall.
- 31(W) x 30(H) (brass) — Worn.
- Well cut brass, in trapezoidal form, in a modern setting.
- John Sadler, d. 1 Oct 1640.

1. Formerly in chancel, see Stephenson (514); Davidson-Houston (*SAC* 79 106) - with illustration and transcription.
2. John Sadler was admitted vicar of Patcham 1608-26, and of Ringmer 1627-40, see Dunkin (*SAC* 26 75); some give year of death and burial as 1642.
3. Patron of 212N was John Sadler's wife Mary whom he married in 1613. She was widow of Edward Fenner.
4. His daughter Anne married John Harvard, founder of Harvard University.
5. This setting of 212N is dated 1957.

Ringmer, 212O Ledger for Rev. Henry SNOOKE, d. 1727
- Nave floor, West end.
- 98(W) x 199(L) — Worn: diagonal cracks.
- M.I. on black (marble?) slab, set head to West.
- Rev. Henry Snooke, vicar of Ringmer, d. 16 Oct 1727, aet 70.

1. Sawyer (*SAC* 29 206) with transcription.
2. For licence to marry Henry Snook, clerk and Mary Short, of Lewes 11 Jul 1691, see Dunkin (*SAC* 26 75) and Dunkin (*Licences 1670-1729* 133); he left money for the charity school, as did his son (see 212Q) in his will of 1762 (Caffyn 220); Parish Registers are quoted as stating that he was buried (not died) on 16 Oct 1727; for other Snooks see 212M, P and Q.

Ringmer, 212P Ledger for Mary SNOOK, d. 1703
- Nave floor, centre.
- 76(W) x 99(L) — Worn; pitted; legible.
- Head to West; dark freestone.
- Mary Snook, d. 4 May 1703.

1. Mary Snook was wife of Henry Snook, see 212O and Sawyer (*SAC* 29 206); for other Snooks see 212M and Q.
2. M.I. wording 'Praestolantior' altered to 'praestolantur'.

Ringmer, 212Q Ledger for Henry SNOOKE, d. 1763
- Nave floor, East end.
- 74(W) x 99(L) — Mostly illegible; evenly worn, corners cut.
- M.I. (engraved, white infill) on a black slab (marble?), set head to West.
- Henry Snooke, armiger, d. 19 Jan 1763, aet 69.

1. This Henry Snook was the son of Rev. Henry Snook Snr (see 212O); his widow was Rebecca (d.1780) (Farrant 296); for other Snooks see 212M, O and P.

Ringmer, 212R Mural for Richard WYNNE, d. 1679
- Sanctuary, North wall, at head height.
- Size? — Faded.
- An elegant cartouche with a border of scrolls and acanthus; in white marble; at the top, a vase and painted and gilded flame; in the centre, M.I. (20 lines, engraved, black, Latin); cherub's head in centre below; shield-of-arms lost (?) from central corbel.
- Richard Wynne, armiger, of Guydur, Caernarvon, Wales, d. 5 Aug 1679, aet 65; his wife, Elizabeth, d. 1 Feb 1673, aet 57, daughter of William Campion, of Combwell, Kent.

1. In situ - Lambarde (*SAC* 70 161) noting arms and Nairn & Pevsner (588).
2. For Wynne see 212S and 212U.
3. Many of Richard Wynne's ancestors were commemorated at Llanrwst church Denbighshire, see J. Lewis (78ff).
4. JH notes that Richard Wynne married Elizabeth Campion 22 Jul 1641 at Goudhurst, Kent. See IGI.

Ringmer, 212S Ledger for Richard WYNNE, undated [1679?]
- Sanctuary floor, against North wall.
- 84(W) x 207(L) — Cracked but legible.
- Arms, then M.I. (3 lines, engraved), remainder blank, on slab set head to West.
- Richard Wynne, Esq., undated.

1. Relates to 212R; see too 212U.
2. For heraldry, see Lambarde (*SAC* 70 162).
3. This ledger is now completely covered by the sanctuary carpet (2010).

Ringmer, 212T Ledger for Elizabeth CAMPION, d. 1669.
- Sanctuary floor, North side.
- 84(W) x 200(L) — Sound; very good.
- Arms, then M.I. (8 lines, engraved) fill upper 80% of black slab (marble?) set head to West.
- Elizabeth Campion, d. 9 Oct 1669, aet 78; her husband, Sir William Campion; her father, Sir William Stone, of London.

1. In situ - Lambarde (*SAC* 70 162) noting arms; close to 212U but with smaller lettering.
2. This ledger is now completely covered by the sanctuary carpet (2010).

Ringmer, 212U Ledger for Elizabeth WYNNE, d. 1673
- Sanctuary floor, North of centre.
- 98(W) x 200(L) — Sound; very good.
- Arms, then M.I. (10 lines, engraved) fills most of black slab (marble?) set head to West.
- Elizabeth Wynne, d. 1 Feb 1673, aet 57; second daughter of Sir William and Elizabeth Campion of Combwell, Kent, and wife of Richard Wynne, Esq.

1. In situ - Lambarde (*SAC* 70 161) noting arms, then partly-covered by an altar.
2. For her mother see 212T; for her husband see 212R and 212S.
3. This ledger is now completely covered by the sanctuary carpet (2010).

Ringmer, 212V Ledger for Sir Herbert SPRINGETT, d. 1661/2
- Sanctuary floor, South of centre.
- 116(W) x 206(L) — Sound; very good.
- Arms, then M.I. (7 lines, engraved) in upper 50% of a black slab (marble?) set head to West.
- Sir Henry Springett, Bart., d. 5 Jan 1661/2, aet 49; loyal to Church of England, King and Country.

1. In situ - Lambarde (*SAC* 70 161) noting arms.
2. For Herbert Springett see Lower (1867 45); his loyalty earned him a baronetcy; the firmly Royalist M.I. contrasts with the political sentiments of other Springetts - see 212W, X, AA, DD and FF.
3. JH notes that Sir Herbert was MP for New Shoreham 1646 until secluded in 1648.
4. And again in 1660 until his death.
5. This ledger is now completely covered by the sanctuary carpet (2010).

Ringmer, 212W Ledger for Elizabeth WHALE [WHALLEY], d. 1660
- Sanctuary floor, South side.
- 87(W) x 202(L) — Sound; very worn.
- Arms, then M.I. (6 lines, engraved) in upper 40% of a black marble (?) slab, set head to West.

HERE LYETH INTERRED THE BODYE
OF THE MOST VERTUOUS AND PIOUS
M. ELIZABETH WHALE SECOND
DAUGHTER OF S. HERBERT SPRINGET
BARONETT WHO DYED JUNE 14 ANNO
DMI 1660 AGED 22 YEARS

1. In situ - Lambarde (*SAC* 70 161) noting arms, and see W. Berry (*Sussex* 33).
2. Flanked by ledgers to her parents.
3. For Springett see 212V, X, AA, DD and FF.
4. This ledger is now completely covered by the sanctuary carpet (2010).

Ringmer, 212X Ledger for Barbara SPRINGETT, d. 1696/7
- Sanctuary floor, against South wall.
- 84(W) x 171(L) — Sound; worn but legible.
- M.I. (8 lines, engraved) in upper 40% of a black slab (marble?), set head to West.

- Barbara Springett, buried 6 Mar 1696/7, aet 85; wife of Sir Herbert Springett, Bart., of the Broyle Place.

1. For Barbara Springett see Lower (*SAC* 20 45).
2. She was daughter of William Campion of Combwell, Kent.
3. Note corrected digit in last line, from '9' to '8'.
4. For Springetts see 212V, W, AA, DD and FF.
5. This ledger is now completely covered by the sanctuary carpet (2010).

Ringmer, 212Y Anonymous Ledger, dated 1630
- South transept floor, North side, West of 212AA.
- 32(W) x 88(L) — Appears complete; worn.
- M.I. on a cream freestone slab, set head to West.

12 Septem.

1630

1. Note the reversed letter 'S'.

Ringmer, 212Z Mural for Sir Herbert WHALLEY, d. 1689 [Plate 127]
- South or Springett chapel, North wall.
- 115(W); height unknown — Very good; some local losses to festoons (right side).
- In high quality grey marble, an elegant cartouche with 2 cherubim on cornice; other cherubim; garlands.
- Sir Herbert Whalley, Knt, born in Ringmer, died of a fever, 6 May 1689, aet 28, and interred in Trinity Church, Chester; his parents, John Whalley, Esq., and Elizabeth; his grandparents, Sir Herbert Springett, Bart., and Barbary [sic]; his wife, Dame Lucy Whalley.

1. In situ - Lambarde (*SAC* 70 162) noting arms, Nairn & Pevsner (588).
2. In 1684, Herbert Whalley donated Ten Commandments painted onto metal panels to be placed flanking the Communion Table 'in token of his zeal for the Church of England' (Church Guide).
3. Good quality of upper cherubim; lower cherub less good and by another hand.

Ringmer, 212AA Ledger for Thomas SPRINGETT, d. 1643
- South transept floor, North side, immediately East of 212BB.
- 68(W) x 109(L) — Worn edges.
- M.I. (7 lines, engraved) on slate slab, set head to West.
- Thomas Springett, d. 2 Dec 1643, aet 3; son of Herbert Springett, Esq., of Broyle House.

1. For Springetts see 212V, W, X, DD and FF and Lower (*SAC* 20 45).

Ringmer, 212BB Ledger for Dame Mary STAPLEY, d. 1708/9
- South transept floor, North side, immediately West of 212AA.
- 99(W) x 197(L) — Fine.
- M.I. (engraved) on black slab (marble?) set head to West.
- Dame Mary Stapley, d. 20 Mar 1708/9, aet 72; eldest daughter of Sir Herbert Springett, Bart., and wife of Sir John Stapley, of Patcham, Bart., d. 1700; her issue cited are Mary Dobell and one other daughter, unnamed.

1. Drafting errors and alterations - 'Dame' and 'x children'.
2. For summary of Mary Stapley's will see Budgen (*Dobell* 70-1); her bequests included a gift of 'all her litle pictures' to her granddaughters; she requested burial at Ringmer; her issue was - Philadelphia, b 1642, wife of Peter Courthope, Esq., of Danny; Elizabeth, b 1657, wife of Dr Briggs, of Chichester; Mary, b 1659, wife of Walter Dobell, Esq., of Streat; Barbara, b 1661, wife of William Hay, of Glyndebourne, then of Merryk Jenkin, Esq., of Woodstock, Oxford, see Notes & Queries (*SAC* 22 222).
3. See also Sibylla Stapley (212F).

Ringmer, 212CC Anonymous ledger, dated 1626

- South transept floor, below 212EE.
- 53(W) x 86(L) — Cracked; partial remains only?
- M.I. in upper left corner of a grey freestone slab, set head to West.

28 DECEMBER

1626

Ringmer, 212DD Ledger for Mary SPRINGETT, d. 1654

- South transept floor.
- (Engraved area) 91(W) x 118(L) — Very cracked, surface partly lost.
- M.I. (engraved) on freestone slab set head to West.

HERE LYETH THE BODY OF MARY

SPRINGETT WIFE OF THOMAS

SPRINGETT KNT. DAVGHTER OF

JOHN BELLINGHAM ESQVIER

WHO DEPARTED THIS LIFE APRIL[23]

ANO DNI 1654 AGED 63

1. Note reversal of letter 'S' and superscription in line 4.
2. For Springetts see 212V, W, X, AA and FF and Lower (*SAC* 20 45).

Ringmer, 212EE Ledger for Sir John STAPLEY, d. 1701

- South transept floor, against South wall.
- 98(W) x 197(L) — Cracked but legible.
- Head to West; black slab.
- Sir John Stapley, Baronet, d. 22 Aug 1701, aet 73; his wife, Mary, eldest daughter of Sir Herbert Springett, Bart.; issue 10, unnamed.

1. For Mary Stapley see 212BB.

Ringmer, 212FF Mural for Herbert SPRINGETT, d. 1620

- South transept, South wall.
- 132(W) x 286(H) — Very good, colour and gilding visible.
- In coloured marbles, alabaster and other stones; hanging monument; kneeling figure between 2 obelisks; M.I. (shallow engraved, gilded).
- Herbert Springett, Esq., d. 7 May 1620, aet 65.

1. In situ - Horsfield (*Sussex* I 350), Lambarde (*SAC* 70 162) noting arms, Mosse and Nairn & Pevsner (587).
2. Herbert Springett was a successful Lewes lawyer who established his children as members of the gentry (Church Guide); for marriage licence dated 30 May 1613, for Simon Stone, of Middle Temple, Gent. and Elizabeth Springett, daughter of Harbert Springett of St. Mary Westout, Lewes (St. Anne's), see Dunkin (*Licences 1586-1643* 86).
3. Lower (*SAC* 20 35) notes M.I. found at St. Anne's, Lewes in the early 1860s, on a pulpit: 'HAR. BAR. SPRINGAT. GEN.TEL.MAN. MADE. THIS PUL. PET. IN. THE. YEARE. OF. ONR. LORD. 1620'.
4. For Springett see 212V, W, X, AA, and DD.

Ringmer, 212GG Mural for Sir William SPRINGETT, d. 1643 [Plate 128]

- South transept, West wall, facing East.
- 100(W) x 230(H) — Fine; colour lost.
- Hanging epitaph monument in white and grey marbles; frontal bust in oval recess; subject wearing a toga-like costume.
- Sir William Springett, Knt., d. 3 Feb 1643, aet 23, eldest son of Herbert Springett, Esq.; his wife, Mary, only daughter of Colonel Sir John Preud [Proud], Knt., soldier, and Ann, daughter of Edward Fagge of Ewell, Faversham, Kent; issue John Springett and Guiliema Maria Posthuma Springett.

1. In situ - Lower (*SAC* 20 36-46) with illustration and transcription, Mosse, Lambarde (*SAC* 70 163) noting arms and Nairn & Pevsner (587-8).
2. William Springett was twin of Herbert Springett of Lewes; he died of typhus at siege of Arundel; his daughter Guilielma, married William Penn (as in Pennsylvania, USA).
3. Patron of 212GG is William Springett's widow.
4. The toga-like costume is notable for the date.
5. JH notes that for details of Sir John Proud, see *The Visitation of Kent, 1619-21*, ed. Robert Hovenden, 1898 (Harl. Soc.), p. 35. Ann Fagge was his second wife.

Ringmer, 212HH Mural for Ensign H. D. CRUNDEN, d. 1793

- South aisle, South wall.
- 110(W) x 250(H) — Good.
- In white marble; grey back-plate in the form of an obelisk; personification of Pity (Fortitude?) leaning on column; face of column engraved and black.
- Ensign H. D. Crunden, 11th Regiment of Foot, d. 25 Apr 1793, aet 27; son of Richard Crunden, land agent at Glyndebourne and Ringmer, also churchwarden.

1. Formerly against North wall - Horsfield (*Sussex* I 350).
2. Unsigned.
3. Ascription to Westmacott goes back to Horsfield, repeated in later Church Guides and by Nairn & Pevsner (588).

Ringmer Additions

Davidson-Houston (*SAC* 79 106), following *Topographer* (IV 291):
(1) Brass for Sir Thomas Springett, Knt, d. 17 Sep 1639, aet 50 (floor-mounted, near Sadler brass, that is 212N).
Summers (150-51).
(2) Two hatchments, probably for Thomas Hay, MP for Lewes 1768, d. unmarried 9 Feb 1786, and Frances Hay, last of the family, d. 1803. Both buried at Glynde (see NBI).

(213) RIPE, St. John the Baptist

Perpendicular with some Decorated traces - Nairn & Pevsner (588); Ripe was a substantial community - c.200 communicants in 1603, see Renshaw (*Ecclesiastical Returns*), 34 families in 1724 and a population of 296 in 1801.

Ripe, 213A Ledger for Elizabeth WILLIAMSON, d. 1728, and her husband James, d. 1736

- Choir floor, centre, before the main altar.
- 113(W) x 224(L) — Excellent.
- M.I. (19 lines in 3 blocks engraved and centred) on an imposing black (slate?) slab; head to West.

Here Lieth y[e] Body of ELIZABETH
late Wife of the Rev[d] IAMES
WILLIAMSON Rector of this Parifh
and Archdeacon of Lewes.
She was Daughter of the Rev[d]
IOHN VINE formerly likewife
Minifter Here & died Nov 26th 1728
In the 64th Year of her Age

The Memorial of Her Good
Deeds Abideth upon Earth
and in Death Her Hope was
full of Immortality

Here alſo Lieth the Body of the
Revᵈ Iᴀᴍᴇꜱ Wɪʟʟɪᴀᴍꜱᴏɴ A.M.
who was Rector of Ripe 49 Years
Rector of Chalvington 26 Years
& Archdeacon of Lewes 13 Years
He died Nov 15ᵗʰ 1736
Aged 75 Years

1. Noted Horsfield (*Sussex* I 354).
2. The final 7 lines were probably added after James Williamson's death in 1736.
3. He was instituted 23 Nov 1687; for licence to marry James Williamson of Ripe, clerk and Elizabeth Vine of Ripe, 14 Sep 1687, see Dunkin (*Licences 1670-1729* 104); most of Elizabeth Williamson's life seems to have been spent living at Ripe Rectory.

Ripe Addition
Horsfield (*Sussex* I 354).
(1) Thomas Plummer, of Ripe, Gent., d. 4 Feb 1725/6, aet defaced; issue – 2 sons, 6 daughters.
(2) John Acton, son of William, d. 15 Jan 1712, aet 22.

(214) RODMELL, St. Peter
Norman, South aisle pre-c.1200; Victorian restorations and additions - Nairn & Pevsner (590); in 1686, the floors were reportedly decayed (Ford 40); by 1724, the South chancel, belonging to William Bachellor of Lindfield (see 164U) was reported as in very poor state (Ford 144); the parish had c.30 families in 1724 and a population of 256 in 1801; some of the series of ledgers relocated in the sanctuary are partly obscured by an altar step.

Rodmell, 214A Ledger for Henry MONTAGU, d. 1668
- Sanctuary floor, close to the North door.
- 76(W) x 122(L) — Fine.
- M.I. (engraved) on a brown freestone slab; head to West.
HERE LYES BVRYED
HENERY MOVNTAGV
THE 4ᴿᵀᴴ SONNE OF
ZACHEVS MOVNTAGV
AGED A XIᵀᴴ YEARES AND
DECEASED MARCH THE
4ᴿᵀᴴ 1668

1. Eccentric position of some lettering; material as in 214F.

Rodmell, 214B Ledger for John MONTAGUE, d. 1716
- Sanctuary floor, North of centre, partly obscured by a step.
- 89(W) x 122(L) — Fine.
- Arms then M.I. (6 lines, engraved) on a black slab; head to West.
- John Montague, Gent., of St. Thomas Cliffe, Lewes, d. 3 May 1716, aet 66.

1. In situ - Lambarde (*SAC* 71 140) noting arms.

Rodmell, 214C Ledger for Arthur JONES, d. 1746/7
- Sanctuary floor, centre.
- 78(W) x 122(L) — Fine; cracked (diagonal).
- M.I. (8 lines, engraved) in upper 50% of a brown freestone slab; head to West.
- Arthur Jones, d. 13 Mar 1746/7, aet 4; son of Owen Jones, clerk, and Mary.

1. Commemorating an infant death.
2. Eccentric italicisation.
3. JH notes that Rev. Owen Jones was curate of Rommel and Southease, then rector of Ovingdean from 1746-51 (see CCEd).

Rodmell, 214D Grave marker for Charles SKOTTOWE, d. 1767
- Sanctuary floor, North of centre, before the altar.
- 78(W) x 53(L) — Fine.
- M.I. (3 lines, engraved) in a brown freestone slab.
- Rev. Charles Skottowe, 1767.

1. For fuller details of Charles Skottowe see 214I.

Rodmell, 214E Ledger for Rev. William GABBITAS, d. 1825
- Sanctuary floor, immediately before the altar.
- 91(W) x 69(L) — Good.
- M.I. (engraved, black) in freestone slab; head to West.
- Rev. William Gabbitas, M.A., vicar of Oving and rector of Rodmell for 24 years, d. 26 Nov 1825, aet 50.

1. For licence to marry dated 5 Jul 1819 for Rev. William Gabbitas, of Rodmell, clerk, bachelor and Fanny Homewood, of Rodmell, spinster, see Dunkin & Penfold (*Licences* 162).
2. JH notes that William Gabbitas had been curate of Southease, rector of East Wittering 1800-02, rector of Rodmell 1802-25 and vicar of Oving 1817-25 (see CCEd).

Rodmell, 214F Ledger for Thomas? GRUNDY, d. 16..
- Sanctuary floor, South of the centre.
- 59(W) x 122(L) — Very worn.
- M.I. (engraved 2 blocks) on a brown freestone slab; head to West.

HERE LYETH BURY
D THE BODY OF
...MAS GRUNDY

... CEASED ...
DAY OF ..ULY
MDC ..

1. Material as in 214A.

Rodmell, 214G Ledger for Thomas? ALCHORNE?, d. 16??
- Sanctuary floor, at South end of set.
- 67(W) x 122(L) — Very worn.
- M.I. (engraved) in upper 50% of freestone slab; head to West.

HERE LYETH INTER*ED
THE BODY ... HO
MA ..... HORNE WHO
WA..... URIED ...
AUGUST ..

1. The licence to marry for Thomas Alchorne of Hailsham, Gent. and Francis De La Chambre, Lewes, 2 Aug 1677 might identify the subject of 214G, see Dunkin (*Licences 1670-1729* 43).
2. 93MM commemorates one Thomas Alchorne, d. 1735.

Rodmell, 214H Anonymous Ledger, date unknown
- Sanctuary floor, South of 214A-E.
- 78(W) x 178(L) — Very worn.
- M.I. (now illegible) on a brown freestone slab.

Rodmell, 214I Mural monument for Rev. Charles SKOTTOWE, d. 1767 [Plate 129]
- Chancel, South wall.
- 73(W) x 131(H) — Good.
- M.I. (engraved, black, centred) on a thin marble oval panel; unframed; alabaster corbel with an unusual mask relief decoration.
- Rev. Charles Skottowe, B.D., prebendary of Chichester, rector of Rodmell and Slinfold, and master of Warwick Hospital, d. 20 Mar 1767, aet 63; youngest son of Thomas Skottowe, Esq., of Norfolk; his virtues - charity, piety, learning, integrity, etc.

1. Elegant lettering.
2. JH notes that Charles Skottowe MA, BD, was rector of St. Lawrence Pountney and St. Mary Abchurch, City of London, 1747-9; declined mastership of Corpus Christi, Cambridge; prebendary of Chichester 1748-67, rector of Rodmell 1749-67, rector of Slinfold 1760-7 and master of the Leicester Hospital, Warwick, see Venn (1 4 34).

Rodmell Addition
(1) Stephenson (514); Turner (*SAC* 23 176) after Horsfield (*Sussex* I 198); Davidson-Houston (*SAC* 79 107).

Then on a hinge, in South (or Rodmell Place) chancel: note an inscribed brass, on one side original 14th-century engraving, on the other 'Here lies the body of John De La Chambre, Esq., who departed this life the 4th day of December, 1673', presumed lost (for the family see 214G).

(216) ROTHERFIELD, St. Denys
Early 13th century with Perpendicular additions - Nairn & Pevsner (591-2); for plan see *SNQ* (III 51); condition in 1724 reported to be fine (Ford 179); external view dated 1785, shows the church from a great distance, commanding its village with very sparse building immediately round it, see Godfrey & Salzman (Pl. 139); population in 1801 was 1963; ledgers were relocated in the chancel floor during the 19th century.

Rotherfield, 216A Mural monument for Humphrey FOWLE, d. 1756
- Sanctuary, North wall, high.
- c.128(W); (H) unknown — Faded.
- Large M.I. in grey marble set portrait-wise; flanked by fluted Doric pilasters; gadroon ornament on base moulding; fluted, scroll corbels; above, entablature; triglyphs and blank metopes in frieze; double ogive pediment; escutcheon in Baroque frame.
- Humphrey Fowle, Esq., magistrate, etc., d. 5 Jul 1756, aet 73; his wife, Elizabeth, daughter of Sir Thomas Seyliard, Bart., of Boxley Abbey, Kent; their issue - Elizabeth, Humphrey (both dead) and Eleonora.

1. Probably in situ - photograph in Keyser (*SAC* 40 frontispiece), cited by Horsfield (*Sussex* 1 400) and Pullein (126 & 374-399) with transcription and pedigree.
2. Both the lower moulding decoration and the ogival pediment are unusual.
3. For heraldry see Lambarde (*SAC* 67 175).
4. NBI records burial of Humphrey Fowle on 9 Jul 1756 at Rotherfield.
5. See Humphrey's wife Elizabeth at 216B.

Rotherfield, 216B Ledger for Elizabeth FOWLE, d. 1720, and Humphrey FOWLE

- Sanctuary floor, North-East corner.
- 110(W) x 200(L) — Good.
- M.I. (7 lines, engraved) in upper 80% of a black slab; head to West; escutcheon at top.

Here lieth the Body of ELIZABETH FOWLE
Late Wife of HUMPHREY FOWLE of Rotherfield, Esq
She was 3ʳᵈ daughter of Sʳ THOMAS SEYLAIRD
of Boxley ABBY in Kent, Barᵗ, & died yᵉ 20ᵗʰ April
Anno Dom: 1720 Æt 38.

Here lieth the body of HUMPHREY FOWLE …
monument

1. Cited by Pullein (126) with transcription.
2. For heraldry see Lambarde (*SAC* 67 175).
3. NBI records burial of Elizabeth Fowle on 15 Apr 1720 at Rotherfield; she was the wife of Humphrey Fowle, see 216A.
4. The Humphrey Fowle on the M.I. is probably, Humphrey, the son of Humphrey and Elizabeth Fowle who died on 31 Jul 1723 aged 14 years, see Pullein (395).

Rotherfield, 216C Ledger for Thomas THREELE, d. 1658

- Sanctuary floor, North of centre, largely obscured by altar.
- 86(W) x 170(L) — Fine.
- Escutcheon then M.I. (engraved) on a black slab; head to West.

THOMAS THREELE ESQ.
DEPARTED THIS LIFE Yᴱ
13ᵀᴴ OF NOVEMBER 1658
AGED 70 YEARES
Et Dominas rerum Opes honeste partas
honestius profundebat:
Conſilio Auxilio Amicis semper adfuit:
Difficillimis temporibus.
Fidem Deo et Regi
Illibatam conſeruauit
Hec, quisquis Legis, virtutes imitare
Ac Aeternitati prospice

1. Cited by Horsfield (*Sussex* I 400) with 1638 as incorrect death date and by Pullein (124) with transcription and correct date.

Rotherfield, 216D Ledger for Mary VINTER, d. 1690

- Sanctuary floor, South of centre, largely obscured by altar.
- (Visible) 87(W) x 169(L) — Fine.
- M.I. (engraved) in black slab; head to West.

Sacrum
Virginibus Uxoribus et Viduis Exemplar
Hic Jacet
Maria filia Eduardi Goring de Cobden in Coᵐⁱᵗ
Suſſexiæ Armigeri, Dotaria Iohannis Luxford
de Ockley. Armigeri, Vxor De nuo Georgij Vinter
S.T.B. Hujus Ecclefiæ Rectoris: Obijt 10 Octobrⁱˢ
Anno Dom 1690. Ætatis Suis 70

1. In situ - Horsfield (*Sussex* I 400) and cited by Pullein (123-4) with transcription.
2. Wording of M.I.s on 216D-E suggests that 216D was erected before death of George Vinter, who was licensed to marry (George Vinter, of Cowfold, clerk, and Mary Luxford, of Lewes, widow 1 Feb 1675), see Dunkin (*Licences 1670-1729* 25). Previously Mary Goring had married John Luxford at Sullington, 2 Nov 1641 (IGI).

Rotherfield, 216E Ledger for Rev. George VINTER, d. 1691/2

- Sanctuary floor, South end, largely obscured altar.
- 98(W) x 200(L) — Local loss (lower right).
- M.I. on black slab; head to West.

Sub hoc marmore spe
Reſurrectionis requiescit
GEORGIUS VINTER
S.T.B.
Et hujus Eccleſiæ Rector
Qui obyit [sic] 3ᵐᵒ Ianuary
Anno Chriſti 1691
Ætatis 74

1. In situ - Horsfield (*Sussex* I 400) and cited by Pullein (123) with transcription.
2. No references in the M.I. to George Vinter's colourful clerical career marked by a number of startling changes of ecclesiastical allegiance, see N. Caplan, 'George Vinter: A Sussex Vicar of Bray?' *SNQ* (XVI 82-89, 149ff); for his wife and possible dating see 216D. .
3. JH notes that George Vinter's degree of STB as on his wife's memorial and (presumably, although not visible, on his own) is not confirmed by Venn (1 4 305), but it is by Hennessy (126). On institution to Rotherfield in 1673 he is shown as MA (see CCEd).

Rotherfield, 216F Mural monument for Nicholas FOWLE, d. 1656

- South choir wall, near South-East corner; high up.
- 128(W) x c.180(H) — Fine; colour; local losses (escutcheon and lower edge).
- Set portrait-wise in weathered (?), white freestone; M.I. (engraved, Latin) fills a slate panel; moulded frame with slender black panels; cornice with damaged escutcheon; below, between crudely fluted, scrolled corbels, a panel of trophies in relief.
- Nicholas Fowle, d. 10 Dec 1656, aet 63; eldest son of Anthony Fowle formerly of Newick; his widow, Elizabeth, patron of 216F; Nicholas Fowle's service to Rape of Hastings.

1. In situ - Horsfield (*Sussex* I 400), photograph in Keyser (*SAC* 40 frontispiece), Nairn & Pevsner (592) and cited by Pullein (127) with transcription.
2. The address to the spectator – 'studiose lector' - at the beginning of the M.I. is noteworthy as is the explanatory military still-life scene.
3. Nicholas Fowle stands surety for a licence to marry in 1642, see Dunkin (*Licences 1586-1643* 289); widow was patron of 216F and composed the M.I.
4. A ledger fragment (head to West) in the floor nearby may relate to 216F and is engraved: '...o hoc Sarcophago re[quies]cit / [D]e quo amplius cartu[m] lo[quitur] ...', see Pullein(126-7).
5. White (109) ascribes 216F to Thomas Stanton (initials 'TS' at end of M.I., lower right) in comparison with those on Stanton's signed monument for Mrs Robinson (d.1665) at Pangbourne, Berkshire.
6. For heraldry see Lambarde (67 175).

Rotherfield, 216G Ledger for John WICKHAM, d. 1591/2

- Choir floor, South side, West end, largely obscured.
- Inaccessible — Fine.
- M.I. (engraved) in a black slab.
- Rev. John Wickham, d. 25 Feb 1591/2, aet unknown; son of Edward Wickham of Swalclif, Oxford; his first wife, Mary Hovenden; their issue - Margaret, Richard, William, Margery, Alice, Elizabeth; his second wife, Martha Cornwalle; issue - Sarah, Mary.

HIC JACET JOHANNES WICKHAM
FILIVS EDVARDI WICKHAM EX
ANTIQUA FAMILIA WICKHAMORVM
DE SWALCLIFF IN COMITATU OXON
ORIVNDI NATVS CANTVARIÆ
ÆDIS CHRISTI, OXON: ALVMNVS
WESTMONASTERII PRÆBENDARIVS
EX HVJVS ECCLESIÆ RECTOR.
DVAS HABVIT VXORES: MARIAM

HOVINDEN ET MARTHAM CORNWA
LLE EX PRIMA SEX HABVIT LI
BEROS MARGARETAM, RICHARDVM,
WILHELMVM, MARGERIAM, ALICIA
M, ET ELIZABETHAM .
EX ALTERA DVAS TANTUM HABVIT FILI
AS SARAM ET MARIAM OBIIT 25
FEB: ANo ÆTATIS ... 1591

1. In situ - Horsfield (*Sussex* I 400) - with the date 29 Apr 1591 and Davidson-Houston (*SAC* 79 108) with transcription.
2. For heraldry, now illegible, see Lambarde (*SAC* 67 175-6).
3. JH notes that John Wickham was MA of Christ Church, Oxon., rector of Horsmonden, Kent, 1571, of New Romney, Kent, 1572, and of Rotherfield c.1580-91/2, see Foster (*Al. Ox.* 1 4 1625); and prebendary of Westminster, see Horn (*Fasti 1541-1857* II 7 81).
4. See also Pullein (199-203) for record of his life.
5. NBI records burial of John Wickham on 2 Mar 1592 at Rotherfield.

Rotherfield, 216H Ledger for William FERMOR, d. 1686
- Nave floor, central aisle, towards East end, carpeted.
- 90(W) x 190(L) — Fine.
- M.I. on a black slab.

Beneath resteth WILLIAM the son
of ALEXANDER FERMOR ESQ^R of
Walsh als Walshes by MARY daugh^r
of ANTHONY FOWLE ESQ^R of this parish.
He had three wives. MARY PICKERING,
MARGARET BUCK and MARTHA THOMAS.
By the First He had one Son
ALEXANDER, by the Second He had
WILLIAM, ANTHONY and a daughter
FRANCES. By the last He had HENRY
JAMES, CHARLES and JOHN.
He was Born 1624
and Dyed 1686

1. In situ - Horsfield (*Sussex* I 400) – 'prostrate', in nave.
2. Walshes, built 1551, was the home of the Fermors (Farrant 300).
3. See also Pullein (362ff) for record of his life.

Rotherfield, 216I Ledger for Jane THWAITES, d. 1828
- South aisle floor, near font.
- 92(W) x 61(L) — Fine.
- M.I. (6 lines, engraved) fill a small black slab; head to South.
- Jane Thwaites, d. 25 Jan 1828, aet 68; wife of Henry Thwaites, Esq., of Hamsell.

1. Cited by Pullein (123) with transcription.

Rotherfield, 216J Anonymous undated floor slab
- On floor, by North door.
- 72(W) x 188(L) — Fine.
- Iron slab with raised processional crosses, no M.I..

1. In situ - Nairn & Pevsner (592) and cited by Pullein (115 & facing 118) with photograph.
2. Willatts (*SAC* 125 102-104) suggests that the double cross decorative indicates a date in first half of 16th century and that 216J possibly commemorates a clergyman pre-Edward VI.
3. To get the achievement the necessary form, the cross was twice impressed in sand bed.

Rotherfield Additions

Horsfield (*Sussex* I 397-400):

(1) In addition to 216A, he cites a monument to (another) Humphrey Fowle, d. 30 Jul 1712, aet 14, son of Humphrey.

Pullein (120-123)

(2) Thomas and Mary CHOWNE, she d. 1605, perhaps a slab in the Neville Chapel 54(W) x 123(L)?

(217) ROTTINGDEAN, St. Margaret

Norman nave, remainder Early English, much restored by G G Scott, 1856 - Nairn & Pevsner (592-3) and A. Hussey, 'On Rottingdean Church in 1855' (*SAC* 9 67-70); pavement reported as utterly decayed in 1686; the chancel was repaired by Pelling between 1699 and 1724 (Ford 36, 145); the parish had 28 families in 1724 and a population of 543 in 1801; Horsfield (*Sussex* I 188) noted unspecified slabs to Beards in the aisle, probably 217A-C.

Rottingdean, 217A Ledger for Mary BEARD, d. 1772

- Nave floor, towards East end.
- 96(W) x 203(L) — Fine; diagonal crack.
- M.I. (5 lines, engraved) in upper 25% (W) of a black slab; head to West.
- Mary Beard, d. 28 Jan 1772, aet 75; wife of Nicolas Beard, Gent.

1. Perhaps formerly in an aisle - Horsfield (*Sussex* I 188).
2. The Beards, owners of nearby Down House, were prominent Quakers and donated a burial ground; one Nicholas Beard was presented by the churchwarden for non-attendance in the mid 1670s, see Johnstone (4, 18); however, 217A-C suggest that other members of the family were or became Anglicans.

Rottingdean, 217B Ledger for Mary BEARD, d. 1726/7

- Nave floor, against chancel steps.
- 99(W) x 174(L) — Fine.
- M.I. (8 lines, engraved) in upper (W) 40% of a black slab; head to West.
- Mary Beard, of Chaldners (Challoners), Rottingdean, d. 2 Feb 1726/7, aet 68; widow of Richard Beard, Gent.

1. Perhaps formerly in an aisle - Horsfield (*Sussex* I 188).
2. For her husband, see 217C; for licence to marry for Richard Beard, of Rottingdean, and Mary Ade of Iford 4 Jun 1681, see Dunkin (*Licences 1670-1729* 64).
3. See comment on the Quaker Beards under 217A.

Rottingdean, 217C Ledger for Richard BEARD, d. 1713/4

- Nave floor, alongside and South of 217B.
- 98(W) x 174(L) — Fine.
- M.I. (10 lines, engraved) in upper (W) 50% of a black slab; head to West.

Here lyeth Interr'd the Body of

RICHARD BEARD

late of CHALLONERS in this pariſh

of ROTTINGDEANE in SUSSEX Gent

who dyed the 28th of JANUARY Anno

Doni 1713 Ætat 55

And left Behind him MARY his wife

and ELIZABETH his onely daughter

& HEIRESSE

Married to HENRY STREATFEILD

of Chiddingſtone in KENT Gent.

1. Perhaps formerly in an aisle - Horsfield (*Sussex* I 188).
2. For Richard Beard's wife see 217B.
3. See comment on the Quaker Beards under 217A.
4. The word 'heiresse' was inserted early and probably in the same hand.

Rottingdean, 217D Ledger for Rev. Thomas PELLING, d. 1732 [Plate 130]
- Tower floor, centre.
- 98(W) x 200(L) — Good; dirty.
- Escutcheon, then M.I. (8 lines, engraved, Latin) fills surface of a black slab; head to West.
- Thomas Pelling, A.M., vicar of Rottingdean, d. 16 Jun 1732, aet 59.

1. In situ - Horsfield (*Sussex* I 188) and Lambarde (*SAC* 71 143) noting arms.
2. 217D is a high quality ledger.
3. Thomas Pelling was vicar of Rottingdean 1698-1732 (see CCEd); for biography of his father, Edward (1640-1718), a high-church Anglican controversialist and vicar at Petworth (see biography by J.S. Chamberlain in *ODNB*); both of Thomas' sisters married Sussex clergymen.

Rottingdean, 217E Floor slab for Charlotte LOCKWOOD, d. 1827
- Tower floor, North of 217D.
- 62(W) x 153(L) — Worn; stained.
- M.I. (5 lines, engraved) on a grey freestone slab; head to West.

M ...

CHARLOTTE

LOCKWOOD

Died 19th Feb ....

Aged 62 Years

1. Style of lettering looks early 19th century.
2. NBI records burial of Charlotte Lockwood on 26 Feb 1827 at Rottingdean.

Rottingdean, 217F Mural monument for Elizabeth FOTHERGILL, d. 1800
- Sanctuary South wall, above head height.
- 87(W) x 145(H) — Very good.
- M.I. (31 lines, engraved, black) fills a white marble tablet set portrait-wise; unframed; engraved, chamfered border; black baseplate; 2 small white corbels.
- Elizabeth Fothergill, died at Brighton, 2 Oct 1800, aet 59; widow of John Fothergill, Esq., of Handsworth, Staffordshire; issue - 4 sons and 3 daughters, all unnamed; her many virtues, analogies with scriptural Martha and Mary; she died during a short visit to the coast.

1. An unusually long M.I.

Rottingdean, 217G Mural monument for Mary Susanna Charlotte ROSS, d. 1787
- Choir, South wall, low down.
- 43(W) x 60(H) — Fine; faded.
- M.I. (8 lines, engraved, black) on a freestone slab; unframed.
- Mary Susanna Charlotte Ross, d. 25 Jul 1787, aet less than 1 year; third daughter of Alexander and Susanna Ross

Rottingdean, 217H Wall-mounted grave marker for 'E[liz] F[OTHERGILL]', d. 1800
- Choir, South wall, below 217G, partly obscured by the altar rail.
- 49(W) x 62(H) — Scaling.

- M.I. (engraved) on a freestone slab.

E.F.
1800
E.J.O.
1848

1. For Elizabeth Fothergill see 217 F.

Rottingdean, 217I Wall-mounted brass for Fanny HUNTER, d. 1807 [Plate 131]
- Choir, South wall, low down.
- 27.5(W) x 22(H) — Fine, polished.
- M.I. (6 lines, engraved) on a rectangular brass plate, on a wooden mount.
- Fanny Hunter, died at Brighton, 27 Nov 1807, aet 7; eldest daughter of Thomas Orby Hunter, Esq.

1. A rare example of an early 19th-century brass.

(221) RYE, St. Mary

Norman with Perpendicular additions - Nairn & Pevsner (594-6), Butler (*SAC* 22 124-133), VCH (IX 58); for a view from North-East see Godfrey & Salzman (Pl. 142); the church paving was reported as in fine state of repair in 1686 and in 1724 (Ford 44, 100); Horsfield (*Sussex* I 495-6) found the nave aisle in liturgical use but the North chancel with its vaults and M.I.s (but with brasses stripped), was used 'as an engine house, and … for the lumber of the town' and the South chancel (St. Clare) as a parish school; at East end of South aisle, the remains of a chantry used by the Lamb family for burials, restored to church use as a vestry in earlier 19th century, see Butler (*SAC* 22 124-133); Butler (*SAC* 13 288) records a Privy Council order dated 29 Mar 1854, discontinuing burials in the church; the parish had c.200 families in 1724 and a population of 2187 in 1801; the church now looks much as it does in photographs accompanying the article on its architectural history in Borrowman, J., 'A short account of Rye Church' (*SAC* 50 20-40); much of the floor is (still) paved with ledger stones, which are especially dense in the North-East (St. Nicholas) Chapel; there are interesting groups of mural monuments in North aisle and crossing but there is nothing really spectacular amongst what is the largest collection of monuments in East Sussex.

Rye, 221A Wall mounted monument for John THREELE, d. 1654 or 1655
- North transept, against North wall, West of North door.
- 116(W) x 260(H) — Fine: repainted.
- M.I. (engraved, Latin) on a slate panel; set portrait-wise; elaborate architectural freestone frame; above, escutcheon against a fluted frieze; on top, segmented pediment breaking forward from pointed pediment; base mouldings and a high pedestal.
- John Threele, d. 4 Sep 1654 or 1655; son of Thomas Threele, of Levisham (Leasam, Rye), Sussex; his widow, Anne [d.1641], daughter of Sir Henry Waldegrave, of Stanningbath, Sussex; quotes Matt. VII.12.

1. A rare case in Sussex of a chronogrammatic inscription used to indicate the year of death with Roman numerals picked out as follows (I)LMDILILII or MDLLLIIII(I) or MDCLIV or V+ (Butler *SAC* 13 279 says 1654).
2. In situ and heraldry noted by Lambarde (*SAC* 68 235).
3. The Threeles were a celebrated Catholic family, presented for their recusancy, see T.J. McCann, 'Our '*dear Sister*' Anne Threele ...' (*SAC* 125 257-8 on Rye as a Puritan centre); Anne Threele was regarded by the Independent Samuel Jeake as a papist, a fornicator and an infidel, see Allison 'Puritanism in 17th century Sussex: Samuel Jeake ...' (*SAC* 125 127).

Rye, 221B Mural monument for members of the PROCTER family, including James, d. 1809 [Plate 132]

- North transept, high on North wall, facing East.
- Inaccessible — Very good; colour.
- An irregular black baseplate; on cornice, a grey marble draped urn with palmette decorations; M.I. (19 lines, engraved, black) fills a trapezoidal panel; below, 2 decorative corbels and an achievement.
- Anne Procter, d. 2 Feb 1831, aet 78; second daughter of James Lamb, Esq., by his first wife, Anne, daughter of David and Anne Morris; and wife of Nathaniel Procter, Esq., d. 5 Aug 1836, aet 79; their second son, Lieut. James Procter, R.N., lost off the Texel, 18 Jun 1809, aet 26, when in command of H.M. schooner Sealark.

1. In situ - Butler (*SAC* 13 278) and Lambarde (*SAC* 68 235) citing arms.
2. For Anne, wife of James Lamb, see 221PP.
3. 221B is cited by Gunnis (*Dict.* 251) as by John Malcott II, c.1777-? and for Nathaniel Proctor [sic], 1831.
4. A ledger relating to Anne and Nathaniel Procter is also recorded.

Rye, 221C Ledger for Ralph NORTON, d. 1750, his wife Anne, d. 1748

- North transept floor, centre.
- 98(W) x 198(L) — Fine: local losses (lower right).
- M.I. (23 lines, engraved) in upper 80% of a black slab; head to West.
- Ralph Norton, Esq., d. 7 Jul 1750, aet 84; his wife, Anne d. 17 Jul 1748, aet 81; their issue
  - daughters Catherine and Elizabeth.

> Here Lyeth the Body of
> RALPH NORTON Eſq.,
> who Departed this Life
> the 7th day of July 1750
> Aged 84.
> Alſo of ANN his Wife
> who died the 17th day of July 1748
> in the 82d Year of Her Age.
> The Requeſt of the deceaſed
> when living to be laid near
> Each other in the Grave
> having by the wanton Exerciſe
> of Power been denied
> CATHERINE & ELIZABETH NORTON
> the only Daughters & Coheireſſes
> of the Deceaſed
> Compelled an Obedience
> to their Parents Command
> & removed the Body of their Mother
> from the Chancel where firſt depoſited
> to this Place by virtue of a Faculty
> obtained for that Purpoſe
> from the Biſhop of this Dioceſe

1. Perhaps formerly in South transept - Butler (*SAC* 13 283).
2. In the 1630-50s, an earlier Norton, one Anthony, had been an outspoken critic of the dominant puritanism of Rye, see G. Mayhew, 'Order, Disorder and Popular Protest in early modern Rye' (*SAC* 127 171).

Rye, 221D Ledger for [Caroline] DURRANT, d. 18..

- North transept floor, West side.
- 105(W) x 183(L) — Very worn.

- M.I. on a slab; head to West.
- Illegible.

1. In situ - Butler (*SAC* 13 283).

Rye, 221E Ledger for Mercy ODIARNE, d. 1703
- North transept floor, centre, South of 221C.
- 95(W) x 200(L) — Very worn.
- M.I. (14 lines, engraved) fills surface of a freestone slab; head to West.
- Mercy Odiarne, d. 7 Mar 1703, aet unknown; daughter of Mr Thomas Kelly, of Herfield [sic], and wife of John Odiarne, Gent., of Rye; issue - daughters: Christian, Anne, both died as infants.

1. In situ in Butler (*SAC* 13 282) with transcription.

Rye, 221F Mural monument for Hannah PINKERTON, d. 1786
- Crossing, North-West pier, facing North, above head height.
- c.55(W) x 140(L) — Fine.
- M.I. (9 lines, engraved, black) on an unframed tablet in grey-veined marble; above, cornice with flaming urn; below, a plain curved apron; with ball finial as corbel.
- Hannah Pinkerton, d. 18 Oct 1786, aet 22; daughter of the late John Pinkerton, Esq., of North Cave in Yorkshire.

1. Located by Butler (*SAC* 13 279) in North transept, with transcription.

Rye, 221G Ledger for Samuel MILLER, d. 1800
- North transept floor, near North door and North wall.
- c.93(W) x 185(L) — Very worn; losses (upper right).
- M.I. (engraved) fill surface of a brown freestone slab; head to West.
- Largely illegible.

1. In situ - Butler (*SAC* 13 282) with following transcription: Samuel Miller, d. 6 Jun 1800, aet 82; his wife, Mary, d. 25 Mar 1805, aet 73; their granddaughters, Harriett Miller, d. 4 Feb 1794, aet 4; Charlotte Ann Miller, d. 31 Oct 1795, infant; (another) Harriett Miller, d. 2 Mar 1804, aet 2; grandson, John Buckhurst Miller, d. 15 Mar 1805, infant.

Rye, 221H Ledger for the KENNETT family, d. 1820, 1822, etc.
- North transept floor, South of 221G.
- 90(W) x 196(L) — Very worn; cracked.
- M.I. (a few lines, engraved) on a pale grey freestone slab; head to East.
- Part legible only - Anonymous, d. ?? ??? 1822, aet 20; Maria, d. 20 Oct 1820, daughter of John and Hannah Kennet.

1. JH notes that this appears to be the ledger of which a full transcription is given by Butler (*SAC* 13 283-4): Catherine Kennett, d. 11 Dec 1798, aet 41; the first wife of John Kennett, d. 5 Apr 1824, aet 74; his second wife Hannah, d. 13 Feb 1816, aet 47; their issue - Catherine, d. 27 Jan 1820, aet 19; Thomas Woollett, d. 22 Apr 1821, aet 16; Ann, d. 26 Feb 1822, aet 20; Maria, d. 20 Oct 1823, aet 17; Edwin, d. 8 Aug 1832, aet 23 - (Centre of South transept).

Rye, 221I Ledger for John and Elizabeth BUCKHURST, d. 1771 and 1782
- North transept floor, East side.
- 97(W) x 191(L) — Very worn; cracked; repaired.
- M.I. (engraved) fills surface of a brown freestone slab; head to West.
- Largely illegible.

1. In situ - Butler (*SAC* 13 282) with following transcription: John Buckhurst, mercer of Rye, d. 23 Feb 1771, aet 62; his wife, Elizabeth, d. 2 Apr 1782, aet 72; their issue - Elizabeth, John, d. 3 Mar 1808, aet 67, Anne; patron of stone - daughter, Elizabeth; patron of mother's M.I.

Rye, 221J Wall-mounted brass for Louis and Anne MERYON, d. 1824

- North transept, East wall, North-East corner, facing West, at head height.
- 40(W) x 50(H) — Very good.
- A wall-mounted engraved brass; floral ornament in corners.
- Louis Meryon, d. Feb 1824, aet 84; his wife, Anne, aet 50 plus; issue - youngest son, Charles Louis Meryon, M.D. (Oxford), FRS, etc.; daughter, Sarah, wife of William Holloway, quotes Matt. 7. 12.

1. In situ - Butler (*SAC* 13 279) with transcription.
2. The Meryons were the parents-in-law of the local historian William Holloway, author of *A History of Rye*, 1847, see G.S. Bagley, 'The Life ... of William Holloway' (*SAC* 100 24ff.), according to whom Anne Meryon died in 1820.

Rye, 221K Mural monument for Thomas HOLFORD, d. 1780, and his family

- North transept, East wall, facing West, above head height.
- 100(W) x 210(L) — Very good; colour.
- Above, a black baseplate in obelisk form; in centre, grey marble flaming urn in relief on a cornice; M.I. (10 lines, engraved) fills upper 80% of an unframed tablet; undulating lower contour with small corbels and panel of arms.
- Thomas Holford, Gent., of The Friars, Winchelsea, d. 15 Nov 1780, aet 35; his issue - Catherine, Frances and William Howard (all died as infants); Thomas Holford, Lieutenant in 21st Regiment of Foot, died abroad, 3 Sep 1795, aet 20.

1. In situ in Butler (*SAC* 13 279) left of North entrance and Lambarde (*SAC* 68 235) cites arms.
2. Gunnis (*Dict.* 257) attributes 221K, which he dates 1798, to John Marten (1728-1814).

Rye, 221L Ledger for Charlotte PROCTER, d. 1809, her sister and her mother Charlotte, d 1828

- North-East chapel floor, centre, West end.
- 92(W) x 198(L) — Very worn; cracked.
- M.I. on pale brown freestone slab; head to West.
- Charlotte Procter, d. 21 Sep 1809, an infant; daughter of Thomas Procter, of Rye, and his wife Charlotte, d. 21 Oct 1828, aet 40; also Sarah Ann, their second daughter who died in infancy .

1. In situ in Butler (*SAC* 13 285) at West end of St. Clare's Chancel.

Rye, 221M Ledger for Henry WATERMAN, d. 1798, his wife and sister-in-law

- North-East chapel floor, against North wall, towards West end.
- 85(W) x 182(L) — Cracked.
- M.I. (engraved) fills surface of freestone slab; head to West.
- Henry Waterman, Gent., d. 20 Jan 1798, aet 58; his wife, Martha, d. 7 Jul 1802, aet 66; her sister, Elizabeth Swaine, d. 12 Feb 1804, aet 76.

1. In situ in Butler (*SAC* 13 286) at West end of St. Clare's Chancel.

Rye, 221N Ledger for James MEGAW, d. 1808

- North-East chapel floor, near North wall, West end.
- 86(W) x 138(L) — Sound; worn.
- M.I. (engraved) fills upper 80% of a light grey freestone slab; head to West.
- James Megaw, surgeon, d. 26 Jul 1808, aet 65; his widow, Sarah, d. 21 Jan 1826, aet 75, eldest daughter of Thomas Procter, Esq., and his second wife, Sarah.

1. In situ in Butler (*SAC* 13 285) at West end of St. Clare's Chancel.
2. For Thomas Procter see 221L and 221Y.

Rye, 221O Anonymous ledger, no date

- North-East chapel floor, against North wall, towards West end.
- 87(W) x 180(L) — Worn.
- M.I. (engraved) on a slab; head to West.

Under this stone
are interred the remains ...
[etc]

1. In situ in Butler (*SAC* 13 286) at West end of St. Clare's Chancel, no more of the M.I. was legible in Butler's day than is the case now.

Rye, 221P Ledger for James ELLIOTT, d. 1801

- North-East chapel floor, near North wall, towards West end.
- 93(W) x 190(L) — Cracked.
- M.I. (2 sets of lines, engraved) on a slab; head to West.
- James Elliott, wine merchant of Rye, d. 31 Jan 180[1], aet 60; his wife, Sarah, d. 8 May 1814, aet 90.

1. In situ in Butler (*SAC* 13 286, who gives year of death as 1801, at West end of St. Clare's Chancel).

Rye, 221Q Ledger for Rev. Lewis JONES, d. 1759 and his wife Elizabeth, d. 1746

- North-East chapel floor, against North wall.
- 75(W) x 121(L) — Poor; cracked.
- M.I. (14 lines, engraved) in upper 50% of a slab.
- Rev. Lewis Jones, master at Rye Grammar School (35 years), d. 13 Dec 1759, aet 63; his wife, Elizabeth, d. 14 Feb 1746, aet 64.

1. In situ in Butler (*SAC* 13 286) at West end of St. Clare's Chancel and partly illegible in his day.
2. Rev. Lewis Jones was appointed master in 1724, aged 28 (Caffyn 228) and he was curate of Rye and, from 1741-59, rector of Little Horsted.

Rye, 221R Ledger for Edward and Mary SWAINE, d. 1772 and 1773, and descendants

- North-East chapel floor, near North wall and 221Q.
- 99(W) x 194(L) — Badly scaled on South side.
- M.I. (engraved) on upper parts of a freestone slab; head to West.
- Largely illegible: Edward Swaine, Mayor's Sergeant, d. 25 Apr 1772, aet 69; his wife Mary, d. 14 Jan 1773, aet 75; issue - John, his first wife, Ann, d. 10 Jan 1765, aet 28, and his second wife, Mary, d. 24 Jun 1801, aet 55; also, Elizabeth, Mary and Martha, daughters of Edward and Mary Swaine.

1. In situ in Butler (*SAC* 13 286) at West end of St. Clare's Chancel.

Rye, 221S Ledger for Marke SPYE, d. 1657, his wife Elizabeth SPYE, d. 1667, and her second husband, Thomas CROUCH, d. 1682

- North-East chapel floor, near centre of North wall.
- 84(W) x 179(L) — Serious cracks.
- Escutcheons at either end; M.I. in centre; all fills surface of a black slab; head to West.
- Marke Spye, merchant, d. 15 Aug 1657, aet 32, son of John Spye; his wife, Elizabeth, d. 18 Oct 1667; her second husband, Thomas Crouch, Gent., Mayor of Rye, d. 7 Aug 1682, aet 49; their issue - Elizabeth, d. 9 Sep 1682, aet 23, wife of Henry Da[r]ington, Gent.

1. In situ in Butler (*SAC* 13 287) at West end of St. Clare's Chancel.
2. Two shields of arms on the ledger, not noted by Lambarde.
3. Rustic lettering style.

Rye, 221T Ledger for Catherine GREBELL, d. 1732 and Allen GREBELL, killed 1742

- North-East chapel floor, against North wall.
- 100(W) x 177(L) — Sound; stained.
- M.I. (engraved) fills surface of a brown freestone slab; head to West.
- Catherine Grebell, d. 9 Nov 1732, aet 36; wife of Allen Grebell, Esq., jurat, mayor for 10 years, etc., d. 17 Mar 1742, aet 50; their issue - Thomas, 18 May 1729 - 15 Jul 1729, an infant; another son and another daughter still living.

1. Butler (*SAC* 13 287) located 221T at East end of St. Clare's Chancel.
2. For the Grebell family, see 221V; in fact, Allen Grebell was murdered: '[he] fell by the cruel stab of a sanguinary butcher ...' called Breads who had intended to kill the then mayor, James Lamb, see L.A. Vidler, 'The Murder of Allen Grebell' (*SNQ* XI 49-51).

Rye, 221U Ledger for Charles HICKS, d. 1814, and others in the family

- North-East chapel floor, near North wall and 221S.
- 98(W) x 199(L) — Fine.
- M.I. (engraved) on upper parts of a brown freestone slab; head to West.
- Charles Hicks, d. 18 Aug 1814, an infant; his brother James Smith Hicks, d. 18 Jan 1827, aet 11; their parents, Elizabeth, d. 17 Feb 1853, aet 74, and Charles Hicks, d. 18 Dec 1857, aet 75.

1. Located by Butler (*SAC* 13 286-7) in West end of St. Clare's Chancel.

Rye, 221V Ledger for Thomas GREBELL, d. 1724, and members of his and the LAMB family

- North-East chapel floor, near North wall, alongside 221T.
- 112(W) x 198(L) — Sound; marked.
- M.I. (engraved) in upper 80% of a black slab; head to West.
- Thomas Grebell, jurat, d. 7 Oct 1724, aet 59; his wife, Alice, d. 13 Nov 1727, aet 62; their daughter, Martha, d. 12 Feb 1737, aet 40, wife of James Lamb; their issue - Martha, d. 9 Jul 1727, an infant; William, d. 5 Aug 1729, an infant; Grebell, d. 30 Jun 1730, an infant; another William, d. 16 Aug 1732, an infant; Samuel, d. 17 Jan 1737, an infant; John, d. 18 Apr 1771, aet 47.

1. Located by Butler (*SAC* 13 287) at East end of St. Clare's Chancel.
2. For James Lamb see 221PP; for licence to marry for James Lamb, of Shoreham, Gent. and Martha Grebell, of Rye, 15 Oct 1717, see Dunkin (*Licences 1670-1729* 218).

Rye, 221W Ledger for Mary and Daniel DAVIS, d. 1728/9 and 1749/50, and their son, d. 1726

- North-East chapel floor, against South wall, West end.
- 91(W) x 190(L) — Cracks; stains.
- M.I. (14 lines [3 + 9] , engraved) in upper 60% of surface of brown freestone slab, head to West.
- Mary Davis, d. 9 Mar 1728/9, aet 37; wife of Daniel Davis, Gent., d. 12 Jan 1749/50, aet 63; their son (also) Daniel Davis, d. 20 Apr 1726, infant.

1. Located by Butler (*SAC* 13 285) at West end of St. Clare's Chancel, with Jan 1749 for death of Daniel Davis.

Rye, 221X Ledger for Ann LONG, d. 1725, and descendants [Plate 133]

- North-East chapel floor, against South wall, towards West end, partly obscured by furnishings.
- 90(W) x 190(L) — Fine; rough edges.
- Arms, cherub's head and crossed bones, then M.I. (in 2 panels, divided, engraved in

different hands) on a freestone slab; head to the West.
- Ann Long, d. 23 Mar 1725, aet 84; her first husband, Stephen Pigram, of Cambridge, no
dates; her second husband, unidentified; her son, Nathaniel Pigram, jurat of Rye, whose
wife was Jane; their daughter Ann, 7 Dec 1702-10 May 1729; this Ann's husband, John
Baker of Queenborough; another daughter Eliza, d. 11 Nov 1742, aet 42, was first wife of
Thomas Procter; also his second wife, Sarah, d. 22 Jun 1802, aet 86; also Eliza, daughter
of Thomas and Eliza Procter, d. 23 Nov 1733.

1. Located by Butler (*SAC* 13 285) at West end of St. Clare's Chance who also records a Mrs Jane
Underwood, d. 22 May 1770, aet 63.
2. For Thomas Procter see 221Y.
3. 221X commemorates the daughters of Nathaniel Pigram, see 221 FF.

Rye, 221Y Ledger for Thomas PROCTER, d. 1775, and descendants
- North-East chapel floor, near South wall, towards West end, alongside 221X.
- 100(W) x 186(L) — Very worn; rough edges.
- Trumpeting angel on relief panel, then M.I. (engraved in different hands) fills a freestone
slab; head to West.
- Thomas Proctor d. 27 Nov 1775, aet 73; his second wife, Sarah; their issue - another
Thomas Proctor, d. 5 Aug 1751, aet 4; Richard Proctor, d. 18 Aug 1751, aet 1; Mary, d. 9
Nov 1760, aet 8.

1. Located by in Butler (*SAC* 13 285-6) at West end of St. Clare's Chancel.
2. For Procter see 221X.

Rye, 221Z Ledger for Needler and Martha CHAMBERLAIN, d. 1781 and 1839, and their son
- North-East chapel floor, against South wall, centre.
- 90(W) x 184(L) — Sound; stained.
- M.I. (engraved) in upper 50% of a brown freestone slab; head to West.
- Needler Chamberlain, of Rye, surgeon, d. 7 Nov 1781, aet 36; his wife, Martha, d. 2[?] Aug
1839, aet ??; their son, James Edwin Chamberlain, d. 4 Nov 1782, infant.

Rye, 221AA Ledger for Major Richard HAY, d. 1825
- North-East chapel floor, centre of South wall.
- 106(W) x 72(L) — Sound; worn.
- M.I. (engraved) fills surface of a small white freestone slab; head to West.
- Major Richard Hay, late of the Bengal Military Establishment, 6 Feb 1761 - 16 Mar 1825;
his widow, Mary, 11 Jun 1772 - 25 Sep 1827.

1. Located by Butler (*SAC* 13 287) at West end of St. Clare's Chancel.
2. Relates to mural monument 221YYY.

Rye, 221BB Ledger for John CHAMBERLAIN, d. 1794
- North-East chapel floor, along South wall, near 221X.
- 93(W) x 196(L) — Very worn.
- M.I. (engraved) in upper 80% of a brown freestone slab; head to West.
- John Chamberlain, Gent., of Greenwich, Kent, d. 26 Aug 1794, aet 41; his sister, Rebecca
Chamberlain, d. 17 Jan 1790, aet 30; also Needler Chamberlain Watson, Esq.; his widow,
Elizabeth Watson, d. 25 Aug 1808, aet 66; their daughter, Mary Watson, d. ?? ??? 1795,
aet 26.

1. Located by Butler (*SAC* 13 287) at East end of St. Clare's chancel.

Rye, 221CC Ledger for William CHAMBERLAIN, 1831
- North-East chapel floor, near South wall, towards East end.
- 84(W) x 74(L) — Very worn.
- Head to West.
- Illegible.

1. Perhaps related to earlier Chamberlain monuments (221Z, 221BB) at Rye.
2. Butler (*SAC* 13 287) gives William Chamberlain, Obit 30 Mar 1831, aet 86.

Rye, 221DD Ledger for Anne and James LAMB, d. 1755 and 1780
- North-East chapel floor, near South wall, near East end.
- 91(W) x 183(L) — Worn.
- M.I. (engraved) on a slab; head to West.
- James Lamb, the younger, jurat, d. 20 Feb 1780, aet 58; his wife, Ann, d. ?? ??? 1755, aet
  26; his grandson, James Matthew Lamb, d. 16 Sep 1825, aet 45.

1. Located by Butler (*SAC* 13 287) at West end of St. Clare's Chancel.
2. For another James Lamb see 221PP.

Rye, 221EE Floor-mounted brass, on slab, for Mary Jane WATSON, d. 1822, and her parents, etc.
- North chapel floor, near East end.
- 31(W) x 31(H) — Worn.
- M.I. (engraved) on a brass escutcheon, on a freestone slab; head to West; additional
  engraved lines on slab (added later).
- On brass: Mary Jane Watson, d. 16 Sep 1822, aet 15, daughter of William and Margaret
  Watson.
  On slab: William Watson, d. 4 May 1841, aet 69 and Margaret, his widow, d. 18 Dec 1855,
  aet 85; [sister of] John Haddock Lardner, solicitor, d. 13 Jul 1852, aet 58.

1. Brass located by Butler (*SAC* 13 279) in North transept.
2. Slab located by Butler (*SAC* 13 287) at East end of St. Clare's chancel.
3. JH notes that Butler shows (incorrectly) John Haddock Lardner as son of William and Margaret.
   Sussex Marriage Index shows William Watson as marrying Margaret Lardner at Rye on 30 Oct 1802.

Rye, 221FF Ledger for Nathaniel PIGRAM, d. 1756
- North-East chapel floor, near South wall, towards West end.
- 114(W) x 199(L) — Fine.
- An escutcheon, then M.I. (engraved) fill a black slab; head to West.
- Nathaniel Pigram, Esq., d. 26 Mar 1756, aet 82; his wife, Jane, d. 1 Jan 1758, aet 83; their
  daughter, Mary, d. 28 Aug 1754, aet 41; their son (also) Nathaniel Pigram, Esq., d. 13 Dec
  1765, aet 52; their grandson, Nathaniel Pigram Beaver, d. 21 Jun 1768, aet 16.

1. Located by Butler (*SAC* 13 286) at West end of St. Clare's chancel.
2. Formerly near 221X which commemorates his daughters and to 221Y.
3. Final 2 lines of M.I. perhaps added after 1765.
4. JH notes that Nathaniel and Jane (née Palmer) also had a daughter Eleanor (baptised 1713) who
   married John Beaver at Icklesham in 1745. They were parents of Nathaniel Pigram Beaver, see IGI.
5. Heraldry not noted by Lambarde.

Rye, 221GG Anonymous ledger, with an attached brass, no date
- Chancel floor, centre, North side.
- 71(W) x 170(L) — Dirty.
- 1 brass refixed (upside down); 3 indents (M.I.s, arms); on a brown freestone slab; head
  to West.
- No M.I.

1. Perhaps the set of brasses noted by Stephenson (514) as 2 achievements and half shield, late 16th-century, inscription lost.
2. In situ in Davidson-Houston (*SAC* 79 115-16) who notes that the arms suggest Jennings, Jay (or Gay).

Rye, 221HH Ledger for Henry Perch BUTLER and Rhoda Jane BUTLER, d. 1829 and 1847

- Chancel floor, North-East corner, South of 221GG, partly obscured by furnishings.
- 103(W) x 116(L) — Fine.
- M.I. (engraved lines) in upper 50% of a pale grey freestone slab; head to West.
- Henry Perch Butler, Gent., of Rye, d. 20 Dec 1829, aet 66; also Rhoda Jane Butler, d. 7 Jul 1847, aet 70, daughter of John and Rhoda Slade, and wife of Richard Weeden Butler.

1. Located by Butler (*SAC* 13 280) within sanctuary rail.
2. For Rhoda Jane Butler's family see 221 CCC.
3. Henry Perch Butler was baptised at Winchelsea on 10 Dec 1763 and Richard Weeden Butler was baptised at Winchelsea on 28 Jan 1767, both sons of Richard and Susanna Butler, see IGI.

Rye, 221II Ledger for Rev. Edward WILSON, d. 1738/9

- Chancel floor, centre, East of 221HH.
- 100(W) x 155(L) — Worn.
- Escutcheon, then M.I. (engraved) in English and Latin fills a pale brown freestone slab; head to West.
- Rev. Edward Wilson, 15 May 1662 - 5 Jan 1738.

1. Located by Butler (*SAC* 13 281) within the sanctuary rail.
2. For outline biography of Edward Wilson see Butler 1861 275; he was buried 9 Jan 1738; he was probably the donor to the church of plate marked 'EW 1722' and again in 1733, see Couchman (*SAC* 55 204-5).
3. JH notes that Edward Wilson, MA, was rector of East Blatchington 1680-90 and Framfield 1686-1705, and vicar of Rye 1700 - 1738.

Rye, 221JJ Ledger for William BAR[HAM]?, d. 1694, and his children

- Chancel floor, North side, largely under stalls.
- 100(W) x 199(L) — Fine.
- M.I. (engraved) densely in Latin on a black slab; head to West.
- William Barham, d. 19 Jul 1694, aet 43; his wife (from 29 Sep 1678), Elizabeth, d. 26 Feb 1694/5, aet 43, daughter of William Stretton, of Tenterden, Kent; their issue - William, of New Romney, Kent, d. 20 Apr 1717, aet 36; Mary; Susanna, d. 26 Nov 1713, aet 35; Elizabeth, d. 23 Dec 1692, aet 8; James.

1. In situ see Butler (*SAC* 13 281) and Lambarde (*SAC* 68 234) noting arms, which are no longer visible.
2. The extant issue, Mary, Susanna and James, are patrons; perhaps following the death of their sibling William in Apr 1717.
3. The engraved M.I. dates from before Susanna's death in Nov 1717.

Rye, 221KK Ledger for Anne FRANCIS, d. 1704

- Chancel floor, immediately East of 221JJ.
- 100(W) x 170(L) — Fine.
- M.I. (engraved) in upper 80% of a reddish-brown patterned freestone slab; head to West.
- Anne Francis, d. 20 Jun 1704, aet 84; wife of Richard Francis of Lamberhurst; issue - a surviving daughter, Mercy, d. 8 Mar 1734, aet 81, wife of Nicholas Mannooch, of Rye, jurat, d. 24 Dec 1724, aet 69; issue - Nicholas died an infant.

1. In situ, see Butler (*SAC* 13 281).
2. Nicholas Mannooch was ordained deacon in 1680, master of Rye Grammar School from 1680 and Mayor several times between 1690-1704 (Caffyn 227-8).

Rye, 221LL Ledger for Robert HOUNSELL, d. 1727
- Chancel floor, South of centre, near East end.
- 92(W) x 183(L) — Poor.
- M.I. on brown freestone slab; head to West.
- Robert Hounsell, d. 30 Sep 1727, buried Topsham; also, Ann, daughter of Robert and Margaret Hounsell, d. 29 Mar 1730, aet 12; also John, William, Mercy, all died as infants.

1. In situ see Butler (*SAC* 13 281).

Rye, 221MM Ledger for Edward WILMSHURST, d. 1718
- Chancel floor, near South side, East end.
- 94(W) x 174(L) — Worn.
- M.I. on a slab; head to West.
- Edward Wilmshurst, late of Garbary, d. 21 Apr 1718, aet 51; his wife, Elizabeth, only daughter of Thomas Hawks, of Playden; issue - 6 sons and 6 daughters.

1. In situ, see Butler (*SAC* 13 281).
2. For licence to marry for Edward Wilmshurst, of Framfield, clerk and Anne Purchin, of Wartling, see Dunkin (*Licences 1670-1729* 154). .
3. JH notes that the Sussex Marriage Index shows Edward Wimshirt [sic] and Elizabeth Hackes married at Rye 20 Jan 1694/5.

Rye, 221NN Ledger for Mary HOOD, d. 1788
- Chancel floor, at door to South aisle.
- 85(W) x 102(L) — Very worn.
- M.I. on a pale slab; head to West.
- Illegible.

1. In situ, see Butler (*SAC* 13 281).
2. Mary Hood, d. 28 Dec 1788, aet 59, her many virtues.
3. Patron probably a friend.

Rye, 221OO Ledger for Richard, Elizabeth and Humphrey BUTLER, d. 1734, d. 1727 and d. 1734, and others
- Chancel floor, South-East corner, largely obscured by stalls.
- 98(W) x c.100(visible L) — Fine.
- M.I. on slab; head to West.
- Richard Butler, Gent., Common Clerk of Rye, d. 16 Sep 1734, aet 49; his wife, Elizabeth, d. 12 Jun 1727, aet 52; their son, Humphrey, also Common Clerk, d. 25 Nov 1734, aet 25; Richard Butler's nephew, another Richard Butler, Gent., jurat of Rye, d. 25 Aug 1808, aet 72; and his wife, Susanna Butler, d. 12 May 1814, aet 77.

1. In situ, see Butler (*SAC* 13 282).

Rye, 221PP Ledger for Anne and David MORRIS, d. 1733 and 1753, and their children
- Sanctuary floor, partly obscured by altar.
- 102(W) x 140(visible L) — Fine.
- M.I. (8 lines engraved) in upper 50% of a brown freestone slab.
- Anne Morris, d. 1 Jul 1733, aet 31; daughter of Rev. Edward Wilson, vicar of Rye, and wife of David Morris, Gent., d. 11 Oct 1753, aet 58; issue - Anne, David (both d. infants), Anne, wife of James Lamb the younger, jurat; Susanna, unmarried.

1. In situ, see Butler (*SAC* 13 281).
2. For Edward Wilson see 221II whose influence perhaps secured for his daughter this prestigious burial place?

Rye, 221QQ Floor-mounted brasses for Thomas HAMON, d. 1607

- Sanctuary floor, partly obscured by altar.
- 90(W) x 150(L) — Local losses (brass edges).
- A grey freestone slab; in centre, a standing male figure engraved on a brass plate; below, M.I. (6 lines, engraved) on a brass; around edges, some parts survive of a M.I. on a brass band.
- Thomas Hamon, burgess, mayor, trained band captain, etc., d. 20 Jul 1607; his widow, Martha.

1. In situ; 221QQ was noted and M.I. quoted by Jeremiah Milles in 1743 – wrongly called Wilson (Farrant 90); Horsfield (*Sussex* I 495-6); Stephenson (514); Butler (*SAC* 13 280 and 22 127-8); Turner (*SAC* 23 178-9); Davidson-Houston (*SAC* 79 112-14).
2. Thomas Hamon was buried 29 Jul 1607 and some saw visions of spirits at his decease - BL Harl. MS 358. 188, 47 reported fully in Butler (*SAC* 14 25ff).
3. Patron of 221 QQ was widow, Martha; for licence to marry for Thomas Hamon and Martha Thorpe of 5 Jun 1607, see Dunkin (*Licences 1586-1643* 58). .
4. JH notes that Thomas Hamon was MP for Rye in 1597 and 1604 – twice, not three times as in the inscription, see Hasler (2 244). Anne Taylor, wife of a townsman, was accused of procuring his death 'by diabolical means'. (Hasler, op. cit.).

Rye, 221RR Ledger for James BENN, d. 1724, and his wives Susanna, d. 1717, and Anne, d. 1721

- Sanctuary floor, South side, East of 221 QQ, partly under main altar.
- 98(W) x 125(L) — Worn; stained.
- M.I. (engraved) fills a grey freestone slab.
- Susanna Benn, d. 9 Aug 1717, aet 42; second daughter of James Brown, Esq., of Spelmenden, Kent, and wife of James Benn, customs collector of Rye, d. 25 Apr 1724, aet 45; his second wife, Ann, d. 16 Jun 1721, daughter of William Bishop, Esq., of Sedlescombe; issue - a son, died an infant.

1. In situ, see Butler (*SAC* 13 280).

Rye, 221SS Ledger for Elizabeth GLAZIER, d. 1829

- Sanctuary floor, more detail?
- 80 x 29 mostly lost — Fragmentary.
- M.I. (engraved) on a slab.
- Elizabeth Glazier, d. 24 Aug 1829, aet 77.

1. Located by Butler (*SAC* 13 281) in the high chancel.

Rye, 221TT Ledger for Mary PEADLE, d. 1676

- South nave aisle floor, West end, abutting wall and pier.
- 40(W) x 50(L) — Worn; dirty.
- M.I. (engraved) on a grey freestone slab.
- Mary Peadle, d. 6 Dec 1676; wife of Aron Peadle, junior.

1. JH notes that Aaron Peadell married Mary Tew on 8 Jan 1671/2 at Rye (Sussex Marriage Index).

Rye, 221UU Ledger for Henry BRAZIER, d. 1838, and his parents

- Crossing floor.
- 130(W) x 213(L) — Worn.
- M.I. (engraved) fills a freestone slab; head to South.
- Henry Brazier, d. 22 Feb 1838, aged 2 weeks; son of Henry Brazier, d. 10 Feb 1845, aet 43 and Mary Munn Brazier, d. 4 Jan 1846, aet 37; another surviving brother, Frederick.

1. Located by Butler (*SAC* 13 283) in North transept.

Rye, 221VV Ledger for Henry CARLETON, d. 1771

- North transept floor, South side.
- 93(W) x 197(L) — Worn.
- M.I. (engraved) fills a black slab; head to West.
- Henry Carleton, jurat of Rye, d. 22 Oct 1771, aet 78; his wife, Mary, d. 3 Nov 1727, aet 36; their issue - Rev. George Carleton, M.A., jurat and vicar of Rye, d. 27 Nov 1761, aet 43 and his wife, Constance, d. 19 May 1754, aet 22; Mary, d. 1721, infant; Thomas, d. 1726, infant; also Henry, son of George and Constance, died an infant.

1. In situ, see Butler (*SAC* 13 282-3).
2. Henry Carleton (1693-1771) was the grandson of an elder brother of the Guy Carleton of 72I, see biography in Butler (*SAC* 13 275); Henry Carleton's son, George, was born 1718.
3. JH notes that Henry Carleton was vicar of Rye 1744-61, see Venn (1 1 293).

Rye, 221WW Mural monument for John WOOLLETT, d. 1819

- Crossing, North-West pier, facing West, at head height.
- 119(W) x 248(H) — Fine; local damage (fluted panels, flanking).
- On a thin black baseplate with pointed arched top; a white marble panel with arched top, against which, in low relief, heavenly glory opens out over allegorical figures of Hope and Faith (?) against an altar; beneath, a moulding; then M.I. (8 lines, engraved, black) on an ornamental apron; flanking, very short fluted pilasters; signed (lower left and right): 'J. BACON. INVT' and 'S.MANNING. FT'.
- John Woollett, Esq., d. 23 Mar 1819, aet 59.

1. Noted in Horsfield (*Sussex* I 496) 'Hope supported by Religion, in the background, Benevolence administers relief'.
2. Subject of 221WW also the patron of 221XX. Cited by Gunnis (*Dict.* 32) as by Bacon & Manning, fl. 1818-43. Licence to marry dated 18 Oct 1793 for John Woollett, of Rye, Gent., bachelor, age 28 plus and Elizabeth Watson, of Rye, spinster, age 22 plus, see Dunkin & Penfold (*Licences* 480). Nairn & Pevsner (596) - Signed Bacon/Manning, two allegorical women before an obelisk. Transcribed by Butler (*SAC* 13 280): location - on North column separating high chancel from transept.
3. 221WW illustrates the taking up by John Bacon II, in partnership with Manning, of a favoured motif of his father, John Bacon I, a pair of elegantly dressed ladies, a pedestal between them, gazing out of the composition.

Rye, 221XX Wall monument for Elizabeth WOOLLETT, d. 1810 [Plate 134]

- Crossing, South-East pier, facing West, at head height.
- 78(W) x c.140(L) — Very good.
- Against a black arched top baseplate, a draped urn in white marble; below, a wreath on a panel, against a fluted frieze; below, an unframed M.I. (8 lines, engraved); curved lower edge; signed (lower right): 'J.BACON / Junior / LONDON'.
- Elizabeth Woollett, d. 28 Jun 1810, aet 42; wife of John Woollett, of Rye, Attorney at Law.

1. In situ, see Butler (*SAC* 13 280).
2. Patron was widowed husband John Woollett, for whom, see 221WW; for licence to marry dated 18 Oct 1793 for John Woollett, of Rye, Gent., bachelor, age 28 plus and Elizabeth Watson, of Rye, spinster, age 22 plus, see Dunkin & Penfold (*Licences* 480).
3. Cited by Gunnis (*Dict.* 30) as by John Bacon II, 1777-1859.

Rye, 221YY Ledger for William HOPE, d. 1732, and several others

- South transept floor, East side, mostly obscured by altar.
- 100(W) x 177(L) — Local losses (upper left corner).
- M.I. on slab; head to West.
- Illegible.

1. In situ, see Butler (*SAC* 13 283).
2. Butler summarises the M.I. - William Hope, of Ashford, Kent, d. 3 Apr 1732, aet 75; his wife, Elizabeth

d. 20 Apr 1732, aet 73; also, issue of James and Judith Hope (see 221ZZ), Judith, d. 20 Jan 1737, aet 3; Thomas d. 15 Sep 1740, aet 1; also SB 1793; CH 1802; IH 1797; also Walter Elmestone, surgeon, and Freeman of Rye, d. 31 Jan 1769, aet 44; his wife, Elizabeth, d. 10 Dec 1782, aet 62.

Rye, 221ZZ Ledger for James HOPE, d. 1740
- South transept floor, South of 221YY, partly obscured by furnishings.
- 95(W) x 195(L) — Very worn.
- M.I. on a freestone slab; head to West.
- Illegible.

1. In situ, see Butler (*SAC* 13 283).
2. Butler summarises the M.I. - James Hope, jurat of Rye, d. 19 Mar 1740, aet 45; his wife, Judith, d. 29 May 1757, aet 59; also James, d. 17 Sep 1747, aet 3, son of Walter and Elizabeth Elmestone, grandson of James Hope.

Rye, 221AAA Ledger for Thomas HUDSON, d. 1743
- Nave aisle, near crossing, centre.
- 91(W) x 188(L) — Fine.
- M.I. (6 lines, engraved) in upper 25% of a dark grey slab; head to West.
- Rev. Thomas Hudson, A.M., vicar of Rye, d. 13 Oct 1743, aet 48.

1. Located by Butler (*SAC* 13 281) in the nave.
2. For biography see Butler (*SAC* 13 275) - buried 19 Oct 1743.
3. JH notes that Thomas Hudson was vicar of Rye 1738-43.

Rye, 221BBB Ledger for John MYERS, d. 1834
- Nave aisle, near crossing, centre.
- 76(W) x 187(L) — Worn; cracked.
- M.I. (10 lines, engraved) in Latin in upper 25% of a slab.
- Rev. John Myers, vicar of Rye for 40 years, d. 24 Oct 1834, aet 77.

1. In situ, see Butler (*SAC* 13 284).
2. For outline biography of John Myers see Butler (*SAC* 13 276).
3. Perhaps linked with an adjacent object, a grey/brown slab heavily scaled, without M.I..

Rye, 221CCC Ledger for several members of the SLADE family, d. 1777 etc.
- Nave aisle floor, centre.
- 100(W) x 200(L) — Fine.
- M.I. (many lines, engraved in many stages) fills a black slab; head to West.
- George Slade, d. 7 Dec 1777, aet 19; his brother, William Slade, d. 5 Mar 1783, aet 26; another brother, Samuel Slade, d. 1 Jan 1789, aet 25; their parents, Chiswell and Jane Slade; also, Daniel Slade, d. 9 May 1826, aet 72; his brother, John Slade, dates unknown and John's wife, Rhoda Slade, d. 27 Aug 1828, aet 72; his sister, Elizabeth Griffith, d. 10 Jan 1840, aet 84.

1. In situ, see Butler (*SAC* 13 284).
2. For other family members see 221 NNN, OOO, WWW, HH.

Rye, 221DDD Ledger for Thomas KENNETT, d. 1824, and his family
- Nave aisle floor, centre, East of 221EE.
- 119(W) x 182(L) — Scratched; cracked; repaired.
- M.I. (10 lines, engraved) in upper 50% of a black slab; head to West.
- Thomas Kennett, d. 19 Jul 1824, aet 87; his wife, Mary; his son, Charles, d. 23 Oct 1824, aet 55 and Charles' wife, also Mary, d. 11 Sep 1818, aet 44.

1. In situ, see Butler (*SAC* 13 284).

Rye, 221EEE Ledger for Edward HASWELL, d. 1703/4, and his wife Elizabeth, d. 1747
- Nave aisle, centre, West end.
- 100(W) x 107(L) — Very good.
- M.I. (15 lines, engraved) in upper 75% of a black slab; head to West.
- Edward Haswell, d. 12 Jan 1703/4, aet 53; his wife, Elizabeth, d. 15 May 1747, aet 83, widow to her second husband, Thomas Haswell, of Leigh, Tunbridge, Kent.

1. In situ, see Butler (*SAC* 13 284).

Rye, 221FFF Ledger for Ann HADDOCK, d. 1790, and her son Henry, d. 1783
- South nave aisle floor, just North of 221GGG.
- 93(W) x 210(L) — Worn.
- M.I. (9 lines, engraved) in upper 30% of a black slab; head to West.
- Ann Haddock, d. 27 Jun 1790, aet 57; wife of Captain John Haddock; their son, Henry Haddock, d. 19 Aug 1783, aet 18.

1. Located in nave by Butler (*SAC* 13 285) from the old vestry.
2. For the family see 221GGG, HHH, OOO, etc.
3. For the relatively high rental value of Captain Haddock's property in 1785, see R. Davey 250.

Rye, 221GGG Ledger for John HADDOCK, d. 1797, and his father, d. 1812
- South nave aisle floor, just North of 221 HHH.
- 93(W) x 210(L) — Fine.
- M.I. (10 lines, engraved) in upper 30% of a black slab; head to West.
- John Haddock, d. 15 Nov 1797, aet 29; son of Captain John Haddock, 1737 - Jul 1812.

1. Located in nave by Butler (*SAC* 13 285) from the old vestry. Butler's transcription does not include the details of Captain John Haddock.
2. For the family see 221FFF, HHH, OOO, etc.

Rye, 221HHH Ledger for Joseph HADDOCK, d. 1810, and his wife Elizabeth, d. 1841
- South nave aisle floor, just North of 221III.
- 93(W) x 210(L) — Very worn.
- M.I. (engraved) in upper 30% of a black slab; head to West.
- Joseph Haddock, of Playden, d. 28 Nov 1810, aet 40; only remaining son of Captain John Haddock, of Rye; his widow, Elizabeth, d. 17 Jan 1841, aet 71.

1. Located in nave by Butler (*SAC* 13 285) from the old vestry.
2. For the family see 221FFF, GGG, OOO, etc.

Rye, 221III Ledger for Sarah BARNES, d. 1795
- South nave aisle floor, just North of 221JJJ.
- 93(W) x 210(L) — Good.
- M.I. (5 lines, engraved) in upper 25% of a black slab; head to West.
- Sarah Barnes, d. 28 Feb 1795, aet 71.

1. Located in nave by Butler (*SAC* 13 284-5) from the old vestry.

Rye, 221JJJ Ledger for John HOLMES, d. 1816, and his family
- South nave aisle floor, near South door.
- 93(W) x 210(L) — Fine.
- M.I. (engraved) in upper 50% of a black slab; head to West.
- John Holmes, d. 15 Oct 1816, aet 67; his daughter, Charlotte, d. 18 Oct 1802, aet 5; his widow, Anne, d. 22 Apr 1844, aet 81.
1. Located in nave by Butler (*SAC* 13 284-5) from the old vestry.

Rye, 221KKK Ledger for Robert LEWIS, d. 1816

- South nave aisle.
- 92(W) x 120(L) — Worn.
- M.I. (engraved) on a pale cream freestone slab; head to West.
- Robert Lewis, Ordnance barrack-master, d. 29 Feb 1816, aet 60; his grandchildren - Sophia Mary Knott, d. 25 Jun 1828, aet 1; Sydney Knott, d. 13 Nov 1829, aet 4; and Adelaide Knott, d. 24 Aug 1830, an infant; the children of Rev. Robert Rowe Knott and Robert Lewis' daughter Sophia Mary Lewis.

1. In situ, see Butler (*SAC* 13 283).

Rye, 221LLL Ledger for Thomas SHARPE, d. 1738

- South nave aisle floor, far West end.
- 83(W) x 175(L) — Local losses (lower right); stained.
- Skull (engraved), then M.I. (6 lines, engraved) in upper 40% of a pale brown freestone slab; head to West.
- Thomas Sharpe, d. 28 Nov 1738, aet 24; son of another Thomas Sharpe, Gent. and Ann, his wife.

1. For licence to marry 21 May 1712 Thomas Sharpe, of Rye, Gent. and Elizabeth Piggens, of Rye, see Dunkin (*Licences 1670-1729* 204).

Rye, 221MMM Ledger for John YOUNG, d. 1721

- North-East chapel floor, centre of South wall, East of 221AA.
- Dimensions unknown — Sound.
- M.I. (engraved) fills upper 80% of a black slab.
- John Young, Gent., of Rye, d. 28 Oct 1721, aet 61; eldest son of Francis Young, Gent. and Mary; his wife from 1680, Elizabeth, d. 1701, aet 48, second daughter of William Burwash, of Rye, jurat; issue - Francis, d. 1682, aet 1; Mary, 1687 - 1707, died unmarried; Elizabeth, b. 1693, wife from 1714 of Edmund Martin, Jnr, Gent., of New Romney, Kent.

1. Formerly at West end of St. Clare's chapel, Butler (*SAC* 13 286).
2. For licence to marry dated 24 May 1698 which mentions one Elizabeth Burwash, widow, of Rye, see Dunkin (*Licences 1670-1729* 170).

Rye, 221NNN Mural monument for Chiswell SLADE, d. 1787 [Plate 135]

- North aisle, North wall, North-West corner, high.
- 50(W) x 110(H) — Fine; fading.
- M.I. (engraved, black) on a white marble convex tablet; above, an achievement; dark grey baseplate with a low pitched top, projecting sides and a curved base.
- Chiswell Slade, d. 25 Jan 1787, aet 70; his wife, Jane, d. 18 Sep 1792, aet 72, daughter of Daniel Davis of Rye; their issue - 8, of which 3 sons and 2 daughters living in 1787.

1. Located by Butler (*SAC* 13 277) as 'On columns on right of nave'.
2. In situ in Lambarde (*SAC* 68 236) citing arms.
3. 221NNN erected by widow between 1787-92.
4. See 221CCC for issue of Chiswell Slade.

Rye, 221OOO Mural monument for Mary HADDOCK, d. 1823 [Plate 136]

- North aisle, North wall, East end, at head height.
- 61(W) x 51(H) — Serious cracks.
- M.I. (8 lines, engraved, black) on a tablet of sarcophagus form, with 2 lion's feet; rectangular black baseplate; plain cornice; pointed pediment over; below, a ledge on 2 block corbels.
- Mary Haddock, d. 30 Oct 1823, aet 72; daughter of Chiswell and Jane Slade, and second wife of Captain John Haddock.

1. Located by Butler (*SAC* 13 277) on a column on right of nave.

2. 221OOO is located immediately beneath a small monument to Ann Haddock (d.1837), which is signed (lower right): 'SMITH. FT. RYE', which is very close to 221OOO in design; the design is repeated in 221UUU and WWW (both unsigned).
3. Mary Haddock was second wife of Captain Haddock (see 221PPP) and daughter of Chiswell and Anne Slade (see 221CCC & NNN); for Haddock's first wife see 221FFF; for other family members see 221GGG-HHH.
4. Is the backplate of 221OOO a replacement?

Rye, 221PPP Mural monument for Captain John HADDOCK, d. 1812

- North aisle, North wall, East of 221NNN, high.
- 70(W) x 140(H) — Good; colour.
- M.I. (engraved, black) fills grey marble tablet set portrait-wise; dark grey baseplate with pointed top and curved bottom; below, an escutcheon; above, a strong moulded cornice supporting a draped urn.
- Captain John Haddock, d. 29 Jul 1812, aet 75; his first wife, Ann, d. 27 Jun 1790, aet 57; their issue, Henry, d. 19 Aug 1783, aet 18; John, d. 15 Nov 1797, aet 29; Joseph, d. 28 Nov 1810, aet 40; also Elizabeth, Ann and Margaret, all still living after 1812; his second wife, Mary, eldest daughter of Chiswell Slade, Esq.

1. Located by Butler (*SAC* 13 277) on columns on right of nave.
2. In situ in Lambarde (*SAC* 68 236) citing arms.
3. Patrons of 221PPP were John Haddock's daughters Elizabeth, Ann and Margaret; for other family members, see 221FFF-HHH and OOO; for the rental value of John Haddock's property in 1785, see R. Davey (250).

Rye, 221QQQ Mural monument for Thomas OWENS, d. 1769, Mrs Elizabeth WELLER, d. 1781, and Catharine OWENS, d. 1797 [Plate 137]

- North aisle, North wall, at head height, below 221PPP.
- 66.5(W) x 70(H) and 66(W) x 90(H) — Very good.
- Against a mottled grey baseplate with shallow pointed top, M.I. on a tablet (engraved, black) set landscape-wise; above, huge quartered palmettes left and right; a fluted urn adorned with acanthus on a plinth; below, a 2nd M.I. with a curved apron; signed (below): 'FLAXMAN. SCULPTOR'.
- Thomas Owens, Esq., d. 12 May 1769, aet 62; Elizabeth Weller, d. 1 Dec 1781, aet 72; Catharine Owens, d. 31 Jan 1797, aet 89.

1. Located by Butler (*SAC* 13 280) on South column dividing nave from transept.
2. Nairn & Pevsner (595-6) - urn and branch, nothing special.
3. The relationships between these three subjects are unexplained; Catharine Owens is described as Madam Owens and Catharine Owens in the 1785 tax return - not the standard 'Mrs' or 'widow' (R. Davey 251).
4. Cited by Gunnis (*SAC* 97 85 and Dict. 150) as by Flaxman, dates it 1797, ordered by John Norton of Rye, on top a fluted urn wreathed in yew.

Rye, 221RRR Mural monument for James LAMB, d. 1756, and his daughter-in-law

- North aisle, North wall, immediately East of 221PPP.
- 90(W)x 170(H) — Very good; colour.
- M.I. (engraved) on a grey marble panel, set portrait-wise; ogival top; at summit, heraldic supporter; flanking, garlands and scrolls; below, base mouldings then escutcheon on ornamental apron.
- James Lamb, Esq., merchant, mayor, host to royalty, d. 21 Nov 1756, aet 63, buried St. Andrew, Holborn, London; also Dorothy Lamb, also d. on 21 or 22 Nov 1756, aet 39, wife of his eldest son, Thomas; their many virtues.

1. Located by Butler (*SAC* 13 277) at East end of nave.
2. In situ in Lambarde (*SAC* 68 236), citing arms.

3. The patron of 221RRR was probably the eldest son Thomas.
4. See 221PP for James Lamb's wife, Anne.
5. Thomas Lamb, son of James, might well be the person of that name from Rye apprenticed to Peter Sykes, a 'cursitor of ye High Court of Chancery' in Jan 1741-2, see Rice (111).
6. There were 24 cursitors, they were engrossing (formal drafting of documents) clerks, whose job was to draft writs before sealing; Cursitor Street was off Chancery Lane.

Rye, 221SSS Mural monument for Margaret and Peter COLLETT, d. 1770 and 1790, and his second wife, Elizabeth, d. 1841

- North aisle, North wall, high, East of 221QQQ.
- 92(W) x 76(H) — Very good.
- White marble on black; baseplate with pointed top; tablet set landscape-wise with pointed pediment and moulded cornice; M.I. (engraved, black) fills tablet; 3 guttae as corbels each side; signed (lower right): 'SMITH FT'.
- Margaret Collett, d. 6 May 1770, aet 36; first wife of Rev. Peter Collett, rector of Denton and curate of Rye for 30 years, d. 14 Sep 1790, aet 55; issue - 3 died in infancy; his second wife, Elizabeth, d. 11 Feb 1841, aet 95.

1. Located by Butler (*SAC* 13 278) in North aisle, West end.
2. Peter Collett was master of Grammar School, Rye from 1760 to his death in 1790, aged 55, see Caffyn (228 & 291).

Rye, 221TTT Mural monument for Thomas LAMB, d. 1804

- North aisle, North wall, East of 221RRR.
- 81(W) x 130(H) — Very good.
- M.I. (engraved, black) fills a white marble tablet, set portrait-wise; a dark grey baseplate with domed top and ornamental apron; below, escutcheon; above, a moulded cornice and a small urn largely obscured by drapery; signed (below): 'J.BACON Junr Ft / London'.
- Thomas Lamb, Esq., magistrate, d. 29 Mar 1804, aet 84; eldest son of James and Martha Lamb; his wife, Dorothy, sixth daughter of Rev. George Eyles, A.M., vicar of Turkdean, Gloucestershire; issue - Thomas Phillipps Lamb.

1. Located by Butler (*SAC* 13 277) at East end of nave.
2. In situ in Lambarde (*SAC* 68 236) citing arms.
3. 221TTT was erected by Thomas Lamb's only son Thomas Phillipps Lamb; Thomas Lamb was taxed on extensive lands in 1785 (R. Davey 250).
4. J. Bacon II took over his father's shop at his death in 1799 and ran it through to c.1808 when he was joined in partnership by Manning (see 221WW and 221XX).

Rye, 221UUU Mural monument for Elizabeth MORRIS, d. 1827

- North aisle, North wall, at head height, below 221TTT.
- 61(W) x 49(H) — Good.
- Description as for 221OOO, pendant also with 221WWW.
- Elizabeth Morris, d. 4 Aug 1827, aet 65; eldest daughter of Captain J. Haddock; quotes Matt. XII. 6.

1. Located by Butler (*SAC* 13 278) on a column on left of nave.
2. For Captain Haddock see 221FFF and 221PPP.
3. 221UUU is unsigned but repeats the design of 221OOO, which is signed by Bacon; Butler also notes a slab in the nave, from old vestry, for Elizabeth wife of William Morris, of Peasmarsh, Gent., d. 4 Aug 1827, aet 65; also her sister Ann Haddock, d. 27 Dec 1837, aet 71.

Rye, 221VVV Mural monument for William PROSSER, d. 1795, and his family
[Plate 138]
- North aisle, North wall, East of 221TTT.
- 40(W) x 75(H) — Very good.
- A grey marble convex escutcheon set on a matching black baseplate; ogival top; M.I.

(engraved, black) fills escutcheon.

- William Prosser, jurat, of Rye, d. 6 Nov 1795, aet 87; his wife, Hannah, d. 26 Mar 1791, aet 73; their issue - William, Lieutenant in the East India Co., died in battle on the Malabar Coast, 18 May 1775, aet 26; James, d. 3 Dec 1792, aet 35; John, d. 2 Jul 1796, aet 42.

1. Located by Butler (*SAC* 13 278) on column on left of nave.
2. Highly unusual escutcheon format.

Rye, 221WWW Mural monument for Daniel SLADE, d. 1826 [Plate 139]
- North aisle, North wall, East of 221 UUU.
- 61(W) x 50(H) — Fine; fading.
- Description as for 221OOO.

SACRED TO THE MEMORY OF
DANIEL SLADE
WHO DIED ON THE 9TH OF MAY. 1826
AGED 72 YEARS
AND
JANE HIS WIFE,
WHO DIED ON THE 8TH OF MARCH, 1840 [1846?],
AGED 84 YEARS.

1. Located by Butler (*SAC* 13 277) 'On column on right of nave'; unsigned but repeats design of 221OOO, which is signed by Bacon.
2. For Daniel Slade see 221CCC.

Rye, 221XXX Mural monument for Henry LAWRENCE, d. 1781
- North aisle, at head height between windows.
- 82(W) x 39(H) — Very sound; dirty.
- M.I. (engraved, black) on unframed grey marble panel, set landscape-wise; strong moulded cornice.
- Henry Lawrence, Esq., of the Kingdom of Ireland, Lieutenant in his Majesty's 52nd Regiment, d. 4 Aug 1781, aet 20.

1. Located by Butler (*SAC* 13 278) on South wall, South aisle.
2. Have some elements been lost in relocation?

Rye, 221YYY Mural monument for Richard HAY, d. 1825, and his wife Mary, d. 1827
- North aisle wall, above head height, above 221XXX.
- c.75(W); (H) inaccessible — Sound; fading.
- M.I. (engraved) on a panel set portrait-wise; between, plain pilasters; above, pointed pediment; below, 3 roundels in a decorative frieze; base moulding and a plain curved ornamental apron.

SACRED
TO THE MEMORY OF
MAJOR RICHARD HAY
LATE OF THE
BENGAL MILITARY ESTABLISHMENT
BORN THE 6TH FEBRY 1764
DIED THE 16TH MARCH 1825
ALSO OF
MARY HAY (HIS WIDOW)
BORN THE 11TH JUNE 1772
DIED THE 25TH SEPT. 1827

1. Located by Butler (*SAC* 13 278) on a column on left of nave.
2. 221YYY relates to ledger 221AA.

Rye, 221ZZZ Mural monument for William DAVIS, d. 1783

- North aisle, above head height between windows.
- c.60(W) x 100(H) — Fine; local losses (below).
- M.I. (7 lines, engraved, black) of Latin in upper 50% of a rectangular panel of grey marble, set portrait-wise; inlaid border of red hardstone; irregular at foot.
- William Davis, d. 25 Sep 1783, aet 61.

1. Located by Butler (*SAC* 13 278) on left side of pulpit.

Rye Additions

Cited by Butler (*SAC* 13 277-301):

(1) William Dansays, jurat of Rye, d. 28 Aug 1787, aet 72 (column on right of nave).

(2) James Lamb, jurat, mayor, d. 20 Feb 1780, aet 58 (column on left of nave); heraldry noted by Lambarde (*SAC* 68 235) (North aisle).

(3) Mercy Haffenden, d. 29 Nov 1678, aet 74; widow of Richard Haffenden, of Tenterden; wife of George Curtis (chancel, had been lost by Butler's day).

(4) Thomas Hovenden, d. 10 Feb 1797, aet 68, of Hastings (North transept).

(5) Frank Smith, d. 16 Feb 1807, aet 66 and wife Ann, d. 3 Oct 1828, aet 91 (North transept).

(6) Stephen, d. 27 Mar 1778, infant son of Stephen and Mary Tress, of Leisisham [Leasham?] (North transept).

(7) AW 1726 (North transept).

(8) H Shaw, d. 1801 (North transept).

(9) Richard Higgings, Snr, of Chatham, d. 22 Sep 1709, aet 72 (nave).

(10) Sarah Igglesden, wife of Richard, surgeon, d. 17 Nov 1725, aet 37.

(11) John Slade, jurat, d. 17 Oct 1743, aet 57; his wife, Mary, d. 2 May 1743, aet 74, daughter of William and Mary Chiswell; also Elizabeth, wife of Chiswell Slade, d. 19 Oct 1744, aet 24, daughter of Joseph and Elizabeth Viny (nave).

(12) RS 1828 (nave).

(13) JH 1812, MH 1823 (nave, from old vestry).

(14) Mary, wife of Thomas Kennett, d. 8 Mar 1782, aet 43; their daughter, Rebackar, d. 10 Apr 1783, aet 11; also HH 1783 (nave, from old vestry).

(15) William and Sarah Gibbon, d. 3 Jun 1790, aet 33 and ?? ??? 1800, aet unknown (nave, from old vestry).

(16) Sarah Price, d. 22 Oct 1809, aet 85, widow of William Price, Esq. (North aisle).

(17) Meryon Holloway, 31 Jan 1812 - 20 Jun 1828, drowned at Charter House, son of William and Sarah Holloway (East end of St. Clare's chancel).

(18) Ammi Waterhouse, d. 24 Oct 1726, aet 71; her daughter, Mary, d. 20 Nov 1728, aet 32; first wife of Joseph Cooper, Jnr, d. 14 Aug 1741, aet 50; their issue - George, d. 14 Nov 1748, aet 28; Joseph; second wife was Mary, d. 24 Sep 1743, aet 37; issue - Mary, d. 2 Nov 1747, aet 1 (East end of St. Clare's chancel).

(222) SALEHURST, St. Mary the Virgin

Early English and Decorated arcades with clerestory of 1861; Decorated North chapel - Nairn & Pevsner (600-1) and *SNQ* (XV 267) with plan; view from South-East of 1781 in Godfrey & Salzman (Pl. 143); condition in 1686 reported to be fine, although the chancel of Lady Salcall was 'in a most filthy rude manner' and that of Sir Philip Harcourt was also out of repair (Ford 48); in the later 1550s, the Culpepers ordered burials here, see Rice & Godfrey (4 86) - William Culpeper, of Wigsell, d. 1559, left £10 for a tomb to set on his grave in the chapel at Salehurst where his wife Cicely was buried, see Attree & Booker (*SAC* 47 62); in the later 18th century, Hayley noted that ledgers/slabs outside priest's door in 1772, were formerly in Wigsell chapel, in which he saw a slab beneath a tester with indents for brasses; the Harcourts took over Wigsell from the Culpepers in the 17th century and constructed a vault, which, in 1954, was found to contain five 18th-century coffins: Richard Harcourt, d. 12 May 1777, aet 67; Elizabeth, daughter of Sir

Philip Harcourt, d. 4 Mar 1778, aet 70; Phoebe Harcourt d. 10 Dec 1779, aet 70; two others unidentified; in 1861 the ledger slabs in Wigsell chapel, with all those in the chancel, including 222T, were removed to the tower floor, see J.L. Ward, 'Salehurst Church: the Wigsell Chapel' *SNQ* (XIV 112ff), citing L.J. Hodson, *History of Salehurst* 1914 and W.E. Meads, 'History of Salehurst Church' (*Sussex Express* No. 12, 1936); Horsfield (*Sussex* I 585) speculates that proximity of nearby Robertsbridge Abbey meant that the church was not a prestigious medieval burial place; the high quality of the relatively inaccessible Peckham cartouches (222D-F) is remarkable; the parish had c.157 families in 1724 and a population of 1611 in 1801; Willatts (*SAC* 125 102) notes 7 iron slabs here; there are terracottas by Harmer in the churchyard.

Salehurst, 222A Mural monument for Thomas JENKIN, d. 1768
- Verger's vestry, North wall, towards West end, high.
- Inaccessible — Sound; faded.
- M.I. (10 + 10 + 7 lines, engraved, black, centred) on rectangular panel of heavily veined grey marble, set portrait-wise; ogival curved top; 2 large scrolled corbels.
- Thomas Jenkin, A.M., vicar of Salehurst, d. 28 Jan 1768, aet 45; his grandparents, Simeon Ashe, vicar of Salehurst, d. 1727, aged 66 and Winifrid, d. 1717, aet 43; also Stephen Jenkin, A.M.F.A.S, vicar of Salehurst and Selmeston, d. 5 Apr 1827, aet 72; his wife, Anne, d. 15 Nov 1828, aged 80; their issue, Elizabeth Jenkin, died Ghent, Flanders, 17 Nov 1792, aet 6, and Lieutenant William Jenkin, R.M., wrecked in HMS Minotaur off the Textel and drowned 22 Dec 1810, aet 19.

1. Noted by Horsfield (*Sussex* I 585).
2. Commemorating many members of the family over several generations.
3. The Rev. Stephen Jenkin (1756-1827), advertised a private boarding school at Salehurst in 1782 (Caffyn 232).

Salehurst, 222B Mural monument for Jonathan George MICKLETHWAIT, d. 1838, and his wife, Sophia, d. 1808
- Verger's vestry, North wall, at head height, East of 222A.
- 58(W) x 110(H) — Very good; fading.
- M.I. (13 lines, engraved, black, centred) fills a white marble trapezoidal panel; clawed feet; above, an urn in relief; irregular black slate back-plate; signed (lower centre): 'E.GAFFIN. REGENT'S ST. LONDON'.
- Jonathan George Micklethwait, Esq., of Warbrook House, Hampshire, d. 27 Feb 1838, aet 73; his wife, Sophia, d. 15 Aug 1808, aet 32; their issue, Elizabeth and John.

1. Patrons were the children; probably erected after 1838.
2. For family see 222D.

Salehurst, 222C Mural monument for Harriet Jane LUXFORD, d. 1825, and several other members of her family
- North aisle, North wall, East of North door, at head height.
- 112(W) x 135(H) — Very good.
- M.I. (33 lines, engraved, centred, black) on a white marble panel, set landscape-wise; base with 2 scrolled corbels; above, a plain frieze then a pointed pediment with scrolled ends; arms.
- John Luxford, Esq., of Higham, JP, etc., 9 Dec 1756 - 17 Mar 1838; his wife, Catherine Sarah, d. Apr 1861, aged 87; their issue - eldest daughter, Catherine Frances, 28 Mar 1803 - 30 Apr 1830; second daughter, Elizabeth Anne, 23 Jul 1805 - 30 Jan 1846, died at Madeira, buried Madeira; elder son, John Odiarne, 23 Nov 1808 - 14 Apr 1880; third daughter, Harriet Jane, 28 May 1812 - 28 Nov 1825, died at Boulogne-sur-Mer, buried

Peasmarsh; and Lydia Mary, d. 30 Jun 1883, wife of Thomas Foljambe, of Acomb, Yorkshire.

1. Mural tablet to John Odiarne Luxford is in the South aisle.
2. Vault marker is 222S.
3. For heraldry see Lambarde (*SAC* 67 153).

Salehurst, 222D Cartouche to the PECKHAM family of William, and his wife Mary, erected early 19ᵗʰ C.

- North-East chapel, North wall, facing East, high.
- Inaccessible — Fine; fading.
- M.I. (engraved, black, centred) on a white marble convex cartouche, framed by drapery; above, arms; 2 cherubim flanking; below, death's head.

..

..

..

DAUGHTER OF JOHN NEWNHAM

OF MARESFIELD PARK IN THIS COUNTY, ESQUIRE

WHO DIED IN NOVEMBER A.D. MDCCLXV AET LXXV

WILLIAM, JOHN, GEORGE, THOMAS, HENRY,

MARY & ELIZABETH

OF WHOM ALL EXCEPT THE LATTER DIED UNMARRIED

THOMAS WHO WAS SHERIFF OF THIS COUNTY

A.D. MDCCLXIV)

ASSUMED BY ROYAL LICENCE

THE SURNAME & ARMS OF FOWLE

ELIZABETH THE ONLY SURVIVING

CHILD AND HEIRESS OF

THE FIRST NAMED WILLIAM PECKHAM

MARRIED JOHN MICKLETHWAIT

OF BEESTON HALL

IN THE COUNTY OF NORFOLK ESQUIRE

BY WHOM SHE HAD THREE SONS

JOHN, NATHANIEL, AND JONATHAN-GEORGE

1. JH notes that this is a memorial to the family of William Peckham, who died 1765 aged 75, and his wife Mary who also died in 1765 aged 75, see 222V. For their children - William (222R), John (222O), George (222O and 222F), Thomas (222BB), Henry (222O), Mary (222O) and for the children of John and Elizabeth Mickelthwait - John (222H) and Jonathan George (222B).
2. The lines above the transcription are illegible.

Salehurst, 222E Cartouche for William PECKHAM, d. 1679

- North-East chapel, North wall, facing South, West of 222F, high, obscured by furnishings.
- Inaccessible — Fine; fading.
- M.I. (engraved, black, centred) on convex cartouche, framed by scrollwork; above, 2 cherubim flank an achievement.

...

WILLIAM PECKHAM

OF IRIDGE PLACE

IN SALEHURST ESQUIRE

..PROPRIATOR OF THE GREAT ...

OF THIS PARISH

OB. ON THE FIFTH DAY

OF APRIL MDCLXXIX

ÆT LXXV

THE ...

... GIFT OF GOD ...

THROUGH JESUS CHRIST OUR LORD

ROM....23

1. Paired with, but not pendant to 222F.
2. NBI records the burial of William Peckham on 10 Apr 1679 at Salehurst.
3. For family see 222D.

Salehurst, 222F Cartouche for George PECKHAM, d. 1788

- North-East chapel, North wall, facing South, East of 222E, high, obscured by furnishings.
- Inaccessible — Fine; fading.
- Description: close to 222E.

. A VAULT BENEATH …

…

GEORGE PECKHAM

OF IRIDGE PLACE IN THIS PARISH …

OF WHICH HE WAS LAY …

SERVED THE OFFICE OF …

OF THE COUNTY A.D. MDCCLXXIV

OB. ON THE TWENTY EIGHTH

DAY OF MAY MDCCLXXXVIII.

ÆT LXIV.

AT HIS DECEASE THE IRIDGE PROPERTY

DESCENDED TO HIS NEPHEW

JOHN MICKELTHWAIT ESQUIRE

THE SAID GEORGE PECKHAM

MUNIFICENTLY PRESENTED TO THIS CHURCH

ITS RING OF EIGHT BELLS

1. Noted by Horsfield (*Sussex* I 585); pendent to 222E.
2. Cited by Gunnis (*Dict.* 292) as by Latter Parsons.
3. In 1785, one George Peckham was a landowner in the parish (R. Davey 186-7).
4. Very high in quality; paired with, but not pendant to 222E.

Salehurst, 222G Mural monument for Mary SNEPP, d. 1723

- South aisle wall, towards West end, at head height.
- 74(W) x 107(H) — Fine; restored colour.
- M.I. (8 lines, engraved) on upper 50% of a rough grey freestone panel set portrait-wise; moulded frame.
- Mary Snepp, d. 12 May 1723, aged 52 years, wife of Joseph Snepp.

1. Described by Horsfield (*Sussex* I 585) as a black marble tablet in the North chancel.
2. As early as 1530 one Robert Snepp bequeathed a legacy to the nearby 'Chapel of the Rood' (Church Guide).

Salehurst, 222H Mural monument for John and Jane MICKLETHWAITE, d. 1824 and 1819

- Vestry, East wall, above head height.
- 122(W) x c.280(H) — Good; colour; faded.
- Above, a black slate back-plate in obelisk form; at top, small escutcheon over a white marble urn in relief on a M.I. (engraved, black) fills a tablet with ornamental top, set landscape-wise; chalice, serpent (eternity), sun-burst of glory, palmettes; below, corbels with paired ring decorative.
- John Micklethwaite, Esq., lay rector of Salehurst, of Iridge Place, d. 20 Apr 1824, aet 67; his wife, Jane, d. 12 Aug 1819, aet 65, daughter of Josiah Corthine, Esq., of Anlaby, Yorkshire.

1. Noted by Horsfield (*Sussex* I 585); Nairn & Pevsner (601).
2. Paired with, but not pendant to 222I.
3. Hatchments for John and Jane Micklethwaite also in the church, see Summers (151).
4. Ascribed by Gunnis (*Dict.* 332) to Peter Rouw II, 1770-1852.

5. JH notes that John Micklethwaite was also a Magistrate, Deputy Lieutenant of Sussex and Norfolk, and sheriff of Sussex in 1807.
6. For family see 222D.

Salehurst, 222I Mural monument for Anne PECKHAM, d. 1758, and Mary PECKHAM, d. 1779

- Vestry, East wall, above head height.
- 122(W) x c.280(H) — Very good.
- M.I. (engraved, black) fills white marble tablet set landscape-wise; black frame then fluted border; below, base mouldings, then curved apron with escutcheon and ferns; above, cornice, then mourning widow and urn against black backplate in obelisk form.
- Anne Peckham, spinster, of Warbleton, d. 21 Jan 1758, aet 62; Mary Peckham, spinster, of Warbleton, d. 6 Mar 1779, aet 78.

1. Formerly in the North chancel - Horsfield (*Sussex* I 585); close to 222H but not pendant.
2. Patron (after 1779) of 222I was the vicar of Warbleton, Henry Harcourt (for whose family see 222T).
3. Hatchment for Mary Peckham also in the church, see Summers (151); Nairn & Pevsner (601): woman by urn, better architecture than sculpture.
4. For heraldry see Lambarde (*SAC* 67 154).

Salehurst, 222J Ledger for 'S.A.', no date

- Vestry floor, centre.
- Slab: 107(W) x 284(L); Plate: 9(W) x 8(H) — Fine.
- M.I. (engraved) on a very small brass plate on a vast light freestone slab.
- Inscribed:

S.A.

1. JH notes that the NBI has 29 burials of people with the initials SA.

Salehurst, 222K Cast iron slab for Eleaner PECKHAM, d. 1713/4

- Vestry floor, West side, North of 222M, partly obscured by step.
- 63(W) x 170(L) — Worn.
- M.I. (7 lines, cast relief) in upper 40% of a slab: head to West.
- Eleaner Peckham, d. 24 Jan 1713/4, aet 72.

1. Noted by Horsfield (*Sussex* I 585) and Nairn & Pevsner (601).

Salehurst, 222L Cast iron slabs for Silvester PECKHAM, d. 1712/3 and others
[Plate 140]
- Vestry floor, North of 222N.
- 55(W) x 172(L) — Fine.
- M.I. (12 lines, cast relief) in upper 80% of a cast iron slab; head to West.
- Silvester Peckham, d. 17 Mar 1712/3, aet 65.

1. Noted by Horsfield (*Sussex* I 585) and Nairn & Pevsner (601).
2. The slab is unusually thin.
3. Some letters reversed e.g. 'N'.

Salehurst, 222M Cast iron slab for Mary PECKHAM, d. 1689

- Vestry floor, West side, in part beneath an earlier or restored pier.
- 63(W) x 170(L) — Worn.
- M.I. (8 lines, cast relief) in upper 50% of a cast iron slab; head to West.
- Mary Peckham, d. 21 Apr 1689, aet 1; her parents, William and Martha Peckham.

1. Noted in Nairn & Pevsner (601).
2. Willatts (*SAC* 125 102) notes erratic lettering, although the orthography is more accurate than in some cases (e.g. 222C).

Salehurst, 222N Cast iron slab for William PECKHAM, d. 1679
- Vestry floor, near door leading to tower.
- 62(W) x 172(L) — Fine.
- M.I. (6 lines cast relief) across centre of a cast iron slab; head to West.
- William Peckham, d. 5 Apr 1679, aet 75.

1. Noted in Nairn & Pevsner (601) and Horsfield (*Sussex* I 585).
2. For William Peckham's wife see 222CC.

Salehurst, 222O Ledger for Henry PECKHAM, d. 1786, and his siblings George, John and Mary
- Tower floor, West side, North end, near vestry entrance.
- 100(W) x 199(L) — Good.
- M.I. (engraved) in upper 60% of a black slab (marble); head to North.
- Henry Peckham, Esq., d. 4 Dec 1786, aet 54; George Peckham, Esq., d. 28 May 1788, aet 64; John Peckham, Esq., d. 6 Feb 1789, aet 68; Mrs Mary Peckham, d. 30 Jan 1805, aet 79, their sister; all of Iridge Place.

1. Noted by Horsfield (*Sussex* I 585).
2. Mary was unmarried; her title 'Mrs' indicates her higher social status.
3. In 1785, Henry Peckham was recorded as a landowner in the parish (R. Davey 186-7).
4. For family see 222D.

Salehurst, 222P Ledger for John BRABAN, d. 1759, and his son and grandson, both William
- Tower floor, North of font.
- 92(W) x 60(L) — Very worn; damaged (on left).
- M.I. (7 + 8 lines, engraved) fills surface of black slab (slate?); head to West.
- John Braban, Gent., d. 28 Feb 1759, aet 33; his wife, Mary; issue - John, dates unknown, and William, d. 4 Apr 1786, aet 29; his grandson, also, William Braban, d. 28 Oct 1786, aet [?] year and 8 months.

1. Noted by Horsfield (*Sussex* I 585).
2. Final 8 lines of M.I. added after 1786.

Salehurst, 222Q Ledger for Elizabeth BRABAN, d. 1775
- Tower floor, North of centre, West side, South of 222O.
- 100(W) x 199(L) — Worn.
- Arms, then M.I. (8 lines, engraved) in upper 60% of a black slab, head to West.
- Elizabeth Braban, d. 16 Oct 1775, aet 55; daughter of Jonathan and Abigail Steevens, and wife of William Braban.

1. 222Q forms a group with 222R and T (formerly in Wigsell chapel, see 222T).
2. Elizabeth Braban's husband, William Braban, owned property in Salehurst, in 1785 (R. Davey 187).
3. For heraldry, see Lambarde (*SAC* 67 154).

Salehurst, 222R Ledgers for William PECKHAM, d. 1737, and others [Plate 141]
- Tower floor, centre, West side.
- 100(W) x 199(L) — Worn; cracked.
- Arms, then M.I. (5 lines, engraved) in upper 50% of a black slab (marble?); head to West.
- William Peckham, d. 29 Apr 1737, aet 19, eldest son of William Peckham, of Iridge.

1. Horsfield (*Sussex* I 585) notes 222R as to William Peckham, son of William Peckham, 1737, aet 19.
2. For heraldry see Lambarde (*SAC* 67 154).
3. For family see 222D.

Salehurst, 222S Vault Marker for the LUXFORD family, dated 1830

- Tower floor, North-East of centre.
- 92(W) x 110(L) — Fine.
- An arrow pointing South and 2 lines engraved in upper 50% of a pale freestone slab.

LUXFORD

MDCCCXXX

1. For Luxford see 222C.
2. NBI records the burial of Catherine Frances Luxford on 7 May 1830 at Salehurst.

Salehurst, 222T Ledger for Dame Elizabeth HARCOURT, d. 1713

- Tower floor, South of centre, West side.
- 114(W) x 200(L) — Worn; cracked.
- Arms, then M.I. (5 lines, engraved) in upper 50% of a black slab (marble?); head to West.
- Elizabeth Harcourt, d. 17 Aug 1713, aet 64.

1. Formerly in the Wigsell chapel - Horsfield (*Sussex* I 585); removed to tower floor in 1861, see J.L. Ward, 'Salehurst Church: the Wigsell Chapel' (*SNQ* XIV 113).
2. In 1702, Elizabeth Harcourt erected the family gallery above 222T, at her own expense; in a group with 222Q and 222R; another Elizabeth Harcourt [daughter?] was buried 10 Mar 1715, see Hussey (*SAC* 25 160).
3. For heraldry see Lambarde (*SAC* 67 153).

Salehurst, 222U Anonymous ledger, no date

- Tower floor, just North of 222W.
- 83(W) x 112(L) — Very worn.
- M.I. (engraved) hardly legible on a pale freestone slab; head to W?
- Perhaps a date: '... 181.. ?'.

Salehurst, 222V Ledger for William PECKHAM, d. 1765, and Mary, his wife, d. 1765

- Tower floor, South of 222T.
- 114(W) x 200(L) — Very cracked.
- M.I. (9 lines, engraved) in upper 25% of a black slab (slate?); head to West.
- William Peckham, Esq., of Iridge, d. 24 Jan 1765, aet 75; his wife, Mary, d. 7 Nov 1765, aet 75.

1. Engraved after January 1766.
2. For the family see 222D.
3. NBI records the burial of William Peckham on 31 Jan 1765 and Mary Peckham on 7 Nov 1765, both at Salehurst. William Peckham had married Mary Nenham on 1 Sep 1716 at Maresfield, see Sussex Marriage Index.

Salehurst, 222W Ledger for Ann STEEVENS, d. 1712

- Tower floor, East of 222V.
- 56(W) x 111(L) — Worn; chipped.
- M.I. (engraved) in upper 75% of a grey-brown freestone slab; head to West.

[Here?]

Lieth Interrd

ye Body of

ANN

Daughter of

Jonathan & Abigall[sic]

STEEVENS

who Dyed Jan

ye 30th

1712

Aged 3 Years

ten Months.

1. For her mother see 222DD.
2. Note very uneven letter-cutting.

Salehurst, 222X Ledger for Robert FOWLE, d. 1681, and his son, d. 1683/4
- Choir vestry floor, by door to tower chapel.
- 112(W) x 200(L) (arms 55 diameter) — Fine.
- Arms and M.I. (9 + 4 lines, engraved) fills a black marble slab; head to West.
- Robert Fowle, Esq., of Iridge, d. 1 Dec 1681, aet 53, son of Sir John Fowle of Sandhurst, Kent and Ann, daughter of Sir John Wildegoose of Iridge, Knt; his wife, Lucy, daughter of Peter Farnden, Esq., of Selscombe; issue - Robert, d. 13 Feb 1683/4, aet 21; Ann; Lucy.

1. Noted by Horsfield (*Sussex* I 585).
2. Perhaps erected in 1684 after the death of Fowle's son.
3. Both blocks of lettering by same hand.
4. Consecutive entries in the Parish Register show burials on 5 Dec 1681 and 19 Feb 1683/4, see Hussey (*SAC* 25 159).
5. The Fowles appear to have been in dispute with the parson at Salehurst over rights of burial in the chancel during the 1650s, see Hussey (*SAC* 25 161).
6. For heraldry see Lambarde (*SAC* 67 153).

Salehurst, 222Y Floor-mounted brass for Ann LEFROY, d. 1812
- Choir vestry floor, North-West corner.
- 22(W) x 33(L) — Worn; dirty.
- A brass plate (variety of engraved), nailed to floor; head to West.

Here lies the Remains of
ANN LEFROY
daughter of
ANTHONY and ELIZABETH LEFROY
who was Born at
SILVERHILL
in the County of
Sulsex
on the 24th of September
1811
And Died at
SILVERHILL BARRACKS
on the 7th March
1812

1. Pendant with 222Z (Anne's brother).
2. The barracks at Silverhill were extensive, see *SNQ* (XIV 172).

Salehurst, 222Z Floor-mounted brass for Thomas LEFROY, d. 1805
- Choir vestry floor, North-West corner.
- 22(W) x 33(L) — Corroding; lifting; damaged edges (South side).
- A brass plate (variety of engraved); nailed to floor; head to West.

Here lie the remains of
THOMAS [LANG]LEY LEFROY
Son of
Anthony & Elizabeth Lefroy
... born at Appleby in the county of
WESTMORELAND
on the 20th of 1801
and Died at
Silverhill Barracks
on the 17th of February 1805

1. Pendant with 222Y (Thomas's sister).
2. See note on 222Y.

Salehurst, 222AA Floor-mounted brass for Mrs FREWEN, d. 176[9?]
- Choir vestry floor, North-West corner, near West wall.
- 9(W) x 11.5(L) — Corroding; damaged edges.
- A brass plate (5 lines engraved) nailed to floor; head to West.

... AL ..
FREWEN
died 27 april
176..
aged [...]3 years

1. JH notes that this could be Palacia Frewen who was buried at Salehurst on 3 May 1769 (NBI).

Salehurst, 222BB Cast iron slab for Thomas PECKHAM, d. 1662
- Choir vestry floor, North side, South of 222X.
- 53(W) x 170(L) — Very worn.
- M.I. (8 lines, cast relief) across centre of an iron slab; head to West.
- Thomas Peckham, d. 31 May 1662, aet 34.

1. Noted by Horsfield (*Sussex* I 585).
2. Note eccentric lettering c.f. 222CC.
3. For family see 222D.

Salehurst, 222CC Cast iron slab for Mary PECKHAM, 1661/2
- Choir vestry floor, near West wall.
- 56(W) x 168(L) — Fine.
- M.I. (7 lines, cast relief) across centre of slab; head to West.

HERE LYETH THE
BODY OF MARY W
IFE OF WILLIAM
PECKHAM WHO DY
ED MARCH 12
1661
ÆTATIS SVÆ 34

1. Noted by Horsfield (*Sussex* I 585), for husband see 222N.
2. Note eccentric setting and orthography (reversed letter 'C').

Salehurst, 222DD Ledger for Abigail STEEVENS, d. 1742
- Choir vestry floor, centre.
- 90(W) x 162(L) — Very worn.
- M.I. (engraved) in upper 30% of pale freestone slab; head to West.

Here lies the body of
ABIGAIL wife of
JONATHAN STEEVENS
who died july 11 1742
aged 52 years

1. For her daughter see 222W.
2. Roman capitals only.
3. NBI records the burial of Abigail Steevens on 6 Jul 1742 at Salehurst.

Salehurst, 222EE Ledger for Mary BRABAN, d. 1748, and her son, Sivyer, d. 1748
- Choir vestry floor, near West wall, just South of 222CC.
- 79(W) x 191(L) — Very worn; cracked.

- Arms then M.I. (engraved) in sandy freestone slab; head to West.

Here lieth interred the
Body of Mary Wife of
Robert Braban Gent
Who departed this life.
the .... Day 1748
in the .... Year of ...
...
...
...

Here also lieth buried the
body of Sivyer ....
Son of ..... Robert and
Mary Braham He /............ life ...
...day of July 1748
Aged 4 Years

1. JH notes that Robert Braban married Mary Sivyer on 14 Apr 1739 at Bodiam (Sussex Marriage Index) and that they had two children - Mary baptised 17 Jan 1739 and Sivyer baptised 9 Nov 1743, both at Bodiam, see IGI. NBI records the burials of Mary Braban on 4 Apr 1748 and Sivyer Braban on 14 Jul 1748, both at Salehurst. Mary Sivyer was the daughter of Stephen and Mary Sivier and was baptised on 7 Mar 1719 at Bodiam, (IGI).

Salehurst Additions
Horsfield (*Sussex* I 585):
(1) Elizabeth Peckham, d. 1680, aet 64.
(2) John Peckham, d. 1789, aet 68 [222O?].

(224) SEAFORD, St. Leonard
Norman (at West end); the East end of the church was rebuilt in 1861-2 by John Billing - Nairn & Pevsner (603); Lower, 'Memorials of ... Seaford' (*SAC* 7 73-150); plan in *SNQ* (XIII 39); paving reported to be poor in 1686 (Ford 54); ledgers have been removed to accommodate a new floor; murals dating from c.1800 relocated on West tower walls; Horsfield (*Sussex* I 280) notes only Addition (8); the lack of 16th and 17th-century monuments might be attributable to Seaford's economic decline following the changed course of the River Ouse, and although there were 70 families in the parish in 1724 and a population of 847 in 1801; for a view of gravestones at Seaford, St. Leonard, see BL Add. MS 5676-77.

Seaford, 224A Mural monument for Elizabeth HIGGS, d. 1830
- Tower, South wall, high.
- c.60(W) x c.75(H) — Good; faded.
- M.I. (7 lines, engraved) fills unframed white tablet set on a dark grey cretaceous backplate.
- Elizabeth Higgs, d. 10 Mar 1830, aet 39; wife of Joseph Higgs, a master in the Royal Navy.

1. Formerly on North side of Tower arch see Simmons (*SAC* 12 244).

Seaford, 224B Mural monument for Esther ATKINS, d. 1807 [Plate 142]
- Tower, North wall, high.
- c.70(W) x (H) unknown — Very good; faded.
- M.I. (engraved) fills tablet set landscape-wise; delicate inlaid, pink (rance?) edging; cornice and base mouldings; above, a pointed pediment; at top, escutcheon on circular plaque; below, ornamental apron with rance decoration.
- Esther Atkins, d. 15 Apr 1807, aet 31; wife of George Atkins, Esq., paymaster of the 2nd Somerset militia.

1. Formerly on North aisle wall, see Simmons (*SAC* 122 242).
2. Patron of 224B is husband.

Seaford, 224C Mural monument for the sons and families of Thomas and Naomi HURDIS, c.1821 [?]

- Tower, North wall, above head height.
- 108(W) x 97(H) — Very good.
- A black baseplate with pointed top; M.I. (engraved, black) fills white marble tablet; above, cornice and pointed pediment; 2 flat corbels; signed (lower right): 'J.BACON F.t LONDON'.
- Rev. Thomas Hurdis, D.D., canon of Windsor and canon-residentiary of Chichester; his wife Naomi; their issue - Rev. Thomas, vicar of Seaford and vicar of Barcombe, d. 1779, unmarried; William Ditch Hurdis, d. 1785, unmarried; James Hurdis, M.D., d. 8 Oct 1816, aet 77, his wife, Ann, d. 3 Jan 1795, aet 48, youngest daughter of Samuel Clarke, of Hailsham: their issue – eldest son, Thomas Bowyer Hurdis, merchant in the East India Co. and judge of the Sudder Court, died at Fort St. George, 16 Nov 1808, aet 38; his wife, Catherine, lost at sea, 1809, daughter of Nathaniel Thomas, alderman of London; second son, Midshipman Henry Samborne Hurdis, R.N., died at Cape Town, 6 Nov 1795, aet 19; fourth son, Captain James Courtail Hurdis, 2nd battalion 19th regiment, East India Co. Native Infantry, died Cannamore, 16 Aug 1819, aet 38; and fourth daughter, Harriot Thomas Hurdis, died at Dindigul, East Indies, 9 May 1802, aet 19.

1. Formerly on chancel North wall, Simmons (*SAC* 12 243), near a M.I. for Sarah Hurdis, 22 Aug 1778 - 11 Feb 1851, wife of Captain George Clarke Hurdis, daughter (1) of late Harry Chambers, of Kingston, Surrey.
2. Thomas Hurdis, vicar of Seaford 1733-73, d. 1784, was buried in Chichester Cathedral with his wife Naomi 1715-81, daughter of William Ditch of Bishopstone, see Lower (*SAC* 7 135); Thomas Hurdis was uncle of the poet Rev. James Hurdis (31B, see *ODNB* entry); other close family members are commemorated on a nearby tablet; the second daughter of James and Anne Hurdis died in 1821, an event not recorded on 224C which may therefore predate it.

Seaford, 224D Mural monument for Colonel John CARNEGIE, d. 1823, his wife, Catherine, d. 1824, and his sister, Margaret, d. 1828

- Tower, North wall, East of 224C, at head height.
- 95(W) x 78(H) — Very good.
- M.I. (13 lines engraved black) on a white marble tablet; black baseplate with straight top; cornice; 2 small corbels.
- Colonel John Carnegie, formerly of 11th Light Dragoons, d. 29 Sep 1823, aet 67; son of Sir James Carnegie, of Southesk, Bart.; his wife, Catherine, d. 25 Dec 1824, aet 71; his sister, Mary, d. 6 Feb 1828, aet 67, eldest daughter of Sir James Carnegie.

1. Formerly on chancel South wall, East end, Simmons (*SAC* 12 243), near a M.I. for Margaret, wife of Captain James Carnegie, d. at Brighton 27 Feb 1828, aet 48, first daughter of late James Gillespie, of Kirkton, Fife.
2. The Carnegies of Southesk and Northesk were a prominent military family, see *ODNB* entry on William Carnegie, 7th Earl of Northesk by Kenneth Breen; another James Carnegie was vicar of Seaford 1824-64 and prominent in town business, see Lower (*SAC* 7 117).

Seaford Additions

Also reported in Simmons (*SAC* 12 244) as inside the church:
(1) An unnamed daughter of Henry and Laetitia Bill, Gent., d. 21 Aug 1676, an infant (nave floor).
(2) Laetitia, wife of Henry Bill, d. 23 Aug 1676, daughter of Sir James Colbrond, Bart. (nave floor).
(3) Thomas Hurdis, buried 21 Jun 1734, an infant, son of Rev. Thomas Hurdis and Naomi his wife (nave floor).
(4) Elphick family c.1650-58 (nave floor and North aisle).
(5) Evernden family c.1650-58 (nave floor and North aisle).
(6) Rev. Thomas Evans, d. 1 Oct 1815, aet 66, vicar of Seaford 38 years (near North aisle).

(7) Elizabeth Champion, d. 31 Aug 1784, aet 16, daughter of Alexander Champion, of Walthamstow, Essex (porch).
(8) Mary Stevens, d. 1 Jan 1781, aet 68, wife of Richard Stevens for 47 years, and other unnamed females; from a rail in the churchyard, moved to the then vestry, also noted in Horsfield (*Sussex* I 280).
(9) For additional lost M.I.s (Elphick and Harison families) see Sir Egerton Brydges in *Topographical Miscellanies* 1, 1792.

(225) SEDLESCOMBE, St. John the Baptist

Perpendicular, restored by Norman & Billing 1866-74 - Nairn & Pevsner (604); in good state of repair in 1686 and 1724 (Ford 50, 115); the parish had c.50 families in 1724 and a population of 510 in 1801; 225E was restored to its original location after the rebuilding.

Sedlescombe, 225A Mural monument for Mary DYKE, d. 1642
- South aisle, South wall, West of South door, at head height on.
- 80(W) x 65(H) — Fine; repairs.
- M.I. (16 lines, engraved, black, Latin) fills an unframed rectangular panel (marble/alabaster?); black slate backplate; 2 small block corbels.
- Mary Dyke, d. 5 Apr 1642, aet 21; daughter of Peter Farnden, armiger; wife of Robert Dyke, Gent., and mother of William Dyke.

1. Erected by her widowed husband Robert.
2. According to the seating plan made in 1632, the Farndens occupied a pew in the centre aisle towards the front of the nave, see Godman (*SAC* 52 96).

Sedlescombe, 225B Mural monument for George BARNSLEY, d. 1724
- Tower, North wall, high.
- 80(W) x 90(H) — Very worn.
- M.I. (many lines engraved) on a square freestone panel; backplate with pointed top; base; 2 tiny moulded corbels.
- M.I. now illegible.

1. Perhaps originally floor-mounted; relocated in the 1870s?
2. The following M.I. is reported: 'GEORGE BANNESLEY Eccl ... OLM CATHED MAGD' (Church Guide).
3. JH notes that George Barnsley had been rector of Markshall, Essex, 1670-4; he was rector of Sedlescombe 1674-1724, of Northiam 1677-92/3 (Venn 1 1 94), prebendary of Hove Villa 1696-1724 and founder of the church school at Sedlescombe (Caffyn 235).

Sedlescombe, 225C Mural monument for Mary FARNDEN, d. 1630
- Tower, North wall, beneath 225B.
- 130(W) x 35(H) — Very worn.
- M.I. (engraved) on an unframed rectangular freestone slab.

IN HVMBLE & A LOWLY SOVLE WITH GRACES MANY MOE
WERE FOVND IN HER WHOSE BONES DOE LY ENTOMBED HEER BELOW
MARY BY NAME SHEE CALLED WAS & MARY LIKE HER ACTIONS
CHRIST WORD IN HEART SHEE LODGED FAST BEINGE PATIENT IN AFFLICATION
DORCAS FOR WORKES OF PIETY & LYDIA FOR HER CARE
TO HEARE X^T WORD ATTENTIVELY & LOVE THE MESSENGER
A BLESSED & A IOYFVLL DEATH SVCCEEDS A LIFE OF GRACE
IN VERTVES SCHOOLE HER LIFE SHE SPENT IN PEACE ENDED HER RACE

1. Perhaps originally floor-mounted; relocated in the 1870s?
2. M.I. given in Church Guide as commemorating Mary Waters, born at Brede, daughter of John Waters, wife (1616) of John Farnden, ironmaster and churchwarden of Sedlescombe, lived at Brickwall.
3. For Farnden see 225A.

4. JH notes that the Sussex Marriage Index shows Mary Waters marrying Peter Farnden at Sedlescombe on 18 Jun 1616 rather than the John Farnden in the Church Guide. The NBI records the burial of Mary Farnden on 12 Jul 1630 at Sedlescombe.

Sedlescombe, 225D Mural monument for Col. Thomas SACKVILL, d. 1692/3

- North-West chapel (vestry), West wall, at head height.
- 60(W) x 150(H) — Fine; some details fragile, detached and repaired.
- An achievement over a curved pediment, over a cornice; below, M.I. panel set portrait-wise, flanked by scrolls and foliage; base moulding; below that, a cherub's head draped and tasselled.
- Colonel Thomas Sackvill, d. 3 Jan 1692, son of Sir Thomas Sackvill and Joan Boyce; his wife, Margaret, daughter of Henry Compton, (brother of the Earl of Northampton), and widow of Anthony Roper of Eltham, Kent; Sisley Sackville, daughter of Robert, Earl of Dorset.

1. Formerly on chancel East wall - Horsfield (*Sussex* I 526); in situ by 1927 in Lambarde (*SAC* 68 217).
2. Thomas Sackvill was presented in the mid 1670s for not repairing the churchyard fence, see Johnstone (13); they were the leading family in the parish occupying an important pew, see plan in Godman (*SAC* 52 96). .
3. JH notes that various works of reference give different names to this wife of Sir Thomas. According to the History of Parliament, she was Elizabeth, daughter of Samuel Boys of Hawkhurst, see Henning (3 378). Thomas Sackvill(e) had been a captain in the royalist army, a JP for Sussex and Westminster, and was MP for East Grinstead in 1689, and 1690-3, see Henning (op. cit.).

Sedlescombe, 225E Cast iron slab for William BISSHOP, d. 1664, his wife and great grand-daughter

- North aisle floor, towards the West end, partly obscured by furniture.
- 60(W) x 150(L) — Fine.
- M.I. (3 bands of raised lines) on an iron slab; head to East.
- William Bisshop, buried 14 Nov 1664, son of John Bisshop, Gent.; his wife, Elizabeth, buried 21 May 1639, daughter of Edward Hause, Gent.; their great granddaughter, Sarah, (daughter of their grandson William), d. 20 Dec 1669.

1. In situ - Horsfield (*Sussex* I 526) alongside a stone slab; close to where the family rented a pew in the mid 17th century.
2. Orientation is unusual.
3. Willatts (*SAC* 125 101) notes reversed 'C'; she dates it 1669 (104).
4. JH notes that William and Sarah have the surname spelled Bishop in the NBI. Could the double SS be another eccentricity of the iron founder ?

(227) SELMESTON, St. Mary

A Perpendicular church; major 19th-century restorations under Rev. William Douglas Parish; South aisle of 1867 - Nairn & Pevsner (604-5); parish had 17 families in 1724 and a population of 130 in 1801; many of the original M.I.s on stone slabs and tablets were re-located and refashioned on brasses during the 19th-century restoration.

Selmeston, 227A Wall-mounted brass for Matthias CALDICOTT, d. 1808

- Nave, East wall, South-East corner facing West, at head height.
- 49(W) x 31(H) — Very good.
- M.I. (5 lines, engraved, in red / black) on a brass plate; ornament; at the top, a cross.
- Matthias Caldicott, Gent., of Sherington in Selmeston, d. 19 Feb 1808, aet 53.

1. Horsfield (*Sussex* I 334) noted a neat mural monument; 227A replaced that [1860s?].
2. The Caldicotts owned property at Selmeston since at least 1785 (R. Davey 193).

3. For licence to marry dated 7 Feb 1778 for Matthias Caldicott, of Selmeston, Gent., bachelor, age 21 plus and Mary Mockett, of Selmeston, spinster, age 20 plus, see Dunkin & Penfold (*Licences* 74).
4. JH notes that the Sussex Marriage Index shows licence and marriage both in the name of Matthew Caldicott.

Selmeston, 227B Ledger for Matthias CALDICOTT, d. 1719

- Chancel floor , near North wall, close to sanctuary rail.
- 55(W) x 100(L) — Fine.
- Escutcheon, then M.I. (4 lines, engraved) fills a pale freestone slab.
- Matthias Caldicott, Gent., of Sherrington, d. 2 Feb 1719, aet 65.

1. A 1860s recutting of an earlier ledger?
2. One Matthias Caldicott had first purchased Sherrington in 1626 (Farrant 308); see Matthias Caldicott, of Selmeston and Katherine Nutt of Selmeston, licence to marry of 1 Nov 1679.
3. Lambarde does not mention the arms on this slab.

Selmeston, 227C Wall monument for Dame Beatris BRAY, dated 1532 [Plate 143]

- Chancel North wall.
- 191(W) x 201(H) x 66(D) — Fine; local damage; extensive restorations (M.I.).
- In freestone; arched and panelled recess; M.I. (2) on back wall; Tudor arch; foliage in spandrels; flanking, attached, faceted pilasters; another M.I. (1) in frieze; above, cresting; plain ledger; below, tomb-chest with further M.I. (3); 4 decorative quatrefoils.

(1 top)

: QVID...AS : OMNIA
: IN : OLIM : DEI : FACIT

(2 centre)

1532

HERE LYETH DAM BETRIS BRAY
SVMTYME THE WYFFE OF SYR
EDWARD BRAY DAWETER OF
RAFFE SHERLEY OF WYSTON
WYFE OF EDWARD ELDERTON
VERMIS .... SISDDDDDIEDCS
16 NATABEATRISATSVVS

(3 bottom)

OSMIHIDEFUNCT E VIVI IMPLORANT SALVTEM ...
FEL.CTINANOVEPIIANUS .... EVIATE VOLVNT TE

1. In situ - Horsfield (*Sussex* I 334); originally used as an Easter Sepulchre.
2. M.I.s corrupted by restorations, perhaps undertaken when 227B was recut.
3. In type, to be compared with 120G.

Selmeston, 227D Floor-mounted brass for Matthias CALDICOTT, d. 1719

- Chancel floor, before rail.
- 223(W) x 8(L) — Good.
- M.I. (engraved) on a strip of brass set North/South.
- Matthias Caldicott, of Sherington, Selmeston, d. [2 Feb] 1719, [aet 65]; his wife, Katherine d. 1743; issue - Matthias, d. 1723; William, d. 1719; Katherine, d. 1772; Edward, d. 1686, etc.

1. A replacement [1860s?].
2. For Matthias Caldicott see 227B; for the family see 227A.

Selmeston, 227E Floor-mounted brass for Catherine and Mark SKINNER, both d. 1819

- Chancel floor, centre.
- 61(W) x 94(L) — Good.

- M.I. (engraved, red/black paint) on brass strip round edge of black slab; gilded cross in centre; head to West or East.
- Catherine Skinner, d. Aug 1819, infant; daughter of Mary Skinner, d. Sep 1819, aet 26; and James Skinner, Esq., of Sherrington; also their daughter, Sarah Ann Skinner, d. 26 Oct 1837, aet 21; also James Skinner, Esq., of Sherrington in Selmeston, d. 5 Nov 1873, aet 88; motto: 'In affectionate remembrance'.

1. For licence to marry dated 29 May 1781 for James Skinner, of Alfriston, surgeon, bachelor, age 24 plus and Mary Newnham, of Alfriston, spinster, see Dunkin & Penfold (*Licences* 384); the property Sherrington passed to Mary Hawes, wife of James Skinner of Alfriston in 1811 (Farrant 308).
2. 227E is a replacement (1860s).

Selmeston, 227F Floor-mounted brass for Ann COX, d. 1741 [Plate 144]

- Nave floor, just West of chancel step.
- 82(W) x 85(L) — Good.
- Arms (engraved) on centre of black slab; head to West; M.I. (engraved, red/black paint) on brass strips on top and sides;.
- Ann Cox, d. 1741, aet 57; daughter of Robert and Elizabeth Rochester, and widow of William Cox of Stanstead, Kent.

1. In situ in Lambarde (*SAC* 70 149) noting arms.
2. 227F appears to be a 18th-century ledger, cut off, the M.I. transferred to a 19th-century brass, the original escutcheon remains.
3. For licence to marry for John Acton, of Ripe, Gent. and Anne Rochester, of Selmeston, dated 12 May 1710, see Dunkin (*Licences 1670-1729* 199).
4. Datable 1860s?

Selmeston, 227G Brass grave marker for Ann MOCKETT, d. 1796 [Plate 145]

- Nave floor.
- 15(W) x 15(L) — Good.
- M.I. (engraved red paint) on brass lozenge ; crosses (red paint).
- Ann Mockett, d. 1796, aet 26, wife of Henry Mockett.

1. 227G is 1 in a set of 4 (others commemorating later deaths); datable 1860s?.

Selmeston, 227H Floor-mounted brass for Henry ROGERS, d. 1639 [Plate 146]

- South aisle floor.
- 43(W) x 18(L) — Good.
- M.I. (engraved) on a brass plate; head to West.
- Rev. Henry Rogers, vicar of Selmeston for 32 years, d. 6 May 1639, aet 67.
A painefull preacher ...

1. Noted by Stephenson (514) and Davidson-Houston (*SAC* 79 116) as in situ; refixed inverted?
2. M.I. includes Henry Roger's name in the form of what appears to be his signature (copied from the parish records suggests Church Guide); this Henry Rogers not to be confused with another clergyman of the same name of Herefordshire, 1584-1658, for whom see *ODNB*.
3. 227H is an original 17th-century brass amongst 19th-century versions.

Selmeston, 227I Ledger stone for Mary ROCHESTER, d. 1683/4

- Vestry floor, partly obscured by furnishings.
- 78(W) x 148(L) — Very worn.
- M.I.s (engraved) on a pinkish freestone slab; set North-South.
- Mary Rochester, d. 7 Mar 1683, aet 6; daughter of Robert Rochester, Jnr and his wife, Elizabeth.

1. Formerly in chancel - Horsfield (*Sussex* 1 334).
2. See too 227I2 and 227J-K.
3. The measurements for 227I include 227I/2.

Selmeston, 227I/2 Ledger stone for Elizabeth ROCHESTER, d. 1725

- Vestry floor, alongside 227J.
- See 227I — Good.
- M.I. (engraved) fills a polished, pinkish freestone slab, set East-West.

HERE ALSO LYETH
INTERED Yᴱ BODY OF
ᴹᴿˢ ELIZAᴮᴱᵀᴴ ROCHESTER
WIDOW OF ROBERT
ROCHESTER LATE OF
LVDLAY GENT. WHO
DEPARTED THIS LIFE
Yᴱ 13ᵀᴴ DAY OF MAY 1725
AGED 77 YEARS MOTHER
OF THE ABVE SAID MARY

Selmeston, 227J Ledger stone for Henry ROCHESTER, d. 1646

- Vestry floor, alongside 227I/2.
- 76(W) x 41(L) — Sound; damaged edges.
- M.I. (engraved) fills a polished black freestone slab; 11 lines of epitaph set East-West; 3 lines set North-South.
- Henry Rochester, d. 28 May 1646.

1. Formerly in chancel - Horsfield (*Sussex* I 334).
2. For the Rochesters, see 227I, I2 and K.
3. An eccentric Latinised M.I.
4. JH notes the last lines of epitaph: '*No sooner christned but possession / I took of th heavenlie habitation*' presumably indicate death at a very young age.

Selmeston, 227K Ledger stone for Henry ROCHESTER, d. 1703

- Vestry floor, amongst others.
- 68(W) x 47(L) — Cracked.
- M.I. (10 lines, engraved) fills a polished black freestone slab; set North-South.
- Henry Rochester, of Selmeston, d. 10 Sep 1703, aet 45; his wife, Susanna, d. 23 May 1726, aet 78, daughter of William Markwick, Esq., of Wannock in Jevington.

1. Formerly in chancel - Horsfield (*Sussex* I 334), see too 227I-J.
2. Place names in M.I. italicised (Wannock and Javington).
3. William Markwick of Jevington stood surety for a licence to marry in 1642, see Dunkin (*Licences 1586-1643* 290); for licence to marry for Henry Rochester, of Selmeston and Susan Markwick, of Jevington 6 Sep 1678, see Dunkin (*Licences 1670-1729* 50); for William Markwick of Jevington, see 147B.
4. For the Rochesters of Jevington, see 147D-E.

Selmeston, 227L Ledger stone for Elizabeth CALDICOTT [?], date unknown

- Vestry floor, near door.
- 62(W) x 111(L) — Very worn.
- Traces of M.I. (engraved) in a slab, set North-South.
- Illegible.

1. JH notes that the very indistinct stone seems to be for Elizabeth, eldest daughter of Samuel Caldicott Gent., and Elizabeth, his wife. Another daughter (name indecipherable) is mentioned later. Date illegible.

Selmeston, 227M Ledger stone for a member of the CALDICOTT family
- Vestry floor, partly obscured by furnishings.
- 93(W) x 193(L) — Very damp.
- M.I. (engraved) on a slab, set North-South.
- Hardly legible.

1. 227M may commemorate the sister of Samuel Caldicott; a date of 1772?

(234) SLAUGHAM, St. Mary
13th-century side aisle widened in 1857-60; South chapel (Covert) of 1613 - Nairn & Pevsner (606-7) and Horsfield (*Sussex* I 258); condition fine in 1724, including the chancels (Ford 152); the parish had 80 families in 1724 and a population of 560 in 1801; 234D-F rivals West Firle as the most important set of Elizabethan monuments in Sussex; the Coverts were related to the Pooles at Ditchling, also tomb patrons (see 77I); for the church and family see W.A. Dengate, *Slaugham, a parish in Sussex* and M Girouard, 'Renaissance Splendour in Decay, the Ruins of Slaugham' (Country Life 9 Jan 1964 70-73).

Slaugham, 234A Mural monument for Rose de BLAQUIERE, d. 1818
- South nave aisle wall, near West end, at head height.
- 32(W) x 38(H) — Fine; faded.
- M.I. (3 lines, engraved, black) on unframed white marble lozenge; rectangular black backplate; above, cherub.
- Rose de Blaquiere, 26 Oct 1813 - 11 Feb 1818.

1. Formerly [?] on chancel North wall, probably one of several tablets removed in 1879.

Slaugham, 234B Mural monument for Mary ELLISON, d. 1821 [Plate 147]
- South nave aisle wall, South-West corner, at head height.
- 43(W) x 59(H) — Fine.
- M.I. (10 lines, engraved, black) on a white marble tablet set portrait-wise in a moulded metal frame; marble corbel below; all set within a cast or stamped tin border with a cherub in a pointed pediment.
- Mary Ellison, d. 9 Apr 1821, aet 24; daughter of Robert Ellison.

1. Formerly [?] on chancel North wall, probably one of several tablets removed in 1879.
2. The only such metal frame identified in this survey.
3. The small white marble grave markers in the choir, perhaps relate to this family.

Slaugham, 234C Mural monument for Dionysius BARTLEE, d. 1773 [Plate 148]
- North nave aisle wall, West end, high.
- 93(W) x 92(H) — Fine.
- M.I. (5 lines, engraved, black) on a white marble tablet; a modest moulded border; set landscape-wise; above, ambitious moulded entablature; below, base moulding and 2 scrolled corbels.

Near this Place are
Inter'd the Body of
DIONYSIUS BARTLEE
who Died March the 25th
1773. Aged 73 Years.

1. Formerly [?] on chancel North wall, probably one of several tablets removed in 1879.
2. Splendid lettering with an error ('are').

Slaugham, 234D Wall monument for Richard COVERT, d. 1547 [Plate 149]

- Sanctuary North wall, West of 234E.
- 183(W) x 223(H) — Good; colour lost; local damage (brasses).
- In freestone; straight, crested top; below, a Tudor arch with quatrefoils in the frieze, over a niche; 11 brasses on the back wall (4 escutcheons, 4 figures (Richard Covert & his wives 1-3), 2 M.I.s; 1 Resurrection; below, a chest with more brasses (now blank) and 3 ornamental panels on its front; facetted pillars flank the niche.
- Richard Covert, Esq., d. 7 Jun 1547; his first wife, Elizabeth, daughter of Sir John and Elizabeth Fagge; his second wife, also Elizabeth, daughter of George Neville, Lord Bergavenny; his third wife, Jane, daughter of William Ashburnham, Esq.; his fourth wife, Blanche, daughter of John Vaughan of Bergavenny, Esq.

(Right hand figure) Richard
NOLI DAMNARE REDEMPTOS
(Next to Richard his first wife) Elizabeth Fagge
QUI VENISTI REDIMERE PERDITOS
(Next, his second wife) Elizabeth Neville
NUNC CHRISTE TE PETIMUS MISERERE QUAESUMUS
(On extreme left his third wife) Jane Ashburnham
DEUS IN MISERICORDIA TUA SEMPER SPERAVI
(On small Brass underneath)
HEC FILIA WILLI ASSCHEBURNEHAM ARMYGERY
TERCIA UXOR RICHARDI COVERT ARMYGERY
CUIUS ANIME PROPICIETUR DEUS AMEN
(on large central Brass)
HERE LYETH RICHARD COVERT ESQUIER AND ELIZABETH FIRST WYFE OF YE SAYD RIC ONE OF THE DOWGHTERS & HEIERS OF JOHN FAGGE ESQUIER & ELIZABETH HIS WYFE, & ELIZABETH SEC[O]NDE WYFE OF Yᴱ AFORE SAYD RIC COVERT THE DOWGHTER OF GEORGE NEVYLE KNYGHT LORD BURGEVENNE & JANE ASCHEBURNHAME DOWGHTER OF WILLIAM ASCHEBURNEHAM OF ASCHEBURNHAM ESQUIER ALSO BLANCHE VAWHAN THE DOWGHTER OF JOHN VAWGHAN OF BURGEVENNE ESQUIER LAST WIFE OF THE SAID RICH WHICHE SAYDE RIC DECESSED THE VII DAY OF JUNE Aᵒ D[OMI]NI 1547 ON WHOS SOULL IH[ES]U HAVE MERCY.

1. In situ, see Horsfield (*Sussex* I 258); Stephenson (514-5) suggests that 234D might have first been erected c.1525 with a brass for third wife Jane after her death in 1527; Davidson-Houston (*SAC* 79 120-24) and R.H. D'Elboux, 'The Covert Brasses: Slaugham' (*SNQ* XIV 80-2) build on this argument suggesting that the original monument, displayed until c.1527 the brasses of Richard Covert, the first and second wives, the Resurrection and the Covert arms, with the main inscription added in 1547 (after Richard Covert's death); distribution of brasses does not seem original or authentic.
2. For a drawing of a detail see Andre (*SAC* 42 14).
3. For Covert details see J. Cooper (*SAC* 47 120ff).
4. See too Lambarde (*SAC* 69 199), noting arms.
5. 234D forms the space taken by the Easter Sepulchre, built to receive the sacred elements of the mass from Good Friday until Easter morning; this location also filled by the Bray and Marwick monuments at Selmeston and Hamsey.
6. The Coverts held the manor of Slaugham from 1495-1735 when they sold to Sergison.
7. Richard Covert inherited the estate from his cousin John Covert.
8. Issue of Richard and Blanche, his 4th wife, were - John, George and Elizabeth.

Slaugham, 234E Wall monument for Jane FETYPLACE (COVERT), d. 1586/7 [Plate 150]

- Sanctuary North wall, North-East corner, East of 234D.
- 142(W) x 218(H) x 24(D) — Worn; some colour.
- In a range of materials: cretaceous (Petworth marble) Doric columns on base mouldings; decorative alabaster inserts in frieze; pointed pediment with rosettes & an oval lozenge over crisp entablature mouldings; rectangular panels (now blank) in frieze; 2 Doric columns on bases, between which, on the back wall, brass plates - 2 escutcheons & a female kneeling figure, at a prayer-desk and a M.I.; below, a ledger; below that, chest on plinth decorative with crowns.
- Jane Fetyplace, d. 25 Jan 1586/7; daughter of John Covert, of Slaugham; her first husband,

Sir Francis Fleming; her second husband, Sir John Fetyplace; also her nephew, William Covert.

1. In situ, see Grimm drawing of 1787 (BL Add. MS 5672 f.3R) and Horsfield (*Sussex* I 258); noted by Stephenson (515); Turner (*SAC* 23 179); Lambarde (*SAC* 69 199), noting arms; Davidson-Houston (*SAC* 79 124-5); Mosse; Nairn & Pevsner (607).
2. Jane Fetyplace was daughter of John Covert (d. 1558) and his first wife Elizabeth daughter of John Cooke, of Rustington; she was granddaughter of Richard and Blanche Covert (234D); patron of 234E was Jane Fetyplace's nephew and executor William Covert; the Coverts held the manor of Slaugham from 1495-1735, when they sold to the Sergison family (see 234I); the Fettiplace monuments are at Swinbrook, Oxford.
3. The relationship between 234E and 234F is puzzling, close in date and both classicizing in type; standard Elizabethan composition; as at West Firle, a brass figure rather than a carved effigy.

Slaugham, 234F Wall monument for Richard COVERT, dated 1579 [Plate 151]
- South aisle, South-East corner, against South wall.
- 320(W) x 356(H) x 35(D) — Fine; no colour.
- An architectural frame around a set of achievements; trophies, skulls and kneelers; entablature with decorated frieze (rosettes, strapwork) on fluted composite columns; high pedestals with decorated panels (strapwork on face; grotesque urns and beasts on returns); arms on back wall; panel with date (engraved) '1579'; below, the name initials of a row of children: 'R, W, W, I, T, M, A, F & A, M, E, A I, E, D, M & C'; children as kneelers, facing East, some at prayer-desks, many with prayer-books.

1. Relocated into the Covert Chapel, which was built only in 1613; originally there was simply a West wall across the present South aisle.
2. In situ, see Grimm's drawing of 1787 showing heads missing from female kneelers numbered 1, 7 and 8, starting from left (BL Add. MS 5672 f.10R) and in Horsfield (*Sussex* I 258); Turner (*SAC* 23 179-180).
3. Restored by rector in 1874-86; Mosse; Lambarde (*SAC* 69 199) noting arms; Esdaile (*EMS* 86).
4. Mercer (223 & 228) groups 234F with monuments to Anthony Cave, d. 1568, Stanford-on-Avon, Northants and Thomas Wylmer, d. 1580, Staverton, Northants, noting the innovation of posing kneelers on the back wall rather than the floor; Nairn & Pevsner (607).
5. The initials correspond with: Richard, William, Walter, John, Thomas Mynors, Alexander, Francis, Ann, Mary, Ellen, Ann, Joan, Elizabeth, Dulcibella, Margery, Cicely; Richard Covert's first wife was Ann Hendley, with whom the above issue; his second wife was Cicely Bowes; his third wife is not referred to on 234F; Richard Covert was first of two sons of John Covert (d. 1558) and Elizabeth Cooke, see J. Cooper (*SAC* 47 129 and pedigree on 144).
6. J Cooper (*SAC* 47 133) quotes Richard Covert's will (TNA PRO PROB 11 Arundel f.14, proved 26 Apr 1580): '£10 to Flynton (in fact 'Flynte') for making my tomb, for which I have already paid him £20' (TNA PRO PROB 11/62/117r-118r); for Flynte's own will, noting that Covert was a creditor, see (TNA PRO PROB 11/63/30).
7. The IPM for Richard Covert, Esq., d. 10 Sep an. reg. Elizabeth 21, notes that his son and heir is Walter, aet 30 in an reg Elizabeth 22; one Ann Covert, widow, late wife of John Covert, has also died; Richard Covert's widow's will dated 1583 (Salzman *Inquisitions* 117ff).
8. The vast size and high all-antica quality of 234F are outstanding.
9. The lack of a M.I., or even of a place for one is puzzling - reflecting an early loss or disruption around the relocation of 234F into the newly-built chapel after 1613, or an interrelation with 234E.

Slaugham, 234G Mural monument for William ELLISON, d. 1817
- South aisle wall, near East end, West of 234F, at head height.
- 82(W) x 91(H) — Very good.
- Against a yellow and grey-veined marble backplate with pointed top, a white marble lamp on a straight cornice; below, M.I. fills an unframed white tablet; drops at bottom edge; signed (lower edge): 'R.SHOUT. London fecit'.
- Captain William Ellison, R.N., d. 29 Jan 1817, aet 52; his brother, Robert.

1. Probably one of the four 'modern' mural monuments to rector's family noted by Horsfield (*Sussex* I 258).

2. Probably removed in 1879 from North chancel, below which, in present choir, there are square white marble grave markers, one initialled 'W.E.'.

3. 234G is signed by the London maker R Shout, who also made 123H (the Swiney monument at Hartfield); Gunnis (*Dict.* 350-1) describes late works by Shout as dull and unadventurous.

4. M.I. alludes to William Ellison's gout and gives a very long account of an heroic naval battle.

5. Patron of 234F is William Ellison's brother Robert, see 234H.

Slaugham, 234H Mural monument for Sarah and Robert ELLISON, d. 1813 and 1808

- South aisle, South wall, West of and alongside 234G.
- 76(W) x 92(H) — Cracked and restored (backplate); local losses.
- Description as for 234G.
- Sarah Ellison, d. 8 Mar 1813, aet 77; widow of Rev. Stanhope Ellison, rector of Wittersham and vicar of Boughton, Kent; also Robert Ellison, d. 2 Jun 1808, aet 6, son of Rev. Robert Ellison, rector of Slaugham, and his wife Sarah.

1. Probably one of the four 'modern' mural monuments to rector's family noted by Horsfield (*Sussex* I 258).
2. Probably removed in 1879 from North chancel.
3. 234G is signed, so 234H is also by Shout of London.
4. In restoration in 2006.
5. JH notes that Rev. Stanhope Ellison and his wife Sarah (née Wilby) were parents of William (see 234G) and Rev. Robert, whose wife was Sarah (née Potter).

Slaugham, 234I Mural monument for Janette Elizabeth SERGISON, d. 1846

- South choir aisle arcade, near East end, facing South, high.
- c.70(W) x c.160(H) — Good.
- A black backplate in stunted obelisk form, above, a white marble urn, draped; straight cornice breaking forward over an unframed tablet, set landscape-wise; M.I. fills tablet; curved apron; signed (lower right backplate): 'S. MANNING SC / YORK TERR. R[egent's] P[ark]'.
- Janette Elizabeth Sergison, d. 10 May 1846, aet 39; wife of Rev. William Sergison, rector of Slaugham.

1. Probably one of four tablets removed from chancel North wall in 1879.
2. The Sergisons, also at Cuckfield, bought the Slaugham estate in 1735; for other land-owning at Slaugham in 1785, see R. Davey 194-5.
3. Patron of 234I is the husband, William Sergison.
4. For Samuel Manning Snr (1788-1842), his large practice and his dull output, see Gunnis (*Dict.* 252-3).

Slaugham Additions

Horsfield (*Sussex* I 258) notes:
(1) Rev. Owen Evans, d. 21 Sep 1793, aet 57.
(2) Ann Evans, d. 20 Mar 1794, aet 89, mother of Owen, see (1).
(3) Francis Griffiths Matcham, d. 15 Feb 1808, aet 12, of Ashfold Lodge, a nephew of Nelson.
(4) Horatio Matcham, d. 11 Oct 1814, aet 18, brother of Francis, see (3).

(239) SOUTH MALLING, St. Michael

Mediaeval church rebuilt 1626-8 (some Decorated remains at West end); consecrated in 1632 as a Puritan foundation, the living maintained by a bequest from John Stansfield (see Lewes All Saints) - Nairn & Pevsner (608-9); plan in *SNQ* (III 247); South Malling was held in plurality with Glynde from 1683-1760; 22 families in 1717 and a population of 348 in 1801; 239E-G refer to the several generations of Kempe, owners of nearby Malling Deanery (1648-1826); some M.I.s refer to now-removed pews (239F); Burrell noted that the chancel monuments were reordered in 1775; Horsfield (*Sussex* I 343) found nothing noteworthy at South Malling.

South Malling, 239A Mural monument for William BRODIE, d. 1827

- Nave, South wall, West of South door, above head height.
- 105(W) x 78(H) — Very good; faded.
- M.I. (7 lines, engraved, black) on a white marble tablet of sarcophagal form; dark grey backplate; light, engraved border; 2 finials as corbels; cornice over; pointed pediment; palmettes in corners; escutcheon in pediment.
- William Brodie, Esq., of Malling Cottage, d. 3 May 1827, aet 61; his son, Francis William Brodie, died Calcutta, 16 Aug 1822, aet 3.

1. In situ in Lambarde (*SAC* 70 161) noting arms.

South Malling, 239B Mural monument for Richard RUSSELL, d. 1759 [Plate 152]

- North wall, towards West end, at head height.
- 48(W) x 49.5(H) — Very good.
- M.I. (5 lines, engraved) in Latin and Greek, on black marble, elliptical panel, set landscape-wise; suspended from it, a circular heraldic medallion.

H.S.E.
RICARD[s] RUSSELL - M.D. - S.R.S.
Obiit Ætat: ANNO - 72 - A.C. 1759.
Θαλασσα κλυζει Ιανθρωτων [recte τανθρωττων] κακα
H.S.P.

1. Formerly next to the East window (Church Guide), now over site of Russell vault.
2. The words 'H(aeres) s(uus) p(osuit)' indicates a date after 1760 for 239B, which was not apparently noted by Burrell in 1775, see W.H. Challen 'Richard Russell' (*SNQ* XIV 73-78); the Sussex antiquaries have rarely agreed on the details of Russell's biography - Horsfield (*Lewes* I 326-7) and (*Sussex* I 132-3); A. Dale, 'Doctor Richard Russell, the Founder of Modern Brighton' *SNQ* (XIV 16-18), Challen (above); see now J.H. Farrant in *ODNB* - Richard Russell, 26 Nov 1687- 21 Dec 1759; buried 25 Dec.
3. Easily confused with another physician of the same name ([?]1714-71).
4. Richard Russell's issue was 5 daughters and 2 sons between 1720-35; he was long-term supporter of the political interests of Duke of Newcastle in the county; his wife was a Kempe, owners of Malling Deanery and his first son William Kempe, Sergeant-at-law [patron of 239B?], took the surname Kempe, after Richard Russell's death; Richard Russell was trained in part at Leiden and was FRS.
5. See his De Tabe Glandulari, (Oxford 1750, English edition 1753), which used the Euripides quotation on the title page that appears on 239B, the text of which (from *Iphigenia in Tauris*, 1193), refers to Russell's career as a physician specialising in the salt-water cure; not quoted directly, but the final word, pa?ta, is omitted because Richard Russell could not claim that the sea off Brighton was a universal remedy, see Currey (*SAC* 36 246).
6. Small heraldic crest not noted by Lambarde.

South Malling, 239C Ledger for Wm KEMPE, d. 1691

- Nave floor, East end, North side.
- 92(W) x 188(H) — Worn.
- M.I. (6 lines, engraved) in upper 30% of a black slab; head to North.
- William Kempe, Esq., d. 6 Nov 1691, aet 66.

1. The Kempes were owners of Malling Deanery.

South Malling, 239D Mural monument for Mary KEMPE, d. 1775

- Chancel North wall, at head height.
- 95(W) x 49(H) — Fine.
- M.I. (9 lines, engraved, black) in Latin on light grey tablet set landscape-wise; moulded

frame; chamfered corners.
- Mary Kempe, d. 28 Oct 1775, aet 47; wife of William Kempe, lawyer.

1. Erected by William Kempe.

South Malling, 239E Ledger for Dorothy SPENCE, d. 1685, and others
- Chancel floor, South-East corner.
- 96(W) x 163(H) — Scratched.
- M.I. (many lines, engraved) covers a black slab; head to East.
- Dorothy Spence, buried 10 Jul 1685, youngest daughter of Sir Houland Roberts, Bart., of Glassenbury, Kent, and wife of John Spence II, Esq., the son of John Spence I; also, Byne, d. 1721, aet 39, daughter of Sir G Walker, Bart., and first wife of John Spence III, Esq.; their issue - youngest son, Benjamin, d. 1721; eldest son, William, died aet 9; third son, Henry, d. 7 Jul 1761, aet 42; also, Mary Spence, d. 24 Dec 1751, aet 23, second daughter of John Spence III by Graciana, his second wife; also, Henrietta, d. 27 Oct 1775, aet 58, daughter of Sir Thomas Frederick, Knt., and wife of Luke Spence, Esq.

1. And see 239G.

South Malling, 239F Mural monument for Annette Jane HORT, d. 1810
- Chancel South wall, above head height.
- 56(W) x 78(H) — Fine; faded.
- M.I. (10 lines, engraved, black) on a white marble oval tablet, set landscape-wise; below, a base moulding and corbel with ring decoration; above, a flaming urn in relief on a base mould.
- Annette Jane Hort, d. 15 Jun 1810, aet 5.

1. Patron of 239F was Annette Jane Hort's mother.

South Malling, 239G Ledger with attached brasses for Luke SPENCE, d. 1800, and others
- Nave floor, East end, South side.
- Ledger: 99.5(W) x 163(H); Upper brass: 32(W) x 39.5(H); Lower brass: 32.5(W) x 16(H) — Very good.
- A slab; head to South; from South end, M.I. (4 lines, engraved) in stone; in centre, upper brass, with many engraved lines; then another M.I. (3 lines, engraved) in stone; then lower brass; also set in centre; finally, another M.I. (4 lines, engraved) in stone.
- Luke Spence, Esq., d. 28 May 1800, aet 84; his granddaughter, Harriet, d. 11 Sep 1797, aet 28; also, William Spence, buried 16 Jul 1677; also, Audry Barksted, d. 7 Aug 1691, aet 26, daughter of John Spence I, and wife of John Barksted; also, John Spence, armiger, 23 Sep 1683 - 15 Jun 1741; also, John Spence I, d. 3 Aug 1691, aet 67; his wife, Ruth, d. 6 Apr 1693, aet 63.

1. A remarkable composite memorial over many generations.
2. Luke Spence was the major landowner at South Malling in 1785 (R. Davey 150).

South Malling, 239H Ledger for Sarah KEMPE, d. 1794
- Nave floor, centre, near East end.
- 89(W) x 111(H) — Cracked (diagonal from top right).
- M.I. (12 lines, engraved) on a black slab; head to South.
- Sarah Kempe, d. 10 Jul 1794, aet 25; wife of William Kempe, Esq., Serjeant at Law, impropriate rector of South Malling; their issue, 4 unnamed children.

1. For licence to marry dated 17 Sep 1787 for William Kempe, of South Malling, serjeant-at-law, widower and Sarah Mackrell, of South Malling, spinster, age 19, see Dunkin & Penfold (*Licences* 247).
2. William Kempe was the son of subject of 239B.

South Malling Additions

Noted in D'Elboux (*SAC* 86):

(1) Brass inscribed for Audrey Barkstead, d. 7 Aug 1691, aet 25, formerly in chancel, now in a private college in Lewes having been removed during 1873 restoration of the church; noted by Burrell, who adds that the chancel monuments were reordered in 1775 (pp. 121-4).

(2) Brass for William Spence, d. 16 Jul 1677, 9 lines of Latin, illustrated and noted as on ledger, head to South, South-West of communion rail, all part of reordering noted under (1) above (pp. 123-4).

(3) Brass for John Spence, 23 Sep 168? - 15 Jun 1741, 6 lines of Latin, all as for (2). John Spence, was son of another John Spence, who was brother of Audrey Barkstead (see (1) above), by Mary, daughter of Sir John Fagge of Wiston; John Spence had 2 wives, issue from each (pp. 124-5).

(241) SOUTHEASE, St. Peter

Norman, some Jacobean box pews - Nairn & Pevsner (608); the paving was defective in 1686 (Ford 38); the parish had 14 families in 1724, in which year the church was reportedly in decent order (Ford 152); the population was 108 in 1801; Horsfield (*Sussex* I 196-7) notes unspecified M.I.s to incumbents.

Southease, 241A Ledger for John WILLARD, d. 1673

- Sanctuary floor, North side.
- 87(W) x 192(L) — Very worn.
- M.I. (9 or 10? lines, engraved) in upper 30% of a sandy freestone slab; head to West.

IOHN WILLARD AGED 80

YEARES, RECTOR OF SOUT

HEASE, AN EMINENTE DIVINE

AND PAINEFULL PREACHER OF

GOD HIS WORDE GR E.TLYE BELO

VED FOR HIS CHARITIES TO THE

POOR ...

...

...

...

1. Ledger of a standard size.

Southease, 241B Grave marker for Edmund ROSE, d. 1596

- Sanctuary floor, South side.
- 53(W) x 29(L) — Very worn.
- M.I. (engraved) on a small freestone slab; head to East.

...

RECT. ECCLE ...

... DO 159.. SEPT 11

...

...

1. Church Guide identifies this as for Edmund Rose, rector of Southease 1577-1596.
2. JH notes that CCEd, NBI and Hennessy (139) all show him as Edmund.

Southease, 241C Floor monument for Edward BOUGHEN, d. 1653

- Sanctuary floor, South side, West of 242B.
- 81(W) x 162(L) — Very worn.
- M.I. (6 lines, scratched) at upper end of a freestone slab; head to West.
- Edward Boughen, D.D., clergyman (Woodchurch), d. 9 Nov 1653.

HERE LYETH THE BODY
OF EDWARD BOUGHEN DOCTER
OF DEVINITY AND PARSON OF
WOODC[H]URCH HE DE
PARTED THIS LIFE NOVEMBER
THE 9TH 1653

1. Church Guide notes that Edward Boughen, b. 1587, was subject of a biography by Anthony à Wood.
2. Edward Boughen was vicar of Bray, then of Woodchurch, Kent and a lifelong Royalist and high churchman; he was in Oxford during the Civil War and a pamphleteer and commentator on theological texts; his association with Southease is unknown; he was perhaps an associate of John Willard? see 242A and W.H. Godfrey, 'The burial place of Edward Bowen' (*SNQ* VI 52), used as source by church guide; JH notes that he was prebendary of Chichester 1638-53, see Horn (*Fasti 1541-1857* II 26 4).
3. NWS Cranfield's biography in *ODNB*; name of wife not known; son Edward.
4. Ledger of a standard size.

(244) STANMER Parish Church

The church underwent a radical remodelling in 1838 - Nairn & Pevsner (460-1); for a view from the North-East see Godfrey & Salzman (Pl. 150); Samuel Tufnell (d.1765) who supplied the house with a chimney piece in 1725 cannot have made any of the monuments here, Gunnis (*Dict.* 401); for other aspects of the manorial context see S. Berry 'Stanmer House and Park, East Sussex ...c.1710-1805' (*SAC* 143 239ff); c.1760, the village comprised nine houses and one farm; in 1801 the population was 105; Horsfield, visiting just before the remodelling, mentions no monuments at Stanmer.

Stanmer, 244A Mural monument for Sir John PELHAM, d. 1580, his wife and his son Oliver, d. 1584/5 [Plate 153]

- North aisle wall, at head height.
- c.118(W) x c.176(H) — Fine; many repairs.
- At the top, an achievement on a circular plate with a scrollwork base; below this, an entablature on Doric columns, framing three figures kneeling at a prayer-desk (2 male to the left, 1 female to the right); below, M.I. (many lines, engraved, black) on apron below; arms; at the foot, as a corbel, a decorative panel with Latin motto.
- Sir John Pelham, d. 13 Oct 1580; husband of Judith, daughter of Oliver St. John of Bletsowe, Bedfordshire; their issue, Oliver Pelham, d. 19 Jan 1584/5.

1. In situ in Lambarde (*SAC* 71 141) noting arms.
2. Apparently moved to Stanmer from Holy Trinity, Minories, City of London, Nairn & Pevsner (461), at an unknown date; Minories was a Royal Peculiar, united with parish of St. Botolph's Aldgate in 1899, *SNQ* (IV 137).
3. See the IPM for Sir John Pelham d. 12 Oct an. reg. 22 Elizabeth I; his son and heir is Oliver, aged 8 months in 1580; John Pelham's will required decent and seemly burial without pomp or superstition.
4. Oliver was perhaps named for John Pelham's business partner [and brother in law], Oliver, Lord St. John of Bletsoe, see Salzman (*Inquisitions* 114) who was a considerable patron of monuments.
5. The Pelham family acquired Stanmer in 1712/13, see S. Farrant, 'The building of Stanmer House ...' (*SAC* 117 196).
6. JH notes that Sir John Pelham was MP for Sussex in 1571, a JP from 1565, and Sheriff of Surrey and Sussex 1571-2, see Hasler (3 193).

Stanmer, 244B Engraved Brass for Deborah GOFFE, d. 1626

- Sanctuary North wall.
- 26(W) x 12(H) — Fine.
- M.I. (5 lines, engraved, white) within a beaded moulded decorative frame; below, an empty field.
- Deborah Goffe, d. 8 Nov 1626, aet 39; wife of Stephen Goffe, preacher.

1. Noted by Stephenson (515), in situ in Davidson-Houston (*SAC* 79 129) with illustration.
2. Stephen Goffe's own dates seem never to have been added to the empty field. For details of Stephen Goffe see Dunkin (*SAC* 26 88 note 100).

Stanmer, 244C Floor mounted brass for Edward MICHELBOURNE, d. 1700
- Sanctuary floor, before altar.
- Slab: 100(W) x 199(L); Brass plate: 34(W) x 29(H) — Very good.
- Arms and M.I. (4 lines, engraved) in upper 50% of a circular brass plate set on a black slab; head to West.
- Edward Michelbourne, Esq., d. 1700, aet 63.

1. In situ, see F.W.T. Attree, 'Notes on the family of Michelborne' (*SAC* 50 84) pedigree of Michelbourne of Horsted Keynes and Stanmer; Lambarde (*SAC* 71 141) noting arms; Davidson-Houston (*SAC* 79 129-30) with illustration, transcribed and translated.
2. Edward Michelbourne's parents were William Michelbourne and Anne, daughter of Lawrence Ashburnham, of Bromham, Esq; having been lords of the manor for most of the century, the Michelbournes sold Stanmer in 1700 to the Gotts, see 250L and H. Warne, 'Stanmer: a restructured Settlement' (see 250L) (*SAC* 127 202); the estate passed to the Pelhams in 1713.

Stanmer, 244D Mural Monument for Elizabeth SCRASE, d. 1732 [Plate 154]
- Sanctuary, South wall, at head height.
- c.75(W) x c.190(H) — Very good.
- Arms painted on a lozenge on a white marble mount, resting on a black unframed oval panel; M.I. (engraved); below, a decorated white marble corbel with another (metal) escutcheon on a hard stone ball finial; signed (lower right): 'HARGRAVES LEWES'.
- Elizabeth Scrase, d. 17 Aug 1732, aged 43, daughter of Charles Harison, Esq., and Catherine, of Lewes; widow of William Scrase, buried at Brighton; and brother of Charles Harison, Esq., of Sutton; her son, Henry, d. 23 May 1793, aged 68.

1. In situ - Lambarde (*SAC* 71 141) noting arms.
2. Charles Harison stood surety for marriages in Feb 1686/7, Jul 1688, Nov 1692 and Jun 1694, see Dunkin (*Licences 1670-1729* 111, 142, 153).
3. Its style suggests that 244D post-dates the death of Henry Harison (subject's son) in 1793.
4. Cited by Gunnis (*Dict.* 188) as by Isaac Hargraves, fl. 1792-6, perhaps his earliest known work [?].
5. Addition 2 is an earlier Harrison monument.

Stanmer Additions
Noted in Dunkin (*SAC* 26 88):
(1) Cuthbert Lancaster, parson of Stanmer, d. 21 Jan 1613/4 (on stone in sanctuary).
(2) James Harrison, rector of Stanmer, d. 17 Mar 1638 (on stone in sanctuary).

(250) STREAT Parish Church
Early history is obscure; over-restored; South aisle of 1854 - Nairn & Pevsner (610-11); view from North-West in Godfrey & Salzman (Pl. 155); VCH (VII 115); condition reportedly fine in 1724 when patron was William Dobell of Folkington (Ford 154); the Streat estate was built up by the Dobells during the earlier 17th century (see 250A-B); the manor passed to the Lanes after the marriage of Dr Thomas Lane to William Dobell's niece, Mary, in 1748 - Budgen (*Dobell* 1ff) and Radcliffe (*SAC* 66 123-135); the parish had 25 families in 1724 and a population of 112 in 1801; Horsfield (*Sussex* I 233-4) notes only the Dobell vault on North side of chancel and the M.I.s on coffins (see Additions), curiously, not the monuments.

Streat, 250A Mural monument for Mary DOBELL, d. 1764 [Plate 155]

- Nave North wall, East of North door, above head height.
- 114(W) x 290(H) — Excellent, faded.
- Much of it in coloured marbles; in centre, a M.I. on white marble framed rectangular panel; below, an ornamental apron with pair of cherubs; above, arms and an urn in low relief; decorated with garlands and rocaille work, all of highest quality.
- Mary Dobell, d. 20 May 1764, aet 74: widow of William Dobell, Esq.; issue - 1 daughter, still living; her virtues, piety, etc.

1. Probably in situ in rebuilt church; see *Gent's Mag* visit dated 1804 in Gomme (324); Horsfield (*Sussex* I 233-4) locates it next to 250B and notes its quality; Lambarde (*SAC* 71 148) arms noted and Nairn & Pevsner (611).
2. 250A was erected by the subject's daughter, another Mary, still owner of the manor in 1785 (R. Davey 197 but see note on 250B) and forms a pair with 250B (note the reference in M.I. l.1), but probably not by the same hand, some 12 years later.

Streat, 250B Mural monument for William DOBELL, d. 1752

- Nave North wall, East of 250A.
- 170(W) x 310(H) — Excellent; faded.
- An arch-topped M.I. in moulded frame; decorated borders; below, apron with 3 cherubim; above, a broken pediment enclosing an achievement; on the cornice flaming lamps (left and right); urn in centre; decorated garlands and swags throughout; in marbles, mainly white but also grey, pink and yellow.

In the adjoining Dormitory
Amidst a Long Series of worthy Ancestors
Rest the Remains of
WILLIAM DOBELL Esq late of FOLKINGTON
In this County
A Gentleman
Who for his Publick and Private Virtues
Was equalled by few, excelled perhaps by none;
He shin'd remarkably
In the love of his Country, In a Zeal for the Church
In Piety, Integrity, Honesty, Disinterestedness,
And a constant Regularity of Life and Manners.
He died the 16th of June 1752 in the 68th year
of his Age
Belov'd by the Good, Esteem'd by the Unprejudiced
Lamented by most
He married MARY the Daughter and Heiress of WILLIAM FINCH Esq
of TENTERDEN in KENT
By who [sic] he had two Daughters.
BARBARA and MARY
The former died before her father the 28th of September 1749
Aged 22, and lies buried near him
Her personal, religious and social Accomplishments were such
As an Attempt to describe, would in Reality lessem [sic]
The Second surviv'd him
This Monument was erected by the Widow,
and Mother Mrs MARY DOBELL
AD
MDCCLIII

1. Probably in situ in rebuilt church, see *Gent's Mag* visit dated 1804 in Gomme (324); Horsfield (*Sussex* I 233-4); Lambarde (*SAC* 71 148) noting arms and Nairn & Pevsner (611).
2. A group of manors owned by Sir William Thomas of Folkington (see 108E and H) passed under the terms of his will to William Dobell, his nephew, in 1706; William then made Folkington his place of residence (Budgen *Dobell* 29 xiii ff.) although the Dobells continued to use Streat for burials

and owned property on Lewes High Street; he gave a silver flagon to Folkington church in 1732, see Couchman (*SAC* 55 152) and his wife gave plate to nearby Westmeston church in 1747, see Couchman (*SAC* 54 247); for William Dobell's gift to the charity school see Caffyn (248).

3. Like 250A, 250B is of very high quality; erected in 1753 by William's widow (see 250A) and also commemorates Dobell's second daughter Barbara (d. 1749).

4. The patron, William Dobell's widow Mary, was also executrix of Sybilla Stapley (see 212F) - Budgen (*Dobell* 44).

5. JH notes that William Dobell's only surviving daughter, Mary, was declared insane in 1773 and the estates at Streat and at Folkington were managed by her husband's family, also her cousins, the Lanes; 250C was perhaps first inscribed soon after 1798, then again after 1805 and finally after 1833; at Mary's death in 1796, the estates passed to Lancelot Harison (see Farrant 222-3).

6. According to his account book, see W.H. Blaauw, 'Streat Place, the ancient mansion of the Dobells' (*SAC* 4 98-9), Dobell paid Mr Blownupp for marble fireplaces in Jan 1714.

Streat, 250C Mural monument for Thomas LANE, d. 1779, and descendants

- North chapel, North wall, above head-height.
- c.87(W) x 197(H) — Excellent.
- M.I. (22 lines, engraved) on a simple unframed panel; in grey slate apron below, a cherub; above, broken pediment in white and grey marbles, with achievement.
- Thomas Lane, Esq., M.D., of Southover, Lewes, d. 1779, aet 74; his wife, Mary, d. 1798, aet 84, daughter of Walter Dobell, merchant of London; their son, Thomas Lane, Esq., of Bradbourne Place, Kent, and of Streat, d. 11 Jun 1805, aet 50; also, his widow, Mary, died at Southampton, 4 Oct 1833.

1. In situ in rebuilt church, see Horsfield (*Sussex* I 233-4), 'neat' and on North chancel wall; Lambarde (*SAC* 71 148) noting arms.

Streat, 250D Ledger for Susannah PENFOLD, d. 1800

- South aisle floor, now obscured by carpet and, in part, built into the restored church.
- (Exposed fragment) 68(W) x 75(L) — Worn.
- M.I. (engraved) on a sandstone slab; head to South.

In Memory of
Susannah
the Wife of Mr. PETER PENFOLD
of Fletching & Daughter of
the late Mr. JOHN MARCHANT
who died July 26th. 1800.
Aged 26 Years.
To name her Virtues ill befits our grief
What was our bliss can now give no relief
Death can't disjoin whom CHRIST hath joined in love
Life leads to death and death to life above,
In heaven's happier place frail things despite
...... in future life the ...
..... expectation therefore we'll wait
... to meet

1. For licence to marry dated 10 Jun 1793 for Peter Penfold, of Chailey, farrier, bachelor, age 22 plus and Susanna Marchant, of Streat, spinster, age 18 plus, consent given by Philadelphia Marchant, mother of Susanna, for whom see 250H, see Dunkin & Penfold (*Licences* 332).

2. For her father see 250F.

Streat, 250E Fragment of a ledger for an anonymous subject

- South aisle floor, near 250D, obscured by carpet.
- 77(W) x 79(L) — Worn, broken.
- Traces of M.I. (engraved) in freestone slab; head to West.
- Illegible.

Streat, 250F Mural monument for John MARCHANT, d. 1793 [Plate 156]
- South aisle, South wall, high up.
- 48(W) x 66(H) — Very good.
- M.I. (engraved) on oval slate panel; rectangular moulded stone frame; floral decoration in corners.
- John Marchant, of Streat, yeoman, d. 25 Jan 1793, aet 66.

1. Pendant with 250H.
2. Lettering variations suggest that 250F and H were perhaps erected after 1798 and 250H engraved after 1805.
3. For John Marchant's properties at Streat, in 1785, see R. Davey (197).

Streat, 250G Mural monument for Richard MARCHANT, d. 1811 [Plate 156]
- South aisle, South wall, high-up, below 250F.
- 104(W) x 67(H) — Cracked, pitted, faded.
- M.I. (engraved) on a rectangular unframed stone tablet.
- Richard Marchant, d. 14 Mar 1811, aet 38; son of John Marchant and Philadelphia; his wife, Emma, d. 25 May 1848, aet 67.

1. For Richard Marchant's parents see 250F and H; M.I. for his wife Emma, added later.

Streat, 250H Mural monument for Philadelphia MARCHANT, d. 1805 [Plate 156]
- South aisle, South wall, high up, alongside 250F-G.
- 48(W) x 66(H) — Very good.
- M.I. as for 250F.
- Philadelphia Marchant, d. 8 Nov 1805, aet 64; wife of John Marchant.

1. Pendant with 250F, for which see comments.

Streat, 250I Fragment of a ledger for an anonymous subject
- South aisle floor, West end, obscured by carpet.
- 78(W) x 63(L) — Worn.
- Traces of M.I. (engraved) in freestone slab; head to West.
- Illegible.

Streat, 250J Ledger stone for Ann TILDEN, d. 1772
- Nave floor, centre.
- 56(W) x 99(L) — Worn, faded.
- M.I. 5 lines, engraved) in centre of a sandstone slab; head to West.
- Ann Tilden, d. 13 Dec 1772, aet 76.

1. Noted by *Gent's Mag* visit dated 1804 in Gomme (324).

Streat, 250K Iron ledger for Sarah SAUNDERS, d. 1731/2
- Nave floor, East of centre.
- 53(W) x 149(L) — Fine.
- M.I. (14 lines, low relief) on 75% of an undecorated cast-iron slab with indented edge; head to West.
- Sarah Saunders, d. 8 Feb 1731/2, aet 56; daughter of Thomas Saunders, Gent., of Wadhurst.

1. Noted by *Gent's Mag* visit dated 1804 in Gomme (323); Willatts (*SAC* 125 101-1, 108) with transcription and comments on lettering; Horsfield (*Sussex* I 233-4) and Nairn & Pevsner (610-11).
2. The M.I. has between 8-10 letters per line, irrespective of word breaks; the digit '8' is especially uncertain.

3. Saunders was from Wadhurst where her family were ironmasters and where members of the family are commemorated by iron slabs (see 270E etc.).

Streat, 250L Iron ledger for Martha GOTT, d. 1732/3, and descendants [Plate 157]

- Nave floor, at chancel step.
- 108(W) x 214(L) — Very good.
- Of unusually large size; M.I. (24 lines, centred) in raised relief on an undecorated cast iron slab.
- Martha Gott, d. 11 Feb 1732/3, aet 78; eldest daughter of Thomas Western, Esq., and widow of Peter Gott, Esq.; issue - third son, Thomas Gott, Esq., d. 19 Mar 1733, aet 49; sixth son, Robert, d. 14 Jan 1714/5, aet 21; surviving - Maximilian, William, Martha, wife of William Hugessen Esq., Mary and Sarah, unmarried; also Elizabeth, d. 27 Aug 1754 aet 75.

1. In situ, in rebuilt church, see *Gent's Mag* visit, dated 1804 in Gomme (324); Horsfield (*Sussex* I 233-4); Nairn & Pevsner (611).
2. For Martha Gott's ancestry see pedigree in Lambarde (*SAC* 68 282-3).
3. The Gotts had briefly been owners of Stanmer, see S. Farrant (*SAC* 117 195-6); Martha Gott's son Samuel sold Stanmer to the Pelhams in 1713.
4. 250L must post-date 1754 when Martha's daughter Elizabeth died; she was heiress of Gott's furnace at Lamberhurst, where 250L must have been made.
5. Willatts (*SAC* 125 102, 108) claims that 250L is the largest cast-iron slab in the UK.

Streat, 250M Ledger for Maria DOBEL, d. 1639/40

- Nave floor, North of chancel step.
- 50(W) x 83(L) — Worn, pitted.
- M.I. (engraved) in West 50% of a freestone slab.

HIC IACET
CORPVS MARIA[E] DO
BEL FILIA GVALTERI
DOBEL ARMIGERI
ET ANNÆ VXORIS
EIVS OBIT 163..
ATAT [sic] 4[?] RESVRGAM

1. Noted by *Gent's Mag* visit dated 1804 in Gomme (324).
2. 250M can be identified with the monument noted in Radcliffe (*SAC* 66 127).
3. For her sister see 250N.
4. No arms appear on 250M, despite armigerous status claimed in the M.I.. .
5. NBI records burial of Mary Dobell on 17 Feb 1640 at Streat.

Streat, 250N Ledger for Barbara DOBEL, d. 1636

- Nave floor, South of chancel step.
- 38(W) x 53(L) — Fine, pitted.
- M.I. (engraved) on a freestone slab; head to West.

HIC IA[CET] CORP
VS BARBARIÆ DO
BEL FILIA GVALT
ERI DOBEL ARMIGE
RI ET ANNÆ UX
ORIS EIVS OBIIT
1636 ATAT [sic] 1 RE
SVRGAM

1. Noted by *Gent's Mag* visit dated 1804 in Gomme (324).
2. Barbara Dobel, an infant daughter of one Walter Dobell; for her sister see 250M; Barbara was buried 26 Nov 1639, see Radcliffe (*SAC* 66 127).

Streat Additions

Cited by Horsfield (*Sussex* I 233-4).

(1) M.I. for Elizabeth Vinal, 24 Oct 1637-26 Jun 1663, wife of William Vinal, of Kingston, Gent., married 19 Jun 1655; daughter of Walter and Ann Dobell.

(2) Walter Dobell, armiger, d. 5 Jun 1661, aet 53.

Noted by *Gent's Mag* of 1804 in Gomme (324).

(3) Mrs Elizabeth Cogger, d. 25 Aug 1753, aet 74, related to the Gotts of Streat;

(4) John Sixsmith, 1729, aet 16.

(5) An iron slab for Mrs Mary Gott, spinster, daughter of Peter and Martha Gott, d. 13 Jul 1768, aet 77 (perhaps in confusion with 250L).

(254) TARRING NEVILLE, St. Mary

An Early English church - Nairn & Pevsner (611); in 1724 it was reported that the chancel was in poor condition (Ford 1182); the parish had 11 families in 1724 and a population of 74 in 1801; members of the Geere family were parsons and land-occupiers at Tarring Neville through several generations (1785 - R. Davey 197); they also held Pett (see List of Rectors at Pett church: 1750 - Augustin Diones Geere; 1774 - Diones Geere); not all of them were wholly virtuous - in 1675, a churchwarden at Rottingdean presented one Dionys Geere as a non-attender at church, see Johnstone (18), and C. Brent (84) notes that someone of that name was charged with assault in the 1790s; note the grave markers for the daughters of the Rev. Dionis Geere II in front of the main altar: 'E.G.', 'A.G.', 'M.G.' and 'G.G.'.

Tarring Neville, 254A Ledger for Diones GEERE and his wife Dina, both d. 1743 [Plate 158]

- Chancel floor, centre.
- 101(W) x 200(L) — Very good.
- M.I. (19 lines, engraved) fills a black slab; head to West.
- Diones Geere, of Hayton [sic], d. 5 Jul 1743, aet 69; son of (also) Diones Geere, late of Rottingdean; his wife Dina, d. 29 Dec 1743, aet 60; only son and heir, Rev. Dionysius Geere.

1. M.I. given in Horsfield (*Sussex* I 335).
2. The patron of 254A (after 1743) was the son, Rev. Dionysius Geere (see 254B), who was 34 when his parents died.
3. 234A is a spectacular ledger; a finger points to the actual place of burial of Dina Geere; the flourishes or 'striking' in the final line are without rival in East Sussex.

Tarring Neville, 254B Wall-mounted ledger for Rev. Diones GEERE, d. 1764, his wife Grace, d. 1794, and children

- Chancel North wall.
- 92(W) x 169(H) — Very good.
- M.I. (20 lines, engraved) in upper 80% of a black slab (slate?); moulded stone top set into wall.
- Rev. Diones Geere, rector of South Heighton cum Tarring Neville and rector of Pett, d. 30 Sep 1764, aet 55; his wife, Grace, d. 3 Mar 1794, aet 79; issue - Elizabeth, d. 30 May 1762, aet 16, Anne Tooby, née Geere, d. 25 Sep 1797, aet 50; Grace, d. 30 Jun 1805, aet 54; and Mary, d. 18 Nov 1809 aet 54.

1. M.I. given in Horsfield (*Sussex* I 335).
2. 254B was perhaps commissioned following the death of Elizabeth Geere in 1762.
3. Perhaps wall-mounted as a consequence of 19th-century work in the choir.

(255) TELSCOMBE (VILLAGE), St. Laurence

Nave and chancel Norman, North aisle and chapel added in late 12th century - Nairn & Pevsner (611); VCH (VII 77); a view from North-East, isolated in downland in Godfrey & Salzman (Pl. 160); unpaved North aisle, chancel fine in 1686 (Ford 38); parish had 6 families in 1724 and a population of 89 in 1801.

Telscombe (Village), 255A Floor monument for Susanna POVEY, d. 1703

- Against North wall, near North-East chapel.
- 99(W) x 180(L) — Worn, pitted.
- M.I. (3 lines, engraved) in upper 40% of a blacked up freestone slab; head to North.
- Susanna Povey, d. 13 Dec 1703; daughter of Sir Orn[?] Biron, Bart.; and wife of [Josiah] Povey, clergyman.

1. Formerly in chancel floor - Horsfield (*Sussex* I 191).
2. Josiah Povey, d. 1727, was rector of Telscombe 1697 - 1727 and curate of Rodmell 1715-25; he left provision for teaching the children of Telscombe; Caffyn (1998 249); Josiah's brother was Charles Povey (c.1651-1743), writer and entrepreneur (biography by Mark G. Spencer in *ODNB*).
3. No details of Sir O. Biron, Bart. have been traced, and as far as can be ascertained, there has never been a baronet with this name (Biron or Byron).
4. Note high quality lettering on the M.I.
5. JH notes that Susanna Biron married Charles Legard on 7 Jan 1685 at St. Katherine Creechurch, London. Presumably Charles Legard died, as Susanna Legard married Joshua [sic] Povey on 6 Nov 1695 at St. Martins-in-the-Fields, London.

Telscombe (Village), 255B Mural monument for Rev. Thomas and Elizabeth HIGGINS, d. 1787 and 1800

- On North wall, North-East corner.
- 110(W) x 210(H) — Very good.
- Above, a black obelisk with scrolled escutcheon; grey-veined cornice over M.I. (8 + 4 lines, engraved, black) filling unframed tablet on grey scrolled brackets; final 4 lines added after 1800.
- Rev. Thomas Higgins, A.M., rector of Telscombe and vicar of Piddinghoe, d. 15 Jun 1787, aet 46; his widow, Elizabeth, d. 30 Jan 1800, aet 64, daughter of Rev. Hugh Colley.

1. Formerly on chancel South wall - Horsfield (*Sussex* I 191).
2. In situ in 1930 - Lambarde (*SAC* 71 140) noting arms.
3. For Rev Hugh Colley see 255C.

Telscombe (Village), 255C Mural monument for Rev. Hugh COLLEY, d. 1779

- North wall, North-East corner, East of 258B.
- 87(W) x 144(H) — Sound; faded.
- Above, a grey-veined point pediment; M.I. (10 lines shallow engraved) on white tablet set portrait-wise; yellowish frame; grey-veined base mouldings; curved apron; single corbel.

In Memory of
the Revd Hugh Colley A.M.
Who was many years rector of this Parish
and Vicar of Peddinghoe
He died on the first Day of March 1779
in the 75th Year of his Age
Blessed are the Dead, who die in
the Lord, yea, saith the Spirit
from henceforth, for they rest from their
labours and their Works do follow them

1. Formerly on chancel North wall - Horsfield (*Sussex* I 191).
2. JH notes that Hugh Colley was rector of Telscombe and vicar of Piddinghoe 1740-79.

Telscombe (Village), 255D Ledger for Thomas CREW, d. 1782
- Chancel floor, at steps.
- 215(W) x 96(H) — Sound; worn; faded.
- M.I. (9 lines, engraved) fills very long, pale freestone slab, set landscape-wise.

Beneath this Stone are deposited the Remains

of M[r] T<small>HOS</small>. C<small>REW</small> who Died the 27th Dec[r]

1782 Aged 48 Years

Likewise the Remains of M[rs] H<small>ONNOR</small> E<small>LIZ</small>[H] D<small>AY</small>

who departed this Life on the 30th April 1815

in the 75th Year of Her Age

Likewise the remains of M[r] R<small>ICHARD</small> D<small>AY</small>

who departed this Life on the 26th Oct[r] 1816

in the 77th Year of His Age

1. Formerly on chancel South wall - Horsfield (*Sussex* I 191).
2. For Thomas Crew, see 258E.

Telscombe (Village), 255E Mural monument for Thomas CREW, d. 1782, and others
- Nave, South wall, West of chancel arch, at head height.
- 90(W) x 158(H) — Very good.
- Above, urn in relief; below, M.I. fills unframed oval tablet; black baseplate follows contour of whole composition; signed (on corbel): 'A.LAMBERT / Brighton'.
- Thomas Crew, d. 27 Dec 1782, aet 48; his wife, Honnor Elizabeth, d. 30 Apr 1815, aet 74; her second husband, Richard Day, d. 26 Oct 1816, aet 76.

1. TPQ for 255E is 1816.
2. No other monument is signed by A. Lambert in East Sussex survey, although 195A is signed W. Lambert & Son (after 1829).

(258) TICEHURST, St. Mary
Mostly of the 14th century - Nairn & Pevsner (612), VCH (IX 256); for a view of 1785 see Godfrey & Salzman (Pl. 161) from South-East; a 1686 report noted that the great chancel belonging to Mr Hartridge was in poor repair and Mr Apsley's and another smaller chancel also needed some work (Ford 116); the sanctuary paving was still poor in 1724; some of the May monuments are unidentifiable; one Thomas May ordered his own burial in the South chapel in 1551, see Rice & Godfrey (4 238), another was lord of the manor in 1785 (see R. Davey); for the earlier ancestral history of the many Roberts commemorated at Ticehurst see Tittler; see Willatts (*SAC* 125 102) for the iron slabs here; the parish had 150 families in 1724 and a population of 1436 in 1801.

Ticehurst, 258A Ledger for Rev. Thomas LORD, d. 1729, his widow Hannah, d. 1750 and daughter Hannah, d. 1796
- North aisle floor, by North door.
- 100(W) x 195(L) — Very worn; right corner lost.
- M.I. (engraved) on a black slab; head to North.
- Rev. Thomas Lord, vicar of Ticehurst, d. 4 Nov 1729, aet 62; his widow, Hannah, d. 30 May 1750 aet 88; their daughter, Hannah, d. Jun 1796.

1. Noted by Hodson & Odell (70) with transcription.
2. Thomas Lord was vicar from 1718.

Ticehurst, 258B Ledger for Rev. Ossory MEDLICOTT, d. 1770

- Nave floor, opposite North door.
- 100(W) x 201(L) — Very worn.
- M.I. on black slab; head to North.

Beneath lie[th]
The Revd Ossory Medlicott A.M.
Vicar of this Pariſh
who died May [22] 1770
Aged [85]

...
...
...

1. Noted by Hodson & Odell (70) with transcription.
2. JH notes that Ossory Medlicott was MA of Trinity College, Dublin, see Burtchaell & Sadleir (2 572). He was vicar of Ticehurst 1738/9-70 (CCEd).
3. NBI records the burial of Ossory Medlicott on 26 May 1770 at Ticehurst.

Ticehurst, 258C Anonymous floor slab

- North aisle floor.
- 54(W) x 104(L) — Very worn; damaged edges; local losses (lower right corner).
- M.I. (engraved) in brown freestone; head to East.

To the [Memory of] ...
W[?]ILL[IAM] ..... [W]L[S]
B......
.....
.....
.....RM
Lye[TH?]
N....

Ticehurst, 258D Ledger for Dame Elizabeth COURTHOPE, d. 1690

- North-East (Courthope) Chapel floor, near North aisle, partly obscured by furnishings.
- 85(W) x 171(L) — Damaged edges; local loss (South-East corner).
- M.I. (6 lines engraved) in upper 30% of a black slab; head to North.
- Dame Elizabeth Courthope, d. 18 Dec 1690, aet 67; wife of Sir George Courthope.

1. Noted by Horsfield (*Sussex* I 592) and Hodson & Odell (63) with transcription.
2. Courthopes of Whiligh (between Ticehurst and Wadhurst) were associated with that property from 1512 (Farrant 321) and were buried in this chapel for more than 400 years (Church Guide p.11); for their property at Ticehurst in 1720 and 1796, see Steer (10 & 23).
3. A view of Whiligh, South front, 1874 in Godfrey & Salzman (Pl. 163); Whiligh is a building now much enlarged.
4. JH notes that Elizabeth was daughter of Henry Hawes, merchant, of London, see Henning (2 146).

Ticehurst, 258E Mural monument for Sir George COURTHOPE, d. 1685

- North-East (Courthope) chapel, North wall, West side, above head height.
- 85(W) x 131(H) — Fine; local losses.
- M.I. (engraved, Latin) fills a black tablet set portrait-wise; scrolled and foliate alabaster frame flanking; above, moulded cornice with broken scrolled pediment and achievement; below, base moulding and shallow apron with scrolled decoration.
- Sir George Courthope, d. 18 Nov 1685.

1. Noted by Horsfield (*Sussex* I 592) and by Hodson & Odell (62) with transcription; for heraldry see Lambarde (*SAC* 69 150).
2. M.I. cites George Courthope's loyalty to the Stuarts and his court service, see Courthope (*SAC* 51 65-98 and edited by S.C. Lomas published by RHS; note the similarity between final lines of his

memoir, written in 1679, and the text of the M.I. which suggests that the M.I. was written by George Courthope himself (transcribed at p. 95); 258E was erected in the subject's own lifetime and is perhaps by the same maker as 258F; George Courthope's wife was Elizabeth Hawes (they married in 1643); issue - 4 sons (2 died as infants) and 2 daughters; George Courthope gave the church a very large silver flagon dated 1684 (Church Guide 16).

3. Sir George (knighted in 1661) was MP for Sussex in 1656, and for East Grinstead in 1659, 1660 and 1661; he was JP for Sussex 1646-9 and Deputy Lieutenant 1660-85, see Henning (2 146).

Ticehurst, 258F Mural monument for Sir George, d. 1642, and Lady Alice COURTHOPE [Plate 159]

- North-East (Courthope) chapel, North wall, East of 258E, above head height.
- 90(W) x (H) inaccessible — Good.
- M.I. (engraved, Latin) fills a black tablet set portrait-wise; alabaster frame; flanked by scrolls; beneath, foliage; above, an unusual arched entablature with frieze and cornice supporting a generous achievement.
- Sir George Courthope, d. 12 Oct 1642; his wife Alice, daughter of George Rivers, of Chafford, Kent.

1. Noted by Horsfield (*Sussex* I 592) and by Hodson & Odell (62) with transcription; for heraldry see Lambarde (*SAC* 69 150).
2. The patron of 258F is the subject of 258E; 258E and F by same maker?
3. This George Courthope was knighted in 1641 and was grandson of John Courthope who had inherited the Whiligh estate from his father-in-law in 1512.

Ticehurst, 258G Mural monument for George and Albinia COURTHOPE, d. 1714 and 1717 [Plate 160]

- North-East (Courthope) chapel, East wall, South of East window, above head height.
- 90(W) x (H) inaccessible — Good.
- A cartouche with scrolled frame; above, a generous achievement; M.I. (engraved, black) fills both cartouche and ornamental apron.
- George Courthope, Esq., late of Whiligh in Ticehurst, d. 13 Sep 1714, aet 68, eldest son of Sir George Courthope, Knt; his widow, Albinia, d. 11 Jun 1717, eldest daughter of Sir William Eliot, of Busbridge, Surrey; their only son, George Courthope, Esq.

1. Noted by Horsfield (*Sussex* I 592), Nairn & Pevsner (612) and Hodson & Odell (63) with transcription; for heraldry see Lambarde (*SAC* 69 150).
2. For the Courthopes see 258D-G.
3. A daughter, Frances, d. 1723, aet 14.
4. The herald John Le Neve (*Monumenta Anglicana*, 1717-19) notes that Thomas Green (c.1659 - c.1730) supplied him with the M.I. for 258G, hence the attribution given in Gunnis (*Dict.* 179) and see too Clive Easter, 'Notes on the Monuments and Career of Thomas Green of Camberwell: some recent Discoveries' (*Church Monuments* XVI 2001 75).

Ticehurst, 258H Ledger for Samuel NEWINGTON, d. 1754, his widow Anne, d. 1757

- Floor between North-East (Courthope) chapel and chancel.
- 98(W) x 188(L) — Damaged edges; a hole (near East end).
- M.I. (engraved) in upper 80% of a slab in an unusual dark grey stone; head to West.

Here lieth the Body of
SAMUEL NEWINGTON
Surgeon of this Pariſh who
departed this Life *December* yᵉ 2
1754 Aged 37 Years and 6 Months
Here also lieth the Body
of *ANNE* Reli[ct] of the afoeſaid
SAMUEL NEWINGTON
who was Afterwards Married

to *THOMAS HUNTLEY*
on Saturday Oct. 2ⁿᵈ 1756 and
Died Saturday Feb 26ᵗʰ 1757
Aged 36 Years and 6 Months

1. In situ? - Horsfield (*Sussex* I 592).
2. Cited by Hodson & Odell (64) with transcription.
3. The Newington family shared burial rights in the North-East chapel with the Courthopes and the Astleys.
4. Samuel Newington took Richard Winch as an apprentice in Dec 1746, see Rice (210).
5. Sussex Marriage Index records the marriage of Thomas Huntley and Ann Newington, widow, on 2 Oct 1756 and NBI records burial of Ann Huntley on 5 Mar 1757 and Samuel Newington on 6 Dec 1754, both at Ticehurst.

Ticehurst, 258I Ledger for Mary EDGAR, d. 1710
- Chancel floor, East of choir stalls, next to 258H.
- 100.5(W) x 201(L) — Fine; scratched.
- M.I. (12 lines, engraved) of unusually large lettering in upper 80% of a black slab; head to West.
- Mary Edgar, d. 7 Jul 1710, aet 86; daughter of Thomas Woodcock, Esq., of Newtimber; widow of her first husband, William Hartridge, Gent., buried Ticehurst; and widow of her second husband, Myles Edgar, Gent., buried Ticehurst.

1. Cited by Hodson & Odell (65) with transcription.
2. NBI records burial of William Hartridge on 30 Apr 1687, Miles Edgar on 27 Jan 1708 and Mary Edgar on 12 Jul 1710, all at Ticehurst.

Ticehurst, 258J Ledger for Samuel ROBERTS, d. 1783, and his wife Martha, d. 1815
- Chancel floor, South of 258I.
- 100(W) x 202(L) — Good.
- Arms, then M.I. (9 lines, engraved) in upper 80% of a black slab; head to West.
- Samuel Roberts, Esq., of Borzell, d. 9 Dec 1783, aet 55; his wife, Martha, d. 18 Feb 1815, aet 87.

1. Cited by Hodson & Odell (65) with transcription.
2. For a view of Boarzell in 1783, a house now destroyed, see Godfrey & Salzman (Pl. 162).
3. Heraldry not listed by Lambarde.

Ticehurst, 258K Mural monument for John ROBERTS, d. 1810
- Sanctuary, North wall, above head height.
- c.90(W); (H) unknown — Fine.
- M.I. (8 lines (4 + 4), engraved, black) in upper 60% of an unframed grey marble tablet set landscape-wise on a small corbel; above, backplate with escutcheon.
- John Roberts, Esq., of Borzell, d. 5 Feb 1810, aet 52; only son, (also) John Roberts, Esq., d. 7 Apr 1839, aet 40.

1. Cited by Hodson & Odell (65) with transcription.
2. For heraldry see Lambarde (*SAC* 69 149).

Ticehurst, 258L Ledger for Robert COLES, d. 1697
- Chancel floor, West of sanctuary rail.
- 66(W) x 38(L) — Very worn; scaling.
- M.I. (engraved) fills a small black slab.
- Robert Coles, d. 14 Sep 1697, aet 25; son of Dr Gilbert Coles and Mary.

1. Cited by Hodson & Odell (65) with transcription.

Ticehurst, 258M Ledger for John ROBERTS, d. 1741 [Plate 161]
- Chancel floor, centre, West of sanctuary rail, between 258J and N.
- 101(W) x 201(L) — Stained; cracked (centre).
- Arms, then M.I. (7 lines, engraved) on a splendid white slab, veined grey; head to West.
- John Roberts, of Bozell, d. 21 Mar 1741, aet 29; son of John Roberts Jnr, Esq., and Lucy.

1. Noted by Horsfield (*Sussex* I 592) and Hodson & Odell (65) with transcription; Lambarde does not note heraldry.
2. This material is highly unusual in this survey.
3. John Roberts, the father, is designated Junior and Esq.; John Roberts, the son, is not designated 'esq'.
4. Note spelling of 'Bozell' c.f. 258N and Q.

Ticehurst, 258N Ledger for John ROBERTS, d. 1732
- Chancel floor, next to 258M.
- 102(W) x 199(L) — Fine.
- M.I. (engraved) in a black slab; head to West.
- John Roberts, Esq., of Bozell in Ticehurst, d. 22 Oct 1732, aet 46; son of John Roberts, Esq. and Bridget.

1. Noted by Horsfield (*Sussex* I 592) and Hodson & Odell (64) with transcription; for heraldry see Lambarde (*SAC* 69 149).

Ticehurst, 258O Ledger for Mary ROBERTS, d. 1666
- Chancel floor, South of 258L, against sanctuary rail.
- 74(W) x 185(L) — Worn.
- A space at upper end, then M.I. (10 + 5 lines, engraved) in remainder of a brown freestone slab; head to North.
- Mary Roberts, d. 20 Jul 1666 and buried 24 Jul; second daughter of John Busbridge, Esq., of Etchingham; and wife of Walter Roberts, Esq., of Ticehurst; also their son, Edmund, buried 5 Dec 1666.

1. Sussex Marriage Index records the marriage of Walter Roberts and Mary Busbridge on 9 Jun 1653 at Ticehurst.

Ticehurst, 258P Ledger for Anna ROBARTES, d. 1658/9
- Chancel floor, South of 258N.
- 51(W) x 102(L) — Fine.
- M.I. (7 lines, engraved) in upper 50% of a small black slab; head to West.
- Anna Robartes, d. 16 Feb 1658/9, an infant; only daughter of Walter Robartes.

1. A small ledger, for an infant.
2. Cited by Hodson & Odell (64) with transcription.

Ticehurst, 258Q Ledger for John ROBERTS, d. 1728
- Chancel floor, near and South of 258P.
- 101(W) x 202(L) — Fine.
- Arms, then M.I. (11 lines, engraved) fills a black slab; head to West.
- John Roberts, Esq., of Bozell in Ticehurst, d. 30 Mar 1728, aet 65; his wife, Bridgett, daughter of Samuel Boys, Esq., of Elford in Hawkhurst; issue - Mary, John, and Walter.

1. Noted by Horsfield (*Sussex* I 592) and Hodson & Odell (65) with transcription; for heraldry see Lambarde (*SAC* 69 149).

Ticehurst, 258R Ledger for John and Thomas ROBERTS, d. 1661 and 1664/5
- Chancel floor, South of 258O.
- 65(W) x 133(L) — Fine.

- M.I. (7 lines engraved, then space, then 7 lines, engraved) on a brown freestone slab; head to North.
- John Roberts, d. 6 May 1661 and buried 10 May; son of Walter Roberts, Esq., of Ticehurst; his brother, Thomas, d. 10 Mar 166[4/5] and buried 15 Mar.

1. Cited by Hodson & Odell (64) with transcription.
2. Like 258O, in style and lettering.
3. JH notes the poor carving of year date for Thomas Roberts but NBI records burial of John Roberts on 18[sic] May 1661 and Thomas Roberts on 15 Mar 1665, both at Ticehurst.

Ticehurst, 258S Ledger for Edward MAY, d. 1685
- South-East (or Pashley) chapel floor, North-East side, carpeted over.
- 95(W) x 197(L) — Deep exfoliation; lettering lost.
- M.I. (engraved) on a black slab with a diagonal white vein.
- Edward May, d. 7 Nov 1685, aet 22; son of Edward May of Pashley.

1. Noted by Horsfield (*Sussex* I 592) and Hodson & Odell (66-7) with transcription.
2. Pashley Manor, between Etchingham and Ticehurst, was sold to one Thomas May in 1543 but passed to the Wetheralls in 1795 when Caroline May married the Rev. Richard Wetherall; the Mays were buried in this chapel, starting with 258Y.
3. Note licence to marry for Edward May, of Ticehurst, and Elizabeth Paine, of Lewes, spinster 8 Sep 1683; Edward May soon died too, young, see Dunkin (*Licences 1670-1729* 78).
4. NBI records burial of Edward May on 10 Nov 1685 at Ticehurst.

Ticehurst, 258T Ledger for Francis MAY, d. 1759, and his wife Mary, d. 1782
- South-East (or Pashley) chapel floor, West side, carpeted over.
- 100(W) x 200(L) — Fine.
- Arms, then M.I. (engraved) in upper 60% of a black slab; head to West.
- Francis May, Esq., of Pashley in Ticehurst, d. 23 May 1759, aet 42; his widow, Mary, d. 12 Nov 1782, aet 68.

1. Noted by Horsfield (*Sussex* I 592) and Hodson & Odell (67) with transcription; for heraldry see Lambarde (*SAC* 69 150).
2. For family, see comments under 258V.

Ticehurst, 258U Ledger for Anne MAY, d. 1694
- South-East (or Pashley) chapel floor, next to and South of 258T, carpeted over, obscured by furnishings.
- 92(W) x 186(L) — Fine.
- Arms, then M.I. (engraved) fills surface of a black slab; head to West.
- Anne May, d. 10 Apr 1694, aet 74; daughter of John Shephard, Gent., of London; and widow of Edward May, Esq., of Pashley; their issue - Susanna.

1. Noted by Horsfield (*Sussex* I 592) and Hodson & Odell (65) with transcription; Lambarde (*SAC* 69 150) cites heraldry which is now obscured.
2. For family, see 258S.
3. Patron is Anne May's daughter (Dame) Susanna May 258S.

Ticehurst, 258V Ledger for Susanna and Mary MAY, d. 1754 and d. 1761
- South-East (or Pashley) chapel floor, next to and South of 258W, carpeted over.
- 91(W) x 198(L) — Condition unknown.
- Black slab with indents for lost brasses.
- Susanna May, d. 22 Apr 1754, aet 9; and Mary May, d. 4 May 1761, aet 13; both daughters of Francis and Mary May.

1. Noted by Hodson & Odell (67) with transcription.
2. For Francis and Mary May see 258T.

Ticehurst, 258W Ledger for Dame Susanna MAY, d. 1718

- South-East (or Pashley) chapel floor, East of centre, carpeted over.
- 89(W) x 186(L) — Worn.
- M.I. on a black slab; head to West.
- Dame Susanna May, of Pashley, d. 9 Aug 1718, aet 64; daughter of Edward May, Esq., of Ticehurst; and widow of Sir Richard May, Knt.

1. Noted by Horsfield (*Sussex* I 592) and Hodson & Odell (67) with transcription; Lambarde does not describe heraldry, which is here displayed on a lozenge, signifying that it is for a woman.
2. For family, see 258Z.

Ticehurst, 258X Ledger for Frances SCAFE and Eleanora HOLLIST, both d. 1819

- South-East (or Pashley) chapel floor, North-East corner, under carpet.
- Dimensions unknown but standard size — Stained; very worn; cracked.
- M.I. (engraved) on a brown freestone slab.

> IN MEMORY OF
> FRANCES AND ELEONORA
> [DA]UGHTERS OF THE LATE
> [THOMAS] MAY OF PASHLEY ESQUIRE
> FRANCES RELICT OF
> JOHN SCAFE ESQUIRE
> BARRISTER AT LAW
> OBIIT JUNE XXII MDCCCXIX
> AGED LXVII YEARS
> ELEONORA RELICT OF
> [RICH]ARD HOLLIST ESQUIRE
> [ONE OF] HIS MAJESTYS COUNSEL
> AND A BENCHER [OF]
> [THE] HONOURABLE SOCIETY
> [OF] THE MIDDLE TEMPLE
> [OBIIT] JULY II MDCCC[XIX]
> AGED [L]XXII YEARS

1. Cited by Hodson & Odell (66) with transcription.
2. Two sisters reached old age and died within ten days of each other.
3. NBI records burial of Frances Scaife[sic] on 26 Jun 1819 and Eleanor Hollist on 6 Jul 1819, both at Ticehurst.

Ticehurst, 258Y Wall-mounted brasses for Adrian MAY, d. 1653

- South-East (or Pashley) chapel, East wall, near North-East corner, at head height.
- Arms: 24(W) x 27(H); M.I.: 52(W) x 20(H) — Polished; worn.
- M.I. (engraved) on 2 rectangular brasses; mounted on a slate(?) slab.
- Adrian May, Gent., d. 19 Dec 1653, aet 24; second son of Anthony May, Esq., of Pashley in Ticehurst.

1. Noted by Horsfield (*Sussex* I 592) and Hodson & Odell (65) with transcription; for heraldry see Lambarde (*SAC* 69 150).
2. In situ in Davidson-Houston (*SAC* 80 118).
3. For family, see 258S.
4. 258Y appears to be the earliest May monument in the family chapel.

Ticehurst, 258Z Slab for anonymous member of MAY family, date unknown

- South-East (or Pashley) chapel floor, against South wall, partly obscured by furnishings.
- 64(W) x 187(L) — Worn.
- Arms (cast relief) on a cast iron slab.
- Edward May, d. 28 Jul 1692, aet 6; and Anne May, d. 22 May 1693, a few days old; both issue of Sir Richard May, Knt., and Dame Susanna.

1. Noted by Hodson & Odell (67) with transcription; cited by Willatts (*SAC* 125 105) as a rare case of arms unaccompanied by a M.I.; noted in Nairn & Pevsner (612) and cited by Lambarde (*SAC* 69 150).
2. Arms identified as those of May (Church Guide and Lambarde).
3. For Dame Susanna May see 258W.

Ticehurst, 258AA Wall-mounted ledger for Henry MAY, d. 1795
- South-East (or Pashley) chapel, South wall.
- 101(W) x 210(H) — Fine.
- Arms (very large) and M.I. (5 lines, engraved) on a black ledger now supported by a stone ledge with brackets; arrowhead decoration in corners.
- Henry May, Esq., of Pashley, d. 6 Jun 1795, aet 43; younger son of Francis and Mary May.

1. Cited by Hodson & Odell (66) with transcription.
2. It is unclear why this May ledger has been wall-mounted.
3. Lambarde does not list heraldry.

Ticehurst, 258BB Ledger for Walter ROBERTS, d. 1699/1700
- Chancel floor, between choir stalls.
- 100(W) x 200(L) — Worn.
- Arms, then M.I. (14 lines, engraved) fills a black slab; head to West.
- Walter Roberts, Esq., of Bozell in Ticehurst, d. 15 Mar 1699/1700, aet 44; his first wife, Lucy, daughter of Robert Fowle, Esq., of Eridge, Salehurst; no issue; his second wife, also Lucy, daughter of Walter Dobell, Esq., of Streat; their issue - a daughter, Lucy.

1. Noted by Hodson & Odell (65) with transcription.
2. For licence to marry for Walter Roberts, Jnr, of Ticehurst, Gent. and Lucy Fowle of Salehurst 14 Apr 1684, see Dunkin (*Licences 1670-1729* 82).

Ticehurst, 258CC Anonymous ledger, date unknown
- Chancel floor, immediately West of 258BB.
- 97(W) x 190(L) — Stained; very worn.
- M.I. (engraved) in brown freestone slab.
- Illegible.

Ticehurst, 258DD Ledger for Joseph NEWINGTON, d. 1790
- Nave floor, centre aisle, at entrance to chancel.
- 92(W) x 183(L) — Stained; very worn.
- Arms, then M.I. (18 lines, engraved) on a brown freestone slab.
- Joseph Newington, Gent., of Withernden, Ticehurst, d. 7? Mar 1790, aet 83; his wife, Mary, d. 28 Dec 1776, aet 71, daughter of Joseph Tompset, of Ticehurst; their issue - 5 sons and 5 daughters including - Zebulon, Mary, Samuel, Sarah, Benjamin, Elizabeth, Ann; 18 grandchildren; 6 great grandchildren.

1. Formerly in North chancel, Horsfield (*Sussex* I 592), with dates for wife Mary (d. 1788, aet 72).
2. Not noted in Hodson & Odell.
3. The 1785 tax return describes Joseph Newington as owner of Wishenden (R. Davey 201).
4. Lambarde does not mention the heraldry.

Ticehurst, 258EE Ledger for Benjamin DRY, d. 1719
- Nave floor, centre aisle, towards East end.
- 100(W) x 197(L) — Good.
- Arms, then M.I. (6 lines engraved) in upper 50% of a black slab; head to West.
- Benjamin Dry, Esq., d. 14 Jul 1719, aet 62.

1. Noted in Hodson & Odell (67) with transcription.
2. Lambarde does not mention the heraldry.

Ticehurst, 258FF Ledger for Henry APSLEY, d. 1692

- Nave floor, centre aisle, West of 258EE.
- 96(W) x 198(L) — Fine.
- Arms, then M.I. (4 lines, engraved) in upper 50% of a black slab; head to West.
- Henry Apsley, Esq., d. 19 Feb 1692, aet 42.

1. Formerly in the North-East chapel, Horsfield (*Sussex* I 592), a burial space shared with the Newingtons and Courthopes.
2. Noted in Hodson & Odell (64) with transcription.
3. Apsleys were lords of the manor of Hammerden, from 1605 until well into 18th century (Church Guide 11).
4. Lambarde does not mention the heraldry.

Ticehurst, 258GG Anonymous ledger, date unknown

- Nave floor, West of crossing.
- 78(W) x 168(L) — Stained; very worn.
- Traces of M.I. (engraved) on brown freestone slab.
- Illegible.

Ticehurst, 258HH Ledger for John SPRINGETT, d. 1826

- Nave floor, cross aisle, South side.
- 119(W) x 193(L) — Stained; worn; local losses.
- M.I. (engraved) on a brown freestone slab, set landscape-wise; head to West.
- John Springett, of Rowley in Ticehurst, d. 23 Apr 1816, aet 72; his wife, Ann, d. 21 Feb 1844, aet 89.

1. Noted in Hodson & Odell (70) with transcription.

Ticehurst, 258II Ledger for Samuel BEALY, d. 1636

- Nave floor, cross aisle, South of 258HH.
- 93(W) x 217(L) — Very worn; local losses.
- M.I. (4 lines, engraved) on upper parts of a freestone slab.

HERE LIETH [I]NTERRED THE
BODY OF S[AM]UEL BEALY BATCHELOR
IN DIV[INITY W]HOE DECEASED THE
SIX DAY [OF AUGU]ST ANNO DOM ...

1. Noted by Hodson & Odell (70) with transcription.
2. Other lines have been lost.
3. JH notes that Samuel Beeley, BD (various spellings) was vicar of Newchurch, Romney, 1612-16, and vicar of Ticehurst, 1614-36, see Foster (*Al Ox* 1 1 101).
4. NBI records burial of Samuel Beal on 23 Aug 1636 at Ticehurst.

Ticehurst, 258JJ Ledger for Hannah PAGET, d. 1823

- South aisle floor, near West end.
- 72(W) x 186(L) — Worn.
- Traces of M.I. (engraved) on a pale brown freestone slab; head to West.

SACRED
TO THE MEMORY OF
M^{RS} H.... PAGET
WHO D[EPARTED] THIS LIFE
ON ... BRUARY

...

1. NBI records burial of Hannah Paget on 17 Feb 1823 at Ticehurst.

Ticehurst, 258KK Mural monument for Samuel NEWINGTON, d. 1811
- South aisle, West wall, near South-West corner, above head height.
- 91(W) x 79(H) — Fine; local cracks (upper parts).
- M.I. (engraved) in upper 50% of a white marble tablet, unframed.
- Samuel Newington, of Ticehurst, d. 8 Jul 1811, aet 72.

1. Noted in Hodson & Odell (68) with transcription.

Ticehurst, 258LL Mural monument for Christopher GAWTHROP, d. 1792, his wife Eliza, d. 1795
- Nave, West wall, South of tower arch, high up.
- Inaccessible — Fine.
- In freestone, M.I. (engraved) on an unframed tablet, breaking forward; above, an entablature and a pointed pediment supporting an urn in relief; below, base mouldings, then 2 scrolled brackets against the engraved baseplate.
- Rev. Christopher Gawthrop, B.D., fellow of Lincoln College, Oxford and vicar of Ticehurst, d. 25 Mar 1792, aet 58; his widow, Eliza, d. 19 May 1795.

1. Noted in Hodson & Odell (68) with transcription.
2. Erected by widow of Christopher Gawthrop.
3. Vicar at Ticehurst from 1776-92, he occupied the Parsonage in 1785 (R. Davey 199).

Ticehurst Additions:
Noted by Horsfield (*Sussex* I 592):
(1) William Roberts, of Bozell, Esq., d. 1750.
(2) Zebulon Apsley, d. 1768, aet 92 (see 258DD).
(3) Thomas Newington, d. 1802, aet 89.
(4) Edward May, son of Richard, d. 1692, aet 6 (for Richard May see 258W)
(5) Anne May, daughter of Richard, d. 1693 (for Richard May see 258W)
(6) Susanna May, daughter of Francis, d. 1754, aet 9 (for Francis May see 258T and 258AA)
(7) Mary May, daughter of Francis, aet 13? (for Francis May see 258T and 258AA)

(263) TWINEHAM, St. Peter
Early Tudor brick - Nairn & Pevsner (614); repaired and some pews rebuilt in 1721, see Turner (*SAC* 18 154); reportedly in very good condition in 1724 (Ford 155) when there were 26 families; a population of 238 in 1801; Horsfield (*Sussex* I 248) makes a general reference to the Stapley slabs here; the Stapleys, long established at Twineham, included amongst their number Anthony, one of five Sussex MPs to vote in favour of the execution of Charles I in 1648/90; the will of one Richard Stapley of 1546 included the words: 'I will yt the greater stone to be laid upon me and the lesser stone upon my wiff', see Rice & Godfrey (4 261).

Twineham, 263A Mural monument for Richard STAPLEY, d. 1762, and his wife Martha, d. 1793
- South chancel-arch buttress, facing West, above head height.
- 100(W) x 198(H) — Good; local losses (top decoration); fading.
- M.I. (engraved, black) on a cream, oval tablet; black obelisk as backplate; above, arms; below, base mouldings.
- Richard Stapley, of Hickstead, d. 30 Jan 1762, aet 48; his wife, Martha, d. 3 Feb 1793, aet 86.

1. In situ, see photograph in Grayling (*SAC* 59 115); Lambarde (*SAC* 71 157) noting arms.
2. For the diary 1682-1724 of a great-uncle of this Richard Stapley of Hickstead see E. Turner, '... The Diary of Richard Stapley ...' (*SAC* 2 102-128) which includes a genealogy of the family; continued in

Turner (*SAC* 18 151-162) where the diary is taken over by this Richard Stapley in 1743.
3. NBI records the burial of Richard Stapley on 4 Feb 1762 and Martha Stapley on 14 Feb 1793, at Twineham.

Twineham, 263B Mural monument for Barbara WOOD, d. 1803
- Nave, South wall, just West of chancel arch, very high.
- 30(W) x 72(H) — Good; faded.
- M.I. on an unframed cream marble panel; 2 block corbels; above, straight moulding supports arms.
- Barbara Wood, d. 25 Apr 1803, aet 30; wife of James Wood, of Hickstead.

1. In situ, see photograph in Grayling (*SAC* 59 115); Lambarde (*SAC* 71 157) noting arms; Horsfield (*Sussex* I 248) not located.
2. Barbara Wood's husband was owner of Hickstead in 1785 (R. Davey 202).

Twineham, 263C Ledger for Anthony STAPLEY, d. 1733
- Nave floor, centre, at chancel arch, near Stapley pew.
- 83(W) x 188(L) — Worn.
- M.I. in upper (W) 60% of a pale freestone slab; head to West.

HERE lyeth [inter]red
the Body of
ANTHONY STAPLEY
of Hickstead Gent who
Died Dec[r] 22nd 1733
Aged 29[?]
HERE also lyeth
Interred the Body of
JOHN STAPLEY junior
of Hickstead Gent who
Departed y[e] Life March
y[e] 20th 1748
Aged 22
Years

1. Anthony Stapley was author of a diary transcribed by Turner (*SAC* 18 151-162).
2. He came into the estate in 1724; his son records (p.159) his death, as above; buried 26 Dec 1733.

Twineham, 263D Ledger for members of the STAPLEY family, date unknown (18th c.)
- Nave floor, West of 263C.
- 99(W) x 208(L) — Very pitted and worn.
- M.I. in upper 50% of a grey freestone slab.
- Illegible.

Twineham, 263E Ledger for Jane STREATFEILD, d. 1720 and her son Richard
- Nave floor, West end.
- 99(W) x 199(L) — Worn.
- M.I. (engraved) on a black slab; head to West.

Here Lyeth Interred the Body
of JANE Wife of
RICHARD STREATFEILD Gent Daughter
to ANTHONY STAPLEY gent by JANE
His wife who Departed this life
September 10
1720
Aged 35 years,
Also RICHARD Their son an infant

1. Anthony Stapley notes in his diary that his wife was buried next to her daughter Jane Streatfeild in 1729, see Turner (*SAC* 18 155-7) and that 'A stone was put over [her] grave by William Hazlegrove, of Shoreham, stonecutter, which cost [him] £5 ... discharged the same day'.

Twineham Addition
(1) A plain stone in chancel floor with brass indent commemorating Rev. John Gowry d. 1757, buried in crypt.

(264) UCKFIELD, Holy Cross
Almost completely rebuilt by Woseley in 1839, but for tower and some ancient walls - *SNQ* (4 90-91); Nairn & Pevsner (614-5); for view of old church from North-East see Godfrey & Salzman (Pl. 166), see too Turner (*SAC* 12 9); for a parish with just 40 families in 1717 and a population of 811 in 1801 the wealth of 18th-century mural monuments is astonishing; they must all have been reinstalled: are any of those scrolled escutcheons original? Ledgers presumably lost in the rebuilding (an exception is 264N); indeed, Horsfield (*Sussex* I 369) reported that the chancel and nave abounded in M.I.s and monuments.

Uckfield, 264A Mural monument for Martha GRAEBKE, dated 1779
- South-West lobby, East wall, at head height.
- 86(W) x 153(H) — Dirty; faded; some cracks.
- In pale brown freestone set portrait-wise; an unframed M.I. tablet with a scrolled top, a base moulding and an ornamental apron.

> *Sacrum ...*
> *...et...*
> *uxoris suae ...*
> *Martha Graebke*
> *hoc Monumentum*
> *eſc.....oluit*
> *Ephraimus Graebke raris*
> *bellicae Chiru....s*
> *Multis illabor ...*
> *1779*

1. Formerly on an external wall.
2. Close in its design to 264C.
3. For a licence to marry dated, 15 Jan 1779, for Ephraim Gruebke, of Meeching, surgeon, aged 36, bachelor and Martha Braker [?], of Meeching, spinster, aged 26, see Dunkin & Penfold (*Licences* 179); Sussex Marriage Index gives this as Martha Brooker and Ephraim Graebke.
4. Date of death unclear but NBI records burial of Martha Grabekey on 25 Jun 1779 at Uckfield.

Uckfield, 264B Mural monument for Rev. John and Lucy LLOYD, d. 1738 and 1746
- South-West lobby, on staircase, facing South, above head height.
- 70(W) x 130(H) — Very weathered; stained.
- In sandy freestone; framed tablet with convex face, moulded entablature and pointed pediment; below, a thick base moulding and 2 scrolled corbels.

> TO THE MEMORY
> of the Revd Mr John Lloyd M.A.
> and Lucy His Wife
> Daughter of Alexan^r Shoebridge Gent.
> He was
> by the Appointment of Y^e charitable
> worthy Founder Anthony Saunders
> (D.D.) the first Master of the School
> endowed & settled in this Parish

and afterwards rector of Maresfield
...d in both those Stations in a
[manner] suitable to the trust committed
to [him] and after living many Years, very
h[os]pitably in this place,
He dyed Octb: 27: 1738 Aged 55 Years,
She dyed [..]m: 29: 1746 Aged 67 Years

1. Formerly on external wall of chancel, South-East of East window, see Turner (*SAC* 12 19).
2. For licence to marry for John Lloyd, of Buxted, clerk and Lucy Shoebridge, of Buxted, 17 Nov 1710, see Dunkin (*Licences 1670-1729* 319); the marriage took place on 23 Nov 1710.
3. Caffyn (1998 315) notes that John Lloyd (d.1738) was first master of Saunders' charity school and later curate at Uckfield.
4. For Saunders see 47E and Dunkin (*SAC* 26 20).
5. JH notes that John Lloyd was curate of Uckfield and then rector of Maresfield 1728-38, see CCEd.

Uckfield, 264C Mural monument for Edward, Philadelphia and Sarah INSKIP, d. 1764, 1732 and 1757

- North-West lobby, on staircase, facing North, above head height.
- 92(W) x 180(H) — Fine; very weathered.
- In pale brown freestone, close to 264A in type.

In
MEMORY OF EDWARD INSKIP,
GENT who died MAY 28th 1764, AGED
63 YEARS
Alſo of PHILADELPHIA his Wife,
who died Nov 20[?]th 1732 Aged 30 Years:
And alſo of SARAH his ſecond Wife
who died May 15th 1757 Aged 62 Years
He had Iſsue by his firſt Wife two Sons
viz
JOHN who took the ſurname of LADE,
And was created a BARONET after
succeeding to the eſtate of his Mother's
Uncle SIR JOHN LADE Baronet; and
EDWARD who died in his infancy

1. Formerly on an external wall.
2. Close in form to 264A.
3. For Sir John Lade, see 273C and Crossley & Saville (xii-xiv)..
4. NBI records the burial of Edward Inskip on 31 May 1764, Philadelphia Inskip on 24 Nov 1732 and Sarah Inskip on 17 May 1757, all at Uckfield.

Uckfield, 264D Mural monument for Elizabeth JACKSON, d. 1756 [Plate 162]

- North aisle, North wall, at head height.
- 87(W) x 125(H) — Very good.
- In grey marble; in centre a rectangular M.I. tablet (5 lines, engraved) and a slim black raised moulded frame; plain flanking pilasters end in scrolled brackets; below, an ornamental apron with polished black finial as corbel; above, no cornice or entablature, but a pointed pediment.
- Elizabeth Jackson, d. 26 Nov 1756, aet 44; wife of Thomas Jackson, Esq.

Uckfield, 264E Mural monument for Rev. David BAYFORD, d. 1792

- On East pier, between nave and North aisle, facing South, at head height.
- 43(W) x 83(H) — Good; fading.
- An unframed oval M.I. tablet (10 lines, engraved, black) on a small scrolled corbel.
- Rev. David Bayford, curate of Uckfield, d. 28 Nov 1792, aet 24.

Uckfield, 264F Wall-mounted brasses for John FULLER, d. 1610 [Plate 163]

- Now against the North choir wall.
- Slab: 88(W) x 204(H): Brass 1: 19(W) x 24(H); Brass 2: 22(W) x 62(H); Brass 3: 62(W) x 26(H); Brass 4: 53(W) x 29(H) — Fine.
- Four brasses set on a black slab, with chamfered edges: top, (1) an escutcheon, with the motto 'IOHN FULLER'; below that (2) standing portrait of John Fuller, hands in prayer, in a fur-trimmed gown, (3) a brass M.I. with John Fuller's charitable bequests, (4) a brass epitaph - didactic (11 lines).
- John Fuller, Gent., of Uckfield, d. 6 Apr 1610, aet unknown; quotes 1 John 3, 11-13.

1. Formerly on the floor, within the sanctuary rail, set North-South; Horsfield (*Sussex* I 369); Turner (*SAC* 12 17-8).
2. Noted by Stephenson (517); Turner (*SAC* 23 186-7) - with transcription; Davidson-Houston (*SAC* 80 126-7) - with illustration and Nairn & Pevsner (615); for heraldry see Lambarde (*SAC* 67 166).
3. John Fuller established his family in Sussex; his charitable donations included Chiddingstone (see too 264P), Penshurst in Kent, Isfield and Uckfield; John Fuller is supposed to have died at Lewes - Turner (*SAC* 12 17-8).
4. Gideon Mantell was inspired by Fuller's epitaph to pen a short impromptu - Lower (*SAC* 25 102).

Uckfield, 264G Mural monument for John and George EGLES, d. 1712 and 1727/8

- South choir wall, towards East end, above head height.
- 74(W) x 158(H) — Very good; colour restored.
- In grey-veined marble; M.I. (12 lines) in upper 50%; straight top and chamfers; base moulding and ornamental apron; above, a scrolled escutcheon.
- John Egles, 18 Apr 1709 - 28 Jul 1712, 'buried under the family seat'; George Egles, 30 Mar 1710 - 4 Mar 1727/8, 'buried under this monument'; both sons of John Egles, Gent. and Mary his wife.

1. Willatts (*SAC* 125 112) notes that the Egles monuments were moved to the South side during 1839 restoration of church; for heraldry see Lambarde (*SAC* 67 166).
2. For licence to marry of John Egles, Gent., of Uckfield, and Mary Goring, of Barcombe, spinster, 17 Apr 1708 see Dunkin (*Licences 1670-1729* 197).

Uckfield, 264H Mural monument for Rev. Henry COURTHOPE, d. 1804

- South choir wall, alongside and West of 264G.
- 134(W) x 278(H) — Very good; heraldic colour.
- Composite white marble M.I. panel with arched top; black surround; white marble architrave; flanked by Tuscan columns on very high pedestals with moulded blocked corbels; above, broken pointed pediment and scrolled escutcheon; below, a straight frame moulding.
- Rev. Henry Courthope, A.M., vicar of Brenchley, Kent, d. 15 Nov 1804, aet 64, buried at Uckfield; second son of George Courthope, Esq., of Whiligh, Sussex; his wife, Mary, d. 29 Apr 1830, aet 82, youngest daughter of William Peckham, Esq., of Arches, Sussex; issue - Mary, d. 1 Nov 1825, aet 48.

1. Noted by Horsfield (*Sussex* I 369); for heraldry see Lambarde (*SAC* 67 166).
2. Turner (*SAC* 12 20) in situ, gives death dates of Mary Courthope, mother and daughter as 1836 and 1826 respectively. Dates above are as on the monument and are confirmed by NBI.
3. 264H is a puzzling composition given the seeming death dates of the subjects; perhaps the lower section was added after 1825 to accommodate the lengthy epitaph for Henry Courthope's daughter; wife/mother was patron in both cases.
4. For this family see Ticehurst (248).

Uckfield, 264I Mural monument for members of the WILSON Family, erected 1770

- South choir wall, alongside and just West of 264H.
- 98(w) x 184(H) — Very good.
- Black rectangular frame around a white marble tablet set portrait-wise with heraldry on top.
- This monument was erected by Sir Thomas Spencer Wilson, 6th Bart. in memory of his sister, Barbara Wilson, d. 5 Mar 1730, aet 6; his sister, Anne Wilson, d. 26 Oct 1744, aet 19; his father, Sir Thomas Wilson, 4th Bart., d. 6 Oct 1759, aet 77; his brother, Sir Edward Wilson, 5th Bart., d. 1 Jun 1760, aet 42, unmarried; his mother, Dame Elizabeth Wilson, d. 4 Jul 1768, aet 78.

1. Noted by Horsfield (*Sussex* I 369); for heraldry see Lambarde (*SAC* 67 167).
2. Formerly on North side of chancel window, see Turner (*SAC* 12 20).
3. The Wilsons lived in Uckfield.
4. Earlier Baronets commemorated at Eastbourne, see genealogy in Blencowe (*SAC* 12 240-1).
5. JH notes that Sir Thomas Spencer Wilson, patron of this monument, was born in Uckfield, in 1726. He entered the army, and in 1796 became a full General. He died in 1798 and is buried at Charlton, Kent. See Cockayne (*Baronetage* III 171).

Uckfield, 264J Mural monument for Mary ELLIS, d. 1718

- Nave, East end, against choir wall, facing West, at head height.
- 74(W) x 114(H) — Good.
- Elegant small tablet with gilded lettering, within a grey marble frames; flat pilasters; base mouldings and decorated apron; above, an escutcheon on a stand against a pointed grey backplate.
- Ms Mary Ellis, d. 19 Dec 1718, aet 61.

1. Noted by Horsfield (*Sussex* I 369); the familiar emphasis in town parish churches on charitable bequests, also noted in Turner (*SAC* 12 18).
2. For heraldry see Lambarde (*SAC* 67 167).

Uckfield, 264K Mural mounted slab for John-Barham EGLES and Mary EGLES, both d. 1721

- Now against East nave wall, below 164J, partly obscured by recent wooden extension to chancel steps.
- (Visible) 84(W) x 99(H) — Good.
- Unframed white marble slab; M.I. (only 13 lines visible, engraved and black).

Here
Lyes Interred
JOHN-BARHAM *and* MARY EGLES
Son and Daughter
of GEORGE EGLES *of Shoosmith's in*
the Pariſh of Wadhurst, Suſsex,
Gent, by BARBARA, *his Wife*
JOHN-BARHAM EGLES, *died 3rd* MAY *1721,*
in the 4th year of his age.
MARY EGLES *died 20th* MAY *1721,*
in the 3rd year of her Age.
Thomas Goring Egles Who [?lieth] ...

1. Formerly a floor slab? For Egles, see comments on 264G.
2. For licence to marry for George Egles, of Uckfield, Gent., bachelor and Barbara Gooley, of Uckfield, 4 Mar 1717, see Dunkin (*Licences 1670-1729* 324).
3. The family monuments were moved to the South aisle during 1839 restoration, see Willatts (*SAC* 125 112).

Uckfield, 264L Mural monument for Dorothy ELLIS, d. 1731/2

- South-East chapel, North wall, facing South, high up.
- 70(W) x c.140(H) — Good.
- Ornate; slate and column marbles; lettering (?gilded); inverted scrolls on the flanking pilasters; above, 3 overlapping cornices, a scrolled escutcheon on a pedestal and 2 gilded, flaming lamps; below, base mouldings on a complex corbel with volutes and an acanthus boss.
- Dorothy Ellis, d. 14 Feb 1731/2, aet 73; she had sister(s).

1. See 264J and F for other charitable bequests also noted in Turner (*SAC* 12 18).
2. For heraldry see Lambarde (*SAC* 67 167).

Uckfield, 264M Mural cartouche for John EGLES, d. 1750 [Plate 164]

- South aisle, South wall, near East end, at head height.
- 69(W) x 154(H) — Very good.
- In white marble; Baroque gilded scrollwork; M.I. (lines, engraved and black) filling the double convex face; above, an escutcheon, flanked by cherubim; another at the foot.
- John Egles, Esq., of Copwood, d. 5 Aug 1750, aet 73; his wife, Mary, d. 6 Sep 1744, aet 71, daughter of George Goring, Esq., of Barcombe; issue, 1 daughter, Mary, wife of Richard Beard Streatfeild, second son of Henry Streatfeild, Esq., of Chiddingstone, Kent.

1. John Egles had settled at Copwood c.1708 and it was inherited by Richard Thomas Streatfeild (see 264O), a nephew of a descendant, after 1789; he demolished it (Farrant 325).
2. 264M is noted by Horsfield (*Sussex* I 369); for heraldry see Lambarde (*SAC* 67 167).
3. Noted in Turner (*SAC* 12 19), subject identified as (probably) the son of Gabriel (see 264N); gives Mary's death date as 1774, notes 2 predeceased sons.
4. For John Egles' descendants see 264P.
5. Despite general high quality of the cutting, the cherubim faces are quite crude.
6. 264M is memorable for its confident use of the Baroque ornamental language.
7. In 1793, one Edward Egles established a cotton manufactory in South Street, Lewes (L. Davey 52).

Uckfield, 264N Wall mounted slab for Gabriel EGLES, d. 1707

- South aisle, rests against South wall, beneath 264M.
- 75(W) x 176(H) — Fine.
- Cast iron slab; M.I. (8 lines over an escutcheon); cabled edge.
- Gabriel Egles, Esq., d. 7 Aug 1707, aet 64.

1. Noted by Horsfield (*Sussex* I 369); Nairn & Pevsner (615); *SAC* 121 19 - then in the chancel; for heraldry see Lambarde (*SAC* 67 167).
2. Willatts (*SAC* 125 100, 112) notes a rare case of rope used to cast decorative edge.
3. 264N was transferred to South side of church during 1839 rebuilding, as were later marble mural monuments to Egles.

Uckfield, 264O Mural monument for Richard Thomas STREATFEILD, d. 1813, and his wife Anne, d. 1848

- South aisle wall, at head height, West of 264M.
- 79(W) x 180(H) — Very good; colour visible on arms.
- In white marble with a scrolled escutcheon above; lightly moulded M.I. tablet (engraved and black) filled; above, cornice and escutcheon; below, base mouldings, and an ornamental apron with scalloped edge, also inscription.
- Richard Thomas Streatfeild, Esq., of the Rocks and Copwood, d. 26 Aug 1813, aet 53, buried Chiddingstone, Kent; his first wife, Jane Esther, d. 26 Oct 1796, aet 26, daughter of Admiral Sir Chaloner Ogle, Kt, of Worthy, Hampshire; no issue; his second wife, Anne, d. 6 Jul 1848 and buried at Kensal Green Cemetery, Paddington, Middlesex, daughter of Robert Shuttleworth, Esq., of Barton Lodge, Lancashire; issue - Anne, Rosa-Sophia, Richard-Shuttleworth, Georgiana-Charlotte, Sidney-Robert, Thomas-Brand (d. 3 Feb

1811, infant, and buried at Chiddingstone) and Gertrude Harriet, a posthumous child; Anne subsequently married Richard Prime, Esq., of Walberton, issue - three children.

1. Richard Thomas Streatfeild demolished Copwood (see 264O) and built Rocks, a house near Uckfield; in turn his son Richard Shuttleworth Streatfeild (d. 1851), demolished Rocks and employed Smirke to replace it with a new house still standing in 1860, see Turner (*SAC* 12 19-20).
2. For heraldry see Lambarde (*SAC* 67 167).

Uckfield, 264P Mural monument for Richard Beard STREATFEILD, d. 1770, and his family

- South aisle wall, at head height, towards West end.
- 100(W) x 215(H) — Excellent.
- In grey-veined marble, a rectangular M.I. tablet (engraved and black); flanked by fluted Doric pilasters; below, base mouldings, finials, an ornamental apron with a column escutcheon and 2 cherubim; above, a plain frieze with raunce inset and cornice supporting urn and 2 flaming lamps.
- Richard Beard Streatfeild, Esq., of Copwood, d. 10 Jan 1770, aet 60; his widow, Mary, d. 3 Aug 1789, aet 74, daughter of John Egles, Esq., of Copwood; issue - Mary, d. 13 Mar 1740/1, an infant; and Elizabeth, d. 14 Mar 1741/2, an infant; all buried Chiddingstone, Kent.

1. Noted by Horsfield (*Sussex* I 369); for heraldry see Lambarde (*SAC* 67 168).
2. Mary, the daughter of John Egles (264m) carried Copwood estate into Streatfeild family through her marriage with Richard Beard Streatfeild. The estate passed to his son Richard Thomas Streatfeild (264N), see Turner (*SAC* 12 19-20); for other Egles monuments see 264M, K, G and N.
3. Note the high quality of the carving of 264P - do the lower cherubim belong?

(265) UDIMORE, St. Mary

Norman nave with early 13th-century chancel - Nairn & Pevsner (615-6); a view in Godfrey & Salzman (Pl. 167); see too VCH (IX 173); Horsfield (*Sussex* I 512) reports a former South aisle; chancel paving reported to be poor in 1686, especially at East end, repairs undertaken by 1724 (Ford 116); parish had 36 families in 1724 and a population of 321 in 1801; as he passed in 1777, Grose noted the Freebody brasses (265I). 265C, F, G and H refer to the mememto mori in their M.I.s, an unusual thematic concentration.

Udimore, 265A Mural monument for William Cooper WOODHAMS, d. 1826, and his wife Catherine, d. 1870 [Plate 165]

- Nave, North wall, above head height.
- 83(W) x 95(H) — Very good.
- White on black marble; M.I. (engraved, black), final lines added, on tablet with pointed pediment and palmettes; backplate with pointed top and curved apron; a cornice over a trapezoidal panel on a base; signed (lower right): 'J.SMITH RYE'.
- William Woodhams, of Pelsham House, Peasmarsh, d. 3 Jan 1826, aet 43; his wife, Catherine, d. 1 Feb 1870, aet 78; their issue - 5 children.

1. Noted by Horsfield (*Sussex* I 512).
2. Cited by Gunnis (*Dict.* 357) as by Smith of Rye.
3. For issue see 265B.

Udimore, 265B Mural monument for Sarah and William WOODHAMS, d. 1822 and 1830, and others

- Nave, North wall, East of 265A.
- 82(W) x 138(H) — Very good.
- M.I. (26 lines, engraved, centred) on a rectangular panel, set portrait-wise on backplate

with domed top; moulded cornice over panel; draped urn over; signed (lower right): 'J. SMITH RYE'.
- Sarah Woodhams, d. 9 May 1822, aet 65; wife of William Woodhams, of Tufton Place, d. 14 Jan 1830, aet 70; their grandsons, William Wilson Woodhams, d. 20 Jan 1815, aet 7 and Peter Waters Woodhams, d. 25 Jul 1821, aet 2; their granddaughters, Catherine Cooper Woodhams, d. 18 Jun 1836, aet 13, and, Eliza Woodhams, d. 15 Dec 1847, aet 22; all children of William Cooper and Catherine Woodhams, Pelsham House, Peasmarsh.

1. Noted by Horsfield (*Sussex* I 512).
2. Erected between 1822-30.
3. Cited by Gunnis (*Dict.* 357) as by Smith.
4. See too 265A.

Udimore, 265C Floor-mounted brass for John FREBODYE, d. 1612/3
- Nave, East end, at foot of pulpit.
- Slab: 86(W) x 168(L); Brass: 46(W) x 12(L) — Fair.
- Brasses mounted on a freestone slab; head to the West.
- John Frebodye, d. 12 Mar 1612/3, aet 57.

1. Noted by Horsfield (*Sussex* I 512); Turner (*SAC* 23 187) notes the brass, or part of it.
2. Seen in nave by Davidson-Houston (*SAC* 80 129).
3. The reference to the memento mori in the final line ('Hodie mihi cras tibi') is rare amongst Sussex M.I.s.

Udimore, 265D Wall-mounted brass for Martha JORDEN, d. 1635
- Nave, North wall, partly obscured by furnishings.
- Slab (irregular): 65(W) x 100(L) — Very damaged. Brass: 32(W) x 11.5(H) — Fine.
- M.I. engraved on a brass plate screwed to a cretaceous limestone slab.

Here lyeth ye body of Martha
Iorden Davghter of Wilm
Iorden of Vdimer who
Dyed the 26 of Iune
1635

1. In 1777, Grose noted brasses to the Jordens at Udimore (Farrant); a medieval hall house at Udimore called Jordan's was demolished c.1928 - J.E. Ray, 'Notes and Queries: Hastings' (*SAC* 70 218-9).
2. Davidson-Houston (*SAC* 80 129-30) noted 265D together with a companion brass, a little larger, to her sister Margaret Jorden, 1636 d. 9 Dec 1636, aet 4, which was also noted in Horsfield (*Sussex* I 512) (see Addition).

Udimore, 265E Ledger for John FREBODY, d. 1621
- Sanctuary floor, North-East corner.
- 48(W) x 18(H) — Worn.
- M.I. (engraved) in cream slab; head to East.
- John Frebody, buried 20 May 1621, son of Richard Frebody, of Udimore; his wife, Ann Pery, daughter of John Pery; no issue.

1. Noted as floor-slab mounted by Turner (*SAC* 23 187), with death-date 26 May following Horsfield (*Sussex* I 512).

Udimore, 265F Floor-mounted brass for Sarah BRABON, d. 1626
- Sanctuary floor, South-East corner.
- Slab: 70(W) x 131(L) — Repaired Brass: 36(W) x 42(L) — Worn and lifting.
- M.I. (engraved, Latin and English) on brass plate; set on a black freestone slab; head to East
- Sarah Brabon, died in childbirth, 14 Oct 1626, aet 24; daughter of John Burdet and Margaret and coheir of William Burdet; and wife of John Brabon, vicar of Udimore; her many virtues.

1. Grose notes brasses to the Burdets at Udimore (Farrant) (see Addition 2).
2. 265F is roughly in situ in Horsfield (*Sussex* I 512).
3. John Burdet was patron and composer of the epitaph.
4. M.I. transcribed by Turner (*SAC* 23 187).
5. In chancel in Davidson-Houston (*SAC* 80 129).

Udimore, 265G Mural monument for [Mary] MARSHALL, d. 1798 [Plate 166]

- Chancel, East wall, South side, facing West.
- 50(W) x 73(H) — Worn.
- M.I. (engraved) on an oval marble panel; more M.I. in the border; lettering crudely cut.
- Widow Marshall, d. 9 Mar 1798, aet 98; patron Benjamin Cooper, Gent., of Udimore.

1. The subject was not included in the 1785 tax return (R. Davey 204-5).
2. For the patron see 265H; it is unclear why Cooper was patron of 265G.
3. NBI records a Mary Marshall (age not stated) buried on 12 March 1798 at Udimore.

Udimore, 265H Mural for Benjamin COOPER, d. 1799, and his widow Sarah, d. 1837

- Nave, South wall, West end, close to chancel arch, high.
- 76(W) x c.150(H) — Very good.
- M.I. (engraved) on oval marble plaque; dark grey-green veined baseplate; above, another smaller, heart-shaped panel with motto with a ribbon tie inlayed at top; below, 2 prominent white corbels.
- Benjamin Cooper, Gent., of Udimore, d. 13 Mar 1799, aet 37; his widow, Sarah, d. 24 Sep 1837, aet 77.

1. Noted by Horsfield (*Sussex* I 512).
2. Benjamin Cooper occupies a property of Lady Compton in 1785 (R. Davey 204).
3. Final 7 lines of M.I. added?

Udimore, 265I Ledger and brasses for John FREEBODY, d. 1578, John Freebody, d 1715/6, and Elizabeth Freebody, d. 1741

- Nave floor, South-East corner, under 265H.
- 82(W) x 175(L) — Good.
- M.I. (engraved) on upper 55% of freestone slab; head to West; 2 brass plates attached to East end (upper brass for John Freebody d. 1578; lower brass for John Freebody d. 1715); M.I. on slab for Elizabeth Freebody, d. 1741.
- John Freebody, d. 28 Sep 1578, aet 80; another John Freebody, Gent., of Knellstone, d. 5 Jan 1715/6, aet 57; one Elizabeth, widow of a John Freebody, d. 5 Feb 1741, aet 85; her son, Thomas Freebody, Gent., of Knellstone, laid the tombstone in 1756.

1. In part, 265I may include material originally located in the churchyard.
2. Horsfield (*Sussex* I 512) following Grose (1777 Diary in Farrant p. 120), notes a monument at Udimore for Thomas Freebody, of Knellstone, d. 22 Nov 1765, aet 72, the last of that name; the Freebodys were possessors of the estate for 400 years.
3. The earliest brass noted by Turner (*SAC* 23 187) was floor slab mounted and for the father of John Freebody (d. 1578), who was Richard Freebody - also cited by Horsfield (*Sussex* I 512).
4. 265I was in situ in Lambarde (*SAC* 71 169) citing arms and in Davidson-Houston (*SAC* 80 128 & 130).
5. The patron of 265I was Thomas Freebody, perhaps the last of that name, as suggested by Horsfield; the Freebody family of Udimore attained gentry status only in the 18th century, for example, one John, yeoman, was licensed to marry in 1639, see Dunkin (*Licences 1586-1643* 256).

Udimore, 265J Mural commemorating the children of James SMITH, d. 1832, his wife Hannah, d. 1805, and their children

- Nave, South wall, East of South door, very high.
- Inaccessible — Very good.
- M.I. (engraved) on upper 80% of a unframed white marble tablet, set portrait-wise; above, moulded cornice supporting draped urn; black slate backplate with pointed top; base moulding; 2 corbels; signed (lower right): 'HINCLIFF SCULP^r HAMST^d R^d LONDON'.
- James Smith, Esq., of Rye, d. 15 Jan 1832, aet 65; his wife, Hannah, d. 25 May 1805, aet 32; issue - Harriett, d. 6 Nov 1797, an infant; Ann Firminger, d. 20 Oct 1804, aet 4; James Firminger, d. 13 Aug 1808, aet 6; Samuel, d. 8 Feb 1814, aet 22; Charlotte, d. 18 Oct 1818, aet 20; also Mary Woodhams Brazier, d. 6 Jul 1825, aet 32, the wife of William Brazier.

1. Cited by Gunnis (*Dict.* 202) as by John Ely Hinchliffe.
2. For licence to marry dated 20 Oct 1790 for James Smith, of Bodiam, age 23 plus and Hannah Woodhams, of Udimore, age 18 plus, see Dunkin & Penfold (*Licences* 388).

Udimore Additions
Noted by Turner (*SAC* 23 187):
(1) Brass on floor slab for Margaret Jordan, daughter of William Jordan, d. 9 Dec 1636 (see under 265D).
Noted in Lambarde (*SAC* 71 169) and Davidson-Houston (*SAC* 80 128) in chancel:
(2) Brass for John Burdett, d. 4 Jan 1605/6, aet 30; his father, William; his wife, Margaret, daughter of John Horrold; issue of John Burdett - William, baptised 30 Nov 1604; Clement, baptised 5 Aug 1597; Mary, baptised 11 Feb 1599; Ann, baptised 1 Jan 1601; Sara, baptised 27 Aug 1603.

(269) UPPER DICKER - No Monuments Found

(270) WADHURST, St. Peter & St. Paul
13th-14th century aisles and chancel added to Norman nave - Nairn & Pevsner (616-17); restorations by Slater 1858; for a plan with monuments marked see *SNQ* (XII 179); the village had c.200 houses in c.1760 and a population of 1677 in 1801; the church contains more than 30 cast iron slabs, the largest collection in the county and in the UK, see Lower (*SAC* 2 199-200) and Willatts (*SAC* 125 102); the important family groups are Luck, Barham, see Fitzgerald-Uniacke (*SAC* 56 110-160), Newington, Saunders and Bucher.

Wadhurst, 270A Mural monument for Ann and John Wells LUCK, d. 1768 and 1771
- Porch, West wall, at head height.
- 123(W) x 174(H) — Fine; painted.
- M.I. (engraved, black) on a framed freestone(?) tablet; the remainder in moulded terracotta; an urn within a broken scrolled pediment; ornamental apron; corbels.
- Ann Luck, d. 27 Nov 1768, aet 77; wife of John Wells Luck, Gent., d. 9 Mar 1771, aet 86.

1. 270A appears to be by Jonathan Harmer of Heathfield, although the composite motifs are not identifiable from corpus published by Remnant in *SAC* 100.
2. Remnant (*SAC* 100 53) rejects the attribution to Harmer.
3. M.I. refers to 270B.
4. 270A is cited by Gunnis (*Dict.* 188), Willatts (*SAC* 125 103) and Wace (48).

Wadhurst, 270B Floor slab for Ann and John Wells LUCK, d. 1768 and 1771

- Porch floor.
- 91(W) x 184(L) — Very worn.
- M.I. in cast iron slab; head to West.

I.W LUCK
1771
A LUCK
1768

1. M.I. refers to 270A.
2. In situ, see Willatts (*SAC* 125 103), *SNQ* (XII 179) and Wace (47).

Wadhurst, 270C Mural monument for Mary Georgiana LUCK, d. 1817 [Plate 167]

- Porch, East wall, North of 270D, at head height.
- 101(W) x 170(H) — Very good; colour restored.
- In painted terracotta; above, floral cartouches and a cherub against a rounded pediment; fluted Doric half-columns flank a M.I. on a straight framed tablet set landscape-wise (in white marble?); below, a base moulding and ornamental corbels.
- Mary Georgiana Luck, d. 15 May 1817, aet 9; daughter of George Luck, Esq., and Mary who d. 15 Jul 1836, aet 65.

1. Final 3 lines added later.
2. 270C is from the workshop of Jonathan Harmer of Heathfield, Remnant (*SAC* 100 53) and Gunnis (*Dict.* 188). See also Wace (48). For heraldry see Lambarde (*SAC* 67 160).
3. The cherubim and vases motifs in the pediment are from the moulds now in Barbican House, Lewes, see Remnant (*SAC* 100 pls. II & IV).

Wadhurst, 270D Mural monument for Richard LUCK, d. 1793, and his brothers George, d. 1807, and John, d. 1805

- Porch, East wall, South of 270C, at head height.
- 124(W) x 176(H) — Very good.
- In painted and gilded terracotta; M.I. (engraved, black) on marble tablet; above, an urn within a broken, scrolled pediment; flanking, decorated scrolls; below, an ornament, inscribed apron and corbels.
- Richard Luck, Gent., Lieutenant in the Sussex Militia, d. 3 Jun 1793, aet 37; second son of John Luck, Esq., Captain in the West Kent Militia, and grandson of John Wells Luck; George Luck, Esq., d. 30 May 1807, aet 54, eldest son of John Luck; and John Luck, d. 24 Jan 1805, aet 49, third son of John Luck.

1. 270D uses elements also seen in 270A and 270C.
2. Attributed here to Jonathan Harmer of Heathfield, composite motifs not identifiable from corpus in *SAC* 100; attribution to Harmer rejected by Remnant (*SAC* 100 53); cited by Gunnis (*Dict.* 188); see also Wace (48).
3. Richard Luck owned Pitthouse in 1785 (R. Davey 207).
4. Lines added to the apron.

Wadhurst, 270E Floor slab for Ann SAUNDERS, d. 1677

- South aisle floor, West end.
- 56(W) x 172(L) — Fine.
- M.I. (raised relief) in centre of cast iron slab, rough at both ends, head to West.
- Ann Saunders, d. 7 Aug 1677, aet 73; her late husband, Nicholas Saunders of Pell .

1. In situ *SNQ* (XII 179).
2. For Nicholas Saunders see 270WW.

Wadhurst, 270F Floor slab for A. BURGIS, d. 1634

- South aisle floor, against West wall, partly obscured by furnishings.
- 65(W) x 188(L) — Fine, many graffiti added.
- A single motif of initials ('A.B.') and date (1634), on a cast iron slab, repeated six times in an irregular arrangement, supplemented by graffiti; head to the West.
- Graffiti include: 'M L / 1735'; 'R ^{W} B / 1777'; 'EB / 1716'; 'E ^{D} B / 1709' and 'I.B / 1764'.

1. In situ *SNQ* (XII 179); Willatts (*SAC* 125 107).
2. 270F probably relates to a member of the Burges family, see Wace (47) who identifies AB as A. Burgis or Burgess from the burial registers for the same date; for RWB (Richard Walter Burgis) and IB (Jane Burgis) see 270CC.
3. The graffiti presumably record eighteenth-century family members.
4. For the composition see 270R and 270S.

Wadhurst, 270G Floor slab for Ann BARHAM, d. 1675

- South aisle floor, towards West end, abutting 270F.
- 57(W) x 182(L) — Fine.
- M.I. (raised relief) in centre of a cast iron slab, some rough casting; 2 escutcheons at East end; head to West.
- Ann Barham, d. 18 May 1675; daughter of David Barham, Gent., of Snape, Wadhurst.

1. Noted by Horsfield (*Sussex* I 413-4).
2. In situ *SNQ* (XII 179) and Wace (46).
3. For David Barham see 270MM.
4. Ann Barham was baptised 10 Aug 1655, see Fitzgerald-Uniacke (*SAC* 56 127-8).
5. Willatts (*SAC* 125 104) notes that Barham arms on 170G are not from same casting block as on 270FF (1648). For this heraldry see Lambarde (*SAC* 67 159).

Wadhurst, 270H Floor slab for John BRABAN, d. 1677/8

- Nave floor, central aisle, towards West end.
- 63(W) x 174(L) — Fine.
- M.I. in relief on a cast iron slab; head to West; a line added.
- John Braban, d. 8 Mar 1677/8, aet 18; second son of Edward Braban, of Salehurst; also 'EL', 1713.

1. In situ *SNQ* (XII 179).

Wadhurst, 270I Mural monument for John NEWINGTON, d. 1780

- Nave West wall, South of tower arch, above head height.
- 142(W); (H) inaccessible — Fine; local damage (middle corbel); colour visible.
- In good quality marble; straight entablature supporting urns; blank frieze; M.I. on tablet; flanking, mock-fluted pilasters; below, escutcheons.
- John Newington, Gent., of Hightown, Wadhurst, d. 17 Feb 1780, aet 85; his first wife, Mary, d. Jun 1759, aet 73, daughter of Joseph Weller, Esq., of Dallington Castle; issue - Joseph, d. Apr 1739, aet 14; his second wife and relict, Anne, daughter of Edward Burgess, Gent., of Wadhurst.

1. All engraved lines appear co-terminal.
2. 270H is probably datable soon after 1780, details of his widow's death were never added.
3. Note the inlay used to create the effect of fluting.
4. For Newington, see 258H, DD and KK at Ticehurst and Harmer terracottas in Burwash churchyard.
5. Anne Newington owned extensive properties in 1785 (R. Davey 207).
6. For heraldry see Lambarde (*SAC* 67 159).

Wadhurst, 270J Mural monument for Judith and John LEGAS, d. 1747 and d. 1752

- Nave West wall, North of tower arch, above head height.
- 109(W) x 203(H) — Very good; faded; heraldry restored.
- in black, white and coloured marbles; M.I. on tablet with arched top; flanking, plain pilasters; ornamental spandrels; above, entablature and scrolled pediment with shell motif; below, escutcheon and corbel.
- Judith Legas, d. 13 Jun 1747, aet 71; her husband, John Legas, Gent., ironfounder, d. 22 May 1752, aet 62; no issue mentioned.

1. Lines for John Legas probably added later but by the same hand; for the slab see 270ZZ.
2. Legas, lived at Old Vicarage in High Street and came to Wadhurst to open iron mines early in the 18th century, see Harper (*Heraldry* 12); and see Cleere & Crossley (204, 205, et al.). His wife's family arms are prominent; Legas arms have been defaced.
3. Lambarde does not describe any heraldry.
4. See too Wace (48).
5. John Legas presented plate to the church in 1748, see Couchman (*SAC* 55 180).

Wadhurst, 270K Floor slab for Edward CHANDLER, d. 1673 [Plate 168]

- North aisle floor, opposite South door, alongside 270L.
- 43(W) x 93(L) — Fine.
- M.I. in relief on cast iron slab; head to West.

EC EC

1673

EC EC

1. In situ *SNQ* (XII 179).
2. EC is identified as Edward Chandler in Wace (47) from the burial registers of the same date.

Wadhurst, 270L Floor slab for John SAUNDERS, d. 1675 [Plate 168]

- North aisle floor, immediately North of 270K.
- 36(W) x 69.5(L) — Worn.
- M.I. in relief in cast iron slab; head to West.
- John Saunders, buried 5 May 1675; son of Nicholas and Philadelphia Saunders, of London.

1. In situ *SNQ* (XII 179) and Wace (47).
2. Patron of 270L is Ann Saunders of Pell, John Saunders' grandmother (see 270E).

Wadhurst, 270M Floor slab for Dorothy ALCHERNE, d. 1688 [Plate 168]

- North aisle floor, alongside and South of 270L.
- 45(W) x 98(L) — Fine.
- M.I. in relief in cast iron slab; head to West.

D.A

1688

D.A

1. In situ *SNQ* (XII 179).
2. DA identified as Dorothy Alcherne in Wace (46) from burial registers of the same date.
3. For the characteristic design of the letter 'A' on 270M, see too 270U.

Wadhurst, 270N Floor slab for T. BARHAM, d. 1647

- North aisle floor, towards East end, partly obscured by nave pier.
- 63(W) x 183(L) — Very good.
- M.I. in relief in a large cast iron slab with very crisp casting; head to East.

T B

1647

TB

1. In situ *SNQ* (XII 179).
2. TB identified as T. Barham in Wace (46) from burial registers of the same date.

Wadhurst, 270O Mural monument for John TOMPSETT, d. 1820, and his wife Ann, d. 1802

- North chapel, West wall, above head height.
- 125(W) x 205(H) — Fine.
- In painted and gilded terracotta; above, an urn on a round pediment, flanked by flames (?); M.I. on a circular lettered tablet with leaves in spandrels; flanking, fluted pilasters; below, base mouldings and apron with fan motif; pine cones as corbels.
- John Tompsett, Gent., of Scrag-Oak, Wadhurst, d. 22 Sep 1820, aet 71; his wife, Ann, d. 23 Dec 1802, aet 48.

1. Cited by Wace (48).
2. M.I. refers to an unmarked vault near the West door.
3. 270O close to 270P.
4. The vase ornament in the pediment appears in the corpus of Harmer motifs, see Remnant (*SAC* 100, Pl. I & 54).
5. Nicholas Barham 1708-88, see Lower (*SAC* 2 219), sold Scrag Oak to James Tompsett in 1741; the property remained with the family for over 100 years (for 1785, see R. Davey 209); another property, Bewmans, belonged to John Tompsett, see map in Steer (13); for licence to marry dated 23 Feb 1774 for John Tompsett, of Wadhurst, Gent., bachelor, age 24 plus, and Ann Maynard, of Mayfield, spinster, age 20 plus see Dunkin & Penfold (*Licences* 424).

Wadhurst, 270P Mural monument for William GURR Junior, d. 1786

- North chapel, East wall, high over door.
- 60(W); (H) inaccessible — Fine.
- M.I. (engraved, black) on unframed oval tablet; above, a vase in terracotta.
- William Gurr, d. 15 Nov 1786, aet 33; son of William Gurr, Snr, d. 17 Nov 1788, aet 67; and Mary, d. 29 Apr 1790, aet 74.

1. Cited by Wace (48).
2. M.I. refers to a stone, of which there is (now) no sign.
3. Compare with terracotta details on 270A, C, D and O.
4. William Gurr owned houses and shops in 1785 (R. Davey 206-7).

Wadhurst, 270Q Floor slab for Richard COOMBER, d. 1763, and his wife Jane, d. 1786

- Nave floor, extreme East end, abutting the chancel step.
- 100(W) x 179(L) — Cracked (North-East corner); damaged edges.
- M.I. (5 + 6 lines, engraved) in upper end and centre of a black stone; head to West.
- Richard Coomber, Gent., d. 4 Oct 1763, aet 61; his second wife, Jane, d. 22 May 1786, aet 91.

1. Previously in chancel; Horsfield (*Sussex* I 413-4).
2. In situ *SNQ* (XII 179) and Wace (47).
3. Later lines added after 1786, but in same hand.
4. Richard Coomber was uncle to John Newington see 270H.

Wadhurst, 270R Floor slab for Mary BARHAM, d. 1658

- Choir floor, North side, West end.
- 59(W) x 177(L) — Fine.
- M.I. in relief in cast iron slab; repeated escutcheon motif; head to the West.

MB 1658

1. MB is identified as Mary Barham, wife of John Barham (270NN), of Scrag Oak in Wace (47) from the burial registers of the same date.
2. In situ *SNQ* (XII 179); Lambarde describes heraldry, but does not identify it, see (*SAC* 67 159).

3. One of a set of slabs now set in front of the choir stalls.
4. For the composition see too 270F and S.

Wadhurst, 270S Floor slab for John DUNMOLL, d. 1625
- Choir floor, North side, East of 270R.
- 63.5(W) x 199(L) — Good.
- M.I. in relief in cast iron slab with initials, a date and the initial 'N' between two escutcheons.

1625
ID

1. ID is identified as John Dunmoll in Wace (47) from the burial registers of the same date.
2. In situ *SNQ* (XII 179).
3. Close in type to 270R but notably long and thin.
4. The meaning of the additional letter 'N', at the East end is unclear - a signature? Perhaps the patron? Surely not the maker?

Wadhurst, 270T Floor slab for Alice BUCHER, d. 1638
- Choir floor, North side, East of 270S.
- 63(W) x 182(L) — Fine.
- M.I. in relief in cast iron slab; lettering in an arched frame; below, a blank compartment.
- Alice Bucher, d. 23 Oct 1638, age unknown; wife of Thomas Bucher.

1. In situ *SNQ* (XII 179) and Wace (47).
2. Composition close to other Bucher slabs (270JJ and 270LL).

Wadhurst, 270U Floor slab for William BARHAM, d. 1701
- Choir floor, North side, East of 270T.
- 83(W) x 204(L) — Fine; some parts poorly cast.
- M.I. in relief on a cast iron slab; raised letters between two heraldic compartments; head to West.
- William Barham, of Scrag Oak, d. 6 Nov 1701, aet 80.

1. In situ; Horsfield (*Sussex* I 413-4), *SNQ* (XII 179) and Wace (46); for heraldry see Lambarde (*SAC* 67 158).
2. Note the Lombardic 'A', as on 270M, and the casting of the arms only partly successful.
3. William Barham outlived his older brother John Barham by some 40 years (see 270EE, FF and NN).
4. Willatts (*SAC* 125 105) notes that 270U is the last and grandest Barham slab, thereafter they erected mural monuments.

Wadhurst, 270V Floor slab for Samuel and Elizabeth NEWINGTON, d. 1714 and d. 1731
- Choir floor, North side, against sanctuary step, largely obscured by organ console.
- 88(W) x 199(L) — Fine (visible parts).
- Arms, then M.I. (engraved) on a slab (material?); head to West.
- Samuel Newington, d. 28 May 1714, aet 71; his wife, Elizabeth, d. 17 Apr 1731, aet 77.

1. Within the sanctuary rail says Horsfield (*Sussex* I 413-4).
2. In situ *SNQ* (XII 179).
3. For Newington, see 270I, 270II and 270RR and Ticehurst.

Wadhurst, 270W Floor slab for John PORTER, d. 1673, and others
- Choir floor, against North wall and sanctuary step, largely obscured by organ bench.
- 86(W) x 197(L) — Very worn; stained; defoliated.
- M.I. (15 lines, engraved) in brown freestone slab; head to West.
- John Porter, of Wadhurst, Gent., d. 1 Aug 1673; son of Thomas Porter of Goudhurst, Gent.; and husband of Katherine, d. 20 Aug 1653, daughter of Thomas Aynscombe, Esq., of Mayfield; their issue, Thomas, d. 18 Feb 1723, aet 81; and Arther, d. 13 Jan 1721, aet 74.

1. Within the sanctuary rail says Horsfield (*Sussex* I 413-4).
2. In situ *SNQ* (XII 179).
3. A freestone ledger is rare at Wadhurst.
4. Probably datable after 1723.

Wadhurst, 270X Mural monument for Mary DAVISON, d. 1651 [Plate 169]

- Sanctuary North wall, at head height and above.
- 87(W) x 204(H) — Good; faded; colour restored above.
- In black, grey and white marbles (alabaster); kneeling effigy turns out from prayer desk to face the altar; flanking, pillars; M.I. (cut shallow) on tablet.

> NEAR THIS PLACE LYETH BVRIED YE BODY OF MARY
> YE DAVGHTER OF IOHN DVNMOLL OF THIS PARISH GENT
> & ANN HIS WIFE; WHO MARIED MICHAEL DAVISON OF
> LONDON MARCHANT BY WHOM HE HAD ISSUE 3
> CHILDREN; ANN, JOHN & MARY WCH MARY BEING
> ONLY LIVING: TO WHOSE MEMORY HER SAD HVSBAND
> DEDICATED THIS SMALL MONVMENT
> OBIIT 14TH APRIL: 1651 ÆTATIS SUÆ 31
> Althov the Earth thy Corps Detaine,
> yet shall wee once more meet againe.
> For to Reioyce and praises singe
> to God in Christ ovr gloriovs King

1. In situ; Horsfield (*Sussex* I 413-4), Nairn & Pevsner 617); Lambarde does not describe heraldry.
2. Flanking pillars (rather than columns) are unusual. Horsfield calls these Ionic; have they been replaced?
3. Patron was husband.

Wadhurst, 270Y Mural monument for Rev. John WILLETT, d. 1742/3

- Sanctuary North wall, above 270X-Z.
- Inaccessible (width close to 270Z) — Very good; dirty; stained.
- M.I. (13 lines, engraved, black, Latin) on simple unframed freestone tablet; arched top; corbels; unframed with arched top.
- Rev. John Willett, A.M., vicar for 28 years, d. 31 Jan 1742/3, aet 69.

1. In situ; Horsfield (*Sussex* I 413-4).
2. Other vicars at Wadhurst are commemorated in and near the sanctuary (see 270Z, AA, BB).
3. For John Willett see Dunkin (*SAC* 26 94-5); educated Wadham College, Oxford; Fellow there 1699-1715; rector of Barlavington 1705-07; vicar of Wadhurst, 1714-42/3; d. 31 Jan 1742/3 and buried, 5 Feb 1742/3, see Foster (*Al Ox* 1 4 1636).

Wadhurst, 270Z Mural monument for Betty SALMON, d. 1813, and her son Rev. William Salmon, d. 1818.

- Sanctuary North wall, East of 270X, above head height.
- 100(W) x c.200(H) — Very good.
- M.I. (12 lines, engraved, black) on a rectangular white marble tablet set landscape-wise; cornice and corbels with natural ornament; above, 2 draped urns in white and an escutcheon; tall backplate with domed top.
- Betty Salmon, d. 3 May 1813, aet 68; her son, Rev. William Salmon, vicar of Wadhurst, d. 2 Jun 1818, aet 53.

1. Noted but not located by Horsfield (*Sussex* I 413-4).
2. Cited by Wace (48).
3. Final 6 lines, added after 1818 [in same hand?].
4. William Salmon instituted 1804; d. 2 Jun 1818, aet 53, see Dunkin (*SAC* 26 95).

Wadhurst, 270AA Floor slab for Rev. James WILCOCKS, d. 1662

- Choir floor, South side, towards East end, mostly obscured by choir stalls.
- 86(W) x 201(L) — Fine (visible areas).
- M.I. (7 lines, engraved) fill upper 25% of a black slab; head to West.
- Rev. James Wilcocks, d. 1662; his wife, Mary.

1. In situ; Horsfield (*Sussex* I 413-4), *SNQ* (XII 179).
2. See too comment under 270Y.
3. For James Wilcocks see Dunkin (*SAC* 26 94): admitted 1650, buried 29 Feb 1661/2; vicar of Goudhurst 1640/1-61/2, see Venn (1 4 405).

Wadhurst, 270BB Floor slab for Rev. Samuel BUSH, d. 1783

- Choir floor, South side, alongside and North of 270AA.
- 95(W) x 198(L) — Good.
- Arms, then M.I. in Latin fills Purbeck (?) slab; head to West.
- Rev. Samuel Bush, A.M., (Wadhurst, 39 years), d. 22 Jan 1783.

1. In situ *SNQ* (XII 179) and Wace (46); for heraldry see Lambarde (*SAC* 67 159).
2. Ambitious Latin M.I., rare for the 1780s.
3. Final 8 lines signed 'SB' as author; for Samuel Bush, see Dunkin (*SAC* 26 95): educated Wadham College, Oxford; instituted 1743.

Wadhurst, 270CC Mural monument for Edward BURGIS, d. 1750

- Sanctuary, South-East corner, above head height.
- 173(W); (H) inaccessible — Fine; stained; repaired.
- M.I. (13+3+5 lines, engraved, black) on a white marble tablet; domed top; set portrait-wise; grey marble frame; below, base mouldings and ornamental apron; above, a cherub within a pointed pediment; no entablature, but scaled and scrolled brackets support a part-frieze; on top, an urn.
- Edward Burgis, d. 22 Apr 1750, aet 71; his wife, Ann, d. 12 Oct 1752, aet 75; their issue - Ann, d. 12 May 1790, aet 80, wife of John Newington; Jane, d. 14 Jul 1764, aet 52; Richard Walter, d. 19 Aug 1777, aet 63.

1. Noted by Horsfield (*Sussex* I 413-4) with date 1740.
2. Cited by Wace (48).
3. 270CC was erected after 1764 by Jane Burgis.
4. For Newington see 270I and 270RR.
5. Burgis was not of Gent. or Esq. status but merited a mural monument in a prominent position.
6. The cherub is of high quality, Remnant (*SAC* 100 54) suggests that the cherub is by Harmer and a later addition to the monument.

Wadhurst, 270DD Mural monument for Ann COURTHOPE, d. 1689, and her husband George, d. 1691

- Sanctuary South-East corner, above head height, West of 270CC.
- 82(W) x 186(L) — Good; rust stains; colour restored.
- M.I. on a white marble tablet, set portrait-wise; light frame and scrolled shoulders; above, a straight ledge and goblet adorned with roses; below, escutcheon on an ornamental apron.
- Ann Courthope, died at Sevenoaks, 18 May 1689, aet 62; daughter of William Brian, Gent.; and wife of George Courthope, Gent., of the Middle Temple, London, d. 24 Sep 1691, buried Boorn, Sussex; issue - George, Ann, Brian, Mary, Catharine, Thomas, James, Edward, John and Henry, all still living; and John, Elianor, Judith and Hannah, all died young.

1. In situ - Horsfield (*Sussex* I 413-4) and Wace (48).
2. Erected by Ann Courthope's second son, Brian Courthope, Gent., of the Inner Temple.
3. The main group of Courthope monuments is at Ticehurst.
4. For heraldry see Lambarde (*SAC* 67 158).

Wadhurst, 270EE Mural monument for John BARHAM, d. 1723/4, and others

[Plate 170]
- South choir wall, in centre, high.
- 170(W); (H) inaccessible — Excellent; colour restored.
- In column and white marbles with pigment and gilding on decorative details and arms; signed (lower left): 'Wm. Palmer, Londini, Fecit'; above, on a curved and broken pediment, 2 mourning putti flank a flaming urn and an achievement; below, crossed trumpets and a crown against clouds; in the centre, an inscribed drapery held by 3 cherubim within a domed niche, flanked by rich fluted Corinthian. columns and a minor order of pilasters; below, elaborate base mouldings, then three elaborate corbels with acanthus decoration.
- John Barham, Esq., of Shoosmith, Wadhurst, d. 10 Mar 1723/4, aet 81; his wife, Lucy, d. 26 Sep 1716, aet 52, daughter of John Chauntler, Gent.; their issue, John d. 22 Aug 1699, aet 20 weeks; Elizabeth, d. 20 Sep 1712, aet 16.

1. Cited by Wace (48).
2. Nairn & Pevsner (617) and Gunnis (*Dict.* 288), ascribe 270EE to Palmer (1673-1739).
3. An ambitious work, erected in 1730 by George Egles, of Shoosmith, Wadhurst - for a view of that house see Godfrey & Salzman (Pl. 169). He was nephew of Barham's wife; the terms of John Barham's inheritance which included £300 to build a monument; see Fitzgerald-Uniacke (*SAC* 56 110-160).
4. Lucy Barham left a bequest to Wadhurst's charity school (Caffyn 254).
5. Lambarde does not describe heraldry.

Wadhurst, 270FF Floor slab for John BARHAM, d. 1648

- Choir floor, South side, West of 270BB.
- 58(W) x 182(L) — Good.
- M.I. (raised relief), then blank arms cast on an iron slab; head to West.
- John Barham, Gent., of Shoosmiths, d. 5 Dec 1648.

1. In situ; Horsfield (*Sussex* I 413-4); *SNQ* (XII 179); Wace (46); illustrated in Lower (*SAC* 2 opposite p.200) and Fitzgerald-Uniacke (*SAC* 56 153).
2. Good quality casting, see Cleere & Crossley (190).
3. Barham arms here not from same block as on 270G (1675), see Willatts (*SAC* 125 104) and see Lambarde (*SAC* 67 159).
4. M.I. ends in initials 'TG' [?].
5. A later John Barham, son of builder of Shoosmiths, was churchwarden in 1670 (bell inscription).
6. For licence to marry for John Barham and Judith Hepden, of Burwash, 29 Apr 1624, see Dunkin (*Licences 1586-1643* 141).

Wadhurst, 270GG Floor slab for Mary SMITH, d. 1666

- Choir floor, South side, West of 270FF.
- 58(W) x 182(L) — Very worn.
- M.I. (raised) between 2 blank arms cast on an iron slab; head to West.
- Mary Smith, d. 11 Sep 1666; daughter of Roger Gostwyke of Sampford Courtney, Devon; and wife of Zachary Smith of Glynde, Sussex; their issue - Rev. John Smith, (Wadhurst, 1662-1713/4).

1. In situ *SNQ* (XII 179) and Wace (47).
2. Casting rough in places.
3. Note use of Lombardic 'A'.
4. JH notes that the son, Rev. John Smith was BA of King's, Cambridge, 1660; Fellow there 1559-62; vicar of Wadhurst 1662-1713/4 and buried there 2 Feb 1713/4, see Venn (1 4 102).

Wadhurst, 270HH Floor slab for Frances PORTER, d. 1717

- Choir floor, South side, West of 270GG.
- 58(W) x 181(L) — Very good.
- Arms, then M.I. (raised) cast on iron slab; head to West.

- Frances Porter, d. 18 Oct 1717, aet 79; daughter of Sir William Colepepyr, Bart., of Aylesford, Kent; her second husband, Thomas Porter, Gent.; Mary Alcron [Alchorne] daughter from Frances' first marriage.

1. Within the sanctuary rail; Horsfield (*Sussex* I 413-4).
2. In situ *SNQ* (XII 179); for heraldry see Lambarde (*SAC* 67 159).
3. Thomas Porter was owner of Dewhurst, a property in the parish; Frances married Thomas Porter in 1672, see Attree & Booker (*SAC* 48 80).
4. The furnace at Riverhall, see view in Godfrey & Salzman (Pl. 168), in Frant parish was sold to one John Alchorne in 1630, see Wright (53); John Alchorne was of Boughton Monchelsea and Frances Porter's first husband from 1667.

Wadhurst, 270II Floor slab for Benjamin NEWINGTON, d. 1777
- Nave floor, extreme East end.
- 99(W) x 168(L) — Good.
- Arms, then M.I. (engraved) in centre of a black slab; head to West.
- Benjamin Newington, Gent., of Towngate, Wadhurst, d. 11 Apr 1777, aet 52.

1. In situ *SNQ* (XII 179); Lambarde does not describe heraldry.
2. For another Newington see 270I.
3. One Joseph Newington owned Towngate etc. in 1785 (R. Davey 210).
4. The claim that 270II is of Purbeck marble can surely be disregarded.

Wadhurst, 270JJ Floor slab for Joan BUCHER, d. 1638
- Nave, East end, close to South Chapel door, partly obscured by lectern.
- 63(W) x 167(L) — Good.
- M.I. cast within an arched and decorated frame on an iron slab; head to West.
- Joan Bucher, wife of Alexander Bucher.

1. In situ *SNQ* (XII 179).
2. 270JJ is of a type favoured for other Bucher slabs (270T and 270LL).

Wadhurst, 270KK Mural monument for Anne TAPSELL, d. 1759, and her daughter Sarah, d. 1755.
- South aisle, East wall, North of East window, above head height.
- 95(W); (H) inaccessible — Good.
- In marbles of mixed colours; a pointed pyramid capped by a black finial; below, M.I. (engraved, black) on a framed tablet; cornice between flanking, inverted scrolls; below, scrolled apron with foliate corbel.
- Anne Tapsell, d. 30 Apr 1759, aet 26; daughter of Paul Legas, Gent., of Wadhurst; and wife of Richard Tapsell, Gent., of Wadhurst; their daughter, Sarah, d. 21 Feb 1755, aet 8 months.

1. Originally on wall at West end ; Horsfield (*Sussex* I 413-4).
2. Cited by Wace (48).
3. For Anne Tapsell's family monuments see 270J and ZZ; Richard Tapsell took over the Legas forge from John Legas.

Wadhurst, 270LL Floor slab for John BUCHER, d. 1640
- South aisle floor, near East end, partly obscured by altar rail.
- 64(W) x 181(L) — Fine.
- M.I. (raised and graffiti) with arched frame and blank arms, cast on an iron slab; head to South.
- John Bucher, Gent., d. Wed 30 Aug 1640; also 'EB' 1750 and 'AB' 1752.

1. Not noted in *SNQ* (XII 179).
2. 270LL is of a type favoured for other Bucher slabs (270T and 270JJ).
3. The M.I.'s reference to the day of the week is unusual.

Wadhurst, 270MM Floor slab for David BARHAM, d. 1643/4
- South aisle floor, centre, towards East end, abuts 270NN.
- 61(W) x 180(L) — Worn.
- M.I. (raised) in an arched frame, cast on an iron slab; head to West.
- David Barham, Gent., d. 18 Feb 1643/4.

1. In situ Horsfield (*Sussex* I 413-4), *SNQ* (XII 179) and Wace (46); illustration of 270MM in Fitzgerald-Uniacke (*SAC* 56 127) and in Cleere & Crossley (190).
2. David Barham was father of Ann Barham (270G); 270MM shows arms of David Barham's mother Courthope, see Willatts (*SAC* 125 104) and Lambarde (*SAC* 67 159); initials 'ABA' and date 1688 scratched in foot relate to David Barham's daughter-in-law Ann; for licence to marry for David Barham and Margaret Keymer, of Chiddingly dated 23 Oct 1613, see Dunkin (*Licences 1586-1643* 88).

Wadhurst, 270NN Floor slab for John BARHAM, d. 1657
- South aisle floor, abutting and West of 270MM.
- 59.5(W) x 177(L) — Fine.
- Repeated motif of an escutcheon cast on an iron slab.

1. In situ *SNQ* (XII 179) and Wace (46).
2. John Barham was nephew of William and David Barham and owned Scrag Oak, Wadhurst.
3. For an earlier example of this type see 270PP.

Wadhurst, 270OO Mural monument commemorating Thomas WHITFIELD'S charity, 1631
- South aisle wall, near East end, at head height.
- 95(W) x 195(H) — Fine; faded; colour restored.
- In grey freestone; flanking below, traces of relief decorative; M.I. on a small panel within a (too) large architectural frame; cornice, base mouldings, apron, baseplate, corbels; above, a small escutcheon and 3 pointed finials.

1. Noted by Horsfield (*Sussex* I 413-4) and Wace (49); for heraldry see Lambarde (*SAC* 67 159).
2. Erected by the parish to mark the charitable foundations of Thomas Whitfield of Worth, (born at Wadhurst); for his monument see 306D.

Wadhurst, 270PP Floor slab for William BARHAM, d. 1617
- South aisle floor, abutting and West of 270NN.
- 57(W) x 183(L) — Fine.
- Arms cast in relief on an iron slab, facing East and West.

1. In situ *SNQ* (XII 179) and Wace (46).
2. Close in type to 270NN.
3. William Barham's elder brother was David Barham.

Wadhurst, 270QQ Floor slab for Helen DUNMOLL, d. 1651/2
- South aisle floor, abutting and West of 270PP.
- 58(W) x 172(L) — Worn.
- Blank compartments for arms either end of M.I. (raised) cast in an iron slab; head to West.
- Helen Dunmoll, d. 6 Feb 1651/2; daughter of David Barham, Gent.; and wife of Joseph Dunmoll, Gent.

1. Noted by Horsfield (*Sussex* I 413-4); in situ *SNQ* (XII 179) and Wace (47).
2. Casting rough in places.

Wadhurst, 270RR Mural monument for John NEWINGTON, d. 1783, and his wife Mary, d. 1794
- South aisle, just East of South door, above head height.
- 120(W) x 300(H) — Fine; colour restored.

- Largely in terracotta; M.I. (engraved, black) on a tablet set landscape-wise; gilded arms and architectural flanking, fluted columns; above a small pointed pediment with 3 flaming urns; below, base mouldings; ornamental apron with escutcheon.
- John Newington, Gent., of Towngate, Wadhurst, d. 7 Feb 1783, aet 55; his wife, Mary, d. 16 Dec 1794, aet 64; both buried at Wadhurst; their son, Joseph erected the monument.

1. In situ, Wace (48).
2. Horsfield (*Sussex* I 413-4) notes a John Newington of Hightown, d. 1780, aet 85.
3. The eccentric ornamental details on 270RR are suggestive of Harmer's work (see 270A etc.).
4. For heraldry see Lambarde (*SAC* 67 159).
5. Newingtons also commemorated by a Harmer terracotta in Burwash churchyard, see Remnant (*SAC* 100 145); for Newington family see 270I and 270II and other monuments at Ticehurst.

Wadhurst, 270SS Floor slab for Ann and David HOLLAN, d. 1664
- South aisle floor, immediately inside the South door.
- 55(W) x 170.5(L) — Worn.
- M.I. (7 lines, in relief) cast in centre of an iron slab; head to West.
- Ann and David Hollan, d. 19 Nov 1664; children of David Holland [sic].

1. Ages not given.
2. In situ *SNQ* (XII 179) and Wace (47).
3. 270SS was perhaps formerly part of 270TT.
4. For licence to marry of David Hollan, of Wadhurst, mercer and Anne Burton, of Wadhurst 23 Sep 1636, see Dunkin (*Licences 1670-1729* 281).

Wadhurst, 270TT Floor slab for Ann HOLLAN, d. 1664
- South aisle floor, alongside 270SS.
- 55(W) x 171.5(L) — Worn.
- M.I. (7 lines, in relief) cast in centre of an iron slab; head to West.
- Ann Hollan, d. 1 Nov 1664, aet 48; wife of David Hollan.

1. In situ *SNQ* (XII 179) and Wace (47).
2. 270TT was perhaps formerly part of 270SS.

Wadhurst, 270UU Floor slab for Nicholas DONMOOLLE, d. 1673/4
- Nave floor, West end, near South door, North of 270TT.
- 55(W) x 155(L) — Worn.
- M.I. (11 lines, in relief) cast between blank compartments for arms on an iron slab; head to West.
- Nicholas Donmoolle, d. 5 Mar 1673/4, aet 50 [?].

1. In situ *SNQ* (XII 179) and Wace (47).
2. Horsfield (*Sussex* I 414) records the year as '1763', incorrectly.
3. Casting rough in places.
4. Close in form to 270VV.
5. Note use of Lombardic 'A'.

Wadhurst, 270VV Floor slab for James ATWELLS, d. 1678
- Nave floor, West end, North of 270UU.
- 57(W) x 156(L) — Worn.
- M.I. (11 lines, in relief) cast between blank compartments for arms on an iron slab; head to West.
- James Atwells, d. 1 Oct 1678; son of John Atwells.

1. In situ *SNQ* (XII 179) and Wace (46).
2. Close in form to 270UU.

Wadhurst, 270WW Floor slab for Nicholas SAUNDERS, d. 1660/1
- Nave, West end, North of 270VV.
- 55(W) x 133(L) — Very worn.
- M.I. (7 lines, in relief) cast in centre of an iron slab; head to West.
- Nicholas Saunders, of Pell, d. 30 Jan 1660/1, aet 65.

1. In situ *SNQ* (XII 179) and Wace (47).
2. Nicholas Saunders was the grandfather of Judith Legas (270J and ZZ); Nicholas Saunders' widow was Ann Saunders (270E).
3. See too 270L.

Wadhurst, 270XX Floor slab for Mary and Elizabeth LUCK, d. 1707 and d. 1709
- Nave floor, West end, North of 270WW.
- 65(W) x 148(L) — Fine.
- M.I. (in relief) below a blank compartment cast in an iron slab; head to West.
- Mary and Elizabeth Luck, daughters, of Edward and Elizabeth Luck. Mary, d. 9 Jan 1707, aet 23; Elizabeth, d. 13 Jan 1709, aet 21.

1. In situ *SNQ* (XII 179), Wace (47) and see Cleere & Crossley (190).
2. For the family see 270A-D.

Wadhurst, 270YY Floor slab for Ann BENGE, d. 1653
- Nave floor, West end, centre.
- 55(W) x 140(L) — Very worn.
- M.I. (8 lines, in relief) cast on an iron slab; head to West.
- Ann Benge, d. 12 Oct 1653, aet 27 [?]; wife of William Benge.

1. In situ *SNQ* (XII 179) and Wace (47).
2. Unusually worn for an iron slab.
3. Other Benge ledgers at Laughton (153A-B).

Wadhurst, 270ZZ Floor slab for Judith LEGAS, dated 1747 [Plate 171]
- Nave floor, centre aisle, in line with South door.
- 92(W) x 198(L) — Fine.
- Brass letters/figures ('I.L / 1747') inlaid on a cast iron slab; head to West.

1. In situ; Horsfield (*Sussex* I 413-4), *SNQ* (XII 179) and Wace (47).
2. This medium is very rare; cited with its mural (270J) by Willatts (*SAC* 125 103); see 270J for a related mural.
3. Judith Legas, d. 13 Jun 1747, aet 71; (her husband was John Legas, d. 22 May 1752, aet 62).

Wadhurst Additions
SNQ XII 17 and Harper (*Heraldry* p. 15):
(1) Iron floor slab to Nicholas Fowle of River Hall; under the oak screen dividing the South chapel from the main body of the church; for Nicholas Fowle see Lower (*SAC* 2 218); Willatts (*SAC* 125 104) notes that Fowle arms are found repeated on slabs at Frant and at Wadhurst (perhaps Addition 2).

(272) WALDRON, All Saints
Mostly Early English; South aisle 1859-62 - Nairn & Pevsner (619); a defective porch pavement, over a grave, was reported in 1686 (Ford 52); the parish had 87 families in 1724 when the church fabric was reported to be fine; the population was 752 in 1801; 4 generations of Dyke family of Horsham are commemorated at Waldron; there are terracottas by Harmer in the churchyard.

Waldron, 272A Wall monument for Major John FULLER, d. 1722

- North-East corner of North aisle, against North wall; partly obscured by banners.
- 194(W) x c.390(H) — Generally very good; M.I. very worn.
- In a selection of rich, coloured marbles; a backplate in grey marble comprising an obelisk with arms; below, a covered sarcophagus, flanked by freestone white urns; M.I. (5 lines, Latin in the basement; 7 lines of English on sarcophagus); no M.I. on obelisk.
- Major John Fuller, son of John Fuller Esq. (no more legible).

1. Horsfield (*Sussex* I 361).
2. Major John Fuller, d. 22 Oct 1722, aet 70, was Major of the Trained Band and Sheriff in 1685; his wife was Elizabeth, daughter of Samuel Fowle of London; their son, also John Fuller, d. 4 Aug 1745, aet 66; his wife, Elizabeth, d. 18 Feb 1727/8, aet 46, was daughter of Fulke Rose, see Ley (*SAC* 13 98).
3. Note absence of figures; a very fashionable, metropolitan piece.
4. [Mistakenly?] located on North aisle, West wall, see Lambarde (*SAC* 70 157).
5. The Fullers were iron founders; the son John Fuller, of Brightling, d. 4 Aug 1746, was MP for Sussex 1713-15, see Crossley & Saville *The Fuller Letters* - which includes family portrait - and Cruikshanks (3 1124).

Waldron, 272B Mural monument for Philadelphia DYKE, d. 1720

- North aisle; South wall, North face, very high.
- Inaccessible — Fine; faded.
- A small, unframed freestone tablet with a moulded and arched top; M.I. (8 lines, engraved, black).
- Philadelphia Dyke, d. 22 Aug 1720, buried at Waldron; widow of Sir Thomas Dyke.

1. The suggestion in the M.I. that 272B was once set below her husband's memorial (272N) is confirmed by Horsfield (*Sussex* I 361).
2. Philadelphia Dyke was a prominent benefactor of the church, see Ley (*SAC* 13 102).

Waldron, 272C Mural monument for Rev. Thomas LEWIS, d. 1818

- Choir, North wall, at head height.
- c.68(W) x c.97(H) — Fair; tablet cracked; local losses to urn moulding.
- Above, a grey marble urn in relief against a black baseplate with pointed top; below, an oval tablet set portrait-wise with a decorated border, a M.I. (20 lines, engraved) all on a small bracket.
- Rev. Thomas Lewis, curate of Waldron for 42 years, d. 3 Jun 1818, aet 66; quotes Timothy IV 7-8.

1. In situ; Horsfield (*Sussex* I 361).

Waldron, 272D Ledger and brass for Thomas DYKE, d. 1632

- Nave, East end, near sanctuary step.
- 74(W) x 158(L) — Slab very worn; brass worn but legible.
- A (Horsham?) stone slab with brass and matrices for other missing brasses; head to West.
- Thomas Dyke, Esq., d. 6 Apr 1632, aet 69; his wife, Joane, daughter of Thomas Walsh, Gent., of Horeham; issue - Abraham, Herbert, Thomas, Margery, Judith, Elizabeth and Sarah.

1. Appears to be in about the original location – Horsfield (*Sussex* I 361); Stephenson (517-18); Turner (*SAC* 23 188); Lambarde (*SAC* 70 156) noting arms and Davidson-Houston (*SAC* 80 130) - a shield by then lost.
2. The Dyke family came from Cumberland and Thomas built Horeham (now largely destroyed) temp. James I - for details of which see Ley (*SAC* 13 100-103); Thomas Walsh, Thomas Dyke's father-in-law, was perhaps the previous owner of Horeham; M.I.s on 272D-E suggest that father, first son and wife all d. 1632, however, according to Couchman (*SAC* 55 216), Joan presented plate to the church in 1638 in memory of Thomas Dyke; had she died in 1632, this would have been a bequest.

Waldron, 272E Ledger and brasses for Abraham and Joane DYKE, d. 1632 and d. 1633

- Nave, East end, near sanctuary step, near 272D.
- Slab: 77(W) x 168(L) — Very worn. Brasses - (i) 40(W) x 12(H); (ii) (lozenge) 19(W) x 17(H), (iii) 47(W) x 14(H) — Worn but legible.
- 3 brasses on a (Horsham?) stone slab; head to West.
- Abraham Dyke, Esq., d. 15 Oct 1632, aet 24; son of Joane Dyke, d. 1 Jan 1632/3, aet 46, wife of late Thomas Dyke, Esq., of Horeham.

1. See comments on 272D.
2. Noted by Horsfield (*Sussex* I 361); Stephenson (518); Turner (*SAC* 23 188); Lambarde (*SAC* 70 156) noting arms and Davidson-Houston (*SAC* 80 131), who notes a copy of the lost M.I. at Society of Antiquaries.

Waldron, 272F Ledger for Thomas OFFLEY, d. 1673

- Nave floor, towards East end.
- 68(W) x 198(L) — Sound; very worn on left side.
- Escutcheon, then M.I. (engraved) fill black slab; head to West.
- Only right-hand fragments of M.I. survive:

...MARBLE

... ERRD THE

... OFFLEY

... OF HVMPHREY

...INGWORTH

... ESQ) WHO

...IVNE 1673

... OF HIS AGE

... SVE BY

...WIFE DAVGHTER

... ARD BATHVRST

... Yᴇ COVNTY

... RELICT OF

... OF THE

... LONDON

...DREN 8 SONS

... OF WHICH

... DAVGHTERS

... LOSSE WITH

... MOTHER

... RIA MUNDI

1. In Lambarde (*SAC* 70 156) noting arms and partly illegible at that date.
2. In the first half of the 17th century, Humphrey Offley purchased the manor of Possingworth, see Ley (*SAC* 13 94-95); for a view of the North-East front in 1785 see Ley (*SAC* 13 facing p.80).
3. JH notes that Thomas Offley, son of Humphrey Offley of Possingworth, Esq., died in June 1673 aged c.37 and was buried on 14 Jun 1673 at Waldron. His wife was Elizabeth, daughter of Richard Bathurst of Finchcocks, Kent, and widow of Richard Thomas of the Middle Temple. They had 8 sons and some daughters.
4. Was 272F installed by Thomas Offley's widow, who d. 1715?

Waldron, 272G Ledger for Catherine and Hugh OFFLEY, d. 1735 and d. 1746/7

- Nave floor, near East end.
- 99(W) x 200(L) — Sound; M.I. and arms very worn.
- Escutcheon, then M.I. (17 lines, engraved) fill black slab; head to West.
- Catherine Offley, d. 1 May 1735, aet 69; youngest daughter of Thomas Lade, Gent., of Warbleton; and wife of Hugh Offley, Esq., of Possingworth, d. 29 Jan 1746/7, aet 71.

1. In situ - Horsfield (*Sussex* I 361); Lambarde (*SAC* 70 156) noting arms.

2. For the family see 272F.
3. According to Ley (1861 95), Catherine Offley d. 1739, aet 70; their only daughter married Stephen Fuller, for whose descent see 272A.

Waldron, 272H Ledger for Richard THOMAS, d. 1677
- Centre of nave floor.
- 83(W) x 204(L) — Very worn, almost illegible; cracks on North side.
- Escutcheon, then M.I. (21 lines, engraved) fill white slab; head to West.
>   Richard Thomas... Templi... Richardi Bathurst... 1677... Frater... posuit

1. Noted by Horsfield (*Sussex* I 361), Lambarde (*SAC* 70 156) noting arms.
2. Richard Thomas' father was also Richard Thomas and of the Middle Temple; Richard Thomas Jnr was son of Elizabeth, daughter of Richard Bathurst, Esq., of Finchcocks, Kent, who d. 1715, see Ley (*SAC* 13 95); her second husband was Thomas Offley (see 272F); a brother was patron of 272H.

Waldron, 272I Ledger for James DALRYMPLE, d. 1781
- Centre of nave floor, partly obscured by pews.
- (Visible): 114(W) x 200(L) — Sound but worn.
- M.I. (14 lines, engraved) in upper 80% of a black slab; head to West.
- James Dalrymple, Esq., of Gatehouse, Mayfield, d. 29 Mar 1781, aet 49; his wife, Cordelia, d. 6 Jun 1802, aet 70.

1. Noted by Horsfield (*Sussex* I 361), even then obscured by pews.
2. Ley (*SAC* 13 95) notes that Cordelia Dalrymple was born Cordelia Apsley and was heiress to the Offley-Fuller descent; she was still the owner of property in 1785 (R. Davey 211).

Waldron, 272J Ledger for Ann COURTHOPE, d. 1675
- Nave floor, West end, partly obscured by pews, cut on North side.
- (Visible): 88(W) x 200(L) — Worn but legible.
- Escutcheon, then M.I. (11 lines, engraved) fill 80% of black slab; head to West.
- Ann Courthope, d. 16 Dec 1675, aet 25; daughter of John Fuller, Esq., of Waldron Sussex; and wife of George Courthorpe, Esq., eldest son of Sir George Courthope, Knt., of Whyligh, Sussex.

1. Noted by Horsfield (*Sussex* I 361), Ley (*SAC* 13 98) and Lambarde (*SAC* 70 157) noting arms.

Waldron, 272K Ledger for Thomas FULLER, d. 1744
- Nave floor, West end, partly obscured by pews, cut on North side.
- (Visible): 88(W) x 200(L) — Worn but legible; large crack running North-South.
- Escutcheon, then M.I. (8 lines, engraved) fill 75% of black slab; head to West.
- Thomas Fuller, Esq., of Mayfield, d. 19 Apr 1744, aet 50.

1. Noted by Horsfield (*Sussex* I 361), even then obscured by pews.
2. Lambarde (*SAC* 70 157) noting arms, with date of 1744.

Waldron, 272L Mural cartouche for Bridget DYKE, d. 1722
- North aisle, West wall, South of 272M, high up.
- c.80(W) x c.140(H) — Sound; very faded.
- Convex Baroque cartouche; framed by drapes and 3 cherubim; above, an escutcheon; M.I. (14 lines, engraved, black) filling 60%.
- [Bridget Dyke], 19 Jun 165? - 3 Nov 1722, daughter [?] of Sir Thomas Dyke; her sister, executrix and patron of the monument, Dorothy Dyke.

1. A monument to Bridget Dyke, d. 1722, wife or daughter of Sir Thomas Dyke, Bart., was noted in the South aisle or on the South wall near the pulpit, see Horsfield (*Sussex* I 361) and Lambarde (*SAC* 70 157).
2. NBI records the burial of Bridget Dyke on 15 Nov 1722 at Waldron.

Waldron, 272M Mural Monument for Sir Thomas and Katherine DYKE, d. 1669 and 1695
- North aisle, West wall, North of 272L, high up.
- c.80(W) x c.140(H) — Fine; faded (M.I. and arms).
- M.I. (17 lines, engraved, black) fills oval convex plaque; below, escutcheon as corbel; above, urn in relief; framed by 2 cherubs, garlands and foliage.
- Sir Thomas Dyke, of Horeham, d. 13 Dec 1669, aet 51; his wife, Katherine Dyke, d. 28 May 1695, aet 76, daughter of Sir John Bramston, of Skreens, Essex, Judge; issue: John, Thomas, William, Mary, Katherine, Elizabeth, Bridget, Sarah, Dorothy, Bridget, Martha and Lucy.

1. Formerly on South wall near chancel; Horsfield (*Sussex* I 361); in situ in Lambarde (*SAC* 70 157) noting arms.
2. Thomas Dyke was third son of the dynastic founder (272D-E) (see Ley 1861 102).
3. Perhaps 297R is by the same hand?

Waldron, 272N Mural Monument for Sir Thomas DYKE, d. 1706
- North aisle, North wall, North-West corner, high up.
- 85(W) x 190(H) — Fine; faded (M.I. and arms).
- Convex Baroque cartouche; drapery and 2 cherubs flanking; above, an escutcheon; below, a death's head with folded wings.
- Sir Thomas Dyke, Bart., of Horeham, d. 31 Oct 1706, aet 57; his widow, Philadelphia, daughter of Sir Thomas Nutt, Knt., of Mays, Sussex; issue: Thomas (died an infant), Catherine (died an infant), Philadelphia, Elizabeth (another) and Thomas; patron of 272N, Philadelphia, widow and mother.

1. Formerly on a pillar in nave, alongside 272B; Horsfield (*Sussex* I 361); in situ in Lambarde (*SAC* 70 157) noting arms.
2. Probably erected soon after 1706 and before the death of Philadelphia Dyke on 22 Aug 1722.

Waldron Additions
Horsfield (*Sussex* I 361).
(1) Samuel Fuller, 1653, in sanctuary – illegible even then.

(273) WARBLETON, St. Mary
Mostly old walls; Early English chancel, Decorated North aisle, remainder Perpendicular - Nairn & Pevsner (619-20); *SNQ* (XIII 315) for plan; a view of 1782 from South-East in Godfrey & Salzman (Pl. 174); condition reported as fine in 1724 report (Ford); Gunnis (*Dict.* 188) and Nairn & Pevsner (619) cite terracotta monument here by Harmer (one subject d. 1813) in churchyard; the parish had c.120 families in 1724 and a population of 908 in 1801.

Warbleton, 273A Ledger for Paul BEESTON, d. 1681
- North aisle floor, opposite South door.
- 98(W) x 201(L) — Pitted.
- M.I. (7 lines, engraved) in band across centre of a black slab; head to West.
- Paul Beeston, Gent., d. 2 Sep 1681, aet 45; charitable bequest (Maidstone, Kent).

1. In situ; Horsfield (*Sussex* I 572); recording a charitable donation to the parish.

Warbleton, 273B Mural for Martha HARCOURT, d. 1796, and her husband Henry, d. 1800 [Plate 172]
- North aisle, North wall, opposite South door, above head height.
- 117(W) x 286(H) — Very good; local losses (head of heraldic supporter); faded.

- In white marble low relief, standing female mourner resting arm on urn; shallow serpentine obelisk as baseplate; below, M.I. (engraved) in 2 stages on tablet, framed, serpentine edging; below that, a fluted base, brackets with dentils; arms in ornamental apron.
- Martha Harcourt, d. 19 Sep 1796, aet 79; wife of Rev. Henry Harcourt, rector of Warbleton, d. 21 Aug 1800, aet 71.

1. Horsfield (*Sussex* I 572) notes 273B as near the Roberts pew.
2. Assume patron to be widowed husband Rev. Henry Harcourt, landowner at Warbleton in 1785 (R. Davey 213).
3. Donor of plate to church in 1776 see Couchman (*SAC* 55 218).
4. JH notes that Rev. Henry Harcourt, MA, was rector of Warbleton 1761-1800 and vicar of Crowhurst 1764-1800.
5. For heraldry, see Lambarde (*SAC* 67 158). There is a hatchment the Harcourts in the church, see Summers (156).

Warbleton, 273C Mural for Sir John LADE, d. 1740 [Plate 173]
- North aisle, North wall, far East end, head height and above.
- 200(W) x 330(H) — Excellent; faded.
- Portrait bust on pedestal adorned with scrolls and foliage, in a shallow arched niche with attached Corinthian columns, variegated marble flanking; outside the columns, scrolls set vertically with foliage; within, simple pilasters in darker grey marble; above, escutcheons (blank) with foliage decoration; at top, coffered pediment (no entablature); globe in centre; lamps flanking; below, decorative base moulding, brackets; ornamental apron with M.I. (engraved).
- Sir John Lade, Bart., of St. Saviour's Southwark, MP, JP, Dep. Lieut. of Southwark and London, etc., d. 30 Jul 1740, aet 78; fifth and youngest son of Thomas Lade, Gent., of Warbleton; no wife; no issue; brother unnamed; his brother's grandson, John Inskip, now also John Lade, Esq.

1. In situ in Horsfield (*Sussex* I 572) and Nairn & Pevsner (620) who point to the high quality of 273C, e.g. the cutting of the portrait & the subtle colour matches in columns and surround.
2. Patron of both 273C-D was John Inskip, who took Lade's name.
3. Attributed by Gunnis (*Dict.* 338) to Rysbrack, dated 1740 and related to a drawing at the V&A.
4. JH notes that Sir John Lade was a controversial politician of varying allegiance, who had made his money in brewing. He was MP for Southwark 1713-14; 1714-22 and 1724-27. As a trustee of Thomas Guy, he helped to establish Guy's Hospital. See Crossley & Saville (xii-xiii) and Cruikshanks (IV 583).

Warbleton, 273D Mural cartouche for John ROBERTS, d. 1688, and wife Anne, d. 1722
- Chancel North wall, West end, above head height.
- 90(W) x 170(H) — Excellent; faded.
- M.I. (engraved) on white marble cartouche; framed by decoration of fabric and cherubim; above, elaborate arms.
- John Roberts, Gent., of the Priory, Warbleton, d. 26 Aug 1688, aet 58; his wife Anna, d. 20 Jan 1722, aet 90, daughter of Thomas Lade, Gent., of Barham, Kent; no issue; their nephew, John Lade, Esq.; his siblings, unnamed.

1. In situ - Horsfield (*Sussex* I 572).
2. As with 273 C, the patron was John Lade, here the nephew.
3. The quality of 273D is very high, e.g. cherub - Nairn & Pevsner (620) call it 'handsome'.
4. For arms see Lambarde (*SAC* 67 157).

Warbleton, 273E Ledger for Thomas BARTON, d. 1735, and his sister Frances, d. 1743
- Nave floor, East end, near North aisle piers, largely obscured by furniture.
- 66(W) x 92(L) — Stained.
- M.I. (engraved) fills a marble slab; head to West.

- Thomas Barton, d. 19 May 1735, an infant; his sister, Frances, d. 29 Apr 1743, an infant; their parents Thomas and Catherine Barton.

1. Two infants aged 3 months and 26 days.

Warbleton, 273F Ledger for Thomas BARTON, d. 1761, and his wives, Catharine, d. 1749, and Frances, d. 1757

- Nave floor, centre, at entrance to chancel.
- 100(W) x 200(L) — Worn.
- M.I. (engraved) in upper 60% of a slab; head to West.

In the Vault under this Stone
lie interred the Bodies of the Rev^d
Mr THOMAS BARTON
many Years Rector of this Pariſh
who departed this Life the ſecond
Day of January 1761
in the 56th Year of his Age.

And both his Wife's
CATHARINE And FRANCES.
The former died the 24th of
July 1749. Aged 40.
The latter the 27th of April 1757.
Aged 58 Years.

1. Datable after 1761?

Warbleton, 273G Ledger for Rev. Richard GREEN, d. 1813

- Chancel floor, against South wall, partly obscured.
- 89(W) x 181(L) — Worn.
- M.I. (engraved) fills a freestone slab; head to West.

SACRED
[TO TH]E MEMORY OF
[RE]V. RICHARD GREEN
[RECT]OR OF THIS PARISH
[WHO D]IED AUG. 28TH 1813
[AGE]D 46 YEARS.

1. JH notes that Rev. Richard Green, MA, was rector of Warbleton 1800-13.

Warbleton, 273H Mural for Thomas ROBERTS, d. 1638

- South wall, near pulpit.
- 84(W) x 163(H) — Local losses (cartouche of arms; lower cornice).
- In coloured marbles and alabaster; Corinthian columns of touch; M.I. (11 lines, engraved) fill a slate tablet; above, elaborate entablature with broken ogival pediment; scrolled ends; achievement in the centre; below, heavy brackets and decorative apron with scrolls.

HERE LIES BVRIED IN THIS
CHVRCH THOMAS ROBERTS
ESQ: SONNE & HEIRE OF S^R
WALTER ROBERTS OF GLAS-
SENBVRIE IN KENT K^T: AND
BARRONET WHO MARRIED
ELIZABETH Y^E SOLE DAVGHTER
& HEIRE OF S^R MATHEW
HOWLAND K^T & DAME ELIZA-
BETH HIS WIFE AND DIED
THE 23TH OF IANVARIE 1638.

1. In situ [?] in Horsfield (*Sussex* I 572).
2. Emphasis on scrolled forms typical of the late 1630s.

Warbleton, 273I Mural for Benjamin Thomas Halcott COLE, d. 1850
- Choir, South wall, above head height.
- Inaccessible — Very good: faded.
- Shallow black slate base; M.I. (10 lines, engraved) on unframed white marble panel; above, simple moulded cornice, pointed pediment; signed (lower right on base): 'WINTER. HASTINGS'.

SACRED TO THE MEMORY OF

THE REV° BENJAMIN THOMAS HALCOTT COLE A>M>

FORMERLY FELLOW OF MAGDALEN COLLEGE CAMBRIDGE

ONE OF THE PREBENDARIES OF CHICHESTER CATHEDRAL

AND DURING 57 YEARS RECTOR OF THIS PARISH.

HE DIED AT BANGOR IN NORTH WALES THE 17 OF AUGUST 1850

IN THE 68TH YEAR OF HIS AGE

TAKE YE HEED WATCH AND PRAY

FOR YE KNOW NOT WHEN THE TIME IS

MARK XIII

(276) WARTLING, St Mary Magdalene

As at Hooe and Herstmonceux, a mediaeval church originally on a coastal rise; Perpendicular North and South arcades; South chapel off chancel now gone (Nairn & Pevsner 621; SNQ IV 1932-33 182 - with plan); state of chancel (belonging to the parson) in both 1686 & 1724 described as poor (Ford 46; 118); the parish had c.100 families in 1724 and a population of 858 in 1801; once the chancel was repaired it was filled with a notable series of tablets for members of the Curteis family, also noted by Horsfield (*Sussex* I 548-9); there are terracottas by Harmer in the churchyard.

Wartling, 276A Mural monument for Thomas LUXFORD d. 1739
- Chancel, across North-West corner, above head height.
- 98(W) x 136 (H) — Excellent.
- M.I. (18 lines, engraved, black) on 80% of a grey-veined and white marble tablet; straight entablature; base mouldings; two simple curved corbels; a dark grey curved apron.
- Thomas Luxford, Esq., of Windmill Hill, Sussex, d. 24 Feb 1739, aet 72; his grandparents, Thomas Luxford, of Windmill Hill and Changed Collins, daughter of Thomas Collins, Esq., of Socknersh, Sussex; eldest son of Richard Luxford, Esq., and Catherine, daughter of Thomas Henshaw, Esq., all of Billingshurst, Sussex; Catherine Henshaw was niece to Joseph Henshaw, bishop of Peterborough.

1. Noted by Horsfield (*Sussex* I 548-9).
2. Patron was George Luxford, presumably Thomas Luxford's heir.

Wartling, 276B Mural monument for Jeremiah and Jane CURTEIS d. 1806 and 1796
- Chancel, North wall, West end, above head height.
- 113(W) x 168(H) — Excellent.
- M.I. (engraved, black) fills an unframed white and grey-veined marble tablet; modest, straight entablature; base mouldings; above, escutcheon on base; below, two fluted scrolled corbels.
- Jeremiah Curteis, Esq., of Rye, d. 31 Dec 1806, aet 71; his wife, Jane Curteis, d. 1 Mar 1796, aet 54, both buried Tenterden, Kent; their only son, Edward Jeremiah Curteis, of Windmill Hill; their grandson, Edward Jeremiah Curteis, d. 7 Aug 1795, aet 4, buried at

Tenterden; a daughter to Edward-Jeremiah Curteis, unnamed.

1. In situ - Horsfield (*Sussex* I 549).
2. Lambarde (*SAC* 68 224) notes arms.
3. 276B-C signal that Edward-Jeremiah Curteis, of Windmill Hill, in succession to the Luxfords (see 276A), is establishing a burial place for his family - and 'its Descent & Alliance' - in succession to Tenterden.

Wartling, 276C Mural monument for Jane Anne Elizabeth CURTEIS d. 1820, her sister Laura Charlotte Darby d. 1847 and others

- Chancel, North wall, East of 276B, above head height.
- 128(W) x 158(H) — Excellent.
- M.I. fills surface of grey and white marble tablet; unframed; straight entablature; base mouldings; 2 fluted, scrolled corbels.
- Jane Anne Elizabeth Curteis, d. 24 Oct 1820, aet 28, buried at Wartling; second daughter of Edward Jeremiah Curteis, Esq., MP; his third daughter, Laura Charlotte Darby, born London, 3 Apr 1795, d. 27 Mar 1847, aet 51, and buried Florence, Italy; her husband as of 11 Apr 1822, William Henry Darby, Esq., of Leap Castle, King's County, Ireland; also, Steuart Boone Inglis, Esq., died at his residence, The Manor House, Inveresk, N[orth] B[ritain], 4 Apr 1828, aet 55, the only son of Capt. John Inglis, RN, of Cramond, N.B.; also his daughter, Mary Barrett Curteis Inglis who was granddaughter of Edward Jeremiah Curteis.

1. Noted by Horsfield (*Sussex* I 549).
2. Very close in type to 276B, less the escutcheon, and surely by the same hand, the pair commemorating the ancestry and issue of the patron Edward Jeremiah Curteis. Paragraphs 2 and 3 of 276C added later (see variations in form of letter '1').
3. For Mary Barrett Curteis Inglis see 276E.

Wartling, 276D Mural monument for Mary Barrett INGLIS d. 1813

- Chancel, North wall, East of 276C, above head height.
- 126(W) x 110(H) — Excellent.
- Against a thin, black baseplate on four black ball corbels; with an arched top; in white marble relief, a sarcophagus on pillared legs, with a moulded top, supporting a draped vase; below, a broad pedestal with a moulded top, supporting an escutcheon with motto; M.I. on the face of the sarcophagus on moulded tablet (9 lines, engraved, black).
- Mary Barrett Inglis 29 Dec 1789 - 17 Aug 1813, aet. 23; eldest daughter of Edward Jeremiah Curteis, Esq.; and wife of Steuart Boone Inglis.

1. In situ - Horsfield (*Sussex* I 548-9) - 'elegant'.
2. Lambarde (*SAC* 68 224) notes arms.
3. Mary Barrett's sisters are commemorated by 276C.
4. 276D was perhaps erected by the widower between 1813-28.

Wartling, 276E Mural monument for Mary Barrett Curteis INGLIS d. 1827 [Plate 174]

- Chancel, North wall, East of 276D, over rail, above head height.
- 90(W) x 75(H) — Excellent.
- Against a thin black baseplate with a pointed top; unframed white marble tablet with pointed pediment, set landscape-wise; squared-off corbels; low relief roses in pediment; below, a straight moulded entablature, M.I. (11 lines, engraved, black); signed (lower right): 'THEAKSTON.SC / PIMLICO.LONDON'.
- Mary Barrett Curteis Inglis, d. 16 Oct 1827, aet 14; only child of Steuart Boone Inglis, Esq., of Inveresk and Cramond, North Britain; and grand-daughter of Edward Jeremiah Curteis, Esq., MP.

1. Horsfield notes that Steuart Boone Inglis d. in 1828, which tends to confirm the dating of 1827.

2. The rose branch above has a bloom and a bud prematurely snapped, symbolising the mother and child, leaving only the bereaved father.
3. Cited by Gunnis (385) as by Joseph Theakston, 1772-1842.

Wartling, 276F Mural monument for Caroline Sarah CURTEIS d. 1825 [Plate 175]

- Chancel, South wall, centre, above head height.
- A mottled dark grey baseplate in obelisk form; a white marble relief with a standing, semi-draped putto mourning over a floral tribute; draped urn with profile relief portrait of the deceased, facing West; base mouldings over a substantial pedestal; M.I. (19 lines, engraved, black) fills a square tablet; below, a moulding, at foot, escutcheon with motto on a grey-veined baseplate.
- Caroline Sarah Curteis, born at Ashford, 16 May 1802, died at Tonbridge Wells, 15 May 1825, the last day of her 23rd year; daughter and co-heiress of Robert Mascall, Esq., of Peasmarsh Place, Sussex; and wife from 29 Jun 1821 of her cousin, Herbert Barrett Curteis, Esq., eldest son of Edward Jeremiah Curteis of Windmill Hill, MP; their only issue, Herbert Mascall Curteis, b. 8 Jan 1823, at Florence.

1. In situ - Horsfield (*Sussex* I 549) - by Bacon.
2. Attributed to Bacon & Manning (Gunnis 32) but appears not to be signed.
3. Heraldry noted by Lambarde (*SAC* 68 225).

Wartling, 276G Mural monument for Mary Jane SMITH d. 1805

- South-East chapel, West wall, above head height on bare wall.
- 63(W) x 124(H) — Good; faded.
- M.I. (10 lines, engraved, black) fills a white marble oval plaque; engraved border; above, flaming urn in low relief; below, ball corbel.
- Mary Jane Smith, d. 31 Jul 1805, aet 16; daughter of Rev. Jeremiah Smith, vicar of Wartling and his wife Ann.

Wartling Addition
Reported in Church Guide and in Survey of August 2001
(1) Mural monument for William Benbrigg (d. 1714) and his wives Rebecca Wenham (d. 1694) and Jane Wenham (d. 1709), at the West end of the North aisle; 47 x 83 (orientation unknown); condition unknown; lettering reported as deeply cut into grey-brown freestone; M.I. unknown. Earlier in the 17th century, the Benbrigges were prominent silver-smiths of Rye, see Kent (33)

(280) WEST DEAN (near Eastbourne), All Saints

Aisleless; Norman nave and early 14th-century chancel - Nairn & Pevsner (621-22), see plan in *SNQ* (IV 237) and views in BL Add. MS 5671 f.80; 5676 f.70; fabric reportedly fine in 1686 (Ford 51 & 183) and again in 1724, when there were just 8 families in the parish and when the patrons (by rotation) were William Dobell, Sir George Parker and Thomas Willard (Ford); the population had risen to 88 in 1801; with the Shurley tomb at Isfield, 280C-D are the most important set of early 17th-century monuments in East Sussex.

West Dean (near Eastbourne), 280A Ledger for Edward ALLFREY, d. 1728/9, and his father Edward, d. 1696

- South entrance porch floor.
- 100(W) x 182(L) — Fine.
- M.I. (11 lines, engraved.) in upper 50% of a black slab; head to West.
- Edward Allfrey, Jnr., of Charlestone, d. 18 Mar 1728/9, aet 59; son of Edward Allfrey, Snr., of West Dean, d. 7 Jul 1696, aet 65.

1. The commemoration of the son (d. 1729), perhaps the patron of 280A, seems to take precedence over that of the father (d. 1696) who was buried nearby but outside the church.
2. For licence to marry for Edward Allfrey, of West Dean and Mary Relph, of Heathfield, maiden, 30 Apr 1698, see Dunkin (*Licences 1670-1729* 170).
3. Note use of French [?] spelling 'Seignior' in M.I. and variant spellings of Allfrey / Allerey.

West Dean (near Eastbourne), 280B Ledger for members of the HARISON family, c.1796-99

- Centre of nave floor, West end.
- 100(W) x 203(L) — Stone fine; lettering worn.
- Escutcheon then M.I. (14 lines [8 lines + 6 lines], engraved) in a freestone slab; head to East.
- Catherine Harison and Elizabeth Harison, d. 1796, daughters of Charles Harison, Esq. and Jane his wife; also Sarah Frances Harison, d. June 22 1798; Jane Harison, d. Dec 1800; Mary Tomkinson, d. 1828, aet 84; Rebecca Harison, d. 1834, aet 97.

1. 280B is in its original location having previously (until 1996) been relocated in the tower wall.
2. Lancelot Harison, Esq., owned extensive property at West Dean in 1785 (see R. Davey 67 and ledger at Folkington, 108G).
3. The crescent moon recurs on arms on 280D.
4. NBI records the burial of five members of the Haris(s)on family at West Dean: Catherine on 18 Feb 1788, Elizabeth on 10 May 1796, Sarah on 26 Jun 1798, Jane on 11 Dec 1800 and Rebecca on 28 Feb 1834. Also Mary Tomkinson is recorded on 8 Mar 1828.

West Dean (near Eastbourne), 280C Mural monument for Susan TIRREY, d. 1637 [Plate 176]

- Nave, North wall, near chancel steps, at head height and above.
- 123(W) x 205(H) — Very good; some damage to upper moulding of plinth, lower left.
- In alabaster and coloured marbles around a M.I. (29 lines, Latin, engraved on slate); above, an achievement and swag within a broken, curved pediment; below, herms flank the M.I., partly obscured by allegorical figures of Labour (left) and Rest, with shovel and torch, the latter with one foot on a death's head, standing on large brackets; below, a scrolly apron with a cherub.
- Susan Tirrey, died 1637; daughter of William Thomas, armiger, of West Dean; and wife of George Tirrey, of Grays Inn; her many virtues.

1. Cited by Horsfield (*Sussex* I 282); Nairn & Pevsner (622) find the allegorical figures 'decidedly funny'.
2. Originally over the pulpit, moved in 1961; condition largely unchanged since 1982.
3. For Susan Tirrey's father, see 280D and for licence to marry for George Tirrey of Greyes Inn, Gent. and Susan Thomas, daughter of William Thomas of All Saints, Lewes, Gent., dated 24 Mar 1636, see Dunkin (*Licences 1586-1643* 228); Susan Tirrey died young, soon after her marriage to George Tirrey who erected 280C immediately afterwards.
4. A similar project to use monuments to establish a dynasty, occurs at nearby Friston (112B-C).
5. NBI records the burial of Susan Tirrey on 24 Apr 1637 at West Dean.
6. For heraldry see Lambarde (*SAC* 70 144).

West Dean (near Eastbourne), 280D Mural Monument for William THOMAS, d. 1639/40 and his wife Anne, d. 1625 [Plates 177 & 178]

- Sanctuary, against South wall.
- 285(W) x 390(H) — Generally very good; local damage to lower projecting mouldings and angels' wings; colour visible throughout.
- 2 kneeling, robed figures at a prayer desk, (William Thomas to East; Ann Thomas to West); on back wall, a black engraved M.I. tablet with scrollwork frames, death's head and escutcheon; in the coffered arch, a scrolled keystone; 2 columns. with black shafts flanking and beyond them, allegorical figures (angels); below, a deeper, then a lesser basement with 2 escutcheons to left and right, set at an angle, and 3 decorative panels of

black touch with M.I.s (engraved); above, an entablature with segmented pediment and a large centred achievement.

- William Thomas, armiger, d. 19 Feb 1639/40, aged 60; his wife of 22 years, Anne, d. 29 Aug 1625, aet c.49, daughter of John Michelborne, Gent., of Chichester, Gent.; their issue - William, Ann, Mary, Susan, Francesca, Elizabeth.

1. In 1777, Grose noted 'several' Thomas monuments here (Farrant); Horsfield (*Sussex* I 282) cites it with full transcription and noted by Nairn & Pevsner (622) and in Lambarde (*SAC* 70 144) noting arms.
2. 280D appears to be in its original location.
3. William Thomas from Lewes, a Clerk of the Peace (*SNQ* XIII 148), was lord of the manor of West Dean in 1611 - but still 'Gent of Lewes' in 1633; see Trayton & Shurley marriage surety in Dunkin (*Licences 1586-1643* 205).
4. Two of the M.I. panels are in the same hand, but a third, on the back wall, is blank suggesting that 280D was erected in the later 1620s, after the death of William Thomas' wife Anne, youngest daughter of John Michelborne by Mary his second wife; first wife, Anne was born c.1576, married. William Thomas in 1605 and d. 29 Aug 1625, aet c.49; her eldest son was another William Thomas, in turn father of Sir William Thomas Bart., for whom see 108E.
5. An ambitious London-made work; hands and faces of the main effigies appear to be plaster, not alabaster.
6. The carving quality of the flanking angels is very high though some of the angled poses of the pairs of cherubs on the underside of the main entablature do not match.
7. About 10 years earlier than 208C.

(281) WEST FIRLE, St. Peter

12th-century North door, 13th-century chancel, 16th-century Gage chapel with late Perpendicular arcade - Nairn & Pevsner (623); for views see BL Add. MS 5676 f.79; 5671 ff.90-91; for a plan see *SNQ* VII 117; the parish had c.100 communicants in 1603, with an additional high number (17) of recusants, see Renshaw (*Ecclesiastical Returns*); in 1724 it was reported that the chancel was being damaged by a collapsed vault, the repairs the responsibility of Thomas Chowne (see 4B, D) (Ford); there were 34 families in 1724 and a population of 494 in 1801; monuments dominated by the remarkable series commissioned from Garret Johnson by John Gage in 1595 to himself and his ancestors and so unusually documented in the Gage archives - first published in *SNQ* (II 175-77), then in Esdaile, 'The Gage Monuments at Firle and their Author' (*SNQ* VIII 1940-41 162-4); the Firle archive is on deposit at East Sussex Record Office; the Gages originated in Gloucestershire and were established at Firle by end of the 1400s; the travails of the unfixed brasses are told in *SNQ* (II 215-16); when Haines saw the set in 1821 they were in a chest in the church, probably in the family chapel, as in Horsfield's day (*Sussex* I 338); having gone missing in 1860 (T Waveing, 'Notes on a brass-rubbing tour in West Sussex' in *Transactions of the Monumental Brass Society* II 296) the set was found at Firle Place c.1895 in various lumber rooms, including brasses for Eleanor Bolne, wife to Sir John Gage II and her two daughters Mary and Elizabeth; as Stephenson points out, the death dates given on the brasses made in 1595-1600 (281B-F), refer to the husband only in each case, although they use the formulation, 'qui obierunt'; the Gages seem to have contacted the maker, Johnson, via their close contacts with the Montagus (White 67 & pls 13-20); Anthony, Viscount Montagu ordered a tomb from Johnson in his will, this was erected at Easebourne in West Sussex c.1593; Montagu was the father-in-law of the Earl of Southampton, whose executors (including Sir John Gage) ordered another monument, also from Johnson, for Titchfield, Hants in c.1594; Montagu's mother was the daughter of Sir John Gage (281F), whose own executor was another Gage, Edward of Bentley, whose tomb is at Framfield (110I).

West Firle, 281A Mural monument for Richard MORTON, d. 1784, and his mother, Annabella TAYLOR, d. 1774

- West chapel, North wall.
- 65(W) x 115(H) — Good.
- M.I. (12 lines, engraved) on an unframed oval plaque in dark grey slate; on a white marble bracket with foliate decoration.
- Rev. Richard Morton, A.M., d. 27 Jun 1784, aet 61; also, Annabella Taylor, 1687-1774, daughter of William Moreton, D.D., bishop of Meath.

1. In situ [?]; Horsfield (*Sussex* I 338); Lambarde (*SAC* 70 152) noting arms, now completely erased; noted by *Gent's Mag* 1814 in Gomme (250).
2. Probably erected after 1784. Lower section of M.I. added later.
3. JH notes that Annabella Moreton, daughter of William Moreton (later Bishop of Meath) and his first wife Mary Atkins, was born in 1687. In 1709 she married William Taylor and their son Richard Taylor Moreton [sic] was born in 1723. As Richard Taylor, he married Frances Scrase at Bishopstone in 1751. See IGI. In the list of vicars of West Firle in Hennessy, he is shown as 'Richard Taylor, or Moreton, B.A.' He was vicar there and of the united parish of Beddingham, 1755-84. The reasons for his changes of surname probably relate to the Moreton inheritance.

West Firle, 281B Brasses, probably for George GAGE and his family, made in the later 1590s

- North-East chapel, West wall, to North of door.
- Arms: 21(W) x 24(H); Lower M.I.: 57(W) x 6(H): Upper M.I.: 15(W) x 7(H); Figure: 68(H) — Fine (upper M.I. - damaged to right); some colour.
- 4 engraved brass plates, evidently a set, on a modern stone slab; a male armoured figure in armour; a rectangular plate of arms and 2 plates with M.I.s.

HIC IACET G...

ANNO DNI

Lower brass

QVID CARO QVID VITA HÆC. FLOS PVLVIS ET VMBRA

1. Formerly on North aisle wall; Davidson-Houston (*SAC* 77 183-6) when, as now, the set was fragmentary.
2. 281B probably commemorates George Gage, one of the nine sons of Sir Edward Gage (281E) and brother of John and Thomas Gage (281D and C).
3. Lambarde does not describe the arms, which are the same as on 281E.

West Firle, 281C Brasses for Thomas and Elizabeth GAGE, both d. 1590
[Plate 179]

- North-East chapel, West wall, to South of door.
- Male: 64(H); Female: 62(H); M.I.: 52(W) x 13(H); Kneeling daughters: 26(W) x 21(H); Male arms: 21(W) x 25(H); Female arms: 15(W) x 17(H) — Fine.
- 6 engraved brass plates, probably a set, on a modern stone slab; standing male and female figures, both with arms over; with her, below, a pair of smaller kneeling figures and a M.I.
- Thomas Gage, armiger, and Elizabeth Gage, both d. 1590; son John and daughters Mary and Elizabeth (unnamed on 281C).

1. Noted by *Gent's Mag* 1814 in Gomme (250); Stephenson (508); Nairn & Pevsner (623); Turner (*SAC* 23 159), then in the church chest; in situ in Lambarde (*SAC* 70 152) noting arms and Davidson-Houston (*SAC* 77 183).
2. The M.I. refers to Thomas Gage, Esq., third son of Edward Gage, Knt; Thomas Gage's wife, Elizabeth, daughter of Sir Thomas Guldeford of Hempstead Place, Kent, was perhaps a descendant of Gage's grandmother Philippa Guldeford.

3. There are no matrices to match these brasses suggesting that 281C was originally on the South wall of the Gage chapel, where the organ has now been installed.

West Firle, 281D Wall tomb for John GAGE, d. 1598, and his wives Elizabeth and Margaret

- North-East chapel, against North wall, North-West corner.
- Tomb chest: 214(W) x 82(D) x 109(H); Arch: 195(H); Plate with 3 brass figures: 78(L); Wall-mounted arms: 25(W) x 30(H); M.I.: 48(W) x 14(H); Shields of arms: 21(W) x 26(H) — Very good.
- A tomb-chest of alabaster and raunce set into a shallow niche with a semi-circular arch over; on the back wall, 4 brass plates; on the surface of the tomb-chest a chamfered slab with 3 brass figures set into its surface; on the face of the chest, simple pilasters and rosettes; M.I. in Latin (engraved, black) in a frieze, under the top slab and on the central pilaster.

M.I. on back wall -
Hic iacet Iohes Gage Armiger et
dvæ Vxores eivs Elizabetha et Mar
gareta qvi obiervnt Anno Dni milesi
mo qvingentesimo nonagesimo qvinto
qvorum animabus propicietvr deus

M.I. - left front
Scio qvod redemptor mevs vivit et in novissimo die de
terra svrrectvrvs svm, et rvrsvm circvmdabor pelle
mea et in carne mea videbo devm salvatorem mevm

M.I. - right front
Qvem visvrvs svm ego ipse et ocvli mei conspectvri
svnt et non alivs reposita est hæc spes mea in
sinu meo iob. cap. 19 versvs: 25

M.I. - centre
IOHES
GAGE
QVI HIC
IACET
FECIT
HEC
MONV
MENTA
ANNO
DNI
1595

1. In situ; *Gent's Mag* 1814 in Gomme (249-50); Lambarde (*SAC* 70 151-2) noting arms; Davidson-Houston (*SAC* 77 181-83) with illustration.
2. The M.I.s suggest that 281D was set up after the death of his wives by the widowed John Gage soon after 1595.
3. Margaret Gage's father was Sir Roger Copley, of Gatton, Surrey; her brass was noted by Stephenson (508) and drawn in André (*SAC* 42 15); she had died by Dec 1581, when John Gage remarried (ESRO SAS/G 8/13). His second wife was Elizabeth, daughter of John Shelley and widow of Thomas Guildford; she may have died in 1595.
4. Extant documents confirm that the maker was Garret Johnson (White 65).
5. The TAQ for the business transaction was Gage's own death (10 Oct an. reg. 40 Elizabeth I - 1598), see Nairn & Pevsner (623) and *SNQ* (II 175-77).
6. The working drawings, (ESRO ACC 5312), include Johnson's annotations, such as: 'This is for Mr. Gage hym selfe and his two wieves...This Stone to be of marble enlayed, the pictures and Scouchtions with the epitaphe to be of Brasse...the marble apperteyninge to thes thre platts are to be made of Mr Gage his owne'; and also Gage's responses, mostly about details of costume.
7. Two important motives for Gage's ambitious campaign of commemoration (see 281B-F) lie in his lack of direct progeny (his heir was his nephew, also John Gage) and his steadfast recusancy, for which he was often fined; in 1580 he was in the Fleet prison 'for obstinacy in popery' and he was apprehended again in 1586.

8. A passage from the text of the Vulgate version of Job XIX 25-6: 'quorum animabus etc ...' is quoted here and in the other Gage monuments of the 1590s, see Sherlock (115).
9. Christopher Whittick of the East Sussex Record Office has kindly supplied information from the Gage MSS and his research. He suggests that the puzzles posed by the M.I. (especially the plural 'obierunt' and the date 1595) may perhaps reflect phrasing supplied to Johnson by John Gage in advance of his own death.

West Firle, 281E Wall tomb for Sir Edward GAGE, d. 1569, and his wife Elizabeth, made after 1595

- North-East chapel, against North wall, North-East corner.
- Tomb-chest: 210(W) x 71(D) x 108 (H); Brass figures: 116(L); Heraldic brass on left: 24(W) x 30 (H); Heraldic brass on right: 22(W) x 26 (H); M.I.: 48(W) x 11 (H) — Very good.
- For description see 281D.

(M.I. a on back wall) -
HIC IACET EDWARDVS GAGE MILES ET
VXOR EIVS ELIZABETHA QVI OBIERVNT
ANNO DNI. 1569. QVORVM ANIMABVS
PROPICIETVR DEVS
M.I.s left and right repeat those on 281D M.I.s left and right.

1. In situ, see *Gent's Mag* 1814 in Gomme (249); Stephenson (508) noting brasses; Lambarde (*SAC* 70 151) noting arms; Mosse (82-3); Davidson-Houston (*SAC* 77 179-81) with illustration; Nairn & Pevsner (623).
2. As was 281D, 281E was erected by John Gage, son of Sir Edward and Elizabeth Gage, in 1595, one of a set of monuments commissioned from Garret Johnson at that time (White 65).
3. 281E commemorates Edward Gage's wife Elizabeth, daughter of John Parker of Ratton in Willingdon, Sussex (see 297H); the M.I. suggests that Edward and Elizabeth died soon after one another, though some sources note another (perhaps first) wife, one Joan Sackville.
4. Sir Edward Gage died 26 Dec 1569 (ESRO SAS/G 19/14), his IPM (Saltzman 46 and Attree 447) state that his daughters were Margery, Lucy, Margaret with Philippa the eldest and his sons were John, Anthony, Thomas, George, Edward, Richard, John II, Robert; his will requires that his sons are brought up in 'the fear and love of God in and of his Catholic Church', and that monuments be erected.
5. The family were unyielding recusants; in 1566, Sir Edward was reported to be receiving communion at home and choosing 'priests from a distance'.
6. Christopher Whittick of the East Sussex Record Office has kindly supplied information from the Gage MSS and his research.

West Firle, 281F Tomb-chest for Sir John GAGE, d. 1556, and his wife Philippa made in the late 1590s [Plate 180]

- North-East chapel, projecting from the East wall, South-East corner.
- Tomb-chest: 217(L) x 126(W) x 104(H of mat from floor) — Very good; local losses (chest panelling).
- Attached by its short end to the East wall of the chapel, a tomb-chest supports 2 full-length effigies; above, on the wall, a stone panel with fluted pilasters, a moulded base, cornice around a circular brass shield & M.I. (engraved) on a rectangular panel; on the tomb-chest, effigies with hands clasped in prayer; Sir John Gage lies to the North side with heraldic supporters at their feet; chest has a gadrooned top edge, alabaster panels with M.I.s; additional heraldic brasses set into the West end. Several M.I.'s, including the text from Job XIX v.25, as in 281D-E.
- John Gage, 1479 - 18 Apr 1556 [some say 1557], Order of Garter, Constable of the Tower of London, Chancellor of Duchy of Lancaster, Lord Chamberlain to Queen Mary I, Privy Councillor to Mary and Phillip.

1. Noted by *Gent's Mag* 1814 in Gomme (249) and Brass noted by Stephenson (508); in situ in Lambarde (*SAC* 70 151) noting arms.
2. Davidson-Houston (*SAC* 77 176-9) with illustration and noting unusual form of 'i' in M.I.; Nairn & Pevsner (623), noting high quality and date of 1595.

3. As with 281D-E, 281F was commissioned from Garret Johnson in 1595 (White 65); the patron of 281F was John Gage, in this case commemorating his grandparents, the founders of Gage influence at court; born in 1479, Gage's marriage in 1502 to Philippa, daughter of Sir Richard Guildford, gave him access to the royal circle; Philippa Gage was sister-in-law of Robert Dudley, Duke of Northumberland; John Gage was loyal to Henry VIII throughout his long career, opposed Somerset in 1549 and welcomed the restoration of Roman Catholicism under Mary I; acted as jailor to Elizabeth I; John Gage d. 18 Apr 1556; buried 25 Apr at Firle, alongside wife; issue - Edward (d.1567, see 281E), James (household official), Robert (c.1518-87) and William and 4 daughters, 1 of whom married Sir Anthony Browne (see 20I).
4. This John Gage started building Firle Place, a new property, not the ancient manor (for John Gage see D Potten in *ODNB*).
5. John Gage's will, dated 20 Feb 1555/6, notes his wish to be buried near to his late wife Philippa, see Rice & Godfrey (2 168).

West Firle, 281G Brass for Mary HOWARD, d. 1638 [Plate 181]
- Nave floor, East end, near North arcade.
- (1 Base): 83(W) x 103(H) ; (2 brass with M.I.): 52(W) x 27(H); (3 figural brass) 19(W) x 45(H) — Fine.
- 2 brasses on a stone slab; the upper with a shrouded corpse (engraved); the lower with M.I. (8 lines, engraved).
- Mary Howard, died at Firle, 28 Jan 1638, aet 36; daughter of William, Lord Eure; and wife (almost 18 years) of Sir William Howard, eldest son of Sir Philip Howard, who was son of Lord William Howard, who was youngest son of the Duke of Norfolk.

1. Noted by *Gent's Mag* 1814 in Gomme (250) and by Stephenson (508); seen in church chest by Horsfield (*Sussex* I 338) and Turner (*SAC* 23 158); drawing of detail in André (*SAC* 42 15); in situ in Davidson-Houston (*SAC* 77 1865-6) with illustration; noted in Nairn & Pevsner (623).
2. The visual memento mori imagery of the shrouded corpse is relatively rare at this date.

West Firle, 281H Brass for Alice LEVETT, d. 1676
- Nave floor, East end, near South arcade.
- Base: 84 x 84; Brass: 49(W) x 18(H) — Fine.
- A small engraved brass on a large stone slab.

> Here lyes Alice Yᴇ wife of
> Tho: Levett Vicar of
> this parish who dyed
> Mᴄʜ 29 1676
> Resvrgam

1. Noted by *Gent's Mag* 1814 in Gomme (250); probably roughly in situ since 281H was seen by Horsfield (*Sussex* I 338) and Turner (*SAC* 23 158) 'under the gallery'; noted by Stephenson (508); in situ in Davidson-Houston (*SAC* 77 186-7) with illustration.
2. Alice Levett, wife of Thomas Levett, the vicar of West Firle 1668-77/8, who stood surety in Jan 1671 and again in Sep 1672, see Dunkin (*Licences 1670-1729* 3 & 12).

West Firle Addition
Horsfield (*Sussex* I 338):
(1) Martha Swaffield, d. 1681, wife of John Swaffield, vicar, slab in South aisle.

(283) WEST HOATHLY, St. Margaret
Norman nave & chancel, Decorated South aisle, 1870 restoration - Nairn & Pevsner (626-7); I.C. Hannah, 'West Hoathly Church' (*SAC* 76 201-211); in 1852, two slabs recorded by A. Hussey, *Notes on the churches in ... Kent, Sussex and Surrey mentioned in the Domesday Book* (239), in use as stepping stones to the tower, by 1940 these were affixed to the vestry wall with a third; by the later 1930s, the Victorian fittings were removed and the stone floor replaced to reveal 'gravestones'

previously obscured by tiles or woodwork; altar rails obtained in Brighton, probably ex-Barcombe church - *SNQ* (VI 23); Willatts (*SAC* 125 102) notes four iron slabs here; the parish had 100 families in 1724 and a population of 794 in 1801.

West Hoathly, 283A Mural monument for Thomas SAWYER, d. 1705, and two later generations

- South nave aisle, South-West corner, West wall, high up.
- 75(W) x 180(H) — Very good.
- M.I. (engraved, black) fills a tablet; unframed; set portrait-wise; below, a grey marble base moulding; ornamental apron with volutes, foliage, a black ball finial and small escutcheon; above, moulded cornice and a broken scrolled pediment; lamp in centre.
- Thomas Sawyer, late of Hoathly Hill, d. 1 Oct 1705; his wife, Mary, d. 24 Mar 1737/8, aet 80; their issue - (sons) Thomas, d. 26 Aug 1728; and Stephen, d. 19 Jun 1761, aet 71; Stephen's widow, Elizabeth, d. 9 Mar 1772, aet 81; their issue, Anne, d. 19 May 1731, aet 3; Stephen, d. 5 May 1772, aet 46.

1. Noted by Horsfield (*Sussex* I 263) with wrong date '1765'; perhaps datable post 1737?.
2. Lambarde does describe the heraldry.

West Hoathly, 283B Mural monument for William GRIFFITH, d. 1720/1

- South nave aisle, West wall, centre, at head height.
- 80(W) x 120(H) — Very good.
- M.I. (engraved, black) on upper 60% of a grey tablet set portrait-wise; moulded frame; domed top and keystone motif; below, an ornamental corbel with escutcheon.
- Rev. William Griffith, vicar of West Hoathly, d. 4 Mar 1720/1, aet 67; his wife, Anne; their issue - William, d. 28 Mar 1696, aet 5; Gainor, buried 23 Mar 1697/8, aet 10.

1. Noted by Horsfield (*Sussex* I 263); in situ in Lambarde (*SAC* 69 197) - noting arms.
2. JH notes that William Griffith was vicar of West Hoathly 1690-1720/1.

West Hoathly, 283C Mural monument for William CLIFFORD, d. 1802

- South nave aisle, North-West corner, West wall, high.
- 80(W) x 150(H) — Fine; faded.
- M.I. (3 lines, engraved, black) on upper 20% of a white tablet set landscape-wise within a dark border; flanked by shallow scrolls; below, a curved apron, small escutcheon, fan decoration and corbels; above, cornice with decorated urn in relief against a dark baseplate with domed top.
- William Clifford, Gent., of Hoathly Hill, d. 24 Jul 1802, aet 50.

1. The Cliffords were owners of Hoathly Hill, etc. in 1785 (R. Davey 112-13).

West Hoathly, 283D Mural monument for George BROOK, d. 1827

- South nave aisle, West wall, below 263C, at head height.
- 77(W) x 51(H) — Sound; faded; local losses (cornice).
- M.I. (12 lines, engraved, black) on simple white marble tablet with moulded cornice; black baseplate; 2 small corbels; signed (lower centre): 'WESTMINSTER MARBLE COMP[Y] EARLS S[T]'.
- George Brook, Gent., of East Grinstead, d. 5 Jan 1827, aet 77; his widow, Catherine, d. 31 Jan 1846, aet 94; their son, John Charles Brook, d. 27 Sep 1843, aet 56.

1. Consistency of the lettering suggests that 263D is datable post 1846.

West Hoathly, 283E Wall mounted brass for Agnes FAULCONER, d. 1635

- Choir, against North wall.
- Slab: 72.5(W) x 173(H); Brass: 42(W) x 29(H) — Fine.
- M.I. (7 lines, engraved) fill a brass panel set on an iron slab; set portrait-wise.

- Agnes Faulconer, buried 22 Sep 1635, aet 39; eldest daughter of Richard Infeld, Gent., of Gravetye and his wife, Katherine Compton; and wife of Henry Faulconer, Esq.

1. Noted by Horsfield (*Sussex* I 263); Turner (*SAC* 23 164) on the church floor; Hannah (*SAC* 76 210) brass set into iron is indeed rare; formerly in the vestry - Davidson-Houston (*SAC* 78 89) with illustration and transcription; Nairn & Pevsner (627); Willatts (*SAC* 125 106) attributes 283E to a London maker and compares it with 8D at Ardingly.
2. Agnes Faulconer was daughter of Richard Infield (see 283M), whose wife was Katherine Compton (see IGI) and she was sister of Richard Infield (see 283N); Henry Faulconer cited on a licence to marry on 14 Aug 1639, see Dunkin (*Licences 1586-1643* 257).

West Hoathly, 283F Anonymous [Thomas?] floor monument, undated
- Sanctuary floor, against North wall, North-West corner.
- Inaccessible under radiator — Very worn.
- Some lettering is visible engraved in surface of a grey freestone slab.
- Illegible.

West Hoathly, 283G Ledger for Richard WOOD, d. 1665
- Sanctuary floor, alongside and South of 263F.
- 62(W) x 133(L) — Pitted; worn; plaster infill.
- M.I. (engraved) in centre of a brown freestone slab; head to East.

...
WOOD SONE ...
RICHARD WOOD
GENT WHO
DEPARTED THIS
...E APREL [TH]E 5
... DOM [1]665

1. Almost obliterated in Horsfield's day (*Sussex* I 263).
2. NBI records the burial of Richard Wood on 7 Apr 1665 at West Hoathly.

West Hoathly, 283H Anonymous iron slab, undated
- Sanctuary floor, alongside and East of 263F.
- 53(W) x 154.5(L) — Very worn.
- M.I. (6 lines, scratched) on upper (East) 25% of the surface of a cast iron slab; head to East.
- Illegible.

West Hoathly, 283I Anonymous floor monument, d. 1625
- Sanctuary floor, East of 263G, partly hidden by altar.
- 84(W) x 165(L) — Worn.
- M.I. (engraved) on upper (East) 25% of the surface of a grey freestone slab; head to East.

HERE LIETH BVRIED TH..
SOMETIME WIFE OF PER...
OF CHIDDINGE IN HAN...
DAVGHTER OF THOMAS ...
DEPARTED THIS LIFE
MARCH 1625 AGED 6..

1. Note reversed form of letter 'S' in 'sometime' and 'this'.

West Hoathly, 283J Ledger for Elizabeth WOOD, undated
- Sanctuary floor, South side, alongside and North of 263K.
- 90(W) x 161(L) — Very worn.

- M.I. (2(?) lines, engraved) on a brown freestone slab; head to East.

HERE LYETH THE BODY OF
ELIZABETH WOOD DAUGHTER

....

MARCH. ....

West Hoathly, 283K Ledger for Richard WOOD, d. 1664

- Sanctuary floor, against South wall.
- 89(W) x 160(L) — Worn.
- M.I. (5 lines, engraved) on upper (W) 25% of a sandy freestone slab; head to East.

HERE LYETH THE BODY OF
RICHARD WOOD GENT WHO
DEPARTED THIS LIFE FEBRVARI[E]
THE 9TH ANO
1664

1. JH notes that he is possibly the father of the Richard Wood on 283G.

West Hoathly, 283L Mural monument for an anonymous couple, probably Richard and Katherine INFIELD, undated

- South aisle, East wall, North of East window, above head height.
- 81(W) x 140(H) — Fine.
- M.I. (6 lines, shallow engraved, gilded) on a rectangular slate tablet; arrow-head ornament in 4 corners; alabaster surround; gilded strapwork at sides; straight cornice; below, apron (cherub mostly missing); above, an achievement.
- No names or dates.

The man attach'd within pale death's precinct
By whom poore liv'd rich lov'd lyes here extinct
Respectlesse fates have alsoe plac'd here
Whose patience god did prove whose love her Pheere
This tyme hath wrovght for them let none be sory
They rest in peace vntill they rise to glory

1. Probably commemorating Richard and Katherine Infield (d. 1625 and 1623), as suggested by Lambarde (*SAC* 69 197) on the basis of the arms; for their marriage see Blaauw (*SAC* 10 154); they are also commemorated by 283N-O.
2. The current anonymity of 283L is curious, there must have been losses.

West Hoathly, 283M Wall-mounted iron slab for Richard INFIELD, d. 1619

[Plate 182]

- South aisle, South wall, at head height, below window.
- 153(W) x 57(H) — Pitted.
- M.I. in border around the empty centre of a cast iron slab mounted landscape-wise.
- Richard Infield, Gent., d. 11 Sep 1619, aet 51.

1. Noted by Horsfield (*Sussex* I 263) and Nairn & Pevsner (627).
2. Willatts (*SAC* 125 101, 104 & 106) draws attention to the variable thickness at the corners of 283M - as a sign of poor workmanship.
3. This Richard Infield was, in fact, the father-in-law of Katherine Culpeper, daughter of Elizabeth Culpeper, commemorated by a brass at Ardingly (8D), for whom see 283O.
4. JH notes that Richard Infield was father of Agnes Faulconer, see 283E.

West Hoathly, 283N Wall-mounted slab for Richard INFIELD, d. 1624/5 [Plate 183]

- South aisle, South wall, West of 263M, at head height, below window.
- 151(W) x 57(H) — Very pitted.
- M.I. with raised lettering in 3 bands, set landscape-wise.
- Richard Infield, Gent., d. 11 Mar 1624/5.

1. Noted in Nairn & Pevsner (627).
2. For marriage of Richard Infield of Gravetye see Blaauw (*SAC* 10 154); for his wife see 283L and 283O; for his father see 283M.
3. For this composition of M.I. on cast iron see 86BB at East Grinstead.

West Hoathly, 283O Wall-mounted ledger for Katherine INFIELD, d. 1623
[Plate 184]
- Against the South aisle wall, East of South door.
- 70(W) x 118(H) x 09(D) — Very good.
- M.I. (5 lines, engraved) in centre of a thick freestone slab painted (?) black.
- Katherine Infield, d. 16 Oct 1623; daughter of Sir Edward Cullpeper of Wakehurst; and wife of Richard Infield, Gent.

1. For the marriage of Katherine and Richard Infield of Gravetye see Blaauw (*SAC* 10 154); Richard Infield, d. 11 Mar 1624; Katherine was born 1597 and married 1619, she was daughter of the subject of 8D, see Willatts (*SAC* 125 106).

West Hoathly, 283P Mural monument for Fasham NAIRN, d. 1823
- South aisle arcade, facing South door, very high.
- 85(W); (H) unknown — Good; local damage (upper left).
- M.I. (7 lines, engraved, black) on a white tablet of trapezoidal form; block corbels; black baseplate; unsigned; draped urn on cornice.
- Fasham Nairn, d. 29 Mar 1823, died an infant; son of Fasham Nairn and Mary Dixon Nairn.

1. Noted by Horsfield (*Sussex* I 263).

(291) WESTFIELD - no monuments found

(292) WESTHAM, St. Mary
Norman nave and South transept; 14th-century North arcade - Nairn & Pevsner (625-6); for plan see *SNQ* (II 115); in 1686, it was reported that everything was in need of repair, including the Thatcher chancel (Ford 51); by 1724, the 'burial place belonging now to Mr Medley extreamely [bad]: [and] promised and ordered to be forthwith repaired'; also, the chancel (owned by Spencer Compton, Esq) was very poor (Ford 185); Victorian installation of a new brick floor and wooden pews on a raised dais resulted in the creation of an area for relocated slabs in the North aisle and slabs from the South-East or from the Priest House Chapel were perhaps also relocated here? The parish had significant communities of papists, nine amongst c. 200 communicants in 1603, see Renshaw (*Ecclesiastical Returns*), and Presbyterians in its total of 49 families in 1724 (Ford) and the population grew fast in the 18th century (293 in 1751 becoming 560 in 1801; inexplicably, Horsfield (*Sussex* I 302-3) cites no monuments at Westham.

Westham, 292A Floor mounted brass for Elizabeth STONSTREET, d. 1644
- North aisle floor, towards West end.
- 42(W) x 17(H) — fine; rusted; stained edges.
- M.I. (6 lines, engraved) on brass, on a stone, head to North.
- Elizabeth Stonstreet, d. 6 May 1644; daughter of William Hamond, Gent., of Westham; and wife of Henry Stonstreet, citizen and mercer of London.

1. Noted by Stephenson (518) and Davidson-Houston (*SAC* 80 136) as in situ.
2. See 292 E,F,K and R for more members of the Hamond family.

Westham, 292B Ledger for George THAYER, d. 1751?
- North aisle floor, beneath West window.
- 90(W) x 181(L) — Cracked; worn.
- M.I. (9 lines, engraved) in upper 60% of freestone slab, head to North.

In Memory of George
Son of George Thayer
of Langney in this
Pariſh Gent and
Ann His Wife
who departed this life
the .... day ...
in the year ...
....

1. JH notes that the year appears to be 1751, which corresponds to the NBI entry for George Thayer, buried 22 Oct 1751 at Westham.

Westham, 292C Ledger for Susanna VINTER, d. 1808
- North aisle floor, East of 292B.
- 85(W) x 177(L) — Worn; cracked.
- M.I. (6 lines, engraved) in upper 30% of freestone slab, head to North; decorated border.

Sacred
To the MEMORY of
SUSANNA the wife of
CAPT GEORGE VINTER B.M.
who ... March 24
1808 37

1. NBI records the burial of Susannah Vintner on 31 Mar 1808, aged 37, at Westham.
2. JH notes that the initials could stand for Bachelor of Medicine.

Westham, 292D Ledger for E... F...., d. 1666
- North aisle floor, far West end.
- 81(W) x 114(L) — Very worn.
- M.I. engraved on a freestone slab, head to East.
- Illegible.

Westham, 292E Ledger for Sarah HAMMOND, d. 1708
- North aisle floor.
- 85(W) x 121(L) — Worn.
- M.I. (6 lines, engraved) in upper 50% of dark grey freestone slab, head to South.
- Sarah Hammond, d. 4 Oct 1708, aet 75; wife of John Hammond, Gent.

1. For Hammond see 292F, K and R.

Westham, 292F Ledger for Philippa HAMMOND, d. 1660
- North aisle floor, East of 292C.
- 67(W) at South end; 48(W) at North end x 182(L) — Very worn.
- M.I. (8 lines, engraved) in upper (South) 30% of an irregular slab, head to South.
- Philippa Hammond, d. 25 Apr 166[0]; wife of [....] Hammond.

1. For Hammond see 292E, K and R.
2. NBI records the burial of Phillippa Hamond [sic] on 27 Apr 1660 at Westham.

Westham, 292G Ledger for children of the FAGGE family, d. 1700, etc.
- North aisle floor, South of 292F.
- 83(W) x 138(L) — Fair.
- M.I. (10 lines, engraved) in upper (W) 60% of pale freestone slab, head to West.

- Thomas Fagge, d. 1700, aet 1; also, Mary Fagge, d. 1706, aet 1; also, Allice Fagge, d. 1728, an infant.

1. Perhaps the children of Thomas Fagge of Wiston, Gent., licence to marry Elizabeth Meres, of Westham, widow, on 1 Dec 1694, see Dunkin (*Licences 1670-1729* 155).
2. For the Fagges see 292H, J and L.

Westham, 292H Ledger for Thomas FAGGE, d. 1705
- North aisle floor, between two windows.
- 84(W) x 196(L) — Cracked; worn.
- M.I. (5 lines, engraved) in upper (North) end of a black slab, head to North.
- Thomas Fagge, Esq., of Glinley, d. 19 Aug 1705, aet 41.

1. Note the characteristic form of the letter 'A', as in 292O.
2. For the Fagges see 292G, J and L.

Westham, 292I Ledger for ... MEERES [?], date unknown
- North aisle floor, alongside 292H.
- 75(W) x 147(L) — Very worn.
- M.I. (engraved) on a pale grey slab, head to East.
- Hardly legible.

1. See comments on 292G and for Meres see 292J and 292L.
2. One Thomas Meere, Gent., d. 2 Apr, an. reg. 39 Elizabeth I [1597], see Holgate (45); Meres also was owner of Glynleigh, Westham, see Farrant (333).

Westham, 292J Ledge for John and Elizabeth MERES, d. 1694 and 1721
- North aisle floor, East of 292H.
- 112(W) x 200(L) — Worn.
- M.I. (11 lines, engraved) in upper 60% of large black slab, head to North.
- John Meres, Gent., d. 25 Mar 1694, aet 56; his widow, Elizabeth, d. 1 Jul 1721, aet 55; her second husband, Thomas Fagge, Esq., of Glinley.

1. Elizabeth Meres was left Glynleigh by John Meres; the house passed to Lady Elizabeth Peachey (d. 1804); see Farrant (333); for her second husband see 292H; for one John, son of Thomas Meere, 1597, see Holgate (45).

Westham, 292K Ledger for William HAMMOND, d. 1652
- North aisle floor, alongside 292J.
- 77(W) x 88(L) — Cracked and worn.
- M.I. (5 lines, engraved) fill a recut grey freestone slab, head to East.
- William Hammond, Gent., d. 3 Nov 16[5]2.

1. For Hammond see 292E, F and R.
2. JH notes that the '5' in 1652 is shown as 'V'.
3. NBI records the burial of William Hammond on 3 Nov 1652 at Westham.

Westham, 292L Ledger for John Meres FAGGE, d. 1750
- North aisle floor, East of 292I.
- 99(W) x 200(L) — Sound.
- M.I. (11 lines, engraved) in the upper (North) 50% of a black slab.
- John Meres Fagge, Esq., late of Middle Temple, d. 18 May 1750, aet 24; eldest son of John Meres Fagge, Esq., and Allice, his wife, of Glinley, in Westham.

1. For Fagge see 292G, H, J, K and M.

Westham, 292M Ledger for Margaret FAGGE, d. 1717

- North aisle floor, under second window.
- 84(W) x 200(L) — Worn.
- M.I. (engraved) fills a freestone slab, head to North, final lines added.
- Margaret Fagge, d. 11 Aug 1717, aet 31; daughter of Sir Robert Fagge, Bart., late of Wiston, Sussex; also, Elizabeth Fagge, d. 22 Jul 1717, aet 21, daughter of Thomas Fagge, Esq., of Glinley; also, Thomas, d. 6 Jun 1749, aet 18, son of John Meres Fagge, Esq., and Allice, his wife, of Glinley.

1. For Fagge see 292G, H, J, K and L.

Westham, 292N Ledger for Elizabeth KIRKHAM, d. 1743

- North aisle floor, alongside 292O.
- 86(W) x 151(L) — Very worn; damage at West end.
- M.I. (5 lines, engraved) in upper (W) 30% of a pale freestone slab; head to West.
- Elizabeth Kirkham, d. 25 Mar 1743, aet 96[?]; husband unnamed.

1. NBI records the burial of Elizabeth Kirkham on 27 Apr 1743 at Westham.

Westham, 292O Ledger for John MERES, d. 1691/2

- North aisle floor, East of 292M.
- 81(W) x 169(L) — Worn.
- M.I. (6 lines, engraved) in upper (North) 30% of black slab; head to North.
- John Meres, Gent., d. 21 Jan 1691/2, aet 81.

1. For Meres see 292I, J and L.
2. Note the characteristic form of the letter 'A', also on 292H.

Westham, 292P Ledger for Anne BEATON, d. 1703/4

- North aisle floor, alongside and East of 292O.
- 85(W) x 172(L) — Cracked; damaged; faint.
- M.I. (7 lines, engraved) in upper 50% of a black slab.
- Anne Beaton, d. 17 Jan 1703/4, aet 70; widow of John Beaton, of Wiston.

Westham, 292Q Ledger for Barbara THOMASON, d. 1646

- North aisle floor, towards East end.
- 64(W) x 162(L) — Worn; faint.
- M.I. (5 lines, engraved in Latin) across centre of grey freestone slab; head to East.
- Barbara Thomason, d. ult [31] Mar 1646; daughter of John Meares of this parish, Gent.; and wife of Miles Thomason, Gent.

Westham, 292R Ledger for .... HAMOND, d. 1686

- North aisle floor, towards East end.
- 71(W) x 170(L) — Sound; very worn.
- Freestone.
- Illegible.

1. For Hammond see 292 E, F and K.

Westham, 292S Ledger for members of the BAKER Family, d. 1709-1786

- Crossing floor, North side.
- Set of stones measures 122(W) x 198(L) — Worn.
- A set of 7 freestone panels, each 65.5 or 66 (H), heads to East, the upper and lower rows with M.I. on a large panel (engraved); smaller, decorated panel to the right; in the centre row, a M.I. on a smaller panel, 2 decorative panels flanking; lower M.I. in epitaph form.
- James Baker, d. 2[?] Aug 1720 or 22; Elizabeth Baker, d. 30 Mar 1709; William Baker, d.

3[?] Jan 1786, aet 76.

1. In 1785, the executors of William Baker owned property here (R. Davey 245).
2. Licence to marry: James Baker, of Willingdon, yeoman and Elizabeth Grinior, of Westham, spinster 26 Apr 1708, see Dunkin (*Licences 1670-1729* 197).
3. NBI records the burial of James Baker on 21 Aug 1720, Elizabeth Baker on 30 Mar 1709 and William Baker on 30 Jan 1786, all at Westham.

Westham, 292T Floor-mounted cross slab inscribed for Abraham KENCHLEY [?], d. 1694

- Choir floor, centre.
- 67(W) x 201(L) — Worn.
- A mediaeval freestone cross slab, M.I. added; head to West.

HIC IACENT

RELIQUAE[?] A–B

KENCHLEY AP...[?]

ET ILLI [?]...

EJUS [?] CE [?] ...

OB: DECIMO SEXTO

OCTOBRIS 1694

ÆTATIS SUAE

TRIGESIMO ...

1. Church Guide notes that 292T [Krenchley?] and another similar, were found in church floor by North porch in early twentieth century.
2. 292T and U are the only examples in the survey of East Sussex monuments of a seventeenth-century reworking of a mediaeval slab; for an incised mediaeval slab in the churchyard at Kenilworth, Warwickshire, appropriated in the nineteenth century see Sunley in *Church Monuments*, XIV 1999 35-6.
3. NBI records the burial of Abraham Kechley on 13 Dec 1642 at Westham.

Westham, 292U Ledger for Philippa HODSON, d. 1602

- South-East chapel floor, East end.
- 93(W) x 175(L) — Worn.
- A mediaeval altar stone; later M.I. (engraved); head to North.

PH. 1602

1. Perhaps the original Norman altar slab, reused in 1602 to commemorate Philippa Hodson, wife of Miles Hodson, rector 1593-1625; 292U remained in church floor until 1903, it was then used as altar table and finally relocated in the floor.
2. 292T and U are the only examples in the survey of East Sussex monuments of a seventeenth-century reworking of a mediaeval slab.
3. Sussex Marriage Index records the marriage of Miles Hodgsone and Philippa Puttenden on 6 Sep 1591 at Hailsham and NBI records the burial of Philip [sic] Hodgesons on 21 Mar 1602 at Westham.
4. JH notes that Miles was also vicar of Hailsham from 1589/90, see Hennessy (76), and prebendary of Fittleworth 1602-16, see Horn (*Fasti 1541-1857* 30).

Westham, 292V Mural monument for John Meres FAGGE, d. 1769 [Plate 185]

- South-East chapel, North wall, North-East corner, above head height.
- 88(W); (H) unknown — Sound; local losses (arms at top).
- Black baseplate in obelisk form; white marble escutcheon with scrolled frame; a white oval unframed tablet with M.I. (engraved, black); below the base moulding, an ornamental apron with more lettering and a black ball finial.
- John Meres Fagge, Esq., of Westham, d. 25 Mar 1769, aet 71; his wife, Allice, d. 2 Oct 1753, aet 55, daughter of Thomas Woodyer, Esq.; issue - eldest son, John Meres Fagge, Esq., of Middle Temple and Trinity Hall, Cambridge, d. 18 May 1750, aet 24; youngest son, Thomas Fagge, d. 6 Jun 1749, aet 17; youngest daughter, Allice Fagge, date of death unknown, an infant; their only surviving child, Dame Elizabeth Peachey, widow of

Sir John Peachey, Bart.

1. In situ; Lambarde (*SAC* 70 134) noting arms.
2. Patron was Dame Elizabeth Peachey, after the death of her husband; she owned Glynleigh (for the Fagge family of Glynleigh, see 292G-J, L, M and O).

Westham, 292W Mural monument for John THETCHER, d. 1649

- South-East chapel, North wall, North-West corner.
- 130(W); (H) unknown; tablet: 68(W) x 76(H) — Fair; restored (at top).
- M.I. (engraved, white) fills black tablet; frame of white marble curtains; flanked by black Corinthian columns with white bases and capitals; entablature and broken segmented pediment; below, white scroll brackets, a white base moulding; black plinth; white ornamental apron with draped skull.
- John Thetcher, Esq., of Priesthawes, Sussex, d. 3 Sep 1649; no issue.

1. John Thetcher was recusant (Church Guide), he built Priesthawse in the parish in the 1590s, using Pevensey Castle stone.
2. For a view from South-East in Godfrey & Salzman (Pl. 178), see too H.M. Whitley, 'Priesthawes' (*SAC* 45 204-8) and Farrant (334); Priesthawse was reputedly a Catholic refuge; for his time in Rome in 1596, with Cardinal Allen, see W. Cooper, 'The Oxenbridges' (*SAC* 12 211); but he appears to have retained his property at Westham, see map of his lands in 1620 in Steer (2).
3. The family took pride in their intermarried relations with other families e.g. Challenor, Lewknor, Oxenbridge, Sackville, Pelham, Colepeper, Stapley, Tresham and Audley, see W. Cooper, 'Notes and Queries - Westham Church' (*SAC* 14 265).
4. His will was addressed to 'The Old Bretheren' and therefore not binding; he made a bequest to the church on condition that the Catholic faith was restored, that the altar stone be resurrected and that masses be said for his soul; John Thetcher also left money to bring Catholic youths from France to England to study; with his death, his family died out at Priesthawes; his heir was his sister Mary Eyston (see *SNQ* IV 159).

Westham, 292X Ledger for Anonymous member of Thetcher family, date unknown

- South-East chapel floor, West side, partly obscured by furnishings.
- 109(W) x 210(L) — Very worn.
- Traces of M.I. (engraved) on a black slab; head to West.
- Almost Illegible.

H[ERE] ... LYETH .. BOD[Y}
O[F] ... [THE]TCHER ...
DI[ED] ... DAY ..
SEPTEMBER [AN]NO DO..
...

Westham, 292Y Ledger for [Miller] BRISTOW, d. 1816, and (probably) his son John BRISTOW, d. 1793.

- South-East chapel floor, North side.
- 81(W) x 136(L) — Very worn.
- Traces of M.I. (engraved) on a grey freestone slab; head to West.
- [Miller] Bristow, d. 8 Mar 181[6], aet [?]2; his son, also unnamed, d. 13 Nov 1793, aet unknown.

1. In 1785, one Miller Bristow occupied Priesthawes Farm, then owned by George Medley, Esq. (R. Davey 245).
2. For a licence to marry dated 18 Nov 1786 for Miller Bristow, of Westham, Gent. and Mary Barnard, of Westham, spinster, which might relate to 292Y, see Dunkin & Penfold (*Licences* 56).
3. JH notes that IGI lists a John Bristow, son of Miller and Mary Bristow, born 30 Apr 1789, baptised at Westham and NBI records the burial of John, aged 4, on 26 Nov 1793 at Westham. Also Miller Bristow, aged 62, buried 15 Mar 1816 at Westham.

Westham, 292Z Ledger for [James?] MILLER, d. 1782
- South-East chapel floor, North side, North of 292Y.
- 79(W) x 139(L) — Cracked; repaired.
- Traces of M.I. (engraved) on a grey freestone slab; head to West.
- Anonymous Miller, d. 17 ??? 1782, aet 82[?]; also Anonymous '..udley esq'.

1. NBI records the burial of James Miller, aged 81, on 4 Jan 1782 at Westham.

(294) WESTMESTON, St. Martin

14th-century, over-restored; East wall modern, rest mediaeval, 17th-century porch - Nairn & Pevsner (628); *SNQ* (XIV 238) - with plan; there were 204 communicants in 1603 when the patron was Mrs Ann Goring of Lewes, widow, see Renshaw (*Ecclesiastical Returns*); 56 families in the parish (with East Chiltington) in 1724 and a population of 368 in 1801.

Westmeston, 294A Ledger for Richard CHALONER, d. 1661 [1664?]
- Choir floor, North side, partly obscured by choir-stalls.
- 71(W) x 159(L) — Very pitted.
- M.I. (16 lines, engraved) in upper 50% of a plain grey freestone slab; head to West.

SACRED THIS TO MEMORIE
OF RICHARD CHALO...
OF THE CHAPPELL ...
GENTLEMAN
HEE LIVED AN ORTHODOX
CHRISTIAN FEARED GOD
HONOVRED THE KING OBEY...
THE CHVRCH AND WALKED
FVLL ROWND OF CHARIT...

HEE DIED OF AN APOPLEXY ...
IN THE 46 YEARE OF H...
AGE ON THE ..2 AND HIS
BODIE WAS IN HOPE OF T..
RESVRRECTION UNTO ...
ETERNALL LIFE HERE INT...
RED THE 14TH OF MAY
1661

1. Noted in situ but with date 1664 by *Gent's Mag* visit of 1808 in Gomme (338) and noted by Horsfield (*Sussex* I 235).
2. The 'Chappell' was presumably a local property (see 294B); note the powerful Royalist sentiments of the M.I. of 294A dated just after the Restoration.

Westmeston, 294B Ledger for Jane CHALONER, d. 1723
- Choir floor, South side, partly obscured by choir stalls.
- 62(W) x 135(L) — Fair.
- M.I. (8 lines, engraved) in upper 50% of a plain sandstone slab; head to West.

Here is Interred the Body of
Ms JANE CHALONER Daughter of
RICHARD CHALONER GENT
Late of Chappel
who Departed this life
September the 23th
1723
Aged 69 years

1. Not noted by *Gent's Mag* visit dated 1808 in Gomme (338).
2. For Jane Chaloner's father, see 294A.

Westmeston, 294C Mural monument for Frances RIDEOUT, d. 1785

- South aisle, South wall.
- 83(W) x 147(H) — Very good; fading.
- M.I. (engraved) fills unframed white marble rectangular tablet; above, a grey-veined marble broken pointed pediment, corbels; curved apron.
- Frances Rideout, d. 5 Jan 1785, aet 27; daughter of Rev. Francis Woodgate, vicar of Mountfield, Sussex; and wife of Rev. Richard Rideout, rector of Westmeston.

1. Formerly on chancel South wall; *Gent's Mag* visit dated 1808 in Gomme (338); Horsfield (*Sussex* I 235).
2. 294C was erected by Richard Rideout, the widowed husband, in the later 1780s; for Richard Rideout's property in 1785 see R. Davey (218); see licence to marry dated 23 Oct 1784 for Richard Rideout, of Westmeston, clerk, bachelor, age 24 plus and Frances Woodgate, of Mountfield, spinster, age 22 plus; he appears to have married again - licence dated 12 Dec 1789 for Richard Rideout, of Westmeston, clerk, widower and Sarah Nicoll, of Mountfield, widow, see Dunkin & Penfold (*Licences* 358).
3. JH notes that Richard Rideout was rector of Westmeston 1783-1809.

Westmeston, 294D Mural monument for William Henry CAMPION, d. 1821

- South aisle, South wall to West of 294C.
- 106(W) x 172(H) — Excellent.
- M.I. (engraved, black) fills a white marble tablet; plain black border; flanking, highly polished white marble Doric half columns; moulded entablature with floral patterns left and right; above, in low relief, a white marble urn against a slate base with a curved top; below, corbels with concentric decoration.
- Rev. William Henry Campion, rector of Westmeston and Streat, died at Milan, 7 Apr 1821, aet 36.

1. Formerly on chancel South wall; Horsfield (*Sussex* I 235).
2. The patronage of 294D is uncertain.
3. A Protestant church was erected in Milan in 1864 in via De Marchi, perhaps associated with a former burial ground?
4. JH notes that William Henry Campion was rector of Westmeston 1809-21 & rector of Streat 1815-21.

Westmeston, 294E Ledger for Elizabeth PACKHAM, d. 1720

- South aisle floor, East end, adjacent to 294G.
- 93(W) x 171(L) — Fair.
- M.I. (11 lines, engraved) on the upper parts of a freestone slab; head to West.

Under here lieth Interred the
Body of Elizabeth Daughter
of Mr John Manning and
Martha his wife *Late of Albarn*
And wife of Henry Packham
of Westmeſton who Departed
this Life March the 24th 1720
Aged [5]4 years

And when I Depart this Life
Pray leet me lie here by my
Dear and Loving wife

1. Roughly in situ, see *Gent's Mag* visit of 1808 in Gomme (338) and noted by Horsfield (*Sussex* I 235) who records her age as 54.
2. Patron was widowed husband (M.I.).
3. Albarn = Albourne?
4. Packham perhaps also spelled Peckham, e.g. the licence to marry of Henry Peckham, of Westmeston, yeoman and Janie Mills, of Hurstpierpoint, spinster 31 May 1722, see Dunkin (*Licences 1670-1729* 237).

Westmeston, 294F Ledger for Mary HAMPTON, d. 1729, and her son

- South aisle floor, East end.
- 60(W) x 76(L) — Fair.
- M.I. (13 lines, engraved) on a freestone slab; head to West.

HERE Lyeth ye Body of
MARY HAMPTON late wife
of WILLIAM HAMPTON
Rector of Ovingdeane
who dyd Jan 1.. 1728/9
Aged 25[?] Years
Here alſo Lyeth ye Body of
ED HAMPTON son of
WILLIAM & MARY HAMP
TON who died March 31
1729 Aged 3 Months.
& of Charles Hampton who dye...
May 29 1729 Aged 5 Months

1. Roughly in situ, see *Gent's Mag* visit dated 1808 in Gomme (338) and noted by Horsfield (*Sussex* I 235).
2. Patron assumed to be Rev. William Hampton; for licence to marry: William Hampton, of Ovingdean, clerk and Mary Mace, of Beddingham, spinster 1 Dec 1724, see Dunkin (*Licences 1670-1729* 247).

Westmeston, 294G Ledger probably for Henry PECKHAM, d. 1725, and his wife Jane, d. 1751

- South aisle floor, East end, adjacent to 294E.
- 98(W) x 171(L) — Pitted; crumbling.
- M.I. (engraved) on a freestone slab; head to West.
- Almost illegible.

...
[b]o[d]y of [HEN]RY [PAC]KHAM
... Departed this ...
November ...
...
... wife ...
... [PECK]HAM ...
... October ...
...

1. Slabs in this location noted by *Gent's Mag* visit dated 1808 in Gomme (338) include those to Henry Packham, d. 2 Nov 1725, aet 56 (husband of 294E) and a later wife Jane Packham, d. 31 Oct 1751, aet 58.
2. NBI records the burial of Henry Peckham on 5 Nov 1725 and Jane Peckham on 4 Nov 1751, both at Westmeston.

Westmeston Additions

Noted by *Gent's Mag* for 1808 in Gomme (338) and by Horsfield (*Sussex* I 235):
(1) Slab for William Challoner, d. 23 Sep 1713, aet 57 or 69; son of Richard and Ann.
(2) Anne Challoner, d. 27 Sep 1696, aet 74, wife of Richard.
(3) Jane Challoner, d. 1723, aet 69, daughter of Richard.
(4) Anne Wilson, d. 12 Oct 1741, aet 68, widow of Edward Wilson, vicar of Rye.
(5) John Martin (Marten), of Stantons, Chiltington, d. 23 Apr 1741, aet 40 (in Martin chapel).
(6) Mary Martin, wife of John, see (5), d. 1 Jul 1766, aet 74 (Martin chapel).

(295) WHATLINGTON, St. Mary Magdalene

Nave and chancel Early English; restored by Tracey in 1862 (Nairn & Pevsner 628-9); view of 1779, see Farrant (336); state of repairs reported to be fine in 1686 (Ford 50). Steeple and roof covering bad in 1724 (Ford 119); the parish had c.23 families in 1724 and a population of 211 in 1801.

Whatlington, 295A Brass for Alice DUNCK d. 1627

- South aisle, East wall, facing West, at head height.
- 39(W) x 18.5(H) — Very good; polished.
- M.I. (8 lines, engraved) on a rectangular brass panel, set landscape-wise.
- Alice Dunck, d. 22 Apr 1627, aet 63; daughter of John Michelbourne of Chichester; and wife of Richard Dunck, of Vine Hall.

1. Formerly mounted on the Manor House pew, Horsfield (*Sussex* I 528); cited by Turner (*SAC* 23 189); noted by Stephenson (518); and in situ in Davidson-Houston (*SAC* 80 137), also illustrated.
2. For another daughter of John Michelbourne see 280d.
3. Alice was b. c.1562; her mother was also Alice; the family were of Chichester and Barcombe.
4. For one Ann Duncke, see 25E.

(297) WILLINGDON, St. Mary the Virgin

Flint, mostly early 14th century - Nairn & Pevsner (629); significant bomb damage during WW2 resulted in repairs and relocations; the medieval church became an attractive commemorative site for the local lords of Ratton, the Parkers, who erected at least 9 monuments, see Horsfield (*Sussex* I 290), nevertheless, in 1724 their family chapel was in poor state (Ford 186); the parish had 28 families in 1724 and a population of 347 in 1801.

Willingdon, 297A Standing monument for Sir Thomas PARKER, [d. 1663], and his grandson Sir Robert Parker, d. 1691, and others [Plate 186]

- North aisle, attached to North wall.
- 90(W) x 295(H) x 67(D) — Very good.
- In pedestal form, in white marble, on a black base; against the wall; M.I. (engraved, black) on 3 sides; base and cornice mouldings; on front face, M.I. flanked by tasselled motif and above, a segmented pediment with escutcheon; 2 more escutcheons wall mounted to sides; on top, a huge decorative urn.
- Thomas Parker, of Ratton, (no dates); his wife, Philadelphia, daughter of Henry Lennard, Baron Dacre of Herstmonceux; his grandson, Sir Robert Parker, of Ratton, Bart., d. 30 Nov 1691, aet 36; his wife, [Sarah], only daughter of George Chute, of Bristocawsway [Brixton Causeway?], Lambeth, Surrey; issue of Robert Parker and his wife - 4 sons and 1 daughter, none named, all still living.

1. Formerly on North chapel, South wall see Lambarde (*SAC* 70 142) noting arms; the reversal of the 2 sets of heraldry from left to right suggest that 197A has been reassembled after bomb damage.
2. Nairn & Pevsner (629) gives a date of 1663, although the forms suggest an early 18th-century date for the monument.
3. A highly unusual design.
4. JH notes that Sir Thomas Parker, 1595-1663, was MP for Seaford in the Long Parliament (1640-48) and that Sir Robert Parker, 1655-91, was MP for Hastings 1679 and 1681. Sir Robert was JP for Sussex, and Deputy Lieutenant, outlawed for treason in 1690, arrested on his return from France in January 1691, and pardoned in that July. See Henning (III 207).

Willingdon, 297B Ledger stone for John GILBERT, d. 1697

- North aisle floor.
- 90(W) x 159(L) — Fair.
- M.I. (8 lines, engraved) on upper 30% of pale grey-brown freestone slab; head to West.
- John Gilbert, d. 27 Oct 1697, aet 90; son of (another) John Gilbert; servant of the Parkers of Ratton for 62 years.

1. For other memorials to servants see e.g. 131A.

Willingdon, 297C Mural monument for Charlotte THOMAS, d. 1800

- North aisle (Ratton Chapel), against North wall, low.
- 71(W) x 100(H) — Very good; faded.
- M.I. (engraved, black) fills a white marble panel set portrait-wise; black frame.
- Charlotte Thomas, died at Lisbon, 17 Apr 1800, buried at Lisbon, aet 20; eldest daughter of Henry Peirse, Esq., of Bedale, Yorkshire; and wife of Inigo Thomas, Esq., of Ratton; her virtues.

1. Unsigned.
2. Gunnis (*Dict.* 420) cites a later monument to Inigo Thomas as made by Henry Weekes (1807-77).

Willingdon, 297D Standing monument for Sir George PARKER, Bart., d. 1726

- North aisle (Ratton Chapel), against North wall.
- 143(W) x 298(H) x 40(D) — Very good; colour.
- All in white and grey marbles; on a moulded base and set portrait-wise, M.I. (engraved, black) with scrolls flanking and escutcheons left and right; above, a moulded cornice and pointed pediment with achievement in centre; above that, on a black base, a decorative urn with flaming top; another M.I. (5 lines, engraved, black) on plinth.
- Sir George Parker, Bart., of Ratton, MP, his loyalty to Queen Anne, d. 18 Jun 1726, aet 49, first son of Sir Robert Parker, Bart.; his wife, Mary, d. 14 May 1727, aet 51, eldest daughter of Sir Walter Bagot, Bart., of Blythfield, Staffordshire, related to Earls of Stafford and Dukes of Buckingham; issue - Walter, d. 19 Apr 1750, aet 55; Thomas; Nicholas; Sarah; Anne; Jane; and Philadelphia.

1. In situ see Lambarde (*SAC* 70 143) - noting arms and Nairn & Pevsner (629).
2. 297D seems intended to relate to the form of 297A, the M.I. added at foot of 297D notes the expiry of the Parker family line in 1750.
3. JH notes that Sir George Parker, 1675-1726, was MP for Sussex 1705-8 and 1710-13. See Cruikshanks (V 96-7), who incorrectly shows his date of death as 14 May 1727 – when his wife died.

Willingdon, 297E Standing monument for Sir Nicholas PARKER, d. 1619/20

- North aisle (Ratton) Chapel, against North wall, North-East corner.
- 227(W) x 342(H) x 39(D) — Fair; local losses.
- In alabaster; an armoured male effigy; reclining, head to West; hands in prayer; black Corinthian columns flanking; below, a tomb-chest; in relief, 3 wives kneeling to East flanked by foliate decoration and blank black panels; above, a straight entablature with 3 escutcheons and 2 rosettes; on the back wall, 2 M.I.s (engraved, white) on slate panels, flank a winged hourglass; flat coffered vault; on top, obelisks, left and right.
- Sir Nicholas Parker, Knt., of Ratton, Willingdon, d. 9 Mar 1619/20, aet 73; his first wife, Joan, daughter of Sir William Courtney, Knt., of Powderham, Devon; no issue; his second wife, Elizabeth, daughter of John Baker, Esq.; no issue; his third wife, Katherine, daughter of John Temple, Esq., of Stow, Buckinghamshire; issue - Thomas John, Robert, Nicholas, Henry, Anne and Mary; laudatory epitaph of Parker name and achievements.

1. In situ & then with iron railings - Horsfield (*Sussex* I 290); also in Lambarde (*SAC* 70 143) - noting

arms; Mosse and Nairn & Pevsner (629).
2. Nicholas Parker was on a trading expedition to the Far East in 1582; knighted for gallantry in the Netherlands in 1591; in 1590s, active in the defence of Cornwall against invasion; Nicholas was patron of the living by 1603, see Renshaw (*Ecclesiastical Returns*) and his son Henry 1604-52 became a political writer (see biographies by T. Borman and Michael Mendle in *ODNB*).
3. 297E is likely to have been extensively restored after bomb-damage.
4. JH notes that Sir Nicholas Parker 1547-1620, was son of Thomas and Elinor Parker – see 297I and 297F. He, knighted in 1591, was appointed a JP for Sussex in 1580, Sheriff 1586-7 and 1593-4, deputy lieutenant 1587, and MP for Sussex 1597. See Hasler (III 173).

Willingdon, 297F Mural monument for Elinor PARKER, d. 1598/9 [Plate 187]
- North aisle (Ratton Chapel), East wall.
- 79(W) x 110(H) — Good; colour; local losses (hands).
- Very flat against the wall in alabaster and brown freestone; in the centre, a tiny female figure in black civil costume with widow's hood, in relief, on cushion, kneeling to right; around her, decorated frame of rosettes, skulls, hour-glasses; lozenge of arms above centre; below, M.I. (engraved, black) on an irregular panel with curved lower edge.
- Elinor Parker, d. 26 Feb 1598/9, aet 83; daughter of William Waller, of Groombridge, Esq.; and widow (20 years) and wife (52 years) of Thomas Parker, Esq., of Ratton; issue - daughter (died an infant), Nicholas and John, both knights; her wifely virtues.

1. In situ see Lambarde (*SAC* 70 142) - noting arms; Mosse and Nairn & Pevsner (629).
2. For her husband, see 297I, her son Sir Nicholas 297E, and her son Sir John 297P.

Willingdon, 297G Ledger for George PARKER, d. 1673
- North aisle (Ratton Chapel) floor, near altar, now carpeted over.
- 109(W) x 208(L) — Very good.
- Escutcheon, then M.I. (engraved) on a black marble slab; head to West.

> HERE LYES INTERR'D THE
> BODY OF GEORGE PARKER OF
> RATTON IN Yᴱ COVNTY OF SVSSEX
> ESQ (ELDEST SON OF OF Sʀ THOMAS
> PARKER Kᵀ) HE MARRIED MARY
> Yᴱ DAVGHTER OF RICHARD
> NEDEGATE SERGᵀ AT LAW BY
> WHOM HE HAD ISSVE FIVE SONS
> & TWO DAVGHTERS & WITH WHOM
> HE LIVED ONE & TWENTY YEARS
> HE LEFT BEHIND HIM TWO SONS. ROBERT & RICHARD ....

1. In situ see Lambarde (*SAC* 70 142) noting arms and giving date of 1673.
2. For George Parker as patron see 297Q.
3. JH notes that George Parker, c.1619-73, was MP for Seaford in 1659 and 1660, JP for Sussex, and deputy lieutenant, 1660. See Henning (III 205).

Willingdon, 297H Three floor-mounted brasses for John PARKER, d. 1558
- North aisle (Ratton Chapel) floor.
- Slab: 118(W) x 176(L); Brasses - Figure: 50(H), M.I.: 29(W) x 12(H) and Arms: 21(H) — Fine.
- Brasses set on large slab of (Horsham?) stone; head to West; male armoured figure, hands in prayer; female figure lost; M.I. (4 lines, engraved); escutcheon of arms.
- John Parker, Esq., d. 5 Oct 1558; his wife, Joanna, d. 6 Nov 1517.

1. At chapel entrance, alongside 297I, Horsfield (*Sussex* I 290); noted by Stephenson (518); in situ in Lambarde (*SAC* 70 142) - noting arms - and Davidson-Houston (*SAC* 80 137-9) - with illustration.
2. The M.I. is confused over John Parker's dates - his will of 5 Oct 1557 was proved on 25 Jun 1558,

his body to be buried at Willingdon, see Rice and Godfrey (4 350); both John Parker's wives appear to have been named Joan, first was Joan Farnefold, and second was Joanne the daughter of Sir Richard Sackville, of Buckhurst; their issue - Elizabeth, wife of Sir Edward Gage, of Firle (see 281E); and one of them, presumably his first wife supposedly died in 1517.

3. John Parker was also father of Thomas, subject of 297I, see Bannerman (*Sussex* 22).

Willingdon, 297I Floor-mounted brasses for Thomas PARKER, d. 1580

- North aisle (Ratton Chapel) floor.
- Slab: 135(W); Brasses: (i) 17(H) and (ii) 10(W) x 49(H) — Fine
- (1) Escutcheon; (2) M.I. in English
- Thomas Parker, of Ratton, d. 16 Apr 1580; his wife, Elinor; daughter of William Waller, of Groombridge, Esq.; issue - Nicholas, another son, and one daughter.

1. Seen by Horsfield (*Sussex* I 290) at chapel entrance close to 297H; Stephenson (518); in situ in Lambarde (*SAC* 70 142) - noting arms - and Davidson-Houston (*SAC* 80 139) - with illustration.
2. For Thomas Parker's wife, Elinor see 297F and for his son Nicholas, see 297E.
3. JH notes that Thomas Parker was son of John Parker – see 297H. Appointed a JP in 1558, he was known as 'Parker the Wild' on account of his having captured a Sussex heretic. He was MP for East Grinstead in 1558. See Bindoff (III 60).

Willingdon, 297J Standing monument for Nathaniel TRAYTON, d. 1757, and his wife Philadelphia, d. 1755

- North aisle (Ratton Chapel), South-East corner, against South wall.
- 167(W) x 288(H) x 25(D) — Very good; colour; local losses (pediment).
- In grey-veined marble against the wall; M.I. (engraved, black) set portrait-wise; arched top, moulded, angled frame and brown marble border; above, 2 fluted, scrolled corbels support a part entablature with broken pointed pediment; at the top, an escutcheon; below, a deep mottled base.
- Nathaniel Trayton, Esq., late of Ratton, d. 26 Mar 1757, aged 57; his wife, Philadelphia, d. 11 Nov 1755, aet 52; daughter of Sir George Parker, Bart., of Ratton; his brother, Edward Trayton, Esq., of Lewes.

1. Patron of 297J was the subject's brother, Edward Trayton of Lewes, who also donated plate to the church, see Couchman (*SAC* 55 157).
2. Nathaniel Trayton was b. c.1700 and through his marriage to Philadelphia became heir to his brother-in-law Sir Walter Parker when that line died out; at Nathaniel's death in 1757 Ratton was left to his brother, Edward (see W.H. Godfrey, 'Trayton of Lewes' *SNQ* III 252).
3. For the last of the Ratton Parkers see 297A and D.
4. 297J shows some notable colour combinations; in form, relates to 297A and D.
5. JH notes that Lambarde does not describe the heraldry - Trayton (granted 1606) impaling Parker.

Willingdon, 297K Ledger for Ann BARNHAM, d. 1704

- North aisle (Ratton chapel), South wall, above 297J.
- Inaccessible — Very good.
- M.I. (engraved, black) fills a very shallow moulded panel set portrait-wise; ogival top with urn, garlands and achievement; below, apron with ferns, lozenge of arms and simple corbel.
- Ann Barham, d. at Isleworth, Middlesex, 16 Apr 1704, aet 69; sixth daughter of Sir Thomas Parker, Knt, of Ratton; her first husband, John Shirley, Esq., of Isfield; her second husband, Francis Barnham, son of Sir Robert Barnham, Knt., of Boughton, Kent; also her nephew, Richard Parker.

1. In situ see Lambarde (*SAC* 70 142) – noting arms.
2. Relates to 297L.
3. Patron of 297K is nephew, Richard Parker.
4. High quality carving.

Willingdon, 297L Grave marker for Anne BARNHAM, d. 1704
- North aisle (Ratton chapel) floor, carpeted, in part obscured by altar.
- 92(W) x 106(L) — Very worn.
- M.I. (3 lines, engraved) in freestone slab; head to West.

Here Lyeth ye Body of
M[rs] Anne Barnham
1704

1. In situ.
2. Relates to 297K.

Willingdon, 297M Mural monument for Sir George THOMAS, d. 1774
- North aisle (Ratton Chapel), South wall, very high.
- c.100(W) x c.200(H) — Very good.
- M.I. (engraved, black) fills an unframed rectangular panel set portrait-wise; escutcheons top and bottom; 2 small black scrolled corbels.
- Sir George Thomas, Bart., of Yapton and of Ratton, Governor of Leeward Islands, West Indies, d. 31 Dec 1774, aet 79; his youngest daughter Margaret, d. 1 Sep 1797, aet 51; her husband, Arthur Freeman, Esq., of Antigua, d. 30 Jan 1780, aet 56; Margaret's Christian virtues.

1. Formerly on North chapel, East wall see Lambarde (*SAC* 70 143) – noting arms.
2. Perhaps originally set on the floor.

Willingdon, 297N Ledger for members of the THOMAS family, d. 1814, etc.
- Chancel floor, against the North wall, partly obscured by furnishings.
- 81(W) x 178(L) — Very good; colour lost.
- M.I. (4 lines, engraved, black) on a freestone slab; head to West.
- H[arriet] T[homas], d. 12 Nov 1828; G[eorge] P[elham] T[homas], d. 7 Sep 1828; G[eorge] T[homas] T[homas], d. 11 Nov 1827; C[harlotte] T[homas], d. 9 Nov 1814.

1. The initials and dates of the individuals listed on ledger 297O.

Willingdon, 297O Ledger for Charlotte THOMAS, d. 1814, and other family members
- Sanctuary floor, close to North wall.
- 136(W) x 66(L) — Good; horizontal crack.
- M.I. (engraved) fills a black slab (slate?); in part, in 3 columns; set landscape-wise; head to North.
- Charlotte Thomas, d. 9 Nov 1814, aet 16, eldest daughter of Inigo and Charlotte Thomas, of Ratton; George Pelham Thomas, d. 7 Sep 1828, aet 14, third son of Inigo and Frances Ann Thomas; Harriet Thomas, d. 12 Nov 1828, aet 21, fourth daughter of Inigo and Francis Ann Thomas; their uncle, Lt. Col. George Thomas Thomas, Esq., Lt-Col, 11th Light Dragoons, died at Ratton, 11 Nov 1827, aet 56.

1. Always within the sanctuary rail.
2. The individuals also commemorated on slab 297N.

Willingdon, 297P Mural monument for Sir John PARKER, d. 1617 [Plate 188]
- Sanctuary, North wall, at head height and above.
- 120(W) x 226(H) — Good; colour restored.
- In alabaster; a kneeling armoured male figure, on cushion, facing East, within a niche; straight entablature over with rose decoration; more roses in coffering above; above, scrollwork and an escutcheon; flanking, panelled pilasters with cord and ribbonwork; plain base; in centre, M.I. (shallow engraved, gilded) fills a square black panel; apron below with grotesque mask; 2 corbels with roses.

- Sir John Parker, Knt., gentleman pensioner of Elizabeth I and James I, captain of Pendenis Castle, Cornwall, d. 15 Oct 1617, aet 69; his elder brother, Sir Nicholas Parker, Knt., of Ratton, Willingdon.

1. In situ see Lambarde (*SAC* 70 141) – noting arms, Mosse and Nairn & Pevsner (629) noting large figure.
2. John Parker was brother of Sir Nicholas Parker, for whom see 297E.
3. JH notes that in addition to an active military life, mainly in Ireland, Sir John Parker was MP for Hastings in 1589, and for the Cornish seats of Truro in 1593, Launceston in 1601, and East Looe in 1604. See Hasler (III 172).

Willingdon, 297Q Mural monument for Lady Margaret WILDEGOOSE, d. 1653

- Sanctuary, North wall.
- 114(W) x 70(H)? — Fine; local losses (pediment); faded.
- M.I. (engraved, black) set portrait-wise, fills white marble panel; plain black frame on 4 sides; flanking, white marble scrolls and garlands; above, white marble broken pointed pediment; below, skull in centre, flanked by fluted scrolled corbels.
- Lady Margaret Wildegoose, d. 16 Aug 1653, aet 61; eldest daughter of Henry Lord Dacre, Baron of Herstmonceux; and widow (44 years) of Sir Anslow Wildegoose; issue - three, all died; also her nephew George Parker, Esq., of Ratton.

1. A widow, and Margaret Wildegoose's 3 children having predeceased her, the patron of 297Q was her nephew George Parker (see 297G).
2. Unusual scroll motif crammed into flanking spaces.

Willingdon, 297R Cartouche monument for Dame Katherine NUTT, d. 1700

- Sanctuary, North wall, above head height.
- 108(W) x 160(H) — Good; colour.
- M.I. (engraved, black) in upper 80% of a white marble convex oval panel with moulded edge; cherubim left and right, their wings crossing the panel frame; below, decorative foliage; at foot, an escutcheon with a Baroque frame.
- Dame Katherine Nutt, d. 2 May 1700; daughter of Sir Thomas Parker, of Ratton; and widow of Sir Thomas Nutt, of Mays, Sussex; issue - Leonard (died); Philadelphia, wife of Sir Thomas Dyke, of Horeham, Sussex; and Katherine, wife of Anthony Bramston, Esq., of Screens, Roxwell, Essex.

1. In situ see Lambarde (*SAC* 70 141), noting arms and Nairn & Pevsner (629).
2. Katherine Nutt's home at Mays House, Selmeston, an early 17th-century building that went through many hands - see Farrant (307).
3. The quality of carving on 297R is very high, e.g. the cherub's wings across the lettering (close to 108C and H).
4. Perhaps 272M is by the same hand?

Willingdon, 297S Cartouche monument for William PARKER, d. 1727 [Plate 189]

- Sanctuary, North wall, above head height, alongside 297R.
- 86(W) x 150(H) — Excellent.
- In white marble, M.I. (engraved, black) fills cartouche in form of a drape and set portrait-wise; a rich frame of 4 cherubim, decorative textile and flowers; above, achievement.
- William Parker, armiger, d. 1 Jan 1727, aet 48, of Lincoln's Inn; son of Robert Parker of Ratton; erected by his heirs.

1. In situ see Lambarde (*SAC* 70 141) noting arms and Nairn & Pevsner (629).
2. The quality of carving on 297S is very high, comparable with contemporary cartouches at Folkington, Streat, Brightling, etc.

Willingdon, 297T Ledger stone for Rev. William BEAN, d. 1768
- Nave floor, near North wall, partly obscured by furnishings.
- 86(W) x 181(L) — Fine.
- M.I. (8 lines, engraved) in upper 30% of a sandy freestone slab; head to West.
- Rev. William Bean, vicar of Willingdon and Arlington, d. 29 Feb 1768; his virtues as a clergyman.

1. JH notes that Rev. William Bean was vicar of Arlington 1738-68 and of Willingdon 1741-68.

Willingdon, 297U Ledger stone for William CARTER, d. 1629
- Nave floor, centre, East end.
- 92(W) x 179(L) — Very worn.
- M.I. (5 lines, engraved) in centre of freestone slab; head to West.
- William Carter, the elder, of Westham, buried at Willingdon 19 Oct 1629.

Willingdon Addition
Noted by Stephenson (518); Davidson-Houston (*SAC* 80 140) with illustration, loose in vestry, engraved on both sides:
(1) A brass for Robert Parker, perhaps engraved on both sides; Stephenson differs from Davidson-Houston who gives, for one side: 'In assured hope of a better … the 16 of Aprill / 1618 in the 17th yeare of his age / De seipso / caelica quae vivo dederat spes gaudia (Christo / auspice) iam cum spes desinit esse fruor; On earth I dreamed of heavenly bliss, Christ guiding me, now dreaming's past and heaven a reality'.
(2) For the other, seemingly more relevant side, both Stephenson and Davidson-Houston give: 'Here lyes the body of Mr Robert Parker third sonne to Sr Nicholas Parker of Wallington [sic] who died ye 22 of Ian 1618 being 18 yeares of age'.

(298) WILMINGTON, St. Mary & St. Peter
Norman chancel, Early English South aisle - Nairn & Pevsner (630) and G. Cooper, 'Illustrations of Wilmington Priory and Church' (*SAC* 4 37-66); the chancel, reported to be in poor state in 1686, was repaired by 1724 (Ford 52, 187); the parish had 35 families in 1724 and a population of 236 in 1801.

Wilmington, 298A Mural monument for Rev. James CAPPER, d. 1835, and his first wife, d. 1787
- North transept, West wall, high up, now enclosed by offices.
- Inaccessible (reported to be large) — Condition appears fine.
- M.I. (engraved, black) fills a rectangular white marble panel; engraved squared border, set portrait-wise.
- Rev. James Capper, M.A., of St. Johns College, Cambridge, prebendary of Chichester, rector of Ashurst, Kent, and vicar of Wilmington for 56 Years, d. 2 Mar 1835, aet 81; his first wife, Catherina Jane, d. 2 Jan 1787, aet 35, eldest daughter of Walter Biddulph, Esq., of Barton-under-Needwood, Staffordshire; his second wife, Ann, d. 16 Jun 1843, aet 80, only daughter of James Nicklin, Esq., of Hackney, Middlesex; quotes Psalms LIV. 4.

1. Probably post-dates 1835; alongside it is another smaller mural monument commemorating James Henry Capper, son of James and Catherine, d. 1835, aged 50 years, and other members of the family, attributed by Gunnis (*Dict.* 292) to Parsons.
2. Travelling between Lewes and Eastbourne in November 1790, Stebbing Shaw noted that James Capper (vicar at Wilmington) received pupils; he was a charitable man; he disbursed food to the poor during the winter of 1794-5; see Caffyn (268, 287-88); for diary of his sister, Mary, see V. Naish, 'Mary Capper's Diary' (*SNQ* XI 90-3, 104-7, 125-7).
3. JH notes that James Capper was vicar of Wilmington 1779-1835, rector of Ashurst, Kent, 1802-35, prebendary of Fittleworth, Chichester Cathedral, 1802-35, and sequestrator of Lullington. See CCEd, Venn (II 1 508), Horn (*Fasti 1541-1857* 2 31).

Wilmington, 298B Ledger stone for Rev. Henry HODSDEN, d. 1740/1

- Chancel floor, near North wall, before rail.
- 100(W) x 200(L) — Good; cracked.
- Escutcheon, then M.I. (12 lines, engraved) fill surface of polished black stone slab; set head to East.
- Rev. Henry Hodsden, vicar of Willingdon and Westham, previously vicar of Wilmington, d. 20 Mar 1740/1, aet 79.

1. Noted in Horsfield (*Sussex* I 326) and in situ in Lambarde (*SAC* 70 149) - noting arms.
2. To match 298C.
3. JH notes that Henry Hodsden was vicar of Wilmington 1698-1720, of Willingdon 1698-1720, and of Westham 1719-41. See CCEd and Venn (I 2 385).

Wilmington, 298C Ledger stone for Rev. William EDWARDS, d. 1731, and his wife Frances [Plate 190]

- Chancel floor, near South wall, before rail.
- 114(W) x 200(L) — Excellent.
- Escutcheon in roundel, then M.I. (12 lines (9 + 3 lines), centred, engraved) on a black polished slab, set head to East.
- Rev. William Edwards, rector of Denton and West Dean, previously vicar of Wilmington, d. 26 Mar 1731, aet 80, 'after 60 years painfull & diligent Labours in the work of the Ministry'; his wife, Frances; quotes I Timothy 4 & 8.

1. In situ see Horsfield (*Sussex* I 326) and Lambarde (*SAC* 70 149) - noting arms.
2. Relaid amongst 19th-century tiles.
3. Frances Edwards d. 1715.
4. JH notes that William Edwards was briefly vicar, ca.1675, then sequestrator of Wilmington, rector of Litlington 1676-87, rector of Denton 1687-1731, and rector of West Dean 1692-1731. See CCEd and Hennessy.

Wilmington, 298D Ledger stone for John SUNDERLAND, d. 1681/2

- Chancel floor, West end, South side of pulpit.
- 86(W) x 63(L) — Good.
- M.I. (4 lines, engraved) in upper 50% of Horsham stone (?) slab; head to North.
- John Sunderland, of Milton Street, buried 7 Feb 1681.

1. Noted in Horsfield (*Sussex* I 326).
2. Set to be legible to incomers through the South door, the date 1621 or 1681 is unclear as is the explanation for the space within the word 'February'.
3. Milton Street is within the parish.
4. NBI records the burial of John Sunderland on 18[sic] Feb 1681 at Wilmington.

Wilmington, 298E Ledger for Rev. John HUBBERSTY, d. 1779, and 2 daughters

- South aisle floor, along South wall.
- 99(W) x 202(L) — Very good.
- M.I. (19 lines, engraved) in upper 75% of polished black slab; fleur-de-lys motif in 4 corners; decorative border; head to West.
- Rev. John Hubbersty, vicar of Wilmington and rector of Folkington, d. 4 Feb 1779, aet 49; his wife, Elizabeth; their issue - second daughter, Katherine, d. 23 Feb 1768, an infant; last daughter, Phillippa, d. 17 Jan 1775, an infant.

1. Noted in Horsfield (*Sussex* I 326).
2. The fleur de-lys motif recurs on other local ledgers, see Introduction and e.g. at nearby Alfriston (4G).
3. JH notes that John Hubbersty was rector of Parham 1761-70, and rector of Folkington and vicar of Wilmington 1770-79. He was also curate of Seaford in 1757 (Caffyn 233).

Wilmington, 298F Ledger for John HONEY, d. 1694, and his wife

- South aisle floor, West end, partly obscured by walling and furnishings.
- (Visible) 78(W) x 168(L) — Very good.
- M.I. (15 lines, centred, engraved) in upper 60% of a polished black slab; head to South.
- John Honey, Esq., late of Ditchling, born Wilmington, buried 14 Nov 1694, aet 68; his wife,
  Anne, died earlier in 1694, first daughter of Sir Thomas Culpepyr, of Folkington, Knt.

1. Noted in Horsfield (*Sussex* I 326).
2. Described as a mural monument with ledger below in Lambarde (*SAC* 70 147) - arms noted.
3. Thomas Culpepere baptised 1600, buried at Folkington 1638, married Elizabeth Goodridge, his
   daughter Anne was b 1632, see pedigree in Attree & Booker (*SAC* 47 72).

Wilmington Additions

Noted in Horsfield (*Sussex* I 326):
(1) Robert Hay, vicar of Alfriston, d. 5 Feb 1735.
(2) Mrs Elizabeth Edwards, d. 1758.
(3) Mrs Mary Hodsden, d. 1743.
Pevsner (630).
(4) Identifies the top of an Elizabethan monument with fluted frieze and steep pediment at West end of
South aisle, perhaps related to 298F.

(299) WINCHELSEA, St. Thomas

The early 14th-century chancel and side chapels remain; otherwise, later
Perpendicular enrichments - VCH (IX 72); Nairn & Pevsner (633-34); for a view of
1784 see Godfrey & Salzman (Pl. 182); John Evelyn reports in his mid 17th-century
diary that the church was 'forlorn ruins'; aisle pavements were in bad repair in
1686 and remained so in 1724 (Ford); during the Peninsula War, a barracks was
established in the town and considerable repairs carried out in the church, and
again in 1850 (Church Guide); the parish had 35 or 40 families in 1724 and a
population of 627 in 1801. See Claude Blair, John A Goodall and Philip J Lankester,
'The Winchelsea Tombs Reconsidered' (*Church Monuments* XV 200 5-30) for a
reconsideration of the fourteenth-century effigies here and comments on the later
history of the building relevant to 299A-V.

Winchelsea, 299A An Anonymous undated ledger

- Nave floor, West end, partly obscured by pews.
- 76(W) x 60(L) — Very worn.
- M.I. (engraved) on a sand-coloured freestone slab; head to West.

...
...
...
...
Aged 42
And of John his Son ...

Winchelsea, 299B Ledger for William WILLES, d. 1752, his wife Jane, d. 1737, and their son, d. 1729.

- Nave floor, East of centre.
- 84(W) x 182(L) — Very worn.
- M.I. (engraved) on a sand-coloured freestone slab; head to West.

... HST
... Primogen.tis Gul.mus Willes
huiusque ecclesiæ Rectoris
... Janae Uxoris ejus: Qui
... vix natus menses (heu)
præpropere [...a]vit die 19 Feb : ry
Ano Dom : 1728
Resurgam
...
...
...
Rectoris
Quo Obiit ...
.. o Dom 1737
... ætat ..
...
Willielm[us] Willes A.M.
Rector [hujus Ecclesiæ
Obiit [12 die] Decembris
Anno 175..

1. Cited in W. Cooper (137) with part transcription.
2. JH notes that NBI records burial of William Willes on 29 Dec 1752, Jane Willes on 22 Apr 1737 and Younge [sic] Willes on 23 Feb 1728/9, all at Winchelsea. The latter is probably William Willes the younger, as a William, son of William and Jane Willes, was baptised at Winchelsea on 15 Jan 1728/9. See IGI.
3. Rev. William Willes was rector of Ore and Winchelsea 1723-52. See CCEd.

Winchelsea, 299C Floor slab for an anonymous child, d. 1758
- Nave floor, North of centre, towards East end.
- 40(W) x 38(H) — Very worn.
- M.I. (engraved) on a small irregular grey stone; head to South.

T. infans
ob. Feb
1758

Winchelsea, 299D Ledger for Sara JORDEN, d. 1633/4
- Nave floor, centre, close to sanctuary rail, North of 299E.
- 47(W) x 90(L) — Worn, cracked, repaired.
- M.I. (6 lines, engraved) on upper 50% of a black slab; head to West.
- Sarah Jorden, d. 18 Feb 1633/4, aet 7; eldest daughter of William and Ann Jorden, of Edimure, Sussex.

1. Cited in W. Cooper (137) with transcription.
2. William Jorden and Ann Burdet licensed to marry dated 14 Feb 1626, see Dunkin (*Licences 1586-1643* 152) and Sussex Marriage Index.
3. Note spelling of Udimore.

Winchelsea, 299E Floor slab and brasses for Margaret JORDEN, d. 1636
- Nave floor (slab), centre, close to sanctuary rail, South of 299D; Sanctuary (brasses), North wall, at head height.
- Stone: 89(W) x 169(L) — Very worn. Brasses: 31(W) x 48(H) — Fine.
- M.I. in sanctuary - inaccessible.

1. M.I. (12 lines, 6 biography, 6 verses, in English) noted by Stephenson (518) as for Margaret, wife of Jeremy Jorden, of Winchelsea, d. 2 Apr 1636, aet 63; their issue - 3 daughters Margaret, Alse, Martha; the sorrow of her bereaved husband.
2. See Davidson-Houston (*SAC* 80 140), with illustrations.
3. Cited in W. Cooper (137) with part transcription.

Winchelsea, 299F Mural monument for Margaret GODFREY, d. 1611

- South aisle, East wall, at head height, obscured by later altar.
- 110(W) x 130(H) — Poor; local losses (heraldry, etc.).
- In coloured alabasters and marbles; M.I. (engraved) on a slate panel; moulded frame; flanking pilasters with ribbon-work and strap-work & mottos over (left): 'CORDE FIXAM'; (right): 'DEO PATR. ...'; below, base mouldings; at foot, decorated apron.

MEMORIÆ SACRVM
OBDORMIT HIC MARGARETA FILIA
GVILIELMI LAMBARD DE WESTCOMB
IN COMITATV CANTII ARMIGERI &
CANCELLARIÆ MAGISTRI VIRI PIETATE
& PRVDENTIA SPECTATISSIMI; VXOR
AVTEM THOMÆ GODFREII GENEROSI
ET HVIVS VILLÆ IVRATI; CVI
LAMBADUM & THOMAM FILIOS PEPERIT
OBIIT DIE 29 IVNII ANNO SAL: 1611
CVM CHRISTO ÆTERNVM VICTVRA.
CONJVGI CHARISSIMÆ
MARITVS MOOSTISSIMVS
CVM LACHRYMIS
POSVIT

1. In situ; cited by Lambarde (*SAC* 68 236-7) noting arms and W. Cooper (137) with transcription.
2. The poor condition cannot hide the high quality of the early 17th-century London carving.
3. JH notes that Margaret was daughter of William Lambard, armiger, of Westcomb in Kent, and wife of Thomas Godfrey, Gent., of this town. She died 29 Jun 1611.

Winchelsea, 299G Grave marker or ledger for Thomas CRUTTENDEN, undated

- South aisle floor, East end, at North end of series (299G-K) mostly obscured by carpeting.
- Inaccessible — Worn.
- Remains of a M.I. engraved in a freestone slab.
- Thomas, son of Thomas Cruttenden, Gent.

1. No Cruttendens of Winchelsea cited amongst parish Marriage Licences, see Dunkin (*Licences 1670-1729*).
2. Thomas Cruttenden perhaps related to those commemorated by 299G and 299I?

Winchelsea, 299H Grave marker or ledger for Catherine CRUTTENDEN, undated

- South aisle floor, East end, to North of centre of the series 299G-K, obscured by carpeting.
- Inaccessible — Worn.
- Remains of a M.I. in a freestone slab.
- Catherine Cruttenden, wife, of Thomas Cruttenden, Gent.

1. See comment on 299G.
2. Catherine Cruttenden was presumably the wife of the Thomas Cruttenden cited on 299G or I.

Winchelsea, 299I Grave marker or ledger for Thomas CRUTTENDEN, d. 1735

- South aisle floor, East end, in centre of series 299G-K, obscured by carpeting.
- Inaccessible — Worn.
- Remains of a M.I. on a freestone slab.
- Thomas Cruttenden, son of Thomas, d. 1735.

1. See comment on 299G.
2. Thomas Cruttenden was probably related to the Thomas Cruttenden of 299G and perhaps husband of Catherine Cruttenden of 299H.

Winchelsea, 299J Floor for Catherine CRUTTENDEN, undated

- South aisle floor, East end, to South of centre of series 299G-K, obscured by carpeting.
- Inaccessible — Worn.
- Remains of M.I. on a freestone slab.
- Catherine Cruttenden, daughter of Thomas Cruttenden, Gent., d. 4 Jan ????

1. See comment on 299G.

Winchelsea, 299K Floor for John CRUTTENDEN, undated

- South aisle floor, East end, at South end of series 299G-K, obscured by carpeting.
- Inaccessible — Worn.
- Remains of M.I. on freestone slab.
- John Cruttenden, son of Thomas Cruttenden, Gent., d. 6 May.

1. See comment on 200G.
2. Probably son of the Thomas Cruttenden of either 299G or 299I.

Winchelsea, 299L Mural monument for John STEWART, d. 1780

- South aisle wall, East of centre, high.
- c.90(W); (H) inaccessible — Fine; water damage.
- In grey-veined and white marbles on black baseplate with pointed top; ornamental apron; M.I. (engraved, black) on 50% of tablet; flanking, flat pilasters; entablature and pointed finials; above, a grey baseplate supports an urn in relief on another triangular plate; below, base mouldings and a decorated apron with achievement.
- John Stewart, Esq., commander of the Mount Stuart, Indiaman, d. 3 Oct 1780, aet 40; fourth son of Charles Stewart, Esq., of Ardsheal, Argyllshire.

1. Cited in W. Cooper (137) with transcription.
2. Patrons were John Stewart's mother and his (unnamed) siblings.
3. Lambarde does not mention the heraldry.

Winchelsea, 299M Ledger for Elizabeth FULLER, d. 1729/30

- South aisle floor, East of centre.
- 49(W) x 82(L) — Very worn.
- A skull, then M.I. (7 lines, engraved) fills 75% of surface of a freestone slab; head to West.
- Elizabeth Fuller, d. 27 Feb 1729/30, aet 16; daughter of Thomas and Judith Fuller.

Winchelsea, 299N Mural monument for Sophia DYNE, d. 1809

- South aisle, South wall, West of centre, high.
- c.85(W); (H) inaccessible — Very good; faded.
- In white marble on a black baseplate with a curved top and pointed bottom; M.I. (8 lines, engraved, black) on a tablet, set landscape-wise; flanking, fluted pilasters on finial corbels; above, a cornice; at top, a draped sarcophagus; below, a pointed apron.
- Sophia Dyne, d. 24 Dec 1809, aet 38; daughter of William Dyne, Esq., of Milton, Sittingbourne, Kent, and his wife, Effield.

1. Cited in W. Cooper (137) with transcription.

Winchelsea, 299O Mural monument for Drake HOLLINGBERY, d. 1821 [Plate 191]

- South aisle, West wall, upper tier, South end.
- Inaccessible — Very good; faded.
- In white marble on a black baseplate with a pointed top; M.I. on tablet; flanking, fluted pilasters; pointed pediment over with quartered palmettes flanking; curved apron with cherub's head.
- Rev. Drake Hollingbery, M.A., rector of Winchelsea, chancellor of the Diocese of Chichester

for 40 years, d. 31 Dec 1821, aet 79.

1. Cited in W. Cooper (138) with transcription.
2. For Drake Hollingbery's wife see 299P.
3. Presumably this is the monument to 'Drake Clerk, 1821', ascribed to George Lupton, c.1742, by Gunnis (*Dict.* 246).

Winchelsea, 299P Mural monument for Elizabeth HOLLINGBERY, d. 1826
[Plate 191]
- South aisle, West wall, upper tier, centre.
- Inaccessible — Very good; faded.
- Description - as for 2990.
- Elizabeth Hollingbery, d. 28 Aug 1826, aet 70; widow of Drake Hollingbery.

1. Cited in W. Cooper (138) with transcription.
2. For Elizabeth Hollingbery's husband see 2990.
3. If 2990 is by Lupton, so must be 299P.

Winchelsea, 299Q Mural monument children of Drake and Elizabeth HOLLINGBERY, d. 1843 and 1844 [Plate 191]
- South aisle, West wall, upper tier, North end.
- Inaccessible — Very good; faded.
- Description - as for 2990.
- Ann Hollingbery, d. 21 Nov 1843, aet 62; John Hollingbery, d. 21 Mar 1844, aet 63; children of Drake and Elizabeth Hollingbery.

1. Cited in W. Cooper (138) with transcription.
2. If 2990 is by Lupton, so must be 299Q.

Winchelsea, 299R Mural monument for Richard and Mary DENNE, d. 1819 and d. 1827 [Plate 191]
- South aisle, West wall, middle tier, South end.
- Inaccessible — Fine; faded.
- A black baseplate with a pointed top and curved base; on a plinth, a M.I. (engraved) on a white marble sarcophagus with wave fluting; block corbels; another M.I. (engraved, black) on a rectangular tablet; separate escutcheon; signed (baseplate lower right): 'S. MANNING ...'.
- Richard Denne, Esq., of Winchelsea, d. 25 Jan 1819, aet 68; his wife, Mary Denne, d. 15 Jul 1827, aet 65; issue - William John Denne, d. 31 May 1855, aet 65; eldest daughter, Anna Maria Denne, d. 16 Apr 1862, aet 76.

1. Cited in W. Cooper (138) with transcription.
2. In situ see Horsfield (*Sussex* I 484) and Lambarde (*SAC* 68 237) - noting arms.
3. JH notes that Richard Denne married in 1783 Mary, daughter of William Steer, Esq., of Northampton. See *BLG* (1850 325).

Winchelsea, 299S Mural monument for Richard Greenland DENNE, d. 1839 and Mary Jane NEWMAN, d. 1834, and her husband [Plate 191]
- South aisle, West wall, middle tier, South of centre.
- Inaccessible — Fine; faded.
- Black baseplate with curved top; M.I. on white marble tablet; flanking, inverted torches; above, an urn flanked by quartered palmettes; below, scroll brackets and bristly foliage; unsigned; no arms.
- Richard Greenland Denne, barrister, Inner Temple, London, d. 5 Dec 1839, aet 44, youngest son of Richard and Mary Denne; Mary Jane Newman, d. 28 Jul 1834, aet 42, youngest daughter of Richard and Mary Denne and wife of Sir Robert William Newman,

Bart., M.P., d. 24 Jan 1848, aet 72.

1. Cited in W. Cooper (138) with transcription.
2. For Richard and Mary Denne, see 299R.

Winchelsea, 299T Mural monument for sons of Nathaniel DAWES, d. 1780-1804 [Plate 191]

- South aisle, West wall, middle tier, North of centre.
- Inaccessible — Fine; faded; rust spots.
- Oval plaque in white marble on a tiny foot; on an unframed rectangular tablet, set portrait-wise; black baseplate with pointed top; ribbonwork at top.
- Nathaniel Dawes, Gent. and his wife, Elizabeth Dawes; their issue - Captain Nathaniel Dawes, died at siege of Bangalore, East Indies, 24 Mar 1791, aet 40; Ensign James Dawes, died at Penin-bar-cum in the battle between Hyder Ally and Col. Baillie, 10 Sep 1780, aet 23; Lieutenant Richard Dawes, wounded against French Fleet on 1 Jun 1794, d. 5 Jun 1794, aet 34; Walter Dawes, died at Macassar, Autumn 1804, aet 40.

1. Cited in W. Cooper (138) with transcription.
2. JH notes that the ages and births correspond with those in IGI.

Winchelsea, 299U Mural monument for Edwin DAWES, d. 1824, his wife Jane, d. 1820, and also George Dawes, d. 1820. [Plate 191]

- South aisle, West wall, middle tier, North end.
- Inaccessible — Fine; faded.
- M.I. on unframed white marble tablet, set portrait-wise; curved apron; black baseplate with pointed top and curved bottom; above, an entablature and ornamental finial with 3 roundels.
- Jane Dawes, d. 17 May 1820, aet 83; wife of Edwin Dawes, d. 30 Sep 1824, aet 75; also George Dawes, d. 17 Nov 1820, aet 59.

1. Cited in W. Cooper (138) with transcription.

Winchelsea, 299V Standing monument for Mrs BALDWIN, d. 1798 [Plate 191]

- Standing on South aisle floor, South-West corner.
- Base - 50 x 50; 170(H) — Fine; faded.
- In white marble; a column topped with an urn.

To the Memory of
Mrs BALDWYN
Wife of Captain BALDWIN
of the King's own Infantry
and Daughter of
General PRESCOTT Governor
and Commander in Chief
in British North America
who died 22 June 1798,
in the 24th Year of her Age
To the Memory also
of their infant Son
this Monument is Erected
as a mark of grateful affection
by her Husband
who in all situations of life
[must] deplore their lot

1. Noted by Horsfield (*Sussex* I 484) and cited in W. Cooper (138) with transcription.
2. The sentiments expressed in the final lines of the M.I. are unusual.
3. Its form compares with a standing monument at Willingdon, somewhat earlier (297D).

Winchelsea Additions
(1) Horsfield (*Sussex* I 484) notes a plain but elegant white marble mural monument to Richard Maliphant, Esq., d. 1823; also noted by W. Cooper (138).
(2) Lambarde (*SAC* 68 236/7) described three hatchments. One was recorded in 1952, but according to Summers (158) is no longer there.
(3) Summers (157) mentions hatchments for General Robert Prescott, and Col. Prescott, both d. 1816.

(302) WITHYHAM, St. Michael and All Angels

Using 14th-century fabric, the church was rebuilt 1663-72, after lightning and a fire on 16 Jun 1663; Sackville chapel completed 1680; South aisle remade in 1841 and there were other 19th century changes - Nairn & Pevsner (637-8); for plan see *SNQ* (IV 113); fabric fine in 1724, but for North chancel (Sackville chapel) (Ford 184); monuments nearly all in North-East Chapel from which earlier examples have been lost; for example, in his will, Robert Sackville, 2nd Earl (1561-1608/9) left provision for a monument costing £200-300 (biography by Michael A.R. Graves in *ODNB*); some early brasses did survive (302B, D and H); the excellent conditions of the monuments, the high rank of the family, the sensational quality of 302J and the fame of the makers of 302 E-G has earned the monuments at Withyham a good deal of antiquarian and art-historical interest; Horsfield (*Sussex* I 395-6) noted that Burrell had found 27 M.I.s in the Sackville vault, see too *SNQ* (IV 113) and Willatts (*SAC* 125 10); for views of the monuments see BL Add. MS 5671 ff.5-11; 5676 ff.44 & 47; Withyham was a large Wealden parish with c.100 families in 1724 and a population of 1074 in 1801. For the history of the family vault, remodelled in 1677 and again in 1815, see Julian Litten in *Church Monuments*, XIV 1999 104-28

Withyham, 302A Wall-mounted iron slab for William ALFREY, d. 1610
- Nave, against West wall.
- 39(W) x 121(L) — Fine.
- M.I. (10 lines, relief) on the upper 30% of a cast iron slab; raised border.
- William Alfrey, yeoman, d. 15 Jun 1610.

1. Formerly on South buttress at East end of chancel - Nairn & Pevsner (639).
2. Brought into church after 1932 (on plan in *SNQ* IV - 302A appears on external East chancel buttress).
3. Willatts (*SAC* 125 100 & 111) interprets the variable thickness of the slab as a sign of inferior workmanship.

Withyham, 302B Wall-mounted brass for Ann SACKVILL, d. 1653
- Sackville Chapel, South wall, at head height.
- 27.5(W) x 21(H) — Fine; local losses (top left corner).
- M.I. (11 lines, engraved) fills a polished rectangular brass plate, with tabs for attachment.
- Ann Sackvill, d. 13 Feb 1653, aet 63, daughter of Sir Robert Johnson, Knt., of the Tower of London; and wife of Thomas Sackvill, son of Thomas Sackvill, Lord Buckhurst, Knight of the Garter.

1. Attachment tabs suggest that 302B is a coffin plate salvaged from the vault after the fire of 1663.

Withyham, 302C Wall-mounted brass for Lady Ann SACKVIL, Countess of Home, d. 1672 [Plate 192]
- Sackville Chapel, West wall, North of 302B.
- 24(W) x 13(H) — Fine.
- M.I. (6 lines, engraved) on a polished rectangular, brass plate; elegant script.

- Lady Ann Sackvil, Countess of Home, 17 Jun 1650 - 22 Aug 1672; wife (from 19 Apr 1671) of Alexander, Earl of Home, Lord Coldinghame.

1. Ann Sackvil's death coincided with the rebuilding of the church, although the family chapel was incomplete until 1680.

Withyham, 302D Wall-mounted brass for Lady Mary SACKVILLE, d. 1632
- Sackville Chapel, West wall, at head height, below 302C.
- 23(W) x 14(H) — Fine.
- M.I. (8 lines, engraved) on a polished rectangular brass plate.
- Lady Mary Sackville, d. 30 Oct 1632, aet 7, daughter of Edward, Earl of Dorset, .

1. Mary Sackville was daughter of the 4th Earl (1590-1652), the prominent courtier, by his wife Mary Curzon, who was Governess of Charles I's children.

Withyham, 302E Mural monument for John Frederick SACKVILLE, 3rd Duke and Earl of DORSET, d. 1799 [Plate 193]
- Sackville Chapel, North wall, West end, above head height.
- 135(W); (H) inaccessible — Excellent.
- Above, 3 mourning putti with the portrait roundel of the deceased against a square back plate; pointed pediment over; M.I. on framed tablet, set landscape-wise, flanked by fluted drums; all on large corbels with arms between; signed (lower right): 'NOLLEKENS FT. 1802'.
- John Frederick Sackville, Duke, KG, etc., many titles and honours, died at Knowle Park, 19 Jul 1799, aet 54, buried at Withyham; his widow, Arabella Diana Cope.

1. Signed by Joseph Nollekens (1737-1823); noted by all commentators - Horsfield (*Sussex* I 395-6); Gunnis (*Dict.* 279); Nairn & Pevsner (638), etc.
2. The preliminary sketches (V&A E.4378 & 4400-1920) suggests that the motif of assembled mourning putti around a portrait roundel was always planned (illustrated in Church Guide).
3. A drawing by Nollekens in the Douce Bequest at the Ashmolean Museum, Oxford is made on the back of a bill relating to the cutting by George Gahagan of the M.I. on 302E, see Physick (152).
4. John Frederick Sackville, 1745-99, was an indolent diplomat (see biography by Gerald M.D. Howat in *ODNB*); heir to the family cricketing traditions; advocate of women's cricket and philanderer; for his wife, Arabella (1769–1825), daughter of Sir Charles Cope, Bart, see 302F, who remarried Charles Earl Whitworth in 1801; their issue - 2 daughters and his successor, George John Frederick (1793-1815), who succeeded as 4th Duke, for whom see 302G.

Withyham, 302F Mural monument for Arabella Diana SACKVILLE, Duchess of DORSET, d. 1825
- Sackville Chapel, North wall, alongside and East of 302E.
- 160(W); (H) unknown — Excellent.
- Black backplate; screen with 2 daughters as mourners; urn on plinth; below, M.I. (engraved) on tablet; signed (on right return): 'CHANTREY. SC.'.
- Arabella Diana Sackville, Duchess of Dorset, d. 1 Aug 1825, aet 57.

1. Attributed to Chantrey (1781-1841) by all commentators - Horsfield (*Sussex* I 395-6); Gunnis (*Dict.* 96); Nairn & Pevsner (639).
2. Some twenty years earlier, Arabella Diana Sackville had been the patron of 302E for her first husband; her daughters by her second husband were the Countess of Plymouth and the Countess De La Warr, who appear here as mourners.
3. 302F is the only East Sussex monument by Chantrey, see Whinney, and illustrates his favoured device for smaller monuments, two female mourning figures flanking an urn.

Withyham, 302G Mural monument for George John Frederick SACKVILLE, 4th Duke of DORSET, d. 1815 [Plate 194]

- Sackville Chapel, North wall, East end, at head height.
- 170(W) x 252(H) — Excellent.
- Against a black backplate with a pointed top, in white marble, a seated, mourning figure (the Duke's mother); against an urn, on a pedestal; above, a small cornice with palmettes left and right, flanking a portrait roundel; below, a deeper cornice on fluted brackets over a M.I. (engraved) on an unframed tablet; signed (on right return): 'FLAXMAN'.
- George John Frederick Sackville, Duke of Dorset, died near Dublin after a fall from his horse, 14 Feb 1815, aet 21, buried at Withyham.

1. Noted by Horsfield (*Sussex* I 395-6) as 'from the chisel of Flaxman'; Gunnis (*Dict.*) does not list as by Flaxman. And see Nairn & Pevsner (638).
2. The 4th Duke was killed in a fall from his horse while hunting and died without issue; for his parents see 302E-F.
3. 302G marks a late career return by Flaxman to his classical style; Dorset's mother appears in Hellenic draperies; in contrast, the roundel, perhaps after a painted portrait, shows Dorset in contemporary dress; despite his huge production of small monuments, 302G is one of only three monuments by Flaxman (1755-1826) in East Sussex (see too 45I and 221QQQ) although Chichester Cathedral has several important works by him - Thomas Ball (mid 1780s), William Collins (1795) and Agnes Cromwell (1800); by the mid 1800s Flaxman's designs were being cut and finished, to a fashionably high degree of polish, by assistants.

Withyham, 302H Wall-mounted brass for Thomas SACKVILLE, d. 1646

- Sackville Chapel, East wall, low down.
- 18(W) x 10(H) — Stained; sound.
- M.I. (8 lines, engraved) on a tiny brass plate, in Latin, floral decoration below.

[C]ORPVS PRENOBILIS THOME SACKVIL..
ARMIGERI QVARTO GENITI FILII THOME
COMITIS DORSESTRIE MAGNI THESAVRARII
ANGLIE & NATI 25 DIE MAII ANNO DOMINI
1571 OBIIT 25 AVGVSTI 1646 EXPECTANS
RESVRRECTIONEM FIDELIVM ET IVSTORVM
IN ET PER IESVM CHRISTVM DOMINVM
NOSTRVM

1. Thomas Sackville was the fourth son of the 1st Earl.

Withyham, 302I Wall-mounted brass for Thomas SACKVILLE, d. 1675

- Sackville Chapel, East wall, below 302H.
- 28(W) x 33(H) — Fine; stained.
- M.I. (32 lines engraved) in Latin, on a brass plate (high copper content).
- Thomas Sackville, 5 Feb 1662 - 19 Aug 1675, died at Saumur, France; seventh son of Richard Sackville, 5th Earl, d. 27 Aug 1677, aet 54 and Frances Cranfield.

MEMORIÆ PIETATI ET POSTERITATI SACRUM,
etc.

1. 302I refers to the subject of 302J and perhaps forms part of it.
2. Thomas Sackville died two years before his father's death.
3. The latter's contract with Cibber (b 1630, came to England in 1660) for Thomas' monument was signed by his widow Frances, dowager Countess of Dorset in 1677, which was the year of the 5th Earl's death.
4. The work was to take no more than 10 months.

Withyham, 302J Freestanding monument for Thomas SACKVILLE, d. 1675, and his father Richard, Earl of Dorset, d. 1677, erected 1678 [Plates 195 & 196]
- Sackville Chapel, freestanding, in the centre.
- The plinth: 348 (East-West); 248 (North-South); The tomb-chest: 120(W) x 229(L) — Excellent; local losses (toes, etc.).
- A tomb-chest on a stepped plinth set East-West; a semi-reclining effigy with a skull, gazing to the East, on a rolled mat, on a polished dark grey ledger; the tomb-chest with white marble panels within a dark grey frame, with his mourning parents kneeling on cushions (father on the North side); portrayals of the siblings in middle relief, dead and alive, kneeling or facing East; on the North side (6 brothers); on the South side (6 sisters); M.I. (engraved, black) on tablets on each short end; East end on patronage; West end, verses on Thomas Sackville's virtues; an achievement on a plaque at the East end; another similar, with details of the Earl, on the other end.
- Thomas Sackville, d 1675, aet 13, thirteenth child and seventh son of Rt. Hon. Richard, Earl of Dorset, d. 27 Aug 1677, aet 55; and Frances, Countess Dowager of Dorset.

1. The Sussex Schoolmaster Walter Gale visited Withyham in July 1750, surveyed the crypt (Sackville vault) and rightly commented in a diary entry that this monument was 'incomparable fine ...', see Blencowe (*SAC* 9 199).
2. 302J is fully described by Horsfield (*Sussex* I 395-6); cited by Gunnis (*Dict.* 102) as by Caius Gabriel Cibber 1630-1700; Esdaile in *SNQ* 1940-41; Nairn & Pevsner (638) review Cibber's contract: he was paid £350, to 'ye well liking of Mr Peter Lilly, his majesty's painter'.
3. The figures represented on the North side are: Charles (1637-1706), 6th Earl; Edward (1644-78); Lionel (died young); Richard (1649-1712); another Lionel (also died young) and Cranfield (died young); on the South side: Elizabeth (died young); Anne (died young); Frances, later Viscountess Lanesborough; Anne, later Countess of Home 1650-72, (for whom see 302C); Mary, later Countess of Orrery and Catherine (died young); the M.I. at the West end refers to 'blasting time', apposite given the lightning strike suffered by the chapel some years earlier, and to Sackville's mother's 'drowned eyes', hence the kerchief carried by the statue representing her.
4. What remains unexplained is the investment in such an ambitious and expensive monument for a younger son, in a family used to child-deaths; Dr. Jane Eade (private communication) points out the importance of the number seven (Thomas was the seventh son), as a perfect number in Christian symbolism, and its place of primacy in a number of philosophies - Zoroastrianism, in Pythagorean geometry and in Juseo-Christian typology - the seven churches (Revelation), deadly Sins, Sacraments, etc. and re: the birthing of males.
5. 302J is Cibber's masterpiece, his only certain monument (Whinney 112-113 & Pl. 72) and the most important sculpture covered by this survey.

Withyham Additions

(1) Iron slab for Richard Gray, parson of Withyham, d. 27 Feb 1582, abandoned at Winchester in the early 1870s seen by F. Arnold, 'Withyham Monumental Slab' (*SAC* 23 320), *SNQ* (IV 113) and noted by Willatts (*SAC* 125 111) as at Withyham, part-covered by choir stalls; probably made at nearby Hamsell, see Addition (2).
(2) Iron slab for Robert Baker (or Bakar), of Withyham, 1585, now at Anne of Cleves Museum, Lewes, rescued from a bakery furnace at Sevenoaks, Kent, perhaps removed from Withyham after 1663 fire; Robert Baker owned Hamsell furnace nearby, measurements close to Addition (1).
(3) Slab in chancel to Nicholas Pennington MA, rector, d. 19 Dec 1722, aet 43, from Wigan, Lancashire see Horsfield (*Sussex* I 396).

(303) WIVELSFIELD, St. Peter and St. John the Baptist
The North aisle is of 1869, otherwise mostly late 13th century; nave lengthened later - Nairn & Pevsner (639-40); in 1724 the condition of the church was fine (Ford 157); the monuments were all relocated from the chantry chapel in the South

aisle to the (West) bell-tower after church restorations of 1868 and refer to five generations of the More/Richbell family, the sequence starting with Thomas Elyot (cited in 303E), whose daughter Margaret (303E and G) married Thomas More (303B and G); the issue of Thomas More's son, Elyot More, is commemorated in 303E,F,G and I and of his daughter, Abigail Richbell, in 303A, C,D and H; for an account of the family home at Morehouse see VCH (VII 122) and Attree (*SAC* 36 44-45), with pedigree of More (p.57) and see Godfrey & Salzman (Pl. 187) for a view of 1787 from the South; the parish had 70 families in 1724; population of 442 in 1801; one Frances More, spinster, by her will of 1723, proved 1727, supported the local charity school (Caffyn 270).

Wivelsfield, 303A Floor slab for Elyott RICHBELL, d. 1716
- Bell-tower floor, against South wall.
- 100(W) x 45(L) — Worn; cracked to right.
- M.I. cut into the surface of a black slab, now reduced in size; head to South.

This S...
Elyott Richbell Gent
Second Son of John Richbell Gent
And Abigail his Wife
Who Departed This Life Jan...
Anno Domini 1715
Aged 42 Y^{rs}

1. Cited by Horsfield (*Sussex* I 229).
2. Elyot Richbell, 25 Apr 1674 - 28 Jan 1715/6, aet 42, was son of John and Abigail (see 303H).
3. 303H as a slab on belfry floor was noted by Attree (*SAC* 36 67).

Wivelsfield, 303B Mural monument for Thomas MORE, d. 1665?
- Bell-tower, South wall, beneath window.
- 106(W) x 82(H) — Worn but sound.
- M.I. (6 lines, engraved) on lower part of oval plaque; local cretaceous(?) freestone; simple moulded rim; above, in relief, an escutcheon.

MEMORIAÆ SACRUM THOMÆ MORE
S [SIC] ARMIGERI
STA LECTOR QUID OPES FACUNDIA
STEMMATA PROSINT
QUID SOBOLES A ME DISCITO
DISCE MORI

1. Originally in chancel see Horsfield (*Sussex* I 229); in situ see Attree (*SAC* 36 64).
2. Thomas More baptised 23 Jul 1592, buried 2 Feb 1664/5 and married Margaret (303E). He was brought before the Archdeaconry Court of Lewes in Jul 1636 for smoking in church during the course of a parish meeting. He confessed and was absolved, see Renshaw (*SAC* 49 63).
3. Lambarde does not mention heraldry.

Wivelsfield, 303C Ledger for John RICHBELL, d. 1712
- Bell-tower floor, against South wall, West of 303A.
- 146(W) x 66(H) — Very worn.
- M.I. on a freestone slab; head to South.

Here lyeth ...
JOHN the Eldest Son ... Gent
And ...
Who departed ...

1. John Richbell 24 Mar 1667 - 8 Aug 1712, aet 45; eldest son of John and Abigail Richbell.
2. 303C noted as in situ by Attree (*SAC* 36 67).

Wivelsfield, 303D Ledger for Frances RICHBELL, d. 1694/5

- Bell-tower floor, against West wall, towards South-West corner.
- 82(W) x 150(L) — Very worn; sound.
- M.I. (5 lines, engraved) on a freestone slab; head to the West; below, an indent [32(W) x 40] for a lost brass.

FRANCES RICHBELL DAVGHTER

OF JOHN RICHBELL GENT

AND ABIGAIL HIS WIFE

WHO DEPARTED THIS LIFE

FEBRVARY THE 11 1694

1. Frances Richbell, 20 Dec 1669 - burial 14 Feb 1694/5, aet 25, see also 303H.
2. For her parents see 303H.
3. Noted as in situ by Attree (*SAC* 36 67).

Wivelsfield, 303E Ledger for Margaret MORE, d. 1680 and descendants

- Bell-tower floor, against West wall, to North of 303D, partly obscured by furnishings.
- 75(W) x 175(L) — Sound; worn.
- M.I. (engraved) fills 75% of a black slab; head to West; final 9 lines added after 1741.
- Margaret More, d. 1680, aet 77, daughter and heir of Thomas Elyott, armiger, of Roygate [Reigate?], Surrey; and wife of Thomas More, armiger, of Wivelsfield; also Thomas Middelton, of Morehouse, d. Sep 1741, aet 34; grandson of Elyott More; and son of John Middelton, of Chailey, and Elyott his wife.

1. Originally in chancel see Horsfield (*Sussex* I 229) who also cites a slab to Margaret More, d. 1671.
2. The association of the 2 M.I.s on 303E is unclear; 303E was seen in situ by Attree (*SAC* 36 65-66) as 2 slabs.
3. The date of More's death is unknown and Elyott More (see 303G) is not cited in M.I.; for a view of More Place see Godfrey & Salzman (Pl. 188); Margaret More was buried 4 Jan 1681 see Attree (*SAC* 36 45); Thomas Middelton (baptised at Chailey 25 Jun 1707 and buried 1 Oct 1741) was her great-grandson; both his mother and grandfather were named Elliott More; Thomas Middleton marks the passing of the estate from More to Middelton; Elyot More was licensed to marry John Middleton, of Chailey, Gent. 12 May 1697.

Wivelsfield, 303F Ledger for Elizabeth MORE, d. 1718

- Bell-tower floor, against West wall, North-West corner, partly obscured.
- 69(W) x 105(L) — Worn; sound.
- M.I. (8 lines, engraved) on a black slab; head to East; final line reversed.

[Hi]c Sita Eſt Elizabetha More

[fili]a Primogenita Elyotti More

[ar]migeri Et Annæ Uxoris Ejus

de Wivelſfield Quæ Obijt Primo

Die Auguſti 1718

Anno Ætatis 46

Post Nubila Cælum

spes nost ...

1. Elizabeth More (baptised 9 Mar 1672) was granddaughter of Margaret More (303E).
2. Attree (*SAC* 36 65) reports reversed on the same slab a M.I. commemorating Edward More 14 Jun 1671 - 8 Nov 1679, son of Elliott and Ann (belfry floor).

Wivelsfield, 303G Mural monument for Elyott MORE, d. 1703

- Bell-tower, West wall, below head height, lower left.
- 83(W) x 83(H) — Generally fine; local losses (& repairs) on right and lower edges.
- Above, arms; M.I. (6 lines, engraved, white) on a freestone slab, now reduced in size and set into the wall.
- Elyott More, armiger, d. 5 Jul 1703, aet 73; son of Thomas and Margaret More.

1. Cited by Rush (*SAC* 22 52).
2. Pedigree states Elyott More baptised 16 May 1630 and buried 7 Jul 1703.
3. A date (possibly spurious) in the 1640s is sometimes cited.

Wivelsfield, 303H Mural monument for John RICHBELL d. 1697/8, and his family

- Bell-tower, West wall, above head height.
- 155(W) x 285(H) — Details replaced; gilding faded; some heraldic colour.
- Arms on a cornice, flanked by urns (not original); entablature of grey marble on 3 pilasters (in rance?) with capitals decorated by symbols of mortality; arched topped black panels with M.I.s (engraved, gilded); decoration in spandrels; below, base mouldings on corbels (not original); in centre, white marble cherub's head.
- Note: all lifespans baptism to burial - John Richbell, Gent. (of London), 31 Aug 1639 - 3 Feb 1697/8, aet 57; his wife, Abigail, 26 Feb 1639/40 - 21 Apr 1715, aet 75, daughter of Thomas More, Esq., of Morehouse; their issue - eldest son, John, 24 Mar 1667 - 8 Aug 1712, aet 45; daughter, Frances, 20 Dec 1669 - 14 Feb 1694/5, aet 25; Elizabeth, 6 Feb 1671 - 28 Jun 1694, aet 24; Elyott, 26 Apr 1674 - 28 Jan 1715/6, aet 42; Ann, 9 Apr 1676 - 16 Apr 1700, aet 24; George, 8 Jun 1679 - 7 Aug 1693, aet 14; all buried Wivelsfield; except George and Elizabeth, buried London.

1. Originally in chancel, see Horsfield (*Sussex* I 229).
2. Patron of 303H was Francis More, Elyott Richbell's aunt and heir.
3. Cited by Rush (*SAC* 22 52); noted as a handsome monument in situ by Attree (*SAC* 36 66-7), with transcription.

Wivelsfield, 303I Floor monument for Ann MORE, d. 1691

- Bell-tower, West wall, partly obscured.
- 70(visible W) x 84(H) — Fair.
- M.I. (11 lines, Latin, engraved, white), final 2 lines (English) reversed, on grey stone slab.
- Ann More, 12 Dec 1691, aet 43; daughter of Edward Paine, armiger, of East Grinstead; and wife of Elyott More, armiger.

1. Cited by Rush (*SAC* 22 52).
2. Ann More was mother of Elizabeth More (see 303F) and grandmother of Thomas Middelton (see 303E).
3. Noted in situ by Attree (*SAC* 36 66).

Wivelsfield Additions
From Attree (*SAC* 36 64ff):
(1) John Attree, d. 26 Jul 1665, aet 45, son of Edward (belfry floor).
(2) Thomas Attree, d. 20 Feb 1765, aet 69 (floor near belfry arch).
(3) Walter More, d. 1591; his wife, Elizabeth, d. Jul 1603 (belfry floor).
(4) Margaret More, 1634-AUG 1671 (belfry floor), see Horsfield (*Sussex* I 229).
(5) Elliot More, son of Thomas, d. 1703 and Anne More, d. 1691 (chancel). But see 303G and I.
(6) Elliot, first son of Elliot More, d. 1679 (chancel).
(7) Thomas Middleton, d. 1741, aet 34 (chancel). But see lower part of 303E.
(8) Tablet for Mary Holey, d. 1787, aet 93 (West nave). See Attree (*SAC* 36 46).

(306) WORTH, St. Nicholas

A major Anglo-Saxon space transformed by Salvin in 1871 - VCH (VII 197); Nairn & Pevsner (641-2); an earlier view from the North-East in Godfrey & Salzman (Pl. 190); condition reported to be fine in 1724, including the Rowsent (Rowfant) estate chancel possessed by Charles Goodwin (Ford 158); the church was re-roofed after a fire in 1987-88 and many monuments are set on modern cast concrete plinths; the parish had c.120 families in 1724 and a population of 501 in 1801; Gunnis (*Dict.* 332, 356 & 360) notes monuments here of the 1830s by Peter Rouw II, Charles R. Smith and Thomas Smith to members of the Ewart and Joliffe families.

Worth, 306A Mural monument for William LAMBE, d. 1823 [Plate 198]
- Nave North wall, near West end, at head height.
- 76(W) x 93(H) — Faded; local damage to base moulding.
- M.I. (12 lines, engraved, black) on an unframed plinth; all in light grey marble; large urn with spiral fluted decoration on a foot; above, a cornice; at top, a pointed pediment with snake for eternity; quarter palmettes flanking; below, straight base moulding.
- William Lambe, Esq., of Tilgate House, Sussex and East Hardwick, Yorkshire, magistrate, bencher of Gray's Inn, etc., d. 16 May 1823, aet 73, buried Clapham.

Worth, 306B Cartouche for Roger BYSSHE, d. 1702/3, and others
- Nave North wall, near West end, above head height.
- c.81(W) x c.183(H) — Very good; colour part-restored.
- M.I. (many lines, engraved) on a double convex cartouche; scrolled drapes all round; above, an escutcheon; flanking, death's heads; at foot, 2 putti flanking a lozenge.
- Roger Bysshe, Esq., of Fenn Place, Worth, d. 21 Mar 1702/3, aet 80; his wife, Ellen, d. 18 Jun 1700, aet 62, daughter of John Parr, Gent., of Kempes, Ireland; their issue - Elizabeth, wife of Francis Wyatt, Esq., of Treemans in Sussex; Hellen, wife of John Shelley, Esq., of Fenn Place; Ellen's niece, Mrs Elizabeth Bradford, d. 18 May 1725, daughter of John Bradford, D.D., and Jane, daughter of John Parr; also Bysshe Shelley, Esq., d. 2 Jan 1733/4, aet 37, son of John Shelley, Esq. and Hellen, no issue.

1. Fenn Place had been in the hands of the Bysshes since the late 1500s.
2. Helen Bysshe married John Shelley in 1692.
3. The Shelleys owned Fenn Place until the mid 1800s (Farrant 344).
4. Patron of 306B was Elizabeth, niece of Mrs Bysshe, d. 1735.
5. Lambarde (*SAC* 69 197) describes the arms as illegible. They have since been restored.
6. Very close in authorship to 39G.

Worth, 306C Mural monument for Elizabeth WHITFIELD, d. 1624
- North transept, West wall, at head height.
- 105(W) x 197(H) — Very good; arms restored.
- In alabaster and slate; M.I. (many lines, English and Latin, gilded, not engraved) on tablet with arched top; straight cornice over; above, an achievement; apron, scrolled and strapped ornament; below, a thick base moulding; no corbel.
- Elizabeth Whitfield, d. 23 May 1624, aet 40; eldest child of Sir Edward Colpeper, of Wakehurst; and 13 years wife of John Whitfield, Esq., of Rowfarnt; their issue - Thomas, John, Robert, Elizabeth, Ann, Mary.

1. Formerly in the South transept [?] see Lambarde (*SAC* 69 193-4 & 196) noting arms.
2. John Whitfield established the family at Rowfant by 1634 see Lower (*SAC* 18 16); the house was enlarged by the architect George Devey, see view of the (largely unaltered) South front Godfrey & Salzman (Pl. 191); see marriage of Elizabeth and John Whitfield, of Roughfant in Blaauw (*SAC* 10 154); Elizabeth Whitfield was baptised 1584, married in 1611 and buried at Worth in 1624, see

pedigree in Attree & Booker (*SAC* 48 98).
3. Patron of 306C is Elizabeth Whitfield's husband, John.
4. 306C is very close to 306D in type.
5. The ledger for Elizabeth Whitfield (306W) appears to be in situ, perhaps near the original location of 306C.

Worth, 306D Mural monument for Thomas WHITFIELD, erected 1631

- North transept, East wall, above head height.
- 79(W) x 109(H) — Very good; paint restored.
- A rectangular alabaster frame; above, a scrolled, reversed support for an escutcheon.
- Thomas Whitfield, Esq.; his wife Mildred, daughter of Henry Manninge, of Greenwich, Esq.; their issue - John who erected 306D in 1631.

1. Formerly in South transept, see Lambarde (*SAC* 69 193) - noting arms.
2. For an account of the family see Lower (*SAC* 19 83-90).
3. 306D emphasises the longevity of the various family lines.
4. For a monument to Thomas Whitfield's charitable bequests see 2700O.
5. 306D is close in type to 306C; with perhaps the same patron, John Whitfield.
6. NBI records burial of Thomas Whitfield on 21 May 1629 at Worth. No entry for Mildred. See 306X - ledger for both.

Worth, 306E Mural monument for John SHELLEY, d. 1713 [Plate 199]

- Nave North wall, just West of the chancel arch, very high.
- Inaccessible — Local damage (cornice)
- A heavy dark grey cornice; scrolled apron; heavy gadrooned base moulding; in centre, moulded corbel; moulded frame in mid grey; whitened lettering on black tablet; no heraldry.
- John Shelley, of Fenn Place, Worth, Esq., born Wolfs-Hill, West Chiltington, 27 Jan 1666, d. 4 Feb 1739; son of Timothy Shelley, Gent., and Catharine, daughter of Edward Michell of Stammerham, Esq.; his wife, Hellen, 16 Apr 1667 - 10 Feb 1742, daughter of Roger Bysshe, Esq., of Fenn Place; their issue - 9 children.

1. Patron of 306E is the estate of the widow, Hellen Shelley, who had married John Shelley in 1692 and brought Fenn Place into the Shelley family (Farrant 344).
2. A later Timothy Shelley was benefactor of the local school in 1767 (Caffyn 271).
3. The gadrooned base moulding of 306E is characteristic.

Worth, 306F Mural monument for Anne HEATH, d. 1602

- Nave, North wall, beneath 306E, at head height.
- 80(W) x 120(H) — Much local damage; restored.
- Freestone frame, strapwork flanking and straight entablature; above, an achievement and flanking part-scrolls; M.I. (shallow-engraving, gilded) on black tablet, set portrait-wise; decorated apron with more part-scrolls.
- Anne Heath, 16 May 1602 - 6 Sep 1602; daughter of Sir Robert Heath, lawyer, and his wife Margaret.

1. Probably in situ, see Lambarde (*SAC* 69 197) noting arms.
2. One Robert Heath, Gent. stands surety for a licence to marry on 4 Oct 1604, see Dunkin (*Licences 1586-1643* 47).

Worth, 306G Mural monument for Leonard GALE, d. 1750, and his wife Sarah and family

- Chancel North wall, East of arch, above head height.
- Plinth: 83(W) x 120(H) — Very good.
- Grey marble unframed tablet; arched and moulded top; below, cherub as corbel; above, a draped urn bearing an escutcheon with some books.

- Leonard Gale, of Crabbet, 12 Nov 1673 - 24 Jun 1750; his wife (since 19 Aug 1703), Sarah, 15 Sep 1680 - 13 Nov 1746; their son, Henry, d. 25 Feb 1749/50, aet 33.

1. In situ, see Horsfield (*Sussex* I 268) and Lambarde (*SAC* 69 193) - citing arms.
2. For the family history see Blencowe (*SAC* 12 45-60), quoting these M.I.s (pp. 59-60), for genealogy see W.S. Ellis 'The Gale Family' (*SAC* 13 307-8), for further children see 306H.
3. Crabbet was purchased in 1698.
4. Family burials were in Worth chancel, see Blencowe (*SAC* 12 57).
5. 306G was erected after 1750.
6. Its carving quality is very high.

Worth, 306H Mural monument for the children of Leonard and Sarah GALE, d. 1715 etc.
- Chancel North wall, towards East end, above head height.
- 70(W) x c.120(H) — Good; cherub cracked.
- M.I. (16 lines, engraved, Latin) in upper 60% of a simple unframed panel with arched top; below, cherub.
- Leonard Gale, 6 May 1715 - 4 Aug 1715; Catherine Gale, 22 Feb 1721 - 14 Jan 1722; Richard Gale, 29 Mar 1723 - 7 Apr 1724; 2 others, both died in the womb; all children of Leonard and Sarah Gale.

1. In situ see Horsfield (*Sussex* I 268).
2. For family see 306G.

Worth, 306I Ledger for Dorothy SMITH, d. 1679
- Chancel floor, at step, on North side, partly obscured by altar rail.
- 100(W) x 175(visible L) — Edges repaired; cracks (centre); very worn (North side).
- Achievement, then M.I. (engraved) on a black slab; head to West.
- Dorothy Smith, d. 9 Jan 1679, aet 25, in childbed; daughter of late Sir Nicholas Weston; granddaughter of Richard, Earl of Portland; and wife of John Smith, Esq., of Crabbet; their issue - Margaret, Dorothy and John, who d. 15 Jan 1679, aet 15 days.

1. Probably relocated but long in chancel see Horsfield (*Sussex* I 268) and Lambarde (*SAC* 69 193) - noting arms.
2. For her daughter see 306K.
3. The M.I. includes the line: 'On whose soule Jesus have mercy', sometimes taken to indicate religious persuasion.

Worth, 306J Ledger for Sir John SMITH, d. 1662
- Chancel floor, at step, South of 306I.
- 99(W) x 175(visible L) — Good, damaged edges.
- Large achievement, then M.I. (3 lines, engraved), in upper (W) 50% of a black slab; head to West.
- Sir John Smith, Knt., d. 12 Nov 1662.

1. Perhaps the father-in-law of Dorothy Smith, see 306I.
2. For Smith see 306L.

Worth, 306K Ledger for Margaret SMITH, d. 1686
- Chancel floor, at step, South of 306J.
- 59(W) x 98(L) — Very worn; scratched.
- M.I. (engraved) on a white marble slab with irregular top; it abuts 306L, head to West.
- Margaret Smith, d. ?? Oct 1686 [7?], aet 6; daughter of John and Dorothy Smith of Crabbet.

1. For Margaret Smith's mother, see 306I.

Worth, 306L Ledger for Sir John SMITH, d. 1662

- Chancel floor, at step, South of 306J and West of 306K.
- 62(W) x 80(L) — Fine.
- M.I. (18 lines, engraved) fills surface of a small black slab; head to East.
- Sir John Smith, Knt, of Crabbet, d. 12 Nov 1662; his first wife, Anne, daughter of Sir Nicholas Parker of Ratton and widow of Adrian More, Esq., of Odiham, Hampshire; no issue; his second wife, Katherine, daughter of Edward Southcote, Esq., of Me[r]stham, Surrey; issue - John, Henry, Richard, Mary, Katherine.

1. For the monument for Smith's father-in-law see 297E.
2. We should perhaps understand 306L as a grave-marker (c.f. 306J).

Worth, 306M Ledger for Elizabeth and William HAMPTON, d. 1729 and 1745

- Chancel floor, at step, South of 306K and 306L, partly obscured by altar rail.
- 100(W) x 197(L) — Good.
- M.I. (16 lines, engraved, Latin and English) fills 75% of a black slab; head to West.
- Elizabeth Hampton, d. in 1729, aet 59; wife (41 years) of Rev. William Hampton, rector and patron of Worth and Plumpton, d. in 1745, aet 87; issue - 16 (unnamed).

1. William Hampton was rector of Plumpton 1692-1745 and Worth 1704-45. See CCEd.
2. His M.I. is in Latin and hers in English.

Worth, 306N Ledger for Roger BYSSHE, d. 1679

- Chancel floor, at step, South of 306M.
- 75(W) x 197(L) — All 3 section edges damaged.
- M.I. (engraved) in white marble slab, in 3 sections; head to West.
- Roger Bysshe, 19 Nov 1668 - 30 Jul 1679; only son of Roger Bysshe, Esq., of Fenn Place and Hellen his wife.

1. For the Bysshe family of Fenn Place see 306B.
2. Is 306N an old M.I. recut onto new slabs?

Worth, 306O Ledger for Anne BYSSHE, d. 1661

- Chancel floor, at step, South of 306N.
- 84(W) x 171(L) — Worn.
- Escutcheons top and bottom; M.I. in centre (9 lines, engraved) on a black slab; head to West.
- Anne Bysshe, d. 28 Oct 1661, aet 32; daughter of Philip Jermyn, Esq., of Lordington in Sussex, Serjeant at Law; and wife of Roger Bysshe, Esq., of Fenn(e) Place.

1. For the Bysshe family of Fenn Place see 306B.
2. Heraldry noted (chancel) by Lambarde (*SAC* 69 192).

Worth, 306P Ledger for Dame Katharine COURTENAY, d. 1672

- Chancel floor, at step, along South wall, partly obscured by altar rail.
- 100(W) x 177(visible L) — Some repairs.
- 2 escutcheons at West end; M.I. (engraved) fills remainder of a black slab; head to West.
- Katharine Courtenay, d. 25 Jun 1672; daughter of Edward Southcott, Esq., of Me[r]stham, Surrey; and, firstly, wife of Sir John Smith, of Crabbett; secondly, wife of Sir William Courtenay, Bart., only son of Thomas Courtenay, Esq., of Powderham, Devon.

1. In situ see Lambarde (*SAC* 69 192) noting arms.
2. M.I. ends with the initials 'OPA', perhaps 'orate pro anima'; see comment on 306I.

Worth, 306Q Mural monument for Susan GOODWIN, d. 1657/8

- South transept, East wall, North side, at head height and above.
- 134(W) x c.220(H) — Very good; heraldic colour.
- M.I. (engraved) on a tablet set portrait-wise; black base moulding and grey fluted corbel; cherub on entablature; curved pediment with achievement.
- Susan Goodwin, d. 12 Feb 1657/8; daughter of Richard Wallop, Esq., of Bugbrooke, Northamptonshire, (Richard Wallop was nephew of Sir John Wallop, KG); and wife of Edward Goodwin, Esq., of Horne, Surrey; their issue - Robert, John, Benjamin and Henry, and two daughters Dorothy and Anne. Their son John Goodwin, Esq., d. 18 Feb 1674; and his wife, Katherine, daughter of Sir Richard Deane, Lord Mayor of London, had one son Deane Goodwin, Esq., d. 22 Jan 1660, and two daughters, Johanna and Sarah. The wife of Deane was Thomasin, daughter of Sir Samuel Oldfield; their issue, John (died and buried at Worth); Deane, Esq., d. 13 May 1692, buried at Worth; Charles, Katherine and Sarah (died and buried at Worth).

1. A good quality late 17th-century tablet.
2. M.I. (lettering all contemporary) suggests that 306Q was erected by Johanna Goodwin, as sole heir of John Goodwin, perhaps after 1692.
3. Reporting the heraldry in Lambarde (*SAC* 69 196) a ledger is also noted in the South transept - now lost?
4. For Thomasin Goodwin (d.1711) see 306Y.

Worth, 306R Mural monument for Catharine BETHUNE, d. 1808 [Plate 200]

- South transept, East wall, South side, at head height.
- 109(W) x 203(H) — Local losses (below).
- In white and grey marbles; backplate in obelisk form with weeping woman and urn; M.I. (engraved) in upper 60% of a framed tablet; decorated apron with tiny lozenge bearing arms.
- Catharine Bethune, d. 31 Dec 1808, aet 62; widow of Rev. George Bethune, LLD, rector of Worth; their issue - unnamed.

1. Noted by Horsfield (*Sussex* I 268).
2. Lambarde does not mention heraldry on this monument, although he does so on 306 S and T.
3. Patrons were unnamed children, perhaps including a later George Bethune mentioned on a nearby monument (post-1858).
4. Catherine Bethune's husband, George Bethune, owned lands here in 1785 (R. Davey 227); for other family monuments see 306S-T.
5. Very close in type to 306S.
6. JH notes that here 'in 63rd year', and on 306T 'aged 63'. Spelling of forename differs between 306 R and T, and in Sussex Marriage Index where it starts with a 'K'.

Worth, 306S Mural monument for George BETHUNE, d. 1803

- South transept, South wall, West of window, at head height.
- 87(W) x 210(H) — Very good.
- Grey-veined obelisk with relief figure of mourning widow and urn; white cornice over M.I. (engraved) on white tablet with grey-veined border; moulded apron with arms; illegible traces of signature (on under face, partly plastered): 'S... London fecit' [South? Strong?].
- Rev. George Bethune, LLD, JP, rector of Worth for 22 years and of West Chiltington, d. 16 May 1803, aet 57; his wife, Catharine, daughter of Rev. Andrew Bethune; their issue - 7 children unnamed, of whom 2 deceased.

1. Noted by Horsfield (*Sussex* I 268) and in situ in Lambarde (*SAC* 69 196) noting arms.
2. Very close in type to 306R.
3. See too George Bethune's ledger (306T). .
4. JH notes that Rev. George Bethune, LLD, formerly of Balliol, Oxon., was a JP for Surrey, rector of Wanstrow in Somerset 1771-81, rector of Brunstead in Norfolk 1780-1803, rector of Worth 1786-

1803 and rector of West Chiltington 1788-1803. See Hennessy (50, 167) and CCEd. He married Katherine [sic] Bethune at Worth on 10 Jun 1771.

Worth, 306T Ledger for George and Catherine BETHUNE, d. 1803 and 1808
- South transept floor, North side.
- 99(W) x 202(L) — Damaged corner (South-East).
- Achievement, then M.I. (engraved), then a second achievement, then a second M.I. (engraved) on polished black slab; head to East.
- Rev. George Bethune, LLD, d. 16 May 1803, aet 57; his wife, Catherine, d. 31 Dec 1808, aet 63; issue - James, d. 1 Mar 1776, an infant; Mary, d. 11 Mar 1786, an infant.

1. In situ see Lambarde (*SAC* 69 197) noting arms.
2. Subjects as for 306R-S.

Worth, 306U Ledger for Charles and John GOODWIN, d. 1731 and 1735/6
- South transept floor, South of 306T.
- 91(W) x 199(L) — Good.
- 2 escutcheons, then M.I. in 2 columns, fills 60% of a black slab; head to East.
- Charles Goodwin, Esq., d. 9 Jun 1731, aet 74; John Goodwin, Esq., Gentleman Usher to the King, d. 7 Jan 1735/6, aet 49.

1. In situ see Lambarde (*SAC* 69 196) noting arms.

Worth, 306V Ledger for Mary GOODWIN, d. 1723/4
- South transept floor, South of 306V, partly obscured by altar.
- 86(W) x 166(L) — Worn; damaged edges.
- Escutcheon, then M.I. (11 lines), fills a black slab; head to East.
- Mary Goodwin, d. 17 Jan 1723/4, aet 65; daughter of Henry Mildemay, Esq., of Grace, Essex; and wife of Charles Goodwin, of Rowvant, Worth.

1. JH notes that a Mary Mildmay married Charles Goodwin on 17 Dec 1691 at St. Martin's in the Fields, Westminster. Although not stated here, it could be that this Charles Goodwin is the one on 306U.
2. The arms, on a lozenge for a woman, and not impaled by a husband's arms, are for Mildmay of Essex, see R. Burke (*Armory* 685).

Worth, 306W Ledger for Elizabeth WHITFELD, d. 1624
- South transept floor, South of 306V.
- 71(W) x 145(L) — Damaged edges; cracks.
- Escutcheon, then M.I. (17 lines, engraved) in Latin and English on a black slab; head to East.
- Elizabeth Whitfield, d. 23 May 1624; eldest daughter of Sir Edward Colepeper; and wife of John Whitfield, armiger.

1. In situ see Lambarde (*SAC* 69 196) - noting arms.
2. For marriage of Elizabeth and John Whitfield 'of Roughfant' see Blaauw (*SAC* 10 154).
3. For her mural monument, perhaps moved from this location, see 306C.
4. The patron of 306W is probably her husband John.

Worth, 306X Ledger for Thomas and Mildred WHITFELD, d. 1629 and 1627
- South transept floor, South of 306W.
- 84(W) x 174(L) — Good.
- Escutcheon, then M.I. (12 lines, engraved) in upper 50% of black slab; head to East.
- Thomas Whitfield, Esq., d. 1 May 1629, aet 83; his wife, Mildred, d. 1 Sep 1627, aet 66.

1. In situ see Lambarde (*SAC* 69 196) noting arms.
2. For Thomas Whitfield's mural monument see 306D, the patron of which is perhaps his son John.

Worth, 306Y Ledger for Thomazin GOODWIN, d. 1711
- South transept floor, South of 306X.
- 98(W) x 201(L) — Very good.
- Escutcheon, then M.I. (11 lines, engraved) on black slab; head to East.
- Thomazin Goodwin, d. 18 Mar 1777, aet 85; daughter of Sir Samuel Oldfield, Knt., of Lincolnshire; and wife of Deane Goodwin, Esq., of Bletchingly, Surrey.

1. Thomasin Goodwin is also cited on 306Q, with issue, not cited here.

Worth, 306Z Mural monument for Johnson TOWERS, d. 1808
- South nave wall, towards East end, above head height.
- 76(W) x 100(H) — Very good; rust.
- M.I. (engraved) in upper parts of an unframed white marble tablet; cornice over; below, escutcheon; at top, flaming lamp in relief.
- Rev. Johnson Towers, A.B., of The Grange, d. 26 Jul 1808, aet 46.

1. Cited by Horsfield (*Sussex* I 268).
2. In situ [?] in Lambarde (*SAC* 69 197) citing arms.
3. JH notes that Johnson Towers, baptised in 1761, succeeded to his father's estates in Kent in 1772. He was awarded BA by Queens' Cambridge in 1783. No details of his ordination have been traced, and he does not ever appear to have held a living. Venn (II 6 214) shows him as having married, but that has not been substantiated. In all, there are more questions about him than answers.

INDEX OF ARTISTS

This index includes all artists (which embraces masons, sculptors and designers of monuments) that are identified in connection with the monuments. Names within the Catalogue are identified by the catalogue number of the monument; names in the Introduction are identified by the roman page number.

INDEX OF PERSONS

This index includes all persons commemorated in the memorials and those mentioned in connection with them, including the patrons who erected the monuments. Names within the Catalogue are identified by the catalogue number of the monument; names in the Introduction are identified by the roman page number. We have not normally included: authors of publications cited, or architects or artists not specifically connected with a monument. We have not attempted to indicate where there are multiple references within a catalogue entry, nor to differentiate when an entry contains references to two or more persons with identical names. Members of the aristocracy have been indexed by the name appearing on the monument; we have not attempted to group them under a family name.

Constable: Barbara 45M; Mary 139/1CC, 156J;
    Sarah 156J; Thomas 98B; William 45M,
    98B, 139/1CC, 156J
Cook(e): Ann 139/1J; Catherine 206G; Edward
    72X; Elizabeth 234E, 234F; George
    139/1J; Jane 186C, 186D; John 234E;
    Mary 206E; Sir Robert 186C; Thomas
    206D, 206E, 206F
Coombe: family 120J
Coomber: Jane 270Q; Richard 270Q
Cooper: Abraham 114O; Afra 186K; Anne
    Elizabeth 140A; Benjamin 265G, 265H;
    Catherine 192B; Charles Herbert 140A;
    Elizabeth 99A, 114O; George 221Add;
    Godfrey Gilbert 99A; Sir John Hutton 120A,
    120K; Joseph 221Add; Judith 186K; Maria
    Charlotte, Lady 120A; Martha 140A; Mary
    140B, 186K, 221Add; Mary Catharine
    Gilbert 99A; Mary Catherine Gilbert 99A;
    Robert 186K; Robert Court 140A; Sarah
    265H; Thomas 140A, 140B, 140C; Thomas
    Lewis 140A; William 140A, 140B, 192B;
    William George 140A
Cope: Arabella Diana 302E; Catherine, Lady
    47F; Sir Charles 47F, 302E
Copley: Margaret 281D; Sir Roger 281D
Cornwalle: Martha 216G
Corthine: Jane 222H; Josiah 222H
Coster: Arthur 11C; Frances 11C; Francis 11C
Cotes: Humphry 40E
Courland: Duchess of 120E
Courtail: John 45L, Pl.33
Courtenay: Dame Katharine 306P; Thomas
    306P; Sir William 306P
Courthop(e): — 139/1N, 270MM; Albinia 258G,
    Pl.160; Alexander 139/1K; Alice, Lady
    258F, Pl.159; Ann 270DD, 272J; Anne
    139/1T; Barbara 130/1Add, 139/1L,
    139/1U; Barbery 139/1C; Brian 270DD;
    Catharine 270DD; Catherine 139/1C;
    Dorothy 139/1T; Edward 270DD; Elianor
    270DD; Elizabeth 139/1K, 139/1T; Dame
    Elizabeth 258D; family 258FF, 258H;
    Frances 139/1K, 139/1L, 139/1T, 258G;
    George 128A, 139/1C, 258G, 264H,
    270DD, 272J, Pl.160; Sir George xvi, xvii,
    258D, 258E, 258F, 258G, 272J, Pl.159;
    Hannah 270DD; Henry 110N, 130/1Add,
    139/1K, 139/1T, 153C, 264H, 270DD;
    James 128A, 270DD; Jane 72M, 139/1K,
    139/1T, 153C; John 139/1L, 139/1U,
    139/1V, 258F, 270DD; Judith 270DD; Mary
    110N, 128A, 139/1T, 264H, 270DD; Peter
    72M, 139/1C, 139/1K, 139/1L, 139/1M,
    139/1N, 139/1T, 139/1U, 139/1V, 212BB,
    Pl.89; Philadelphia 139/1L, 139/1N,
    139/1O, 139/1U, 139/1V, 212BB, Pl.90;
    Thomas 128A, 270DD; William 139/1L,
    139/1O
Courtney: Joan 297E; Sir William 297E

Coventry: Thomas, Lord 39I
Covert: Alexander 234F; Ann 234F; Anne 77I;
    Blanche, Lady 234D, 234E; Cicely 234F;
    Dulcibella 234F; Elizabeth 234D, 234E,
    234F; Elizabeth, Lady 234D; Ellen 234F;
    family xxiii, 234; Francis 234F; George
    234D; Jane 234E, Pl.150; Jane, Lady
    145D, 234D; Joan 234F; John 164B, 234D,
    234E, 234F; Margery 234F; Mary 234F;
    Richard 234F, Pl.149, Pl.151; Sir Richard
    234D, 234E; Thomas Mynors 234F; Walter
    234F; Sir Walter 145D; William 234E, 234F
Cowley: Fanny xvi, 40O
Cowper: William 31B, 31D
Cox: Ann 227F, Pl.144; Henry 39G; Margareta
    39G; Mary 9B, 9C; William 227F
Coxe: Anna Diana 40A; Julia 40A; Thomas 40A
Cragg: Jane 192C; John 192C
Cranfield: Frances 302I
Cranston: Catharine Frances 157P; Catherine
    86G, 157P; Cordelia 26E; family Pl.99;
    James 26E, 157P, Pl.99; John 86G
Crauford/Craufurd/Crawfurd: — 73I, 86; Ann
    73A, Pl.52; Anna 86O, 86V; Anne 73H,
    86V; family 164J; Fanny 164G; George
    73A, 73E, 73H; Gibbs 86O, 86V, 164G;
    Harriot 164G; Harriot-Fanny 164G; Harriot-
    Louisa 164G; Jane 73F, 73G, Pl.53; John
    86O, 164G; Patrick George 73E, 73F,
    73J; Thomas Gibbs 164I; William-Board-
    Edward-Gibbs 164G
Crayford: Robert 16B
Crew: Honnor Elizabeth 255E; Thomas 255D,
    255E
Crisp: John 190Add; Mary 190Add; William
    190Add
Crocker: Elizabeth 32B; James 32B
Croft(s): Catherine 111B; Daniel 111B; Elizabeth
    Frederica 158A; Harriet 158A; James
    158B; Mary Henrietta 158A; Peter Guerin
    158, 158A, 158B, 158C, 158E; Sarah
    158C, 158E
Croker: Elizabeth 32B; James 32B
Cromwell: Agnes 302G; Oliver 195F
Crosby: Susan 4Add
Crouch: Elizabeth 221S; Thomas 221S
Crowhurst: Elizabeth 93X; John 93X
Crunden: H. D. 212HH; Richard 212HH
Cruttenden: Anthony 39T, 45Add, 45I, 45J,
    45O; Catherine 299H, 299I, 299J;
    John 45R, 299K; John (or Anthony) 45;
    Mary 39T, 45I, 45J, 45O, 45R; Nathaniel
    45O, Pl.34; Obedience 45Q; Robert 45Q;
    Thomas 299G, 299H, 299I, 299J, 299K
Crysford: William 99Add
Cumber: Barbara xxii; John xxii
Curteis: Caroline Sarah 276F, Pl.175; Edward
    Jeremiah 276B, 276C, 276D, 276E, 276F;
    Edward-Jeremiah xxi; family 276; Herbert
    Barrett 276F; Herbert Mascall 276F; Jane